PRACTICAL ORGANIC CHEMISTRY

PRACTICAL
ORGANIC CHEMISTRY

by

FREDERICK GEORGE MANN
Sc.D. (Cantab.), D.Sc. (Lond.), F.R.I.C., F.R.S.
FELLOW, TRINITY COLLEGE, CAMBRIDGE,
UNIVERSITY EMERITUS READER IN ORGANIC CHEMISTRY

and

BERNARD CHARLES SAUNDERS
C.B.E., M.A., Sc.D. (Cantab.), D.Sc. (Lond.), F.R.I.C., F.R.C. Path.

LONGMAN
London and New York

LONGMAN GROUP LIMITED
London

*Associated companies, branches and representatives
throughout the world*

Published in the United States of America
by Longman Inc., New York

First Published 1936
Second Edition 1938
New Impressions 1941, 1942, 1943, 1944, 1946, 1947, 1949, 1952
Third Edition 1952
New Impressions 1954, 1955, 1956, 1957, 1958
Fourth Edition 1960
New Impressions 1961, 1962, 1964, 1967, 1970, 1971
New Impression with revisions 1974
New Impression 1975
Reprinted in paper covers, 1978

British Library Cataloguing in Publication Data

Mann, Frederick George
  Practical organic chemistry – 4th ed.
  1. Chemistry, Organic – Laboratory manuals
  I. Title   II. Saunders, Bernard Charles
  547'.0028   QD261   78–40612

  ISBN 0–582–44407–1

Printed in Great Britain by
Lowe & Brydone Printers Ltd, Thetford, Norfolk

NEW IMPRESSION, 1974

The last (4th) Edition of this book appeared in 1960, and has been followed by four New Impressions, the last in 1967. The rapid and ceaseless changing of the presentation of organic chemistry—both theoretical and practical—warranted an entirely new edition, but this would have entailed a massive task, for which neither Dr. B. C. Saunders nor I had time or opportunity to undertake.

The publishers therefore suggested that a new impression should be prepared. This also proved a laborious task, partly because of the many minor changes in nomenclature and—more particularly—the presentation of names that the recommendations of the I.U.P.A.C. required, and partly because all corrections and additions were necessarily limited in length to the space which the original text had occupied.

Several of my chemical colleagues have suggested that a new edition of 'M. and S.' should now deal also with the chief branches of modern spectroscopy. This would be an aim both excellent and impracticable. Students have their own monographs on spectroscopy and their own teachers, whose exposition should clarify the branches of this subject more rapidly and easily than the printed text. An attempt to deal adequately with spectroscopy in this volume would greatly increase its size and probably fail in purpose—the fate of several books whose authors have attempted this ambitious programme.

We are greatly indebted to Dr. D. K. C. Cooper, F.R.C.S., who has critically examined the section on First-Aid to ensure that it now harmonises with modern medical practice.

F. G. Mann,
University Chemical Laboratory,
Cambridge.
March 1973.

PREFACE TO FOURTH EDITION

IN the preparation of this revised and extended edition, we have had in mind two major factors.

First, considerably greater emphasis has been placed on semi-micro techniques and their application to preparations, separations, analysis and physical determinations such as those of molecular weight. We have therefore greatly expanded the section on Manipulation on a semi-micro scale which was in the Third Edition, and we have described many more preparations on this scale, some independent and others as alternatives to the larger-scale preparations which immediately precede them. Some 40 separate preparations on the semi-micro scale are described in detail, in addition to specific directions for the preparation of many classes of crystalline derivatives required for identification purposes. The equipment required for these small-scale reactions has been selected on a realistic basis, and care has been taken not to include the very curious pieces of apparatus sometimes suggested as necessary for working on the semi-micro scale.

Secondly, whilst retaining undiminished the full and clear directions provided for students who are starting the study of practical organic chemistry, we have extended the scope of the work so that it covers most of the needs of students working for an Honours or Special Degree.

To meet the needs of the advanced students, preparations have now been included to illustrate, for example, reduction by lithium aluminium hydride and by the Meerwein-Ponndorf-Verley method, oxidation by selenium dioxide and by periodate, the Michael, Hoesch, Leuckart and Doebner-Miller Reactions, the Knorr pyrrole and the Hantzsch collidine syntheses, various Free Radical reactions, the Pinacol-Pinacolone, Beckmann and Arbusov Rearrangements, and the Bart and the Meyer Reactions, together with many others.

These preparations, with those noted in the Preface to the Third Edition, cover a considerable proportion of the standard synthetic reactions. Most of these preparations come towards the end of Part II (Preparations), and both elementary and advanced students should have no difficulty in selecting the preparative work they require.

In earlier editions, Part III (Reactions and Identification of

Organic Compounds) was designed to give students a thorough training in the *general* reactions of the simpler members of each of the main classes of organic compounds, and in the methods by which an unknown compound could be first allocated to its class and then identified. Clearly, more advanced students will meet a wider range of members of each class of compound, and the final identification must usually be based on the melting-points of crystalline derivatives. We have therefore inserted in the account of each class a note of the types of crystalline derivatives which can be most rapidly and reliably prepared, with full experimental details. Our Tables of Melting-points of derivatives, given at the end of the book, have been very considerably extended, so that the advanced student, who, like the elementary student, must first allocate his unknown compound to its class, can now prepare one or more crystalline derivatives, and complete the identification by reference to these tables. The preparation of these crystalline derivatives gives the student a further and very valuable exercise in semi-micro preparations. It should be emphasised that in Sections 10–27 of Part III, *i.e.*, the sections which are each devoted to one class of compound, the simpler or more common members are still clearly specified, and their reactions discussed, so that again the less advanced student can readily discern the range of the material which is his immediate concern.

For the more advanced student, we have extended the section on Quantitative Semi-micro Analysis, and we have included a section dealing with Special Techniques in Separation and Purification, namely Adsorption Chromatography, Paper Chromatography, and Ion-Exchange Processes.

The use of more complex or more costly articles of equipment, such as catalytic hydrogenation apparatus, autoclaves, polarimeters, ultraviolet absorption spectrometers, etc., has not been described, because the type of such apparatus employed in different laboratories varies considerably, and students must be taught the use of their own laboratory equipment.

In the First Edition of this book, we included a short section to illustrate some of the more simple or the more clearly defined reactions which are promoted by enzymes. It was hoped that this section might stimulate the interest of younger chemists in the preparative value of such reactions, but organic chemists still largely ignore this branch of preparative work. We have now deleted certain portions of this section, and emphasised other portions having greater current interest.

Throughout this **edition the** nomenclature adopted is in general that recommended by the International Union of Pure and Applied Chemistry, and by the Chemical Society (1959).

In the preparation of this edition, we are indebted for much help to many of our colleagues, and in particular to Dr. P. Sykes, Dr. F. B. Kipping, Dr. P. Maitland, Dr. J. Harley-Mason and Dr. R. E. D. Clark. We have maintained the standard which was self-imposed when this book was first written, namely, that all the experiments in the book had been critically examined, and then performed either by the authors, or under their supervision. The heavy load of work which this has involved would have been impossible without the willing, patient, and very considerable help of Mr. F. C. Baker and Mr. F. E. G. Smith.

F.G.M.

Cambridge, 1960   B.C.S.

PREFACE TO THIRD EDITION

FOR the production of this edition, we have made a thorough and critical revision of the whole contents of the book, based on our experience of its use in the laboratory and on the general advance in organic chemical practice. In addition to this general revision, however, we have extended the book in three main directions.

The book as originally planned was intended to meet the needs primarily of pupils in the senior forms at schools and of undergraduates up to the level of a Pass Degree. We have extended Parts II and III dealing with Preparations and with the Reactions and Identification of Organic Compounds so that the book should now cater fully for the needs of students working for Honours Degrees. In particular, the Preparations now include examples of most of the more simple standard reactions: for this purpose we have now added, for example, preparations illustrating the Benzidine Transformation, the Ullmann Condensation, the Benzilic Acid Rearrangement, the Reformatsky Reaction, the Clemmensen Reduction, the Fischer Indolisation Reaction, the Mannich Reaction, and the Diels-Alder Reaction. It is probable that preparative work on a much smaller scale than has hitherto been customary in teaching laboratories will become more common in future. To meet this need, we have added a short section to Part I, describing the design and use of apparatus for this purpose, and we have also included some examples of these small-scale preparations as alternatives to the larger preparations in Part II.

In Part III, dealing with the Reactions and Identification of Organic Compounds, greater emphasis has now been placed on the preparation of suitable crystalline derivatives. Quite apart from the importance of these derivatives for purposes of identification, encouragement is thereby given to the student to gain experience in small-scale preparative work.

We have also added an entirely new section dealing with semi-microanalysis. In our original Introduction (p. ix) we justified the retention of macro-methods of quantitative analysis on the grounds that they formed an excellent introduction to micro-methods and also afforded a valuable training in exact manipulation generally. By now, however, the macro-estimation particularly of carbon and hydrogen and of nitrogen has disappeared entirely from most laboratories. On the other hand, the micro-methods developed so largely by Pregl, and which usually require no more than 5 mgm. of material, necessitate prolonged training and an impeccable experimental technique, and give consistently reliable results only in the hands of full-time analysts. They are consequently unsuitable for students. The semi-micro methods of analysis, which usually require 20–50 mgm. of material, form an ideal compromise for student-training, for the necessary technique can be acquired after only a few attempts. These methods moreover provide the student with very valuable manipulative exercise, and serve as an introduction to the handling of even smaller quantities of material which may arise in his post-graduate work. This section on Semi-microanalysis has been designed and written by Dr. P. Sykes, and is based on his experience of teaching such methods in the Cambridge laboratories. We wish to thank him sincerely for a valuable contribution to this work.

In the original planning of this book we were at pains to ensure that the preparations in particular were designed to afford a minimum expenditure of time, materials and heating. We hope that the economy thus introduced will be especially appreciated in view of the recent heavily increased cost of chemicals, fuel and laboratory service. This increased cost, incidentally, must necessarily increase the attraction of the small-scale preparations referred to above.

We are grateful to our colleagues for many valuable discussions and suggestions: in particular we would mention Dr. F. B. Kipping, Dr. P. Maitland, Dr. G. W. Kenner and Mr. J. Harley-Mason.

We should also like to express once again our sincere thanks for the considerable help we have received from our laboratory assistants, Mr. F. C. Baker and Mr. F. E. Smith.

F.G.M.
B.C.S.

PREFACE TO SECOND EDITION

THE two chief additions which have now been made are the Sodium Carbonate-Zinc Method as an alternative to Lassaigne's Sodium Fusion Method for detecting elements in organic compounds, and the Tables of Physical Constants which have been included in the Appendix. These Tables have been compiled to cover a very much wider scope of organic compounds than those described in this book. In addition to the general utility of these Tables, we hope that they will be of value to students wishing to extend their practice in the identification of organic compounds beyond the range given in Part III of this book. This range has been deliberately limited in order to enable students to obtain a firm grasp of the methods of identifying simple compounds, and these methods have therefore been based almost entirely on chemical reactions alone. When the range of organic compounds to be identified is extended, and particularly when higher homologues are being investigated, identification by the physical properties of derivatives becomes increasingly necessary, and the Tables of Physical Constants should considerably facilitate this extension.

We wish to express our gratitude to the chemists who have made suggestions with regard to the subject-matter of this book: many of these suggestions have now been incorporated in this edition. We would warmly welcome further suggestions for improving its contents.

F.G.M.
B.C.S.

INTRODUCTION

THIS laboratory manual of organic chemistry has been compiled primarily to cover the work required for Part I of the Natural Sciences Tripos at Cambridge University, the General B.Sc. course at London University, and the Pass Degree courses at other universities. At the same time, however, it has been carefully arranged to cover adequately the needs of students proceeding to the M.B. examinations in organic chemistry at the various universities. Moreover, since the introductory work has been given in considerable detail, the book is suitable for senior pupils at schools (more particularly for Higher Certificate and University Entrance Scholarship candidates), and should therefore be sufficient to cover both their school and university needs.

This work is based largely on the authors' experience with the teaching of practical organic chemistry to very large classes of students at Cambridge University. For such classes experimental directions involving the utmost economy in chemicals and apparatus, and also in the students' time, are obviously required. Therefore the whole of the experimental work described in this book has been repeatedly checked by the authors themselves (and for the most part by their classes also) in order to obtain the desired results with a minimum expenditure of materials and time. In the section on Organic Preparations in particular, this detailed investigation of each preparation has frequently enabled unexpected simplifications and economies to be introduced, more particularly as many text-books still contain experimental directions which have frequently remained unchanged since their original publication in chemical journals many years ago, and in which, moreover, occasional errors both in fact and in transcription have thus remained uncorrected. It is almost universally found that departments of organic chemistry are more costly to maintain than other science departments, primarily because of the heavy consumption of organic reagents and solvents, and the economies which have now been effected will, we think, be appreciated by most teachers of practical organic chemistry.

Teachers of chemistry (and of the sciences generally) will have found that many students appear to dissociate their practical work sharply in their minds from their theoretical knowledge. Many

xiii

students of organic chemistry moreover remain familiar with a particular preparation, but fail to appreciate the value or significance of the process of which that preparation is merely one example: for instance, a student may often have a detailed knowledge of the preparation of acetanilide, but be unable to give a general account of the methods of acetylation, or of the practical value of the process of acetylation itself. Consequently in the following pages the description of most experiments (and particularly of the preparations) is preceded by a short account in small print of the chief theoretical considerations involved: in the case of preparations based on one of several alternative methods, a brief account is similarly given of these methods and of their comparative practical value. This combination of theory and practice will, it is hoped, both simplify and elucidate the practical study of organic chemistry, and enable the student to visualise his practical work as an orderly whole and not as a vast number of isolated and unrelated experiments.

Part III, on the Reactions and Identification of Organic Compounds, has been strictly limited to the commoner members of each of the more important classes of organic compounds. This work, consisting chiefly of reactions carried out on the test-tube scale, should be of great value to the student, who, if he carries out the reactions intelligently, should thereby effectively consolidate his theoretical knowledge. Yet students frequently attempt far too ambitious a programme of reactions and more particularly of qualitative analysis, and thus often become lost in the very detailed work on which such programmes are based. We consider therefore that students should master thoroughly the more simple programme given in Part III before proceeding to wider and more detailed systems for the identification of organic compounds.

The comparatively wide prevalence of micro-methods of quantitative organic analysis, applied more particularly to the estimation of the constituent elements in an organic compound, may cause the advisability of including the macro-methods in Part IV to be questioned. Quite apart, however, from the fact that the micro-methods still find no place in many laboratories, we consider that thorough practice in the macro-methods of quantitative analysis to be not only an excellent introduction to the micro-methods themselves, but also a valuable training in exact manipulation generally.

Part V, on Simple Enzyme Reactions, is rather a new departure in practical books of this type. The importance of this section to medical students, biochemists, physiologists, *etc.*, is obvious. We consider, however, that students of chemistry who are not reading any biological subject should have some practical knowledge of a branch of organic chemistry which is of the greatest scientific importance, and the industrial application of which will undoubtedly increase very widely in the future. At present it rarely occurs to such students that an organic reaction can be usefully promoted by the application of anything but the flame of a Bunsen burner!

If students are carefully trained in accurate work, accidents in the laboratory should be of very rare occurrence. Since, however, they can never be entirely eliminated, it is hoped that the First Aid directions given in the Appendix will prove of value, particularly to the junior staff of laboratories, who by virtue of their duties as demonstrators are frequently the first to be called upon to help injured students.

We wish to express our very sincere thanks to Dr. W. H Mills, F.R.S., and to Dr. Hamilton McCombie, for much advice and help in the compilation of this book; to Prof. C. S. Gibson, F.R.S., for suggestions with regard to the needs of medical students; and to Prof. E. L. Hirst, F.R.S., for advice upon certain preparations in the carbohydrate series. We are also greatly indebted to Dr. F. B. Kipping and Dr. P. Maitland for many suggestions based on the experience obtained from their own first-year medical and Tripos classes. We gratefully acknowledge the help we have received from Dr. P. J. G. Mann of the Cambridge University Biochemical Department, who read over the section on Enzymes and made many valuable suggestions, and from Dr. F. J. W. Roughton, F.R.S., and Dr. G. A. Millikan, who kindly furnished the details of experiments concerning carbonic anhydrase.

Our warm thanks are due also to our Laboratory and Lecture Assistants, Mr. F. C. Baker and Mr. F. E. Smith, who have given us great help in the many repetitions of the preparations and the quantitative analyses respectively which were required before this book could attain its final form.

The notes on First Aid have been based on the memorandum *Safeguards in the Laboratory*, compiled by the Science Masters. Association and the Association of Women Science Teachers. This report has, however, been considerably modified and amplified for our purpose, and we are greatly indebted to Dr. F. B. Parsons, M.D., for very kindly supervising our final draft and thus ensuring its medical accuracy.

The authors will welcome criticisms and suggestions from teachers of practical organic chemistry.

Cambridge.   F. G. MANN
    May 1936   B. C. SAUNDERS

CONTENTS

PAGE

Part I. METHODS AND MANIPULATION 1

ADVANCED TECHNIQUES OF SEPARATION AND
PURIFICATION 48

METHODS AND MANIPULATION ON A SEMI-MICRO
SCALE 59

Part II. PREPARATIONS 73

Part III. REACTIONS AND IDENTIFICATION OF ORGANIC
COMPOUNDS 316

Part IV. QUANTITATIVE ANALYSIS 416

SECTION A
MACROANALYSIS 416

SECTION B
SEMI-MICROANALYSIS 465

Part V. SIMPLE ENZYME REACTIONS 509

APPENDIX

PREPARATION OF REAGENTS 524
FIRST-AID, TREATMENT OF FIRES, ETC. . . . 526

TABLES I–XXVIII 533

INDEX 566

SAFETY PRECAUTIONS

to be observed during Laboratory Work.

(1) **Protection of the eyes.** Safety goggles should always be worn over the eyes, especially when carrying out potentially dangerous operations, *e.g.*, vacuum distillations, distillation of large volumes of inflammable liquids, and experiments requiring large quantities of metallic sodium.

For treatment of injuries to the eye, see p. 527.

(2) **Cuts.** Most cuts which occur in the laboratory are caused either by glass tubing, condensers, etc., snapping while being forced through perforated corks, with the result that the broken jagged end cuts the hands holding the cork, or by test-tubes, boiling-tubes and heavier glass cylinders breaking whilst being too forcibly corked, with similar results. Such accidents in either case are avoided by careful working.

For treatment of cuts, see p. 528.

For First-Aid Directions, see p. 526.

ABBREVIATIONS

The following abbreviations are used throughout this book:

b.p.	boiling-point
f.p.	freezing-point
m.p.	melting-point
d.	density (g. per ml.)
g.	gram(s)
l.	litre(s)
mg.	milligram(s)
ml.	millilitre(s)
G.Mol.	gram-molecule
M.	Molar
N.	Normal
Atm.	Atmosphere-pressure
S.T.P.	Standard temperature and Pressure

The density of liquids, unless otherwise stated, is given at 15°C.

The experiments described in Part I have been numbered, as they form a graded series to illustrate the chief manipulative processes employed in practical organic chemistry. The experiments in Parts II–V have not been numbered, as in general a selection must be made from them. In each part of the book, the experiments have been arranged as far as possible in logical order, although occasionally (as in Part IV) this is not necessarily the order of increasing difficulty.

PART I

METHODS AND MANIPULATION

In this part of the book, a brief account is given of the chief manipulative processes which are used in practical organic chemistry. Most of these processes are those which students are likely to use repeatedly in their work. The remainder are not of such frequent occurrence, but are processes with which more advanced students should be familiar: the discussion of the latter processes is given in small print.

It should be emphasised that all the processes here described are considered essentially from the practical standpoint. The student should always acquaint himself with the theoretical basis of these operations, for which he should consult any standard text-book of physical chemistry: this applies particularly to such processes as the distillation of constant boiling-point mixtures, steam-distillation, ether extraction, *etc.*

The experimental operations in organic chemistry which occur with greatest frequency are those which are concerned, directly or indirectly, with the isolation and purification of organic compounds. It is necessary therefore to describe in detail the chief methods of purification. Before doing so, however, the *criteria of purity* (and their observation) must first be discussed, so that when the purification has been attempted, its success can at once be checked and confirmed.

Criteria of Purity. Solid Compounds. The property of an organic compound which is most frequently determined as a criterion of purity is the *melting-point,* because in general it may be said that a pure compound has usually a sharp melting-point (*i.e.,* the substance melts entirely within a range of about $1°C.$), whereas an impure substance has an indefinite melting-point, and will therefore melt slowly and indecisively over a range of several degrees. The actual possibilities which may be revealed by a melting-point determination may be summarised as follows:

A. *Melting-point sharp.*
  (1) Substance chemically pure. This is almost invariably the cause of a sharp melting-point.
  (2) Substance is a eutectic mixture of two or more compounds. The chance of a given mixture containing two compounds

in just the proportion to give a sharp-melting eutectic mixture is so remote that this possibility may be neglected. [Occasionally arbitrary mixtures of two substances which (usually) are chemically related may melt fairly sharply at temperatures intermediate between the melting-points of the two components, but this phenomenon is rarely encountered.]

B. *Melting-point indefinite.*

(1) The substance is *impure*. This is almost invariably the cause of an indefinite melting-point.

(2) The substance is *pure*, but on warming undergoes slight thermal decomposition before the melting-point is reached, and the decomposition products then act as impurities and depress the melting-point.

Experimental Determination of Melting-point. The general method consists in placing the finely powdered compound in a capillary tube, and heating the latter in a bath of a suitable liquid, the temperature of the bath when the compound melts being then noted. The capillary tubes should be very thin-walled tubes, about 8 cm. long, and about 1 mm. in diameter. They can be prepared very easily by heating the centre of a clean dry soft-glass test-tube* in a large brush flame of a Bunsen burner, whilst the ends of the tube are uniformly rotated by the hands. When the central portion of the tube over a length of about 5 cm. has become both soft and moderately thickened by the heating, the ends of the tube are drawn as far apart as the arms permit, the soft portion of the tube being thus drawn out into a long capillary. The latter is then cut into suitable lengths (rejecting any flawed or otherwise unsuitable portions), and one end of each portion is then sealed. This is done by inserting the end of the capillary tube horizontally into the extreme edge of a small steady Bunsen flame for a few seconds, rotating the capillary meanwhile: no difficulty should thus be experienced in obtaining a uniformly sealed strong end to the capillary tube (Fig. 1(A)).

A clean dry porous plate is then broken into fragments† about

---

* A laboratory demonstration of this operation is far better than any written description. The tubes may be bought from many dealers (*e.g.*, A. Gallenkamp & Co. Ltd., Technico House, Christopher Street, London, EC2P 2ER, and Victoria House, Widnes, Lancs; also The Scientific Glass-Blowing Co., 41 Upper Brook Street, Manchester 13), but students should learn to make their own capillary tubes.

† A microscope slide may be used in place of the fragment of unglazed porcelain. The slide has the advantage that it can be washed after each determination and so used repeatedly: the rough surface of the porcelain, however, lends itself much more readily to the pulverisation of the organic material.

3 cm. square. (A supply of the fragments in a dust-tight box should always be freely available in the laboratory.) To fill the capillary with the compound the melting-point of which is to be determined, about 0·05 g. of the compound is placed on one of the fragments of plate, and crushed to a fine powder by gently rubbing it with the flat end of a porcelain spatula or (better) with the slightly bent end of a small flat narrow metal (*e.g.*, nickel) spatula. When a very fine powder has been obtained, sufficient is transferred to the capillary tube (by pushing the open end of the tube through the powder and backing the latter if necessary with the spatula) so that, when the closed end of the tube is tapped on the bench, a length of about 5 mm. of fairly tightly packed material has accumulated at the bottom. This is a rapid operation when the compound gives a fine dense powder: some compounds however, even when pure, have a waxy consistency, and are not easily inserted into a tube of the usual width, in which case a slightly wider capillary (say 2 mm. in diameter) may have to be used. The student should soon be able by experience to select a suitable tube having once obtained the "feel" of the material when crushed on the porcelain. Should the material be inclined to stick in the tube, it can often be rapidly conducted to the bottom by vibrating the tube gently by the cross-wise action of a blunt file or the milled edge of a coin.

The usual apparatus for heating the substance is shown in Fig. 1(B), and consists of a long-necked hard-glass flask **D** to which a thermometer **E** is fitted by means of a cork having a shallow vertical groove **F** cut or filed as shown to allow expansion of the contents of **D**. The best liquid for placing in **D** is medicinal paraffin, which possesses the following very suitable properties: (*a*) it has a low specific heat and therefore the temperature can be easily increased using only a small flame, (*b*) even when hot it

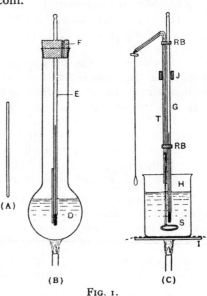

FIG. 1.

is almost non-inflammable, and therefore should the flask break whilst still over the flame, the oil seldom ignites, (c) the oil is non-corrosive, and owing to its low specific heat causes remarkably slight burns even if spilt, while at a high temperature, on the hands. The oil may be safely heated up to about 220°, when it begins to decompose slightly, giving off smoky fumes. For substances melting above this temperature, the flask **D** should contain concentrated sulphuric acid containing a crystal of potassium nitrate to prevent charring and consequent darkening in colour at higher temperatures. Fresh sulphuric acid can be safely heated to about 280°, but its use should generally be avoided in elementary classes. Alternatively, silicone* can be used in place of sulphuric acid for compounds of high melting-point. It is a straw-coloured non-corrosive liquid which can be safely heated to *ca.* 300° without decomposition or ignition.

The capillary tube is then placed as shown against the thermometer **E**, to which it will adhere by the capillary attraction of the oil, the column of powdered material being thus beside the bulb of the thermometer. The oil in **D** is then *slowly* heated, and the temperature, or range of temperature, over which the compound melts carefully noted. It is essential for an accurate determination that the temperature of the oil in **D** should rise *very slowly* as the compound is about to melt. It will therefore frequently save time, particularly if the compound is likely to have a high melting-point, to fill two capillaries with the substance. The temperature of **D** is then raised quickly using one tube, in order to determine the melting-point approximately: the temperature is then allowed to fall about 30°, the second capillary is then substituted for the first, and an accurate determination with the temperature very slowly rising is then made. It is important to note that a second determination is never made by noting the temperature at which the molten material in the capillary solidifies as the oil cools, or by reheating the tube after this solidification has occurred.† A freshly-filled capillary should always be used for each subsequent determination.

The more accurate apparatus shown in Fig. 1(c) is strongly recommended when laboratory conditions enable students to retain their own apparatus over a complete course of work. A glass tube **T**, bent as shown, is fixed by the rubber-bands **RB** to the thermometer **G**. The

---

* Marketed as "DC550 Fluid" by Midland Silicones Ltd., Oldbury, Birmingham, and obtainable from Hopkins & Williams, Ltd, P.O. Box 1, Romford, RN1 1HA.

† For an exception to this statement, see Rast's Method, pp. 437, 438.

glass stirrer **S** is then placed so that the shaft is in the tube **T**, and is connected by a piece of string through the tube as shown, a knot or a cork preventing the stirrer from falling completely to the bottom of the beaker **H** which contains the oil. The apparatus is kept permanently fixed to a small retort stand, which holds the beaker on a gauze-covered ring **I**, and the thermometer and tube by the clamp **J**. The capillary is then placed as before against the thermometer, and the oil gently heated: meanwhile by means of the string the stirrer is kept steadily in motion and the oil well mixed. The thorough mixing of the oil in this apparatus, and the better control of its temperature, give therefore more accurate results than those obtained with the simple apparatus shown in Fig. 1(B).

The electrically heated type of melting-point apparatus, which has certain advantages over the above types, is described on p. 61, Fig. 33.

Experiment 1. Determination of Melting-points.

The student should determine the melting-point of the following compounds:

A (I). *Pure Compounds.*   (*a*) Phenyl Benzoate   M.p.   70°
                    (*b*) Benzoic Acid   121°
                    (*c*) Salicylic Acid   157°

By working in the above order, time will not be wasted by having to allow the apparatus to cool between consecutive determinations.

B (I). *Impure Substances.* Prepare an intimate mixture of (*b*) with about one-third of its weight of (*c*).

(II). *Pure Compounds*, decomposing slightly before melting. Lactose. Melts slowly between about 205 and 215°, with preliminary darkening and subsequent decomposition.

NOTE. When it is suspected that an indefinite melting-point is caused by a pure substance undergoing preliminary decomposition, a fairly accurate result may often be obtained by repeating the determination, having first heated the oil to within 5–10° of the melting-point before placing the capillary in position. The compound is thus exposed to the high temperature for such a short time before melting that only slight preliminary decomposition occurs.

Identification by Mixed Melting-points.

It will be clear that melting-point determinations afford a ready method of identifying minute quantities of a solid compound, if the *probable* identity of this compound is already suspected. Thus if there is reason to believe that a particular substance is, for example, benzoic acid, a small quantity of the substance is mixed with a known sample of benzoic acid, and the melting-point of the mixture determined. If the mixture has the normal sharp melting-point of benzoic acid, then the unknown substance must be benzoic acid itself: if the mixture has an indefinite melting-point, then the unknown substance is not identical with benzoic acid and by acting as an impurity is causing the indefinite melting-point. Identification by "mixed melting-points" is a valuable and frequently used process in organic research work.

Experiment 2. Identification by Mixed Melting-points.

Students should be provided with known (labelled) samples of one of the following series of compounds, the samples being finely ground so that no obvious difference in crystal form, *etc.*, is apparent. They should determine the melting-point of each compound in order to assure themselves that these melting-points lie too near together to enable any one compound to be identified by a simple melting-point determination. They should then be given an unknown compound **A** (preferably in coarse crystals), told that it is one member of the series, and then identify it by mixed melting-point determinations.

SERIES I		SERIES II	
Acetanilide	M.p. 113°	Benzoic acid	M.p. 121°
Acetyl-o-toluidine	112°	Succinic anhydride	120°
m-Toluic acid	111°	Hexacetylmannitol*	120°

SERIES III	
Benzamide	M.p. 130°
Phthalic anhydride	130°
β-Pentacetylglucose†	130°
Urea	132°

Corrected Melting-points. In all the above determinations of melting-points, the values obtained are described as "uncorrected," since no allowance has been made for the fact that the column of mercury in the thermometer is at a lower temperature than that in the bulb. For most purposes it is sufficient to record this uncorrected value, which is usually only slightly lower than the corrected value.

Criteria of Purity. Liquid Compounds.

A pure liquid (which distils without decomposition) will have

* Preparation, p. 142.   † Preparation, p. 141.

similarly a sharp boiling-point which will remain constant until the whole of the liquid has boiled off, leaving no residue. Unlike the melting-point, however, this boiling-point, whilst remaining sharp, may vary in value over a range of several degrees, owing to fluctuations in the barometric pressure. The boiling-point of an impure liquid will depend largely on the physical nature of the impurities. If all the impurities are non-volatile, the liquid will have a sharp boiling-point, and the solid impurities will remain behind when the liquid has evaporated. If the impurities are themselves volatile, then the boiling-point of the liquid may (*a*) remain constant (see below), or (*b*) rise steadily as the liquid boils, or (*c*) rise in a series of definite steps, according to the nature and quantity of the impurities present.

Although a pure liquid has a sharp boiling-point, the converse is not necessarily true: a sharp boiling-point does not always indicate a pure liquid, but may be caused by a constant-boiling mixture of two or more liquids. Such mixtures are common in both inorganic and organic chemistry: thus a mixture of 20·2% HCl and 79·8% of water boils steadily at 110°/760 mm.; a mixture of 60·5% benzene and 39·5% methanol has boiling-point 58·3°/760 mm.; a mixture of 14% of ethanol and 76% ethyl iodide has boiling-point 63·0°/760 mm. The difference between a pure liquid and a constant-boiling mixture can easily be detected by redistilling at a different pressure. A pure liquid under these conditions will change its boiling-point, but the composition of the distillate will necessarily remain unchanged: a constant-boiling mixture will however change both in boiling-point and in the composition of the distillate. This change in composition can then be detected by analysis, density determinations, *etc.*

As a guide to the probable occurrence of a constant-boiling mixture, it should be noted that such mixtures most frequently occur when one of the components contains an hydroxyl (−OH) group. Only aqueous and alcoholic mixtures therefore are likely to have a constant boiling-point.

Experimental Determination of Boiling-point. Unless only minute quantities of the liquid are available (*cf.* p. 60), the boiling-point is usually determined by simple distillation. For this purpose, the apparatus shown in Fig. 2 is assembled. A distillation flask **A** of suitable size is fitted to a water-condenser **B**, the water supply of which is arranged as shown. An adaptor **C** is sometimes fitted in turn to the condenser, so that the distillate may be collected directly into a suitable flask **D**, but the use of an adaptor in this way is seldom necessary. The liquid is then placed in the flask **A** (which should not be more than three-fifths filled), some small fragments of unglazed porcelain* added, the thermometer **E** placed in position, and the flask then heated—either on a water-bath if the liquid has a low boiling-point, or else on a sand-bath, or directly over a wire gauze. The following important points with regard to simple distillation should be noted:—

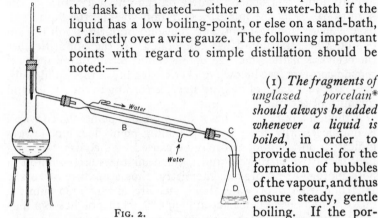

FIG. 2.

(1) *The fragments of unglazed porcelain* *should always be added whenever a liquid is boiled*, in order to provide nuclei for the formation of bubbles of the vapour, and thus ensure steady, gentle boiling. If the porcelain is omitted, the liquid may become superheated, and then suddenly boil with great violence. Fires are often caused by students omitting this precaution when distilling inflammable solvents, which then "bump" so violently that the liquid either pushes the thermometer out of position and boils over, or else shatters the distilling-flask. *Throughout this book, therefore, it is assumed that porcelain is added whenever a distillation is described, and the use of porcelain is mentioned only when it is particularly necessary.*

(2) The thermometer should be so arranged that the top of the bulb is just level with the centre of the side-arm of the distilling-flask.

(3) A water-condenser can be used for any liquid the boiling-point of which does not exceed 140°. Above this temperature, an air-condenser (*i.e.*, a straight glass tube having no jacket) should be used. If a water-condenser is used above 140°, there is always a risk of the condenser cracking at the point where the hot vapour first meets the water-cooled portion.

(4) Low-boiling, inflammable liquids are usually distilled from

* Fragments of unglazed porcelain can be replaced by small dark granules of carborundum (silicon carbide); these ensure steady boiling and remain active when the cold solution is reheated. Their accidental presence in subsequent operations is immediately obvious.

a water-bath for additional safety. Whether a liquid can thus be distilled from a boiling water-bath will depend chiefly on its boiling-point and also on its latent heat, but as a general rule most liquids of boiling-point below 80° may be distilled readily in this way: for liquids of higher boiling-point a sand-bath or direct heating on a gauze is necessary. Thus ethanol (boiling-point 78°) can be distilled from a water-bath: benzene (boiling-point 81°) will boil gently when heated on a water-bath, but not sufficiently vigorously to distil over at an appreciable rate.

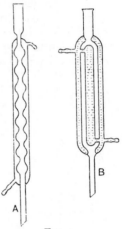

The water-condenser **B** shown in Fig. 2 represents the simplest and cheapest kind, which because of its limited efficiency should be at least 2 feet long. Fig. 3(A) shows a bulb condenser, which, although also cheap, is much more efficient. In Fig. 3(B) is shown the usual double-surface condenser, which, although more costly than the two former condensers, is far more efficient, and need be only one-third to one-half as long as the others. It should therefore be available for reasonably careful students.*

Modifications of the simple distillation are described on pp. 23-24 under Purification of Liquid Substances.

FIG. 3.

Experiment 3. Determination of Boiling-point.

Most students will be familiar with simple distillation from their practical inorganic chemistry. Other students should determine the boiling-point of acetone (56°), using a water-bath and water-condenser, or of benzene (81°), using a sand-bath and water-condenser, and finally of either aniline (184°) or nitrobenzene (210°), using for both these liquids a sand-bath and air-condenser.

Filtration. Before discussing the practical details of the purification of solid substances by recrystallisation, it is convenient to describe here the general methods of filtration. The two principal occasions in organic chemistry when filtration is necessary are:

* A simpler water-condenser having both ends conically ground (cf. (B), p. 45), and a thin-walled inner tube, is lighter and more efficient than those illustrated above.

(A) A solid substance has crystallised from a solution, and it is necessary to separate the crystals (*i.e.*, the solute) from the cold mother-liquor by filtration.

(B) A hot solution has to be filtered to remove traces of insoluble impurities, and kept hot meanwhile to prevent crystallisation of the main solute, which would otherwise choke up the filter.

(A) **Filtration of crystals from the cold mother-liquor.** This type of filtration is almost invariably performed with the aid of a Buchner flask and funnel, by means of which a rapid and almost complete separation can be obtained. The Buchner flask **A** (Fig. 4) consists of a simple thick-walled conical flask with a short side-arm for connection to a water-pump. Into the neck of the flask is fitted the Buchner funnel **B** which consists usually of a cylindrical porcelain funnel, the bed of which is pierced by a number of small holes giving direct access through the stem of the funnel to the flask. Before filtration, one* layer of well-fitting filter-paper is placed in the funnel **B**, and moistened with a few drops of the liquid to be filtered, so that when the suction of the pump is applied the filter-paper adheres firmly to the perforated bed of the funnel, and thus subsequently prevents any solid matter from passing round and under the edge of the paper into the flask and so avoiding filtration. The mixture of crystals and solution is then filtered through the funnel under gentle suction of the pump: when all the mother-liquor has been filtered, some is returned to the vessel which originally contained the mixture, and well stirred to remove any crystals adhering to the sides of the vessel. This portion is then again filtered, and the process is repeated until all the solid material has been transferred to the funnel **B**, and the whole of the mother-liquor has collected in the flask **A**. The action of the pump is then continued until the crystals in **B** are thoroughly drained from traces of the mother-liquor. If a large quantity of material is being collected in the funnel, it should be pressed firmly down, *e.g.* by a clean cork or stopper, during the draining. Students should remember that the speed of filtration is not necessarily proportional to the suction force of the pump. A gentle suction will

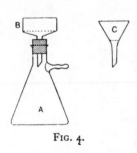

FIG. 4.

---

* Two layers of filter-paper are desirable for aqueous solutions: for organic solvents, however, one layer is usually sufficient.

often cause rapid filtration, whereas increased suction may drag the finer particles of the solute into the pores of the filter-paper, and thus cause filtration to become very slow.

When only a small quantity of solid material has to be filtered from a liquid, the small conical funnel **C**, usually known as a Hirsch funnel, is used in order to collect and drain the material on a very small filter-paper (see p. 68).

One disadvantage of porcelain Buchner funnels (particularly when used in large classes) is the difficulty in detecting and removing solid material which, owing to evaporation of the filtrate, may have collected immediately below the perforated plate. This difficulty is removed in the newer types of funnel which are made of glass, and which have either a transparent glass plate perforated by holes or fine slots, or a plate of fine porous sintered glass. Although the glass funnels are more fragile than the porcelain ones, they will undoubtedly replace the porcelain funnels as they become cheaper.

More advanced students, who may frequently have occasion to filter a very *small* quantity of crystals from a correspondingly small volume of solution, are strongly recommended to use the Irvine filter-cylinder (Fig. 5), which is invaluable for the clean, rapid and complete separation of small crops of crystals. It consists of a glass cylinder **A**, having at the base a simple tap **B**, and at the side a two-way tap **C**, by means of which the cylinder can either be connected directly through to the pump, or alternatively connected through the bottom of **C** to the open air, the pump being simultaneously cut off. A series of Buchner funnels, of various sizes and shapes, fit the top of the cylinder as shown. A mixture of crystals and mother-liquor in a beaker can therefore be filtered as usual through the funnel **D** under suction of the pump. Rotation of the tap **C** then cuts off the suction and relieves the partial vacuum within the cylinder. The mother-liquor can then be run through the tap **B** back into the beaker, the tap **B** closed and **C** opened, thus restarting the suction, and the beaker can then be rinsed out with the mother-liquor, which is filtered again into the cylinder. The process is repeated

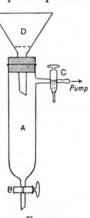

FIG. 5.

until all crystalline material has been transferred to **D**, where it is gently pressed down with the spatula and thoroughly drained. If necessary, the filtrate can be run out of **A**, and the crystals then washed with some other liquid while still under suction on the filter.

(B) **Filtration of hot solutions.** The quickest method of removing traces of insoluble impurities from a hot solution is to filter it in the usual way through a Buchner funnel. The disadvantage of this method is that the heavy porcelain funnel may so chill the solution that crystallisation occurs before filtration is complete and the funnel may become choked with crystals, both above the filter and below in the stem. The disadvantage may be often overcome by boiling a quantity of the pure solvent (particularly if the latter is water) and, immediately before filtration of the solution, placing the filter-papers in the funnel and filtering a moderate quantity of the pure boiling solvent through the funnel into the flask. The solvent is then poured out, and the hot solution at once filtered through the hot apparatus. This preheating of both funnel and flask will often enable a hot solution to be filtered and the clear filtrate transferred into a beaker before any separation of solid matter occurs.

A "hot-water funnel" is a slower and less efficient apparatus for filtering hot solutions. A satisfactory form of the apparatus is shown in Fig. 6, in which the double-walled funnel is heated by blowing steam through the apparatus as shown. A glass filter funnel of the usual type fits snugly into the hot-water funnel. This type has the advantage that, during the filtration of a hot inflammable liquid, the steam generator (and therefore the heating apparatus) can be removed to a safe distance. It should be noted that the inner glass funnel should have a stem so short that it projects only just below the outer metal funnel. If the stem is longer it serves merely to cool the filtered solution, which may then crystallise and completely stop the filtration.

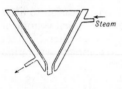

FIG. 6.

For the filtration of small quantities of dilute solution, it is often possible to dispense with the outer heater, and use the ordinary glass funnel which has been heated above a flame immediately before use.

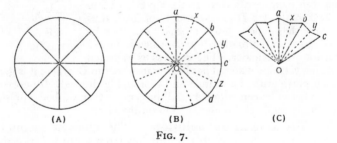

(A)   (B)   (C)

FIG. 7.

The filtration of any solution through the ordinary conical funnel may be hastened considerably by the use of a "fluted" filter-paper, instead of one folded into quarters in the usual way. The folding of a fluted paper may be learnt far more readily by a demonstration in the laboratory than by any written description.

The following is one of the simplest ways of fluting a filter-paper. First make four folds in the paper so that the latter is divided into eight equal sectors (Fig. 7(A)), the two halves of the paper on each occasion being folded *forwards*, so that all the folds tend to be concave. Now take each segment in turn (*e.g.*, **aOb**, Fig. 7(B)) and fold the points **a** and **b** *backwards* until they meet, so that a new convex fold **Ox** is made between them: continue in this way making new folds **Oy**, **Oz**, *etc.*, around the paper. When the complete fluted paper (Fig. 7(C)) is placed in the ordinary conical funnel, it will possess a series of regular corrugations, and only the edges of the folds **Oa**, **Ob**, **Oc**, *etc.*, will be in contact with the funnel.

Purification of Solid Substances.

Recrystallisation. The process of purification by recrystallisation is undoubtedly the most frequent operation in practical organic chemistry, and it is one which, when cleanly and efficiently performed, should give great pleasure to the chemist, particularly if the original crude material is in a very impure and filthy condition. Yet no operation is carried out so badly, wastefully (and thoughtlessly) by students in general, not only by elementary students, but often by research students of several years' experience. The student who intends later to do advanced work must master the process, for unless he can choose a suitable solvent and then successfully recrystallise often minute quantities of material, he will frequently find his work completely arrested.

Students are familiar with the general process of recrystallisation from their more elementary inorganic work. Briefly, it consists in first finding a solvent which will dissolve the crude material readily when hot, but only to a small extent when cold. The crude substance is then dissolved in a minimum of the boiling solvent, the solution filtered if necessary to remove any insoluble impurities, and then cooled, when the solute will crystallise out, leaving the greater part of the impurities in solution. The crop of crystals is then filtered off, and the process repeated until the crystals are pure, and all impurities remain in the mother-liquor.

Students are sometimes puzzled at the extraordinarily general application of the process of recrystallisation, since it may appear to them to depend on the *assumption* that the impurities are more soluble than the main product, and therefore will always eventually be left in the mother-liquor. Consideration will show that this assumption is not necessarily made: the assumption actually made is that the impurities are either more soluble than the main product, or, if less soluble, are present in such small proportion that in spite of the comparative solubilities they will be eliminated by recrystallisation. The two cases may be exemplified thus. Suppose the crude mixture contains 97% of the required compound **A**, and 3% of an impurity **B**. Then if

(1) **A** is less soluble in a given solvent than **B**.

It is clear that repeated recrystallisation will rapidly leave **B** entirely in the mother-liquors, and thus provide a pure sample of **A**.

(2) **A** is more soluble in the solvent than **B**.

Suppose that a given volume of the solvent *when cold* can dissolve 15 g. of **A** and 5 g. of **B**. If 100 g. of the crude product are dissolved in this volume of the hot solvent, and the solution allowed to cool, then (ignoring the small mutual effect on the solubility of each compound caused by the presence of the other) it is clear that 82 g. of **A** will crystallise, whilst the whole of **B** will remain in solution, since the latter is not saturated with respect to **B**.

The choice of a solvent is of course determined primarily by its suitability for the actual recrystallisation of the given crude product. If two or more solvents appear to be almost equally suitable for the recrystallisation, the final choice should depend on the inflammability (and therefore risk in use) of the solvent, and also on its cost. It is assumed that a solvent which might have any chemical action on the compound has already been debarred. The chief solvents normally available are:

Solvent.	B.P.	Inflammability.	Remarks.
Water (distilled)	100°	Non-inflammable	To be used whenever suitable.
Ether	35°	Inflammable	Avoid when possible (see below).
Acetone	56°	,,	Should preferably be dried before use.
Methanol	65°	,,	Toxic
Benzene	81°	,,	,,
Petroleum	Available in fractions of b.p. 40–60°, 60–80°, 80–100°, 100–120°	,,	Frequently called "light petroleum" or "petrol ether." Unless specially purified, contains sulphur derivatives, *etc.*, as impurities.

Solvent.	B.P.	Inflammability.	Remarks.

Acetic acid (glacial)   118°   Not readily inflammable

Ethanol

(a) Absolute ethanol. Anhydrous, but contains some benzene from azeotropic distillation of (b) with benzene.
(b) Rectified ethanol, contains 95·6% ethanol, 4·4% water. Care in using it with hygroscopic substances.
(c) Colourless industrial methylated spirit [I.M.S.], contains 95 vols of (b) and 5 vols of wood naphtha.

Remarks: Hygroscopic. Hot liquid gives pungent fumes. Frequently used to dissolve strong oxidising agents (p. 259).

Chloroform   61°   Non-inflammable   May contain traces of HCl, due to oxidation or hydrolysis.

Carbon tetrachloride   77°   ,,

Carbon disulphide should never be used if any alternative solvent is available, as it has a dangerously low flash-point, and its vapours form exceedingly explosive mixtures with air. Ether as a solvent for recrystallisation is much safer than carbon disulphide, but again should be avoided whenever possible, partly on account of the danger of fires, and partly because the filtered solution tends to creep up the walls of the containing vessel and there deposit solid matter by complete evaporation instead of preferential crystallisation.

Homologous mono-alkyl ethers of ethylene glycol, such as mono-ethyl glycol (or 2-ethoxyethanol), $HOC_2H_4OC_2H_5$, form excellent solvents as they combine to a large extent the solvent properties of alcohols and ethers. The monoethyl and the monomethyl members have the technical names of ethyl cellosolve and methyl cellosolve respectively. Dioxan (or diethylene dioxide) $O\begin{subarray}{c}CH_2CH_2\\CH_2CH_2\end{subarray}O$, and dimethylformamide, $HCON(CH_3)_2$, also possess exceptional solvent properties. The alkylglycols, dioxan and dimethyl-formamide should be used with caution, however, as their hot vapours are poisonous.

Experimental Directions for Recrystallisation. The complete process consists of the following stages, each of which is discussed in full:

(1) *Choice of a Solvent.* No theoretical considerations are of any real use for this purpose, except the very rough generalisation that a solvent will dissolve most readily compounds similar in

constitution to itself: thus alcohol will usually dissolve other hydroxy compounds, benzene will dissolve hydrocarbons, *etc.*, but there are many exceptions to this rule. Therefore the experimental determination is alone of value. Place about 0·1 g. of the crude powdered compound in a clean dry test-tube, and add sufficient of the possible solvent just to cover the compound. If the compound dissolves readily in the cold, the solvent is obviously unsuitable. If it does not dissolve, warm the mixture *gently* over a very small Bunsen flame until the liquid boils: it is advantageous at this stage to hold the forefinger loosely over the mouth of the tube to prevent undue loss of vapour. Continue adding the liquid if necessary until almost all the substance has dissolved. If a large amount of the solvent is required (*e.g.*, one-half to two-thirds of the tube) then the low solubility renders the solvent unsuitable. If an almost clear solution is obtained, cool by immersing the tube preferably in a mixture of ice and water, or alternatively in cold water. (If benzene is the solvent, cold water alone must be used, as benzene will itself crystallise in ice-water.) Shake the mixture gently in the tube. If crystallisation does not rapidly start, the failure may be due to lack of suitable nuclei for crystal-growth. Therefore scratch the tube below the surface of the solution with a glass rod: the fine scratches on the walls form excellent sites for crystal-growth, and crystals often form rapidly after scratching. Repeat this process with various other possible solvents (using a fresh clean tube for each test) until the best solvent has been selected, and then note carefully the approximate proportions of the solute and the solvent for efficient recrystallisation.

Sometimes the crude substance may contain an insoluble impurity, and on cooling the solution it may be difficult to judge how much of the solid matter is merely undissolved impurity and how much is solute which has subsequently crystallised from solution. To avoid this difficulty, the hot solution should be filtered, and should thus always be absolutely clear before cooling is attempted. Therefore filter the hot solution into a clean tube through a *very small* fluted filter-paper contained in a correspondingly small glass funnel, which should have had its stem cut off as that shown in Fig. 6, p. 12 (and for the same reason). Unless the upper part of the filter is cut away to reduce its size to a minimum, a large proportion of the solution will remain held mechanically in the pores of the paper itself and only a few drops of clear filtrate will be obtained.

(2) *Repetition of Recrystallisation on Larger Scale.* Having now determined both the best solvent and also the approximate

proportions of solute and solvent for recrystallisation, the main bulk of the crude material may be recrystallised. If the solvent is water, the material is placed in a beaker or (better) in a conical flask, and a volume of water which is judged to be just insufficient for the purpose is then added, and the mixture gently heated (with the usual addition of fragments of unglazed porcelain) to boiling. More water is then cautiously added until either a clear solution is obtained or until the undissolved material is recognised from the experience gained in (1) as being insoluble impurity. In either case, the boiling solution is then filtered. For this purpose steps must be taken to prevent undue cooling of the solution during filtration, otherwise crystallisation will occur prematurely and choke the filter. This applies more particularly of course if the preliminary test in (1) has shown that crystallisation starts very rapidly on cooling the hot solution. Therefore if a Buchner funnel and flask are used, this apparatus must usually be preheated by the filtration of some pure boiling water, as described on p. 12, or alternatively a heated funnel must be used.

If an organic solvent is used, boiling in an open vessel is obviously not permissible, as the operation would be wasteful in all cases, and dangerous with an inflammable solvent. The crude material is therefore placed either in a round-bottomed bolt-head flask (Fig. 8) or in a conical flask, the solvent added (again in slight deficiency) and a reflux water-condenser fitted to the flask as shown. The mixture is boiled either on a water-bath or over a gauze, and then more solvent added cautiously down the condenser until a clear solution (apart from insoluble impurities) is again obtained. It is then filtered hot as described above.

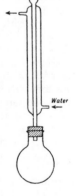

Water

The hot filtered solution is then without delay poured into a lipped beaker or a conical flask (*not into an evaporating-basin*, since it is crystallisation and not evaporation which is now required), the beaker covered with a watch-glass, and then cooled in ice-water. As cooling proceeds, the solution should be stirred from time to time to facilitate crystallisa-

Fig. 8.

tion, and when crystallisation appears complete, the cooling should be continued for *at least* another 15 minutes.

Occasionally the solute may separate (particularly if strong external cooling is rapidly applied) as a metastable oil or syrup, which solidifies on standing although a considerable interval may elapse before crystallisation occurs. This should be avoided, for even if the oil subsequently crystallises well, it will probably occlude a moderate quantity of crude mother-liquor, and its purity will therefore not be high. In such cases it is best to re-heat the mixture until a clear hot solution is obtained, and then allow it to cool spontaneously, stirring and scratching with a glass rod from time to time. It is thus often possible to induce crystallisation to start, and it will then proceed without the production of the less stable oil. During the cooling and scratching, a *minute* quantity of the crude material may occasionally be added to " seed " the solution and thus facilitate initial crystallisation. Formation of an oil or a syrup on attempted recrystallisation is most likely to occur when an entirely new preparation is carried out in the laboratory. When successful recrystallisation is once accomplished, the laboratory becomes " inoculated " with nuclei of the crystals, and subsequent recrystallisation usually proceeds readily.* Hence this difficulty is far more likely to occur in a research laboratory than in one in which routine preparations are repeated at regular intervals.

When an organic substance is found to be freely soluble in one solvent and insoluble in another, a mixture of these solvents (if miscible) will often prove excellent for recrystallisation, the best proportion of the two solvents in the mixture being found by small-scale tests. It sometimes happens, however, that the solute (particularly if it possesses a rather low melting-point) separates from such a mixture as a fine emulsion, which solidifies on further cooling. In such cases, a hot concentrated solution of the crude substance should be prepared in the liquid (*e.g.*, ethanol) in which it is freely soluble, and then the other liquid in which it is almost insoluble (*e.g.*, water) should be added drop by drop with stirring until an emulsion or a cloudiness *just* appears. A clear solution is now again obtained either by warming momentarily, or by adding a *few* drops of the first solvent, and it is then allowed to cool spontaneously: if the cloudiness should reappear, a few more drops of the first solvent are added. A clear solution can thus be maintained until the temperature has fallen so low that crystallisation starts: the solution can then be stirred and cooled without further risk of emulsion-formation. Examples of this process are described for *o*-nitrophenol (p. 172) and amino-azobenzene (p. 209).

When crystallisation is complete, the mixture of crystals and crude mother-liquor is filtered at the pump, again using a Buchner funnel and flask as described on p. 10, and the crystals remaining in the funnel are then pressed well down with a spatula whilst continual suction of the pump is applied, in order to drain the mother-liquor from the crystals as effectively as possible. If it has been found in the preliminary tests that the crystalline material is almost insoluble in the *cold* solvent, the crystals in the

---

* For an example, see p. 143.

funnel, after a short preliminary draining from the mother-liquor, may be quickly washed on the filter with a small quantity of the pure solvent, and the draining continued without interruption. An efficient removal of traces of the mother-liquor can thus be effected.

(3) *Drying of Recrystallised Material.* It is now required to obtain the recrystallised material in a thoroughly dry condition and this can seldom be achieved solely by draining on the filter. One rapid method of drying the thoroughly drained material is to transfer it with the aid of a spatula on to a pad of several thicknesses of drying paper (*i.e.*, coarse-grained, smooth-surfaced filter-paper), place a similar pad on top and then press the material strongly, occasionally transferring it to fresh paper as the earlier sheets become too soiled by the mother-liquor absorbed. The final traces of mother-liquor can then be rapidly removed (if the material is physically and chemically stable up to 100°) by drying in a steam or electric oven. The chief disadvantage of this method however is that the recrystallised material is always apt to become contaminated with filter-paper fibre, and moreover a

well-crystallised material may be crushed by the pressure to a fine powder. If time permits, therefore, the drained material should always be finally dried in a desiccator. For this purpose the simple and inexpensive atmospheric desiccator (Fig. 9(A)) is frequently used: the drying agent employed is usually calcium chloride, or small

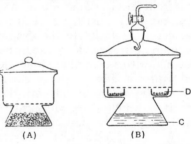

FIG. 9.

uniform fragments of silica gel. The latter are coloured blue with a cobalt salt, and their colour changes to red as the material becomes spent: it can be regenerated by heating. Far more rapid and efficient drying is, however, obtained with a vacuum desiccator of the type shown in Fig. 9(B).

A very effective "universal" filling for vacuum desiccators is obtained by having concentrated sulphuric acid **C** in the bottom of the desiccator, and "flake" sodium hydroxide* **D** in the inverted glass collar supported on the shoulders of the desiccator, the collar then being covered

* Supplied as "flake" or "petal" sodium hydroxide by chemical manufacturers.

with wire gauze. Very rapid drying is thereby obtained, and any acid or basic vapours which may be evolved are absorbed, the interior of the desiccator thus remaining clean and odourless. This is of particular advantage when drying a substance, e.g., an amine hydrochloride, which has been recrystallised from concentrated hydrochloric acid, and which would otherwise fill the desiccator with hydrogen chloride as drying proceeded.

If a compound has been recrystallised from petrol, benzene, etc., some freshly cut shavings of clean paraffin wax should be added to the calcium chloride in (A) or to the sodium hydroxide in **D**. The surface of the wax absorbs organic solvent vapours (particularly the hydrocarbons) and the last trace of such solvents is thus readily removed from the recrystallised material.

When using a desiccator, the recrystallised material in the Buchner funnel should be transferred to a piece of clean glazed paper with the aid of a spatula, and the last traces carefully removed from the sides of the funnel and the damp filter by careful use of the spatula, in such a way that the surface of the filter is not torn or scratched, and that filter-paper fibre does not contaminate the crystals. The latter can then be tipped without loss from the glazed paper on to a watch-glass. If the atmospheric desiccator (A) is used, the open watch-glass should be left in the desiccator to facilitate the evaporation of the solvent. If the vacuum desiccator (B) is used, the watch-glass should always be covered with a second inverted glass, otherwise, unless the air is subsequently admitted very carefully, the sudden draught may sweep the finer crystals off the watch-glass: moreover, the inverted watch-glass will protect the crystals if, during the evacuation of the desiccator, the pump should for any reason cease working and so allow a mixture of air and water to rush back into the desiccator. As a further safeguard, a Buchner flask arranged as a trap (as **K** in Fig. 14, p. 31) should always be fitted between the desiccator and the pump.

(4) *Checking the Purification.* The purity of the dry re-crystallised material must now be determined, as it is possible that repeated recrystallisation may be necessary to obtain the pure material. The purity is therefore checked by a melting-point determination, and the recrystallisation must be repeated until a sharp melting-point is obtained. Should the compound have no well-defined melting-point (e.g., the salt of an organic acid or base), it must be analysed for one suitable component element, until its analysis agrees closely with that theoretically required.

Experiment 4. Choice of Solvent and Complete Recrystallisation. Students should be supplied with distilled water and with the more common organic solvents, and also with the compounds mentioned below. Taking each compound in turn they should decide, by the methods described in (1) above, which of these six solvents is the best for recrystallisation. They should then recrystallise about 5 g. of at least two of the compounds, dry the product, and whenever possible take its melting-point.

Naphthalene, oxalic acid (hydrated), cinnamic acid, acetamide, benzamide, m-dinitrobenzene, p-nitrophenol, toluene p-sulphonamide.

Students should appreciate that this is probably the most important experimental work (for their purpose) described in this book, and it should therefore be performed with great care. Moreover, on subsequent occasions in the laboratory when short periods are available, e.g., during the longer stages of a preparation, they can put this time to valuable use by taking *small* quantities of organic reagents from the side-shelves, and practising for themselves the process of selecting (on a test-tube scale) a suitable solvent for recrystallisation.

Decolorisation by Animal Charcoal.* It sometimes happens (particularly with aromatic and heterocyclic compounds) that a crude product may contain a coloured impurity, which on recrystallisation dissolves in the boiling solvent, but is then partly occluded by crystals as they form and grow in the cooling solution. Sometimes a very tenacious occlusion may thus occur, and repeated and very wasteful recrystallisation may be necessary to eliminate the impurity. Moreover, the amount of the impurity present may be so small that the melting-point and analytical values of the compound are not sensibly affected, yet the appearance of the sample is ruined. Such impurities can usually be readily removed by boiling the substance in solution with a small quantity of finely powdered animal charcoal for a short time, and then filtering the solution while hot. The animal charcoal adsorbs the coloured impurity, and the filtrate is usually almost free from extraneous colour and deposits therefore pure crystals. This decolorisation by animal charcoal occurs most readily in aqueous solution, but can be performed in almost any organic solvent. Care should be taken not to use an excessive quantity

---

* Sometimes termed activated or decolorising charcoal, to distinguish it from wood charcoal, which absorbs gases.

of charcoal, however, as it tends to adsorb some of the solute as well as the coloured impurity.

Students should distinguish carefully between the animal charcoal used for decolorisation, and the wood charcoal which is used for absorbing easily liquefiable gases, and which is therefore used in gas respirators and also, when chilled in liquid air, for obtaining high vacua.

Animal charcoal can usually be used as described above without any serious risk of impurities originally present in the charcoal itself dissolving in the hot solvent, and then separating again with the recrystallised material. To remove such risk entirely, the animal charcoal can be boiled under reflux with dilute hydrochloric acid (1 : 1 by volume) for 3 hours. The mixture is then diluted with hot distilled water, filtered through a Buchner funnel, and washed *repeatedly* with much boiling distilled water until all trace of acid has been removed. It is then well drained and finally dried by heating gently in an evaporating-basin over a sand-bath until a fine dry powder is obtained.

Experiment 5. Decolorisation of Crude Sulphanilic Acid.

"Technical" sulphanilic acid is usually almost black in colour. Place 6 g. of the crude powdered acid in each of two conical flasks **A** and **B** (of about 200–250 ml. capacity), add 100 ml. of distilled water to each, but add 0·5–1 g. of animal charcoal to the flask **A** alone. Heat the two flasks side by side, so that the contents boil *gently* for about 5 minutes and the volume of the solutions is thus only slightly reduced. Now filter each solution rapidly. This can be done in two ways: (*a*) At the pump, using Buchner funnels and flasks which have been preheated by the filtration of boiling distilled water. Pour the filtrates into two beakers and allow to cool spontaneously side by side for comparison. (*b*) Through ordinary conical funnels fitted with fluted filter-papers and preheated by the filtration of boiling distilled water. In this case collect the filtrates directly into two conical flasks. Crystallisation occurs rapidly. When the solutions are cold and crystallisation complete, filter through cold Buchner funnels. Compare carefully the colour of (i) the two hot filtrates before crystallisation starts. (ii) the crystals when filtered and drained. The filtrate and crystals obtained from the flask **A** (using charcoal) should be colourless, whereas those from **B** will both retain a deep brown colour.

A similar experiment can be performed with commercial aniline hydrochloride (or "aniline salt").

Animal charcoal has a further use. Occasionally, when recrystallising a crude product, it is found that the hot solution contains a very fine suspension of an insoluble impurity. This suspension may be so fine that, although apparent to the eye, it passes freely through the usual filter-paper (particularly when a Buchner funnel is used), and thus cannot easily be eliminated. Alternatively the suspension may be easily held back by the filter-paper in the Buchner funnel, but then may rapidly block up the pores of the filter and so arrest filtration almost completely, with the result that crystallisation occurs in the cooling solution while it is still in the Buchner funnel, *i.e.*, before filtration is complete. Both these difficulties can usually be overcome by boiling the solution with a small quantity of animal charcoal. The latter readily adsorbs such fine suspensions, and the hot solution can then be filtered clearly and rapidly through the Buchner funnel.

Sublimation. This process is occasionally used for the purification of solid organic compounds. Its use is necessarily limited to those compounds which on heating pass readily and directly from the solid to the vapour state, with a subsequent ready reversal of this process when the vapour is cooled. A simple form of apparatus which gives good results is shown in Fig. 10. The dry crude material is placed in a small evaporating-basin **A**, which is placed on a wire gauze. **A** is then covered with a filter-paper **B** which is pierced by a number of small holes (about 2 mm. in diameter), made in an upward direction. A glass funnel **C**, the rim of which is rather smaller than the largest diameter of **A**, is then inverted as shown over the paper **B**. The basin **A** is then *gently* heated by a small Bunsen flame, which should be carefully protected from side draughts by screens, so that the material in **A** receives a steady uniform supply of heat. The material vaporises, and the vapour passes up through the holes into the cold funnel **C**. Here it cools and condenses as fine crystals on the upper surface of the

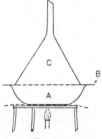

FIG. 10.

paper **B** and on the walls of **C**. When almost the whole of the material in **A** has vaporised, the heating is stopped and the pure sublimed material collected. In using such an apparatus, it is clearly necessary to adjust the supply of heat so that the crude material in **A** is being steadily vaporised, while the funnel **C** does not become more than luke-warm.

For an example of sublimation, see the preparation of anthraquinone, p. 259: for semi-micro sublimation, see p. 69.

Purification of Liquid Substances.

The purification of liquids is almost invariably performed by distillation, and the type of distillation employed will depend largely on the nature of the impurities and in particular whether they are volatile or non-volatile. The commonest impurity in liquid compounds, namely water, should however be removed before distillation whenever conveniently possible.

Drying of Liquid Compounds.

Liquids are almost invariably dried by being kept in contact with a suitable powdered solid dehydrating agent, the dehydration being occasionally facilitated by boiling the liquid gently under reflux. When dehydration is complete, the liquid is either decanted or (better) filtered from the dehydrating agent, and can then at once be further purified by distillation. The commonest dehydrating agents, with their practical limitations, are:

Calcium chloride (granular).	Cannot be used for alcohols, phenols or amines, with all of which it combines. Not advisable for acidic liquids, as ordinary calcium chloride always contains some calcium hydroxide owing to partial hydrolysis during preparation.
Calcium oxide (quicklime).	Usually used for alcohols (see p. 88). Cannot be used for acidic compounds, nor for esters, which it would hydrolyse.
Potassium hydroxide.	Particularly suitable for amines. Obviously cannot be used for any liquids affected by alkalis, *e.g.*, acids, phenols, esters.
Potassium carbonate.	Sometimes used in place of potassium hydroxide for amines, *etc.*, when a strongly alkaline drying agent is to be avoided.
Sodium sulphate (powdered anhydrous).	Can be used on almost all occasions, but its dehydrating action is rather slow.
Magnesium sulphate (powdered anhydrous).	A neutral drying agent, which, like sodium sulphate, can be used on most occasions. Its drying action is more rapid than that of sodium sulphate.
Calcium sulphate ("Drierite").	Applicable to all liquids.
Metallic sodium (preferably as wire).	Used particularly for ethers. Cannot be used for any compound affected by alkalis, or easily subject to reduction (owing to the hydrogen evolved during dehydration).

Liquids are occasionally purified by removing impurities as constant-boiling mixtures, or by shaking with concentrated sulphuric acid and subsequently separating the dried liquid from the acid: the second method is therefore limited to liquids which are insoluble in, and chemically unaffected by, the strong acid (*e.g.*, benzene, anhydrous chloral).

Distillation. If the impurities in a liquid are non-volatile, the liquid may be purified by direct distillation, the impurities remaining in the distilling-flask. This process is therefore essentially the same as a simple distillation for boiling-point determination, and has been already described on pp. 7-9.

If, however, the impurities are themselves volatile liquids, then the separation of these impurities from the main bulk of the required substance is achieved by fractional distillation. If an ordinary distilling-flask, such as that shown in Fig. 2, p. 8, is used for this purpose, however, only a very partial separation of the liquid components of the crude mixture is usually obtained, unless there is a considerable difference in boiling-point between the impurities and the main component. To obtain a much sharper and more complete separation, a fractionating column is employed.

Fractional Distillation. For this type of distillation, the fractionating column is inserted vertically between the flask containing the boiling liquid and the condenser. The principle of a fractionating column is that, as the vapours ascend the column from the boiling mixture below, the higher-boiling components are condensed and returned to the flask, the ascending column of vapour being thus steadily "scrubbed" by the descending column of liquid condensate. The ascending column of vapour becomes therefore steadily richer in the lowest-boiling component, and the descending column of condensate steadily richer in the highest-boiling component. It follows that the prime factor which determines the efficiency of a column is the extent to which the vapour is "scrubbed" by the condensate, and columns are therefore designed to make this "scrubbing" as intimate as possible. Text-books of theoretical organic chemistry frequently illustrate remarkable and weird types of fractionating column which the practical chemist never encounters. For actual use in the laboratory two types of column are recommended. (A) For quick rough separations, or (more particularly) for the separation of two components having a considerable difference in boiling-point, the pear column (Fig. 11(A)) is useful. The increase in cooling surface produced by pear-shaped bulbs causes considerable condensation, and the condensate, steadily dripping down from the lower shoulder of each bulb, comes in moderate contact with the ascending vapour. The efficiency of a column can, of course, be increased by increasing the number of bulbs in the column. (B) For accurate work, the column shown in Fig. 11(B) is probably the most efficient and generally useful type available in most laboratories. It consists of a simple glass column, packed with very short sections of glass tubing, the bore of these sections preferably decreasing steadily up the column. For general purposes, the column itself should be about 11–12 mm. internal diameter, and the glass sections* towards the bottom of the column should be about 5 mm. long and 6 mm. external diameter, and towards the top about 3 mm. long and 5 mm. diameter: the length of the column *actually packed* with the tubes should be about 20 cm., but for low-boiling mixtures this length of the column may be considerably increased, and for high-boiling mixtures correspondingly decreased. To retain the glass tubes in position, it is inadvisable to constrict the column immediately below the tube, as this readily causes "choking" of the column when in use. It is better either to seal across the inside of the column a very fine glass rod, on which the tubes may rest, or (more easily) to have one section of glass tubing rather larger than the rest at the bottom of the column and to fix this permanently in place by fusing it carefully to the wall of the column. The sections *must* be arranged as irregularly as possible in the column: if they tend to arrange themselves regularly they should be well shaken up, otherwise "channelling" of the condensed liquid will occur and the efficiency of the column will be decreased. These sections of glass tubing are preferable to similar sections of metal for two reasons, (*a*) the metal sections, because of their low specific heat, do not condense sufficient of the ascending vapour, and the efficiency of the column falls considerably in consequence; (*b*) if the tube becomes fouled in use, particularly by traces of tarry pro-

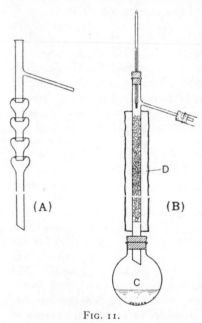

(A)   (B)

Fig. 11.

---

* These glass sections for fractionating columns may be purchased from Messrs. Quickfit & Quartz, Ltd., Quickfit Works, Stone, Staffs, ST15 0BG.

ducts, it can always be cleaned by pouring acids, dichromate mixture, *etc.*, down the column, or even by being allowed to stand overnight immersed in such cleaning agents. For the fractionation of high-boiling liquids it is advisable to have a lagging of cotton-wool **D** around the column as shown.

To use such a column, the crude liquid is placed in a round-bottomed flask **C** having a short wide neck, the usual fragments of unglazed porcelain are added, and the column then fixed in position, great care being taken to ensure that it is mounted absolutely vertically, again in order to avoid channelling. A water-condenser is then fitted in turn to the side-arm of the column, particularly when the components of the mixture have low boiling-points. The mixture is then heated with a *very small* flame, carefully protected from draughts to ensure a uniform supply of heat. It is essential that the initial heating of the liquid in **C** (while it is still mounting the cold column) should not be hurried, as considerable extra condensation occurs while the column is warming up, and the latter may easily choke: when once distillation has started, and a thermal equilibrium has been established between the column and its surroundings, the tendency to choke should disappear. The heating is then adjusted until the distillate is issuing from the side-arm of the column not faster than about 1 *drop every* 4-5 *seconds*. In these circumstances, so efficient a fractionation should be obtained that, when the lowest-boiling fraction has distilled over, distillation completely ceases, as the next lower fraction is refluxing definitely below the side-arm of the column. The heating is then *cautiously* increased, and a sharp rise in boiling-point (and therefore a sharp fractionation) should occur as the second fraction starts to distil. Although in Fig. 12(B) a condenser is shown fitted to the side-arm of the column, this is required only for low-boiling components: for most mixtures, however, the above rate of distillation, necessary for efficient fractionation, will be accompanied by complete condensation in the side-arm of the column, from which the successive fractions may be collected directly.

In using a column of this type, it is essential that the distillation be not hurried. Although the complete fractionation may therefore take a moderate time, yet the fractionation is so efficient that the over-all time for the complete process is very much less than when more rapid columns are used, for in the latter case the fractionation usually has to be repeated several times in order to obtain as complete a result.

Experiment 6. Fractional Distillation of a Mixture of Benzene and Toluene. Fractionally distil about 40 ml. of a mixture of equal volumes of benzene and toluene, using the type of fractionating column shown in Fig. 11(B), in which about 18–20 cm. of the column are actually filled with glass sections, but in which the cotton-wool lagging is not used. Distil *very slowly*, so that the total distillation occupies about 1½ hours. Shield the apparatus very carefully from draughts. Collect the fractions having the b.ps (a) 80–85°, (b) 85–107°, (c) 107–111°. A sharp separation should be obtained, e.g., these fractions should have volumes of about 19, 2, and 17 ml. respectively.

It will be found that the first few drops of the lowest fraction are always cloudy, owing mainly to the fine film of water adsorbed on the glass surfaces within the column.

Distillation under Reduced Pressure. Occasionally a liquid, when distillation is attempted under atmospheric pressure, will undergo partial or complete decomposition before its boiling-point is reached. To overcome this difficulty, the liquid is distilled under reduced pressure, so that its boiling-point shall be definitely below its thermal decomposition point.

It has already been pointed out that a liquid even when subjected to simple atmospheric distillation may become superheated and then "bump" violently in consequence: this danger is greatly increased during distillation under reduced pressure and therefore a specially designed flask, known as a Claisen flask, is used to decrease the risk of superheating. In Fig. 12(A) a Claisen flask **D** is shown, fitted up as part of one of the simplest types of vacuum-distillation apparatus.*

The flask has two necks, the right-hand one carrying a thermometer in the usual way, while the left-hand one carries a stout capillary tube **E**, which is closed at the top by a short piece of pressure tubing and a screw-clip, by which the amount of air passing through the capillary can be regulated. The capillary tube **E** should always be prepared by drawing out a piece of thick-walled capillary tube of about 4–5 mm. external bore, and then adjusting the length of the fine capillary tube below so that it reaches to within 1–2 mm. of the bottom of the flask: it should never be prepared by drawing out an ordinary glass "quill" tube, otherwise the fine capillary so obtained will be too fragile, and will probably snap during the course of the distillation. The side-

* For all vacuum distillations, a trap (cf. K, Fig. 14, p. 31) should be fitted near the pump, in case the water "sucks back".

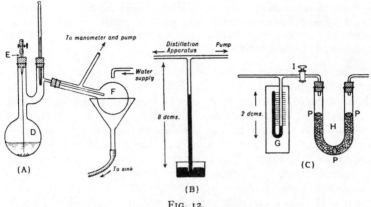

FIG. 12.

arm is then fitted to an ordinary distillation-flask **F**, which serves as a receiver for the distillate. Well-bored rubber stoppers should be used throughout the apparatus, and immediately before being inserted in position should be lightly smeared with a solution of good-quality rubber in benzene to ensure an air-tight fit. (For a ground-glass distilling flask similar to **D**, see Fig. 23(F), p. 46.)

Before performing a distillation, the flask **D** is filled not more than half-full with the liquid, *some fragments of porcelain† added*, and the capillary, thermometer and receiver then placed in position, the side-arm of the receiver **F** being connected through a manometer to an efficient water-pump. As the pressure falls to a steady value, the screw-clip above the capillary **E** is adjusted until a steady stream of fine bubbles is emerging through the lower end of **E**. If it is anticipated that the liquid will boil below about 100°, the whole of the bulb of the receiver **F** is cooled with a stream of water as shown, the waste being collected by a funnel below and run off to the sink. In most cases, however, it is sufficient to have the bulb of **F** dipping into a basin of ice-water. A water-condenser is not necessary with this apparatus if the distillation is carried out slowly. The liquid in **D** is then heated steadily, preferably in an oil-bath, and in these circumstances steady ebullition should occur: the temperature of the vapour and the pressure in the apparatus, indicated by the thermometer and the manometer respectively, should then be read.

† Or carborundum nodules, cf. p. 8.

Examples of the use of this apparatus (or that shown in Fig. 14, p. 31) will be found in the preparation of phenylhydrazine (p. 195), ethyl acetoacetate (p. 264), ethyl malonate (p. 272), quinaldine (p. 300), triethyl phosphite (p. 308) and di-isopropyl hydrogen phosphite (p. 309).

The simplest form of manometer for this purpose is an ordinary barometer tube, as shown in Fig. 12(B): this form has the disadvantages, however, that the surface of the mercury in the tube is easily fouled and then difficult to read, and that in any case an accurate measurement of the long column of mercury is not simple.* A neater and more accurate type of manometer is shown in Fig. 12(C). The mercury is contained in a fine glass U-tube **G** fused to a horizontal cross-piece, which is sealed on one side, and on the other leads through the tap **I** to a thick-walled U-tube **H**, which contains granular calcium chloride in the left-hand arm, and soda-lime in the right-hand arm, the reagents being kept in position by the three plugs of glass wool **P**. To prevent fouling of the mercury surface, the manometer should be placed not directly in line between the distillation apparatus and the pump as in (B), but as a "side-arm" between these two. With this precaution, and with the additional protection by the reagents in **H**, the mercury surface should with care remain clean for years.

When constructing a manometer of the type shown in Fig. 12(C), it is important to apply a very high vacuum (*e.g.*, with a Hy-Vac pump) to the manometer while the mercury in the left-hand (sealed) limb is heated until it boils: unless this is done, traces of air will remain in this limb and cause inaccurate readings. During a distillation, the tap **I** should be kept closed except when a pressure reading is being taken: if it is left open indefinitely, a sudden default by the distillation apparatus or by the pump may cause the mercury in the sealed limb of **G** to fly back and fracture the top of the limb.

Other similar types of manometer, usually reading over a range of about 10–60 mm., are available in many laboratories.

Fractional Distillation under Reduced Pressure. One great disadvantage of the simple vacuum-distillation apparatus shown in Fig. 12(A) is that, if more than one fraction distils, the whole process has to be stopped after collecting each consecutive fraction, in order to change the receiver **F**. This may be overcome by replacing the simple receiving flask **F** by a "pig" (Fig. 13) which collects consecutive

---

* Furthermore, the open exposure of mercury in any apparatus, particularly one in frequent use, is to be avoided, as even at room temperature the mercury gives appreciable quantity of the toxic vapour.

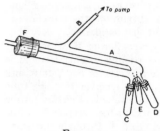

FIG. 13.

fractions without interruption of the distillation. The "pig" consists of a stout glass receiver **A**, which fits either over the side-arm of the Claisen flask or, in the case of low-boiling liquids, over the end of the condenser which is fitted to this side-arm. It has at the top an outlet tube **B** for connection to the manometer and pump, and at the lower end usually three outlet tubes to which are fitted consecutive receivers **C, D, E**.

When distillation starts, the "pig" is so placed that the first fraction collects in **C**. When the second fraction starts to distil, **A** is rotated slightly to bring the outlet tube leading to **D** in the lowest position, so that the second fraction collects in **D**: further rotation then causes the third fraction to collect in **E**. The apparatus however often gives unsatisfactory results, particularly in the hands of students, who frequently find that if a good vacuum is obtained in the apparatus, the "pig" sticks firmly around the cork **F** and refuses to rotate: conversely, easy rotation around this cork usually means a leaky joint at this point, and an unsatisfactory and varying pressure is recorded by the manometer. (The ground-glass fitting **B** shown in Fig. 23(F), p. 46, avoids this trouble.)

For general work, a very satisfactory apparatus for collecting fractions under reduced pressure is the Perkin triangle **C**,* which is shown in Fig. 14, together with the requisite fittings for the complete

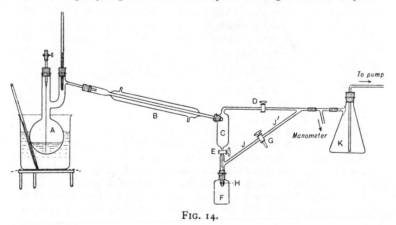

FIG. 14.

* G. A. R. Kon (*Jour. Chem. Soc.*, 1930, 182) described a modification of the Perkin triangle having only two taps instead of the three described above. It may be purchased from Quickfit & Quartz, Ltd., Quickfit Works, Stone, Staffs.

distillation. **A** is a Claisen flask, fitted up as already described, and heated in a beaker of transparent medicinal paraffin, the temperature of which is carefully controlled throughout the distillation.

The Claisen flask is then fitted to a water-condenser **B**, which leads directly into the main receiver **C** of the triangle. This triangle is connected through the upper tap **D** to the manometer and pump, and by the lower tap **E** to a supplementary (bottle) receiver **F**. The tube leading from **E** to the receiver **F** is double-walled: the inner tube gives direct access from **C** through the tap **E** to the receiver **F**, while the outer (annular) tube provides access from **F** through the small holes **H** to the side-arm **JJ′** carrying the three-way tap **G**. **G** is made to give *either* direct access through the tube **JJ′**, *or* access from the outside through **J** downwards to **F**, *or* from the outside through **J′** to the manometer and pump. The triangle is then connected to the manometer (fitted in a "side-chain" as before) and through the trap **K** (a Buchner flask) to the pump. The function of **K** is to "smooth out" slight changes in the pressure, within the apparatus, and also, should the pump default, to prevent water from rushing back into the apparatus.

When distillation starts, the taps **D** and **E** are open, and **G** is turned so as to give direct access from **J** to **J′**. The first fraction therefore runs from **C** through **E**, and collects in **F**. Directly the second fraction starts to distil, **E** is closed, so that this fraction collects in **C**. Meanwhile **G** is turned to allow air to enter through **J** to **F**, which can then be detached and a new receiver **F′** added. If a pump of good capacity is being used, it is sufficient now to turn **G** so as to give direct access again between **J** and **J′**, thus evacuating the new receiver **F′**, which is then ready to receive the second fraction which has been accumulating in **C**. If a rather weak pump is in use, however, this sudden admission of the air from the new receiver **F′** into the rest of the apparatus may cause a moderate rise in the pressure, and a temporary cessation in the distillation, and in these circumstances "bumping" frequently starts (and persists) when distillation recommences. To avoid this, the tap **G**, before being turned, should be connected to a supplementary pump, which will evacuate the new receiver **F′**: rotation of **G** as before now serves to cut off the supplementary pump and simultaneously reconnect the two parts of the apparatus through **JJ′**.

When a more delicate fractional vacuum-distillation is required, the flask and column shown in Fig. 11(B), p. 26, may be used, the side-arm of the column being fitted directly into receiver **C** (Fig. 14). A rubber stopper must then be used to fit the flask on to the fractionating column, and it should also carry a capillary tube leading to the bottom of the flask, to provide the usual fine stream of bubbles to prevent bumping.

Steam-distillation. Many water-insoluble compounds, both solid and liquid, may be readily purified by distillation in a

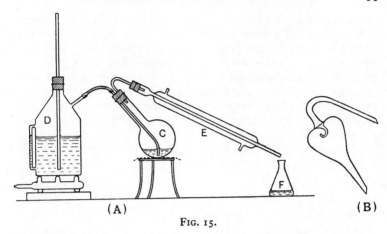

(A)   (B)

FIG. 15.

current of steam, provided that the compound is volatile, and the impurities non-volatile, under these conditions.

The apparatus consists of a round-bottomed flask **C** (Fig. 15 (A)), having a glass inlet tube which reaches almost to the bottom of the flask and which is connected to a steam generator **D**: the flask **C** has also a glass outlet tube, connected in turn to the water-condenser **E**. The flask is clamped at an angle as shown to prevent the solution in **C** from being splashed into the entrance of the outlet tube and thus being blown over mechanically into the condenser: this purpose is achieved more completely if in addition a still-head (shown on a larger scale in Fig. 15(B)) is used in place of the outlet tube, since spray will be trapped in the still-head, and returned as a steady stream of liquid to the flask **C**. (A ground-glass unit combining the steam-inlet and the still-head is shown in Fig. 22(I), p. 43.)

The material to be steam-distilled (mixed with some water if a solid compound, but not otherwise) is placed in **C**, and a vigorous current of steam blown in from **D**. The mixture in **C** is thus rapidly heated, and the vapour of the organic compound mixed with steam passes over and is condensed in **E**. For distillations on a small scale it is not necessary to heat **C**: if, however, the flask **C** contains a large volume of material or material which requires prolonged distillation, it should be heated by a Bunsen burner, otherwise the steady condensation of steam in **C** will produce too great a volume of liquid.

If the organic compound which is being steam-distilled is freely soluble in water, an aqueous solution will ultimately collect in the receiver **F**, and the compound must then be isolated by ether extraction, *etc.* Alternatively, a water-insoluble compound, if liquid, will form a separate layer in **F**, or if solid, will probably crystallise in the aqueous distillate. When steam-distilling a solid product, it is sometimes found that the distilled material crystallises in **E**, and may tend to choke up the condenser: in such cases, the water should be run out of the condenser for a few minutes until the solid material has melted and been carried by the steam down into the receiver.

Experiment 7. Steam-distillation.

Students should carry out the purification by steam distillation of (*a*) crude nitrobenzene or chlorobenzene, or of (*b*) crude naphthalene, *o*-nitrophenol (p. 170) or *p*-tolunitrile (p. 194) as examples of solid compounds which may also be purified in this way. When the distillation is complete, disconnect the tubing (Fig. 15) between **C** and **D** *before* removing the flame from under **D**, otherwise the contents of **C** will be sucked back into **D** as the latter cools.

Ether Extraction. In the course of organic preparations, it frequently happens that an organic compound is obtained either in aqueous solution or (less often) in aqueous suspension; if the organic compound is volatile in steam, or if it is chemically affected by prolonged exposure to hot water, it clearly cannot be isolated by evaporation of the water. If, however, the compound is soluble in an organic solvent which is itself almost completely insoluble in water, then repeated extraction of the aqueous solution with the solvent will eventually transfer the compound almost entirely into the organic solvent. Any water-insoluble solvent may be used for this purpose, but ether is usually the most suitable because (*a*) it is chemically inert and is unlikely to react with the compound, (*b*) owing to its great volatility, it can subsequently be readily removed by distillation without serious risk of simultaneously volatilising the compound.

To extract the substance, the aqueous solution or suspension is placed in a separating-funnel, which may be either cylindrical, Fig. 16(A), or (better) pear-shaped, Fig. 16(B). Ether is then

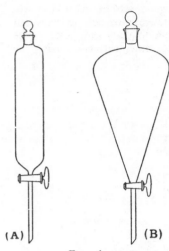

FIG. 16.

added and the mixture *thoroughly* shaken, the stopper at the top of the cylinder being occasionally opened to relieve any pressure of ether vapour caused by the heat of the hands. The mixture is allowed to settle until two well-defined layers have formed, and the lower aqueous layer is then run off and separated as completely as possible. The remaining ethereal layer is run off, preferably by pouring it through the upper neck of the funnel, to avoid contamination with any drops of aqueous solution still remaining in the stem of the funnel below the tap. The aqueous solution is then returned to the funnel, and the extraction repeated, using fresh ether on each occasion, until it is judged that very little of the compound remains in the aqueous layer. It should be borne in mind, however, that if a given volume of ether is to be used for the complete extraction, a far more efficient result will be obtained by a number of consecutive extractions using only a small volume of ether for each extraction, than by one or two extractions using a correspondingly greater volume of ether each time.

The ethereal extracts are then united, dried with a suitable drying agent and filtered. The filtrate is then cautiously distilled, the ether being first distilled and finally the organic compound if volatile: if the compound is solid, the crude residue is purified by recrystallisation. *Very great care must be taken on all occasions when ether is distilled, because of the risk of fire or of an explosion:* full experimental details for this operation are given, both on p. 80 (Preparation of Ether) and on p. 164 (Preparation of Aniline).

Continuous ether extraction and continuous chloroform extraction. When a substance **X** is shaken up with ether and water it will distribute itself according to the relative solubilities in each solvent.

Thus **K** (partition coefficient) $= \dfrac{\text{Conc. in ether layer}}{\text{Conc. in aqueous layer}}$

Now if **K** is very small, the amount of **X** going into the ether layer will also be very small and it would be quite impracticable to carry out more than three or four extractions. This difficulty can, however, be easily overcome by employing continuous ether extraction using the apparatus shown in Fig. 17 (A).

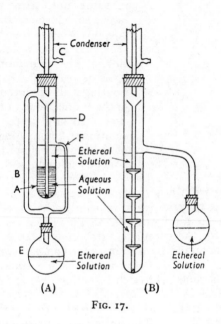

(A)   (B)

FIG. 17.

The ether is placed in the flask **E**. The aqueous solution is placed in the wide tube **A**. On heating **E**, ether vapour passes up the side-tube **B** to the condenser **C**, from whence liquid ether falls through the central vertical tube **D** to the bottom of the aqueous layer in **A**. Small drops of ether ascend through the aqueous layer, and in so doing expose a relatively large surface and extract some of the solute. The ethereal extract gradually increases in bulk, and the upper part of it is returned continuously by the system **F** to the flask **E**. Here the ether is again vapourised and recycled as above. Thus after a large number of cycles the solute will gradually accumulate in the ether in **E** and the solute can then be recovered by normal distillation or evaporation of the ethereal solution.

A convenient alternative apparatus for continuous ether extraction is shown in Fig. 17 (B).

The two forms of apparatus, Fig. 17 (A) and (B), are suitable for any solvent immiscible in and lighter than water. Fig. 18 (A) shows an

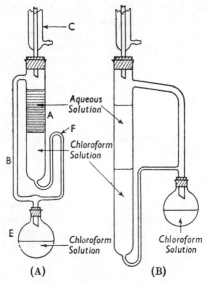

FIG. 18.

apparatus suitable for continuous extraction of aqueous solutions with solvents heavier than water (*e.g.*, chloroform). In this case chloroform is placed in the flask **E**, and the aqueous solution in tube **A**. The chloroform is boiled and its vapour ascends the tube **B**, is condensed and then falls in droplets through the aqueous phase in **A**. When the lower chloroform layer reaches a certain height much of it will siphon through **F** back into **E**. From here the solvent is recycled, and gradually the chloroform in **E** becomes more concentrated with respect to the solute.

A convenient alternative apparatus for continuous chloroform extraction is shown in Fig. 18 (B).

Soxhlet Extraction. Occasionally a crude product (often of natural occurrence) is obtained, from which a particular component may be isolated by repeated extraction with a hot solvent. For this purpose, Soxhlet's Extraction Apparatus (Fig. 19) is usually employed.

The extractor consists of a glass cylinder **A**, terminating at the base in the open tube **B**. Fused within the top of **A** as shown is another tube **C**, having a small hole **D** blown in the side: a fine glass tube leads from the base of **C**, rises about two-thirds of the height of the cylinder to **E**, and then returns past **F** into the open tube **B**.

The crude organic material is placed in a porous thimble **G** (made of tough filter-paper), and the latter placed as shown within the inner tube **C**. The apparatus is then fitted below to a bolt-head flask **H** containing the requisite solvent, and above to a reflux water-condenser **J**.

The solvent in **H** is then gently boiled. The vapour passes up **B**, through the annular space between the tubes **C** and **A**, and so through the orifice **D** into the reflux condenser above. The condensed solvent falls down into the thimble **G**, and slowly fills the body of **C**, being meanwhile heated by the ascending mantle of hot vapour in the annular space outside. When this condensed liquid reaches the top **E** of the fine glass tube, it syphons down into the flask **H**, taking down that portion of the organic compound which it has extracted in **G**. The process then repeats itself indefinitely, more of the organic material being extracted from **G** and transferred to the solvent in **H** on each occasion. Eventually complete extraction of the crude product in **G** is effected, and the extracted compound can then be isolated from the solution in **H** by any of the usual methods.

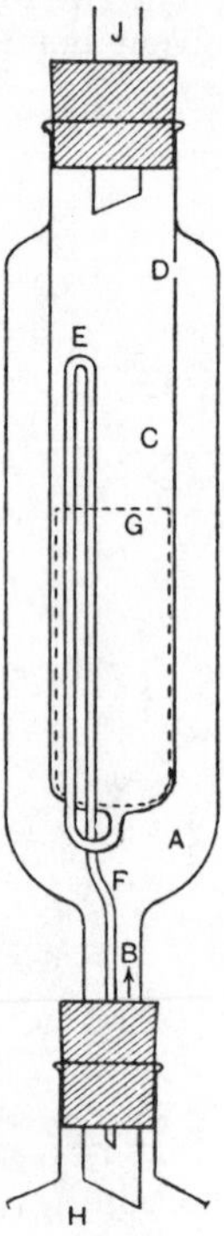

FIG. 19.

NOTE. In the older types of Soxhlet extractor, an external tube ran from **B** up to the top of **C** for conveying the ascending column of hot vapour. This type had the disadvantage not only of being more easily broken, but also that the condensed liquid in **C** received very little heat, and therefore the extraction, being carried out by the lukewarm solvent, was usually very slow.

Stirring. In the course of many organic preparations, a solution or suspension has to be kept continuously agitated either during the addition of a reagent or throughout the main stage of the preparation. For other than small-scale preparations, mechanical stirring is most conveniently employed. For this purpose, a stirrer **S** (Fig. 20) is made of stout glass rod, with the lower end bent at right angles if it is intended to sweep over the flat base of a beaker, or curved (as shown in Fig. 20) if it is to be used inside a round-bottomed flask. Other types can be designed for special purposes, or to allow insertion within a narrow-necked flask. The stirrer may be connected to an electric motor by a pulley **P**, which is particularly useful if a number of stirrers are run off one revolving shaft. It is usually more convenient, however, to secure the stirrer **S** directly to the axis of a small motor, which is therefore clamped perpendicularly above.

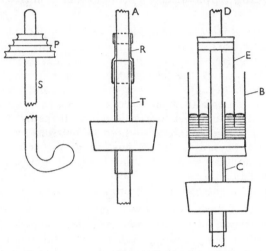

FIG. 20.

It is frequently necessary, however, to stir a solution which is boiling under reflux, and the stirrer must therefore be fitted with a seal to prevent the escape of vapour. This can often be done very simply by means of a short glass tube **T** (Fig. 20) which passes through the cork of the flask, and which serves as a collar within which the stirrer **A** fits quite closely. To prevent the escape of vapour, a short length of rubber tubing **R** (about $1\frac{1}{2}$ inches long) is fitted over the top of the tube **T**: the upper portion of this tube is then turned back over the stirrer as shown in order to grip the stirrer securely. A few drops of glycerol or mineral oil placed between the upper portion of this tubing and the stirrer allow the latter to rotate freely with very little friction.

Alternatively a mercury-sealed stirrer may be employed. Here again a short glass tube **C** is inserted through the cork of the flask to act as a collar for the stirrer. The tube **C** carries a short wide tube **B** which is either fused at its lower end to **C**, or is fixed to it by means of a cork as shown. The stirrer **D** carries a precisely similar tube **E**, the top of which however is now fixed to **D**: the bore of the tube **E** allows it to fit easily within the annular space between the collar **C** and the tube **B**. Mercury is then placed in this annular space to act as a seal whilst the stirrer is in operation.

Assembling Apparatus. The following points should be noted.

(1) *Drying Apparatus.* Simple pieces of apparatus such as flasks are best dried by heating in the large luminous flame of a blowpipe, a current of air, *e.g.*, from compressed air mains, being blown through the flask meanwhile to remove the water vapour, which would otherwise merely recondense as the flask cooled. Apparatus such as condensers, *etc.*, which cannot be so treated, should first be rinsed out with methylated spirit, and then with ether (preferably dried beforehand over calcium chloride and filtered): a brisk current of air is then blown through the apparatus until the ether has completely evaporated.

In most laboratories, drying ovens maintained at about 50° are available for the final drying of glass apparatus of all kinds.

(2) *Corks.** Before using an ordinary bark cork, examine it carefully for flaws: many corks have such deep holes that they are useless. Before boring, always roll the cork thoroughly (under the foot, if a cork-roller is not available) in order to soften it. Never bore a cork right through from one end to another, as the cork-borer on emerging will almost invariably tear the surface of the cork. Therefore bore halfway through from one end, and then start again from the opposite end, rotating the cork steadily each time to ensure that the borer goes symmetrically along the long axis of the cork. With care the two borings should meet exactly.

Never use unprotected bark corks for an apparatus in which a carefully dried liquid is to be distilled, *etc.*, as these corks always contain appreciable quantities of water, which is exuded when the cork comes into contact with a hot liquid. Rubber stoppers should therefore be used in these circumstances.

When boring rubber stoppers, lubricate the borer well, either with aqueous glycerine or with vaseline. Then clean well and dry before using.

Storage of Specimens. Solid compounds after purification should be stored in bottles or in corked specimen tubes, according

---

* For most purposes, the use of corks is now replaced by that of ground-glass apparatus (p. 42 *et seq.*).

to the amount of the compound available. The bottle or tube should at once be labelled, so that the identity of the compound, its melting-point, and any particular details concerning the method of purification employed, are clearly recorded. The label should also record the "tare" (*i.e.*, the weight) of the *empty* bottle or tube, including that of the stopper or cork, so that the total weight of material available can subsequently be determined without removing the substance from the bottle. Stable liquids of high boiling-point can be similarly stored in stoppered bottles or in corked specimen tubes: in the latter case, however, unless the liquid is required again shortly, it is advisable to wax the cork in order to hold it firmly in position and also to prevent the liquid from slowly seeping through the cork itself. For this purpose, the cork should be placed firmly in position, and the inverted tube dipped into some clean paraffin wax which has been heated in an evaporating-basin to about 180°, *i.e.*, until it has become a mobile liquid. After the cork and the extreme end of the tube have been immersed in the wax, the tube is removed and, while still inverted, gently rotated so that the wax solidifies as a layer of uniform thickness.

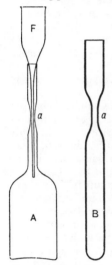

FIG. 21.

The only satisfactory method for storing liquids of low boiling-point (*e.g.*, ethyl bromide) or liquids which are affected by the air (*e.g.*, acetic anhydride, benzoyl chloride, benzaldehyde) is to seal them in special glass bottles **A** (Fig. 21) or tubes **B** according to the amount available. The bottles, of various sizes, can be purchased: the tubes should be prepared in the laboratory from moderately thick-walled glass tubing. The bottle or tube should first be cleaned and dried: then, by carefully rotating the neck in a suitable small blowpipe flame, a constriction *a* (Fig. 21) of about 15–20 mm. length should be made so that the wall of the tubing remains uniformly thick at this point. A test-tube is then drawn out at the centre so that the upper part can be broken off and used as the funnel **F**; the liquid can now be easily poured into **A** or **B**. If the liquid is readily volatile, the bottle or tube must now be placed in ice-water or in ice-salt for several minutes. It is then removed, the lower portion wrapped in a duster to protect the liquid from the heat of the hand, and the neck quickly sealed off at *a*. For liquids of high boiling-point, these precautions are not necessary, although in all cases the constriction *a* facilitates the sealing of the neck.

Students frequently attempt to seal liquids in test-tubes: the latter are, however, usually too fragile for this purpose.

Apparatus having Ground-glass Joints.

Apparatus consisting solely of glass units interlocking by ground-glass joints has for many purposes replaced the older cork- or rubber-stoppered apparatus because its great advantages in use outweigh its much greater cost.

These advantages include: (*a*) *Speed of assembly.* (*b*) *Well-fitting joints*, as these are made to accurate standards and joints of any given size are thus interchangeable. (*c*) *Accurate alignment of assembly*, for the use of incorrectly bored corks is obviated. (*d*) *Freedom from contamination* of liquids by cork and rubber.

The underlying principle of this apparatus is the interchangeable conical ground-glass joint. The same "taper" of 1 in 10 in the diameter is used for all joints, so that the inner unit fits the outer unit with precision. A code is frequently used to designate the cone-size of the joint, *e.g.*, from the small B10 to the large B55. The sizes of greatest general utility are B14, B19 and B24.

Precautions: Students should carefully note the following points in order to minimise breakages.

(1) Ensure that all the individual components in the assembly are adequately supported when in position: the friction between contiguous ground-glass surfaces does not provide adequate support. Therefore always use clamps, the claws of which are lined with rubber or other soft material. When assembling apparatus, allow some play in the clamps until the individual parts are in position, and then secure the position of the assembly by gently increasing the pressure of the clamps.

(2) It is often advisable to lubricate ground-glass joint surfaces with an *extremely* thin film of vaseline. This applies particularly to joints employed in assemblies for distillation under reduced pressure. For distillations under greatly reduced pressures or at very high temperatures it is essential to employ a special lubricant, *e.g.*, silicone grease.

(3) Care must be used when employing alkalis. In these circumstances joints tend to stick unless a lubricant is used. In addition it is advisable to rotate the units comprising the joint at frequent intervals. Apparatus in which alkalis have been used should be dismantled immediately after use.

Although apparatus employing ground-glass joints is excellent for work on a macro scale, it is not always suitable for very small-scale work as the joints are often disproportionately large compared with the rest of the assembly. The semi-micro apparatus described on pp. 59–72 can therefore be considered as being of general utility for this scale of work, especially as the use of corks has been reduced to a minimum.

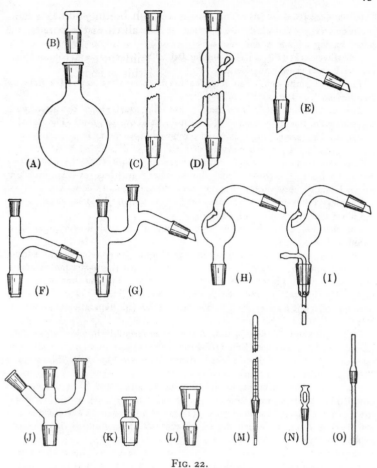

FIG. 22.

Units. * Some of the chief units employed for reasonably simple ground-glass assemblies are:

Round-bottomed flasks (Fig. 22(A)) of various sizes and having necks of various lengths and widths. They can be closed with stoppers (Fig. 22(B)), or fitted with any of the following units: reflux air-condensers (Fig. 22(C)) or water-condensers (Fig. 22(D)); distillation heads, of the simple "knee-tube" type (Fig. 22(E)), or with a vertical joint (Fig. 22(F)) for thermometers, *etc.*, or with

---

* This brief account is intended to give only a general indication of the types of apparatus available. The firm which has pioneered the design and manufacture of ground-glass apparatus is Quickfit and Quartz, Ltd., "Quickfit" Works, Stone, Staffordshire, ST15 0BG, whose catalogues fully illustrate the range of units and assemblies available.

a double neck (Fig. 22(G)) of the Claisen type, for a capillary inlet-tube and a thermometer; steam-splash heads, such as Fig. 22(H) and Fig. 22(I), the latter having an additional inlet-tube for steam-distillation: adaptors having two or three necks (Fig. 22(J)). Similar flat-bottomed flasks and conical flasks are used when more convenient.

The above units can when required be fitted into the neck of a flask by adaptors such as Fig. 22(K) and Fig. 22(L).

The distillation heads Fig. 22(F) and Fig. 22(G) can be fitted with thermometers having a ground-glass cone just above the bulb (Fig. 22(M)). These are expensive, and it is usually more convenient to fit a thermometer pocket (Fig. 22(N)) which consists of a small "well", fitting as shown into the neck of the flask. A *small* volume of mercury is placed in the well just to cover the bulb of a conventional thermometer, and thus provides excellent thermal contact between the thermometer and the sides of the pocket.

Capillary tubes for low-pressure distillations are prepared by drawing out the lower end of the tube (Fig. 22(O)).

Assemblies. Other units are shown in some of the typical assemblies illustrated in Fig. 23.

Fig. 23(A) shows an assembly for boiling a liquid under reflux whilst adding another liquid at a rate which can be clearly seen (*cf.* preparation of acetophenone, p. 253). The outlet **A** allows expansion of the vapour content, and can be fitted with a calcium chloride or soda-lime tube. The outlet **A** can also be used for collecting a gas evolved during the reaction (*cf.* preparation of acetylene, p. 88).

Fig. 23(B) shows a modification of the reflux assembly to allow a gas to be passed through the boiling liquid (*cf.* Fischer-Speier esterification, p. 104). The inlet-tube **A** fits into a three-necked adaptor shown in Fig. 22(J). The stopper **B** can be replaced by a dropping-funnel, *etc.*

Fig. 23(C) shows a reflux assembly with a stirrer fitted. The stirrer **A** is both held in position in the tube **B** and allowed to rotate freely by the lubricated rubber sleeve **C**, as described on p. 39, and is connected to a vertical motor above. The extent to which the stirrer dips into the liquid in the flask can readily be adjusted. The condenser (not shown) is fitted into **D**. This constitutes for many purposes the best type of stirrer. If desired, the rubber sleeve **C** can be replaced by a metal fitting **E** for a horizontal drive. The gas-inlet **F** is closed when not in use.

Fig. 23(D) shows a simple distillation apparatus with an adaptor fitted to the lower end of the condenser. This apparatus can also be used for the recovery of solvents, or for the concentration of a solution with collection of the distilled solvent.

Fig. 23(E) shows a distillation assembly particularly useful for distilling ether from an ethereal extract. When all the ether has distilled over, the dropping-funnel may be replaced by a thermometer for distillation of the residual liquid: the adaptor **A** and the receiver **B** can then be replaced by the simple adaptor shown in Fig. 23(D) and a flask or bottle of suitable size.

Fig. 23(F) shows a similar distillation assembly for isolating a pure liquid which is present in an organic extract and which may finally require fractional

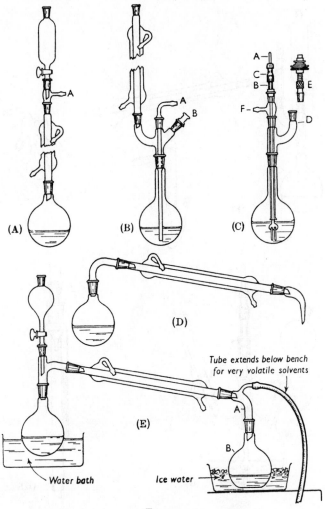

FIG. 23.

distillation under reduced pressure. The lower end of the condenser is fitted with an adaptor of type **A** and a receiver **B** (Fig. 23(E)) whilst the solvent is being distilled. For the fractional distillation of the residual liquid, the dropping-funnel is replaced by a capillary tube, the thermometer is inserted, and then the adaptor **A** (Fig. 23(E)) is replaced by a "pig" **B** (Fig. 23(F)) carrying suitable receivers (of which the cylindrical and the spherical types are shown), or by an all-glass Perkin triangle similar to that shown in Fig. 14, p. 31. If the amount

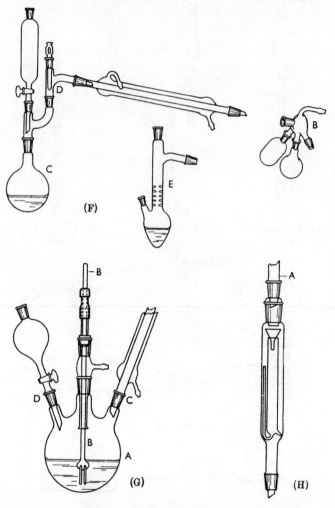

FIG. 23 (*contd.*).

of residual liquid is small, the distillation flask **C** and the still-head **D** can be replaced by a small flask **E** (Fig. 23(F)) the neck of which can have various fractionating devices. The ethereal extract can thus be run into **E** at the same speed as the ether distils over: this process is rather slow, but the small volume of residual liquid can then be directly distilled. The lower side-neck of **E** is subsequently fitted with a capillary tube for the final distillation.

Fig. 23(G) shows a three-necked round-bottomed flask **A** having the two side-arms fitted at an angle. The flask **A** can therefore, for example, carry through its central neck a stirrer **B** and gas-inlet (closed when not in use), and through one side-neck **C** a reflux condenser and through the other neck **D** either a dropping-funnel or a stopper to allow intermittent additions of a solid reagent such as sodium. For fairly large quantities of liquids, this assembly is more robust than a single-necked flask fitted with the three-necked adaptor shown in Fig. 22(J). The gas-inlet is particularly useful for the passage of nitrogen over an easily oxidised liquid.

For extraction purposes, a Soxhlet apparatus (Fig. 23(H)) can be inserted between a flask of boiling solvent and the reflux condenser **A** above. This apparatus is similar in design to that shown in Fig. 19, p. 38: in the type shown in Fig. 23(H) the hot extract continuously overflows through the side-tube into the boiling solvent below, but the syphon type shown in Fig. 19 is also available.

Advanced Techniques of Separation and Purification.

The methods of purification of a crude product by fractional crystallisation (p. 13) and fractional distillation (p. 25) have the advantages that they can, when required, be applied on a large scale. They have the disadvantages that they cannot be rapidly applied to separate, for example, two components of a crude product whose solubilities in a range of solvents are closely similar or whose boiling-points are very close together. Fractional crystallisation may often be impeded (or prevented) by the formation of mixed crystals, and fractional distillation by the formation of constant boiling-point mixtures, or by less definite co-distillation. Purification by sublimation (p. 23) can also be performed on a large scale, but its use is obviously and severely limited to solid compounds having the necessary physical properties.

The various types of *Chromatographic Separation* have been developed partly to avoid the above disadvantages, but (more particularly) to provide methods of separation on a micro-scale. Three methods are described below:

Adsorption Chromatography
Paper Chromatography (p. 50)
Ion-exchange Chromatography (p. 55).
Thin-layer Chromatography (p. 58)

Paper chromatography in particular frequently enables the components of a mixture to be separated and identified when only 1–2 mg. of the mixture are available, the process being independent of the relative solubilities of the components.

ADSORPTION CHROMATOGRAPHY

A mixture can often be separated into its components by utilising their selective adsorption from solution by a suitable substance, such as active alumina: the separation can be readily followed if the components are coloured.

The method consists essentially in allowing a solution of the substance in a suitable solvent to pass slowly down a long column containing the adsorbent material. The tenacity with which this material adsorbs the various components of the mixture may vary considerably, with the result that a sharp separation of the components into coloured zones or bands may result. At this stage, the passage of the solvent may be stopped and the individual zones removed either by careful extrusion of the adsorbent material or by cutting the tube in sections corresponding with the zones. It is usually more convenient to "elute" the components, *i.e.*, by the further passage of the pure solvent

48

(or of a mixture of solvents) to cause each zone to pass down the tube and ultimately to emerge as a solution of the pure component.

If the components are colourless, their separation can often be followed by working in a quartz (or special glass) tube which is placed in the light of a mercury lamp. The separate zones are then often revealed by their fluorescence.

The process of chromatographic separation is illustrated in the following experiment, in which a wider tube than usual is employed to give a reasonably rapid separation within the time normally available to students. The alumina employed is the usual active alumina as supplied by dealers.

Chromatographic Separation of a Mixture of *o*- and *p*-Nitroaniline. Prepare a glass tube **A** (Fig. 24) in which the wider portion has a diameter of 3 cm. and a length of *ca.* 30 cm.: the narrow portion at the base has a diameter of 5–7 mm. Wash the tube thoroughly (if necessary, with chromic acid, followed by distilled water and ethanol) and then dry. Insert a *small* plug of cotton-wool **P** as shown just within the narrow neck of the tube: it is essential that this plug does not project into the wider portion of the tube. Clamp the tube in a *vertical* position.

Mix 100 g. of active alumina with dry benzene until a suspension or slurry of suitable consistency is obtained, and pour this carefully into the tube. Clamp a dropping-funnel just above the top of the tube and allow benzene to run slowly down as the alumina column settles in the tube: the benzene emerging from the bottom of the tube is collected in a conical flask. It is essential that the top of the column should be kept immersed in the solvent, and that the latter passes uniformly down the column without "channelling": a disc of filter-paper can, if desired, be fitted over the top of the column to prevent disturbance of the surface.

Meanwhile dissolve not more than 0·5 g. of a mixture of crude *o*- and *p*-nitroaniline in 30 ml. of dry benzene and then allow this solution to enter the tube slowly through the dropping-funnel. Immediately this solution has all entered the tube, continue running in the pure solvent, and develop the chromatogram by collecting the benzene from the bottom of the tube and running it again through the top of the tube. Continue in this

FIG. 24.

way until the two yellow bands have become distinct and separate during their passage to the lower portion of the column. Then continue the washing with fresh benzene until each band has been separately eluted in about 150 ml. of benzene, that of the *o*-nitroaniline emerging first from the tube.*

Concentrate each of the two solutions (or eluates) to about 20 ml. by distilling off the greater part of the benzene, the distilling-flask being immersed in the boiling water-bath. Then pour the concentrated solution into an evaporating-basin, and evaporate the remaining benzene (preferably in a fume-cupboard) in the absence of free flames, *i.e.*, on an electrically heated water-bath, or on a steam-bath directly connected to a steam-pipe. Wash the dry residue from the first eluate with petrol and then dry it in a desiccator: pure *o*-nitroaniline, m.p. 72°, is obtained. Wash the second residue similarly with a small quantity of benzene and dry: pure *p*-nitroaniline, m.p. 148°, is obtained. Record the yield and m.p. of each component.

NOTE. For more delicate work, highly purified solvents are necessary, but for the above experiment dry technical benzene is suitable.

PAPER CHROMATOGRAPHY

Filter paper is made of highly purified cellulose which, being a polyhydroxy-compound of high molecular weight, both absorbs and retains water molecules strongly. Consequently if a small quantity of mixed solvent (one component of which is water and another being almost insoluble in water) is placed in a tall cylinder and a strip of the filter paper then suspended vertically in the vapour above the solvent in the closed cylinder, the paper will absorb preferentially the water molecules. The film of the solvent molecules on the paper will therefore contain all the solvent constituents, but with a greater proportion of water molecules than that in the original mixed solvent.

A drop of an aqueous solution of the mixture to be separated is now placed near the bottom of the paper strip and allowed to evaporate in the air. The strip is now again suspended in the closed cylinder, but with the bottom of the strip just immersed in the solvent. The capillary action of the paper will cause the solvent to rise steadily up the strip, and during this process the solvent, which now contains the mixture in solution, is continuously extracted by the retained water molecules in the paper. A highly hydrophobic (water-repellent) solute will move up closely behind the solvent-front, whereas a highly hydrophilic solute will barely leave the original point where the drop of the mixed solutes in solution has been dried. In an intermediate case,

* The chromatographic separation should whenever possible be completed in one operation. If, however, shortage of time necessitates an interruption, this can most conveniently be made immediately after the first band has been completely eluted, whereupon the lower end of the tube is closed by a short piece of rubber tubing carrying a screw-clip. Great care should be taken however not to allow even the top of the column to run dry.

however, the extent to which a particular solute has moved, relative to the extent to which the solvent has moved, known as the R_F of the solute, will be a function of the partition coefficient of the solute between the solvent and the film of retained water.

When the ascending solvent-front has reached a convenient height, the strip is removed, the position of the solvent-front marked, and the paper strip dried. The positions of the various solutes, if they are coloured compounds, now appear as clear separate spots. Frequently however, the solutes are colourless, and the position of their spots must be determined by indirect methods, such as their fluorescence in ultraviolet light, or their absorption in such light (when the spots appear almost black), or by spraying the paper with a dilute solution of a reagent which will give a coloured insoluble derivative with the solutes.

The first of the two experiments given below illustrates the separation of amino-acids, now an almost classic example of the use of paper chromatography: the second illustrates the separation of anthranilic acid and N-methylanthranilic acid. Both experiments show the micro scale of the separation, and also the fact that a mixture of compounds which are chemically closely similar can be readily separated, and also can be identified by the use of controls.

The second experiment requires far less time than the first (*cf.* p. 54).

Separation of Glycine (I), ($\pm$) Proline (II), and ($\pm$) Phenylalanine (III)

These three amino-acids are colourless and readily soluble in water:

$$NH_2 \cdot CH_2 \cdot COOH$$
$$(I)$$

$$C_6H_5 \cdot CH_2 \cdot CH \cdot COOH$$
$$NH_2$$
$$(III)$$

$$\begin{array}{c} H_2C\text{——}CH_2 \\ | \qquad | \\ H_2C \qquad CH \cdot COOH \\ \diagdown \quad \diagup \\ N \\ (II) \quad H \end{array}$$

(IV)

like most α-amino-acids, they give marked colours with "ninhydrin" (IV) (systematically 2,2-dihydroxy-1,3-dioxohydrindene), and these colours are used to detect the final position of each acid on the paper strip.

Apparatus. A strong glass cylinder **E** (Fig. 25(A)), which is conveniently about 45 cm. high and about 6 cm. internal diameter, is fitted with a rubber bung **F** having a glass rod **G** which passes through the centre of the bung, and which is bent at the lower end as shown. The paper strip can be folded over the horizontal arm of **G**, and held in position by two plastic clips **H**: alternatively it can be held by two metal paper-clips, but in this case two glass microscope slides should be placed across the strip and under the clips, to protect the paper from the metal.

A 1-litre measuring-cylinder may be used in place of the cylinder **E**, but when the bung **F** is in position, any gap at the lip of the cylinder must be tightly plugged with cotton-wool.

The paper strips (conveniently 40 × 4 cm.) should be cut from

Whatman No. 1 filter-paper, and handled as little and as cleanly as possible.

Spray. For most purposes a simple spray device, based on the ordinary scent-spray, suffices. A finer and less intermittent spray can be obtained using the apparatus shown in Fig. 26. A narrow glass cylinder **J** has a ground-glass

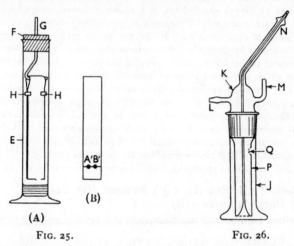

FIG. 25.   FIG. 26.

neck into which the attachment **K** fits securely. This attachment consists essentially of the central neck **K**, which has two short inlet tubes, **L** being horizontal and **M** bent upwards as shown, and a long curved outlet tube **N** which is tapered to a small orifice at the end. The lower part of **K** within the cylinder **J** consists of a tapering tube **P** having a small hole **Q** at one side: the open base of **P** is curved inwards as shown to form a fine capillary-tube which reaches to the upper end of the outlet tube **N**. (Alternatively, the capillary tube can be drawn out from a short length of tubing which fits inside **P**, and is held in position by being lightly fused to the inside lower rim of **P** at two opposite points.) The spraying solution is put into **J**, and the inlet tube **L** connected to a high-pressure air supply. When **J** is grasped in the hand, and the tube **M** closed with the forefinger, a very fine spray is blown from **N**, and its duration can be immediately controlled by thus opening or closing **M**.

Reagents. (A) *Amino-acid solution.* A solution of 5 mg. of glycine, 5 mg. of proline, and 5 mg. of phenylalanine in 1 ml. of water.

(B) *Control solution.* A solution of 5 mg. of glycine in 1 ml. of water.

(C) *Mixed solvent.* A well-shaken mixture of 20 ml. of redistilled *n*-butanol, 9·5 ml. of water, and 5·5 ml. of 95% ethanol.

(D) *Spraying solution.* A solution of 0·2 g. of ninhydrin in a mixture of 99 ml. of redistilled *n*-butanol and 1 ml. of glacial acetic acid.

Method. Draw a light pencil line across the paper strip about 3 cm. from the bottom (Fig. 25 (B)), and mark two points A' and B' 2 cm.

apart symmetrically on the line as shown. By means of a *fine* glass pipette, drop sufficient of solution (A) on the point A' to form a circular zone about 0·5 cm. in diameter. Wash pipette thoroughly, and then similarly place solution (B) on the point B'. Dry the strip in the air.

Now place 35 ml. of the mixed solvent (C) in the clean cylinder **E**, and suspend the strip, as described above, to the horizontal arm of **G** (Fig. 25(A)); adjust the position of the strip so that, when the bung is firmly in position, the bottom of the paper-strip is about 5 mm. above the solvent. Place the cylinder for 5–8 hours in a draught-free place, such as a cupboard, where the temperature is reasonably constant.

Now lower the paper-strip, which has become saturated with the solvent vapour molecules, so that it dips about 5 mm. into the solvent. Then close the cylinder, and set it aside as before for 12–18 hours, by which time the solvent will have risen about three-quarters of the height of the strip.

Then remove the strip and dry it in a stream of cold air, either from a blower, or by pinning it to the lower edge of a fume-cupboard window having a vigorous draught already in operation. Then spray the strip lightly but uniformly with the ninhydrin solution (D) in a fume-cupboard, and dry as before.

The positions of the three amino-acids are shown clearly by the colour of their zones or spots, the proline being yellow and the glycine and phenylalanine being blue. Note the R_F value for each amino-acid:

$$R_F = \frac{\text{Distance moved by centre of solute zone}}{\text{Distance moved by solvent front.}}$$

The control solution (B) is used in this experiment to differentiate between the blue spots of glycine and phenylalanine. It will be seen that the R_F value of phenylalanine is greater than that of glycine.

The position of the spots should be marked in pencil, for the colours fade after some time.

NOTE. The period of 5–8 hours recommended above for attaining an equilibrium between the vapour molecules of the mixed solvent and those absorbed by the paper strip is essential if accurate R_F values are required for identification of mixed amino-acids. To illustrate the separation, as in the above experiment, this period may be reduced to about 2 hours.

Separation of Anthranilic acid and N-Methylanthranilic acid.

Both these acids are colourless, but the "spots" of each acid on a filter-paper strip show up in ultraviolet light as intense blue fluorescent zones. They can also be detected, but considerably less sensitively, by spraying with ethanolic ferric chloride solution, which gives with N-methylanthranilic acid a purple-brown coloration.

N-Methylanthranilic acid is very readily prepared (p. 222). Prepare a sample of this acid and recrystallise it 2 or 3 times from ethanol until it has m.p. 177° and is "pure".

This experiment requires less time than the former, for the paper strip comes into equilibrium with the solvent vapour much more rapidly, and can then be inserted into the solvent without intermediate drying.

Reagents. (A) *Anthranilic acid.* A solution of 20 mg. of the pure acid in 20 ml. of methanol.

(B) N-*Methylanthranilic acid.* A solution of 10 mg. of the acid (recrystallised as above) in 20 mg. of methanol.

(C) *Mixed acids.* A solution containing 10 mg. of each acid in 20 ml. of methanol.

(D) *Mixed solvent.* Add 10 ml. of concentrated aqueous ammonia (*d*, 0·880) to 40 ml. of redistilled n-butanol and thoroughly mix to obtain a complete solution.

Method. Prepare a paper strip from Whatman No. 1 filter paper, as in the previous experiment, and draw a light pencil line about 3 cm. from the bottom (*cf.* Fig. 25(B)). Mark three points A', B' and C' symmetrically on this line, if possible 2 cm. apart. Using the fine pipette, or a capillary tube, apply solution (A) to the point A' to give a damp spot about 0·5 cm. in diameter. Using a thoroughly washed pipette or a fresh capillary tube on each occasion, apply solution (B) and (C) to the points B' and C' respectively. Dry the strip in the air.

Place 40 ml. of the mixed solvent (D) in the chromatogram cylinder, and suspend the dried strip in the closed cylinder (*cf.* p. 223) for at least 30 minutes to allow the paper to come into complete equilibrium with the mixed solvent. Then gently lower the strip until the bottom edge dips about 5 mm. into the solvent. Allow the chromatogram to develop overnight protected from draughts.

Next day, hang the paper from the edge of the fume-cupboard window in the full draught of the fan to dry, and immediately mark the position of the solvent front.

Inspect the paper in ultraviolet light—conveniently in front on a Hanovia ultraviolet strip light—in a dark room. The acids show up as intense blue fluorescent spots. Mark with a pencil the positions of all spots. The position of the two spots arising from solution (C) should be compared with the single spots arising from solutions (A) and (B). It is probable that the solution (B) of "pure" N-methylanthranilic acid may also reveal a faint spot corresponding to anthranilic acid still present in minute traces in the methylated acid (*cf.* p. 223).

Record the R_F values of the two acids: under the above conditions the anthranilic and the N-methylanthranilic acid should have R_F values of 0·28 and 0·55 respectively.

Finally spray the paper with neutral 1% ethanolic ferric chloride solution: the methylanthranilic acid spot develops a purple-brown coloration, whereas the anthranilic acid gives only a very faint pink coloration.

If an alternative mixed solvent is required, shake thoroughly a mixture of 20 ml. of distilled water and 40 ml. of the *n*-butanol, then allow the mixture to separate, and use the upper (organic) layer. Under the above conditions, but using this solvent, the spots are decisively but not so widely separated, for the R_F values for the anthranilic and the methylanthranilic acid are now 0·68 and 0·81 respectively.

ION EXCHANGE

The principle of ion exchange is employed in the separation of organic compounds on a semi-micro scale or micro scale. Broadly speaking, the use of ion exchange materials* is, in some respect, similar to the use of adsorbents in ordinary chromatography. Ion exchange materials are usually described as (a) cation exchange resins and (b) anion exchange resins.

Ion exchange materials are usually resins with acidic or basic groups incorporated into their molecular structures. Such resins are commercially available and are usually made by the co-polymerisation of styrene and divinylbenzene. The latter forms cross linkages between chains of polymerised styrene to give a lattice structure. Suitable groups upon which the exchange principle depend can be introduced either before or after condensation. For example a "sulphonated exchanger" can be prepared from suitably sulphonated monomers or by sulphonating the final resin under controlled conditions. Fig. 27 represents the essential features of such a sulphonate exchanger.

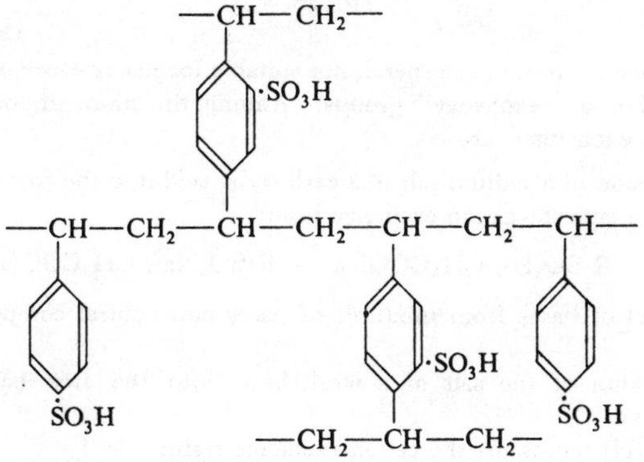

FIG. 27.

Cation exchange resins usually contain as their active principle these sulphonic acid groups although they may contain carboxylic acid groups instead. Those polymers containing —SO_3H groups are known as *strong acid cation resins*, whereas those containing —COOH groups are designated *weak acid cation resins*. Both these cation exchange resins may be looked upon as insoluble acids of extremely high molecular weight. *Anion exchange resins* usually contain as the active exchange principle quaternary ammonium groups (Fig. 28) and may

* The student who is interested in details of the physical principles involved and of further applications of ion exchange should consult *Ion Exchanges in Organic and Biochemistry* by Calvin Calmon and T. R. E. Kressman. (Interscience Publication Inc., New York.)

be regarded as very strong insoluble bases (or salts of such bases) of extremely high molecular weight. Such polymers are designated as *strong base anion resins*. There is also a class of *weak base anion resins* which contain amino groups in place of the quaternary ammonium groups.

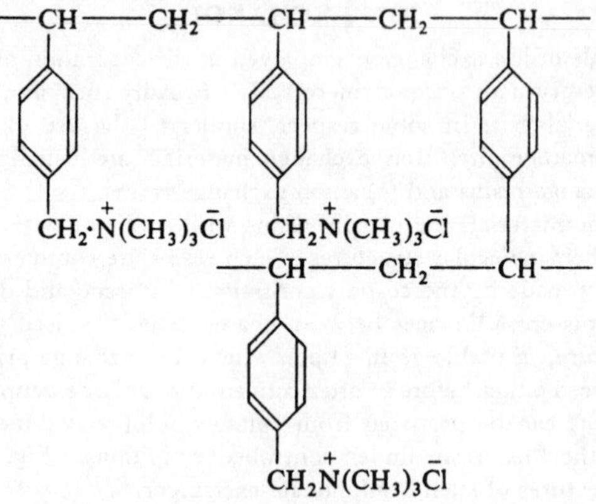

FIG. 28.

Ion exchange resins are, in general, not suitable for macro-work owing to the limited number of "exchange" groups. Among the more important applications of ion exchangers are:

(1) Conversion of a sodium salt of a carboxylic acid into the free acid: *e.g.*, if $R \cdot SO_3H$ represents the cation exchange resin:

$$R \cdot SO_3H + CH_3COONa \rightarrow R \cdot SO_3Na + CH_3COOH$$

(2) Removal of bases from mixtures of bases and neutral compounds such as alcohols.

(3) Conversion of the salt of a weak base into the free base: *e.g.*, if $[R \cdot \overset{+}{N}(CH_3)_3\overset{-}{OH}]$ represents the cation exchange resin:

$$[R \cdot \overset{+}{N}(CH_3)_3\overset{-}{OH}] + C_6H_5\overset{+}{NH_3}\overset{-}{Cl} \rightarrow [R \cdot \overset{+}{N}(CH_3)_3\overset{-}{Cl}] + C_6H_5\overset{+}{NH_3}\overset{-}{OH}$$
$$\downarrow$$
$$C_6H_5NH_2 + H_2O$$

(4) Removal of acids from mixtures of acids and neutral compounds.

Conversion of sodium citrate into citric acid.

This conversion cannot easily be carried out on a semi-micro scale by ordinary chemical means. Liberation of an acid from one of its salts by dil. H_2SO_4 is feasible when the organic acid is insoluble in water (e.g. an aromatic acid) or when it is volatile (e.g. acetic acid). Citric acid is water-soluble and non-volatile and therefore cation exchange is a particularly suitable method of liberating it from its salts.

Method. Prepare a slurry of a strong acid cation resin (such as Amberlite I.R-120(HO)*) in distilled water. Place a thin plug of glass wool at the base of a 50 ml. burette. Now pour the slurry into the burette until the latter is about half full. Open the tap of the burette and pour distilled water through the slurry until all the air bubbles have been removed. Drain off most of the water, but do not allow the resin to become uncovered at any time during this or subsequent operations. Now pass 100 ml. of 10% hydrochloric acid solution through the resin and then wash it thoroughly by passing distilled water down the column until the washings leaving the burette are neutral to methyl orange. Close the tap of the burette. This column is now ready for use. Prepare a solution of 0·05 g. of sodium citrate in 100 ml. of water. Now pass this solution down the column at the rate of 5 ml. per minute by opening the tap of the burette to a suitable extent. Collect the runnings. When all the mixture has been added, wash the column with 50 ml. of distilled water, and add these runnings to those previously collected. Evaporate the combined runnings or "effluent" in order to obtain pure citric acid, m.p. 100°.

The column of resin must now be "regenerated," i.e. the retained ions must be removed by passing an excess of "regenerant" (in this case 10% HCl) down the column as described above. The column is then washed with water and is ready for a new cycle of operations. Note that the column must not be allowed to become dry.

As a corollary to the above it should be pointed out that the exchange is in some instances stoichiometric and therefore the amount of cation in solution can be estimated by passage through a hydrogen exchanger as above and subsequent titration of the acid in the effluent.

(2) *Removal of bases from mixtures of bases and neutral compounds.* The procedure here is essentially the same as in (1) above. The base is retained by the column. Use a solution of 0·05 g. of benzylamine and 0·1 g. of mannitol in 100 ml. of water. The effluent contains only mannitol.

(3) *Conversion of the salt of a weak base into the free base.* Prepare a column of a strong base anion resin (such as Amberlite IRA-400(OH)*) washed with distilled water as above. Drain off most of the water and then allow 100 ml. of $M/2.Na_2CO_3$ solution to pass through the column at 5 ml. per minute. Again wash the column with 200 ml. of distilled water. Dissolve 0·05 g. of aniline hydrochloride in 100 ml. of distilled water and pass the solution down the column. The effluent contains aniline in solution and free from all other ions.

(4) *Removal of acids from mixtures of acids and neutral substances.* Prepare a column of a strong base anion resin and treat it with sodium

* Obtainable from British Drug Houses, Ltd., (Laboratory Chemicals Division), Poole, Dorset, BH12 4NN.

carbonate as in (3). Prepare a solution of 0·025 g. of citric acid and 0·25 g. of glucose in 100 ml. of distilled water. Pass this solution down the column at the rate of 5 ml. per minute. Collect the effluent and wash the column with 100 ml. of distilled water. Add this to the main effluent and distil off the water until a small volume is obtained, then evaporate to obtain pure glucose. [The citric acid is retained on the column and can if desired by recovered in solution by eluting the column with 100 ml. of $M/2$ ammonium carbonate solution.]

Regenerate the column by washing with water, $M/2.Na_2CO_3$ solution, and again with water.

Thin Layer Chromatography

This is used extensively for qualitative analysis, for it is a rapid process and requires simple apparatus. The adsorbent is usually a layer, about 0·25 mm. thick, of silica gel or alumina, with an inactive binder, e.g. calcium sulphate, to increase the strength of the layer. A 1:1 slurry of the absorbent and methanol is commonly coated on glass plates (5 × 20 cm. or 20 × 20 cm.), but microscope slides are convenient for routine work. Various spreading devices are available for the larger plates, or they may be bought ready-prepared. Microscope slides may be prepared by dipping them in pairs back-to-back in the slurry and quickly withdrawing them. The long edges are wiped clean with thumb and forefinger, and the plates separated and placed face-upwards on racks, and the absorbent activated by drying at 110° for 30 minutes; the plates can then be stored in a desiccator.

The mixture to be separated is dissolved in a suitable solvent and spotted on to a pencilled line at the bottom of the t.l.c. plate, ca. 1·0–1·5 cm. from the end. A suitable dropping tube may be made by drawing out the middle of a m.p. tube with a micro-burner and breaking the tube in the middle. The dropper is filled by capillary action and is discharged when the liquid at the tip drops on to the untouched absorbent surface; the spot should be 2–5 mm. in diameter.

When the solvent around the spot has evaporated, the plate is placed vertically in a glass developing 'tank' (a cylinder for small slides) which contains a small quantity of the solvent and is lined with filter-paper dipping into the solvent; the level of the latter is adjusted, preferably with a pipette, so that the lower edge of the absorbent layer is under the solvent but the spot is above this level, and the top of the cylinder is then firmly closed. The solvent rises through the adsorbent layer, and the components of the mixture ascend at different rates depending on their affinities for the adsorbent.

When the solvent has nearly reached the top of the adsorbent layer, the components should be well separated. The relative distance travelled by the components can be increased by using a solvent of higher or lower polarity in the order of increasing eluting power:

petroleum < benzene < chloroform < ether < ethanol

The plate is removed from the tank, the position of the solvent front marked, and the solvent allowed to evaporate from the plate. If the components of the mixture are coloured, the separation is obvious; if colourless, they must be located either by viewing under U.V. or by standing the plate in a closed dry 'tank' containing crystals of iodine, whose vapour makes brown spots show up. The R_F values of the components are determined as before (p. 53).

Methods and Manipulation on a Semi-micro Scale.

INTRODUCTION. When only very small quantities of organic materials are available their manipulation must necessarily be carried out on a correspondingly small scale. This occurs frequently in research problems, but small-scale preparative work is often of value to the student because considerable economy of materials and of time can be achieved. It is emphasised, however, that the proper training for the organic chemist must rest upon the correct understanding and thorough practice of the manipulations on the macro-scale already described, and that he should consider small-scale work as a sequel to and not as a replacement of the above standard techniques.

Preparative work is sometimes divided into three categories. This division is entirely arbitrary and the categories overlap, but they may conveniently be classified thus:

Scale	Remarks
(a) *Macro*.	Usually 1 g. to 200 g. for solids and 5 g. to 200 g. for liquids.
(b) *Semi-micro*.	50 mg. to 1 g. for solids and 1 g. to 5 g. for liquids.
(c) *Micro*.	Below the above limits.

The difficulties of working with small quantities of liquids are much greater than with small quantities of solids. For example a competent worker can, and does in fact, often work with 100 mg. of solid without any special apparatus. With liquids this is often not practicable because of the much greater losses entailed, particularly when it is realised that one ordinary-sized drop weighs about 50–100 mg. The account which follows gives details of modifications of standard apparatus suitable for the semi-micro scale defined above.

General Considerations. With liquids and solutions the most serious losses are due to (a) transference from spherical flasks and difficulties of drainage, (b) retention by filter-papers, (c) absorption by large corks. As containers for small quantities of liquids it is therefore often convenient to use pear-shaped flasks **A** and conical test-tubes or centrifuge-tubes **B** (Fig. 29). (In this and subsequent figures, approximate dimensions are given to indicate a convenient size.)

The transference of a liquid from one vessel to another is best carried out by means of a dropping pipette **A** (Fig. 30). For measuring out a definite volume of liquid it is obviously an advantage to have a calibrated pipette **B** (Fig. 30) of 1 or 5 ml. total capacity. Alternatively, semi-micro burettes reading to 0·02 ml. are particularly convenient for class work.

For the separation of immiscible liquids a small separating funnel of the conventional type should be used whenever practicable, a pear-shaped funnel (Fig. 16, p. 35) of 5–10 ml. capacity being particularly

59

convenient. For separations on a smaller scale a dropping-pipette should be used: for the removal of an upper layer, the bent pipette (Fig. 31) is recommended. An ordinary hand centrifuge may be employed to promote a clean line of demarcation between two immiscible liquids which show a tendency to emulsify.

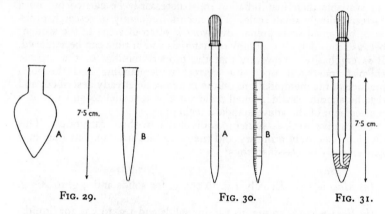

FIG. 29.   FIG. 30.   FIG. 31.

In order to minimise the absorption of liquids by corks, single pieces of apparatus are used wherever possible.

A skilled worker can use a micro-Bunsen burner for most types of heating. Nevertheless, as there is a tendency for a liquid to shoot out of a small test-tube when heated, it is preferable to place the tube in a hot water-bath or in a metal heating block. A small glycerol bath is suitable for distillations and heating under reflux, the glycerol being subsequently easily removed from flasks, etc., by washing with water.

Determination of Boiling-points. The following alternative methods are recommended. (a) Draw one drop of the liquid into a capillary tube so that the drop is about 1 cm. from one end. Hold the tube horizontally and quickly seal this end in a micro-burner. Attach the tube (with the open end upwards) to a thermometer in the melting-point apparatus (Fig. 1(c), p. 3) so that the trapped bubble of air in the capillary tube is below the surface of the bath-liquid. Now heat the bath, and take as the b.p. of the liquid that temperature at which the upper level of the bubble reaches the level of the surface of the bath liquid. (b) Prepare a fairly wide capillary tube **A** (*ca.* 4 mm. × 8 cm.) (Fig. 32). Using a fine pipette insert about 1 cm. length of the liquid into the bottom of the tube. Now place in the tube **A** a fine inverted melting-point tube **B** of about 1 mm. diameter, sealed at the upper end. Fasten the capillary tube to the thermometer by means of a rubber band and place in a melting-point apparatus. Heat slowly until a stream of bubbles rises from the bottom

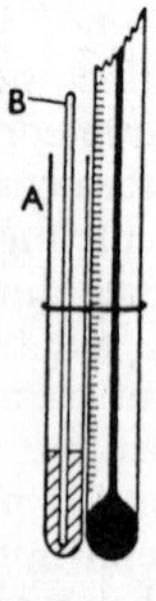

FIG. 32.

of the capillary tube, then remove the source of heat and, as the bath cools, take as the b.p. that temperature at which the liquid recedes into the inverted tube **B**.

Determination of Melting-points. The determination of the melting-point, as described on pp. 2–4, is of course in itself a micro-method. Even so, when working on a very small scale it is advantageous to use either:

(a) Electrically heated melting-point apparatus (Fig. 33), or
(b) Microscope hot stage apparatus (Fig. 34).

(a) Electrically heated melting-point apparatus.

With this type of apparatus (Fig. 33) high temperatures can be reached with safety and the dangers of hot oil or concentrated sulphuric acid are avoided.

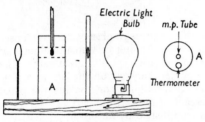

FIG. 33.

A metal cylinder **A** contains two small holes. Into one of these the thermometer is placed and into the other (arranged centrally) is placed the melting-point tube. The cylinder is pierced by a horizontal tunnel so the melting-point tube can be observed during heating. A lens is fixed in front of the horizontal tunnel so that minute changes can be observed on very small amounts of material in the melting-point tube. The cylinder is heated electrically by an insulated resistance, controlled by a rheostat. The melting-point tube is illuminated electrically from behind. After a determination, the metal cylinder and surrounding element can be cooled very quickly by a jet of cold air (from bellows or from compressed air mains).

(b) Determination of Melting-point on Microscope Hot Stage

The advantages of this method are twofold (1) It is possible to observe minute changes in colour and structure before and during the process of melting. (2) It is possible to use a single crystal which, e.g., is often obtained from a semi-micro sublimation.

The instrument (Fig. 34) is fixed by screws on to the stage of the microscope. An electrically heated stage **S** supports a removable rim **R**, and a glass slide **G**. The heating apparatus is connected to a rheostat. A thermometer **T** is inserted into a long cylindrical hole passing below the centre of the stage. Light from the mirror of the microscope passes through the optical condenser below the hot stage and then through a small opening in the latter so as to illuminate the sample.

If the apparatus has not been used for some time, it should be heated to about 140° to drive off any moisture. After cooling, a few crystals of the substance are placed on the glass slide **G**. A small cover glass,

C, is then placed firmly on the slide. The latter is then inserted into the stage in such a position that the sample is directly above the light opening. A glass baffle, **B**, is placed over the sample, so as to protect the microscope lens from too much heat. A large glass cover is then placed completely over the rim **B**. The sample is now brought into sharp focus and the temperature raised by adjustment of the rheostat. As usual when taking melting-points, the temperature should be almost stationary at the actual melting-point.

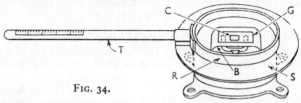

FIG. 34.

Heating under Reflux. For this purpose, a glass water-condenser of length *ca.* 25 cm. can be used. When boiling very small volumes of liquid under reflux, the "cold finger" **A** (Fig. 35) is of great value. The cold finger, if provided with a shoulder, can rest on the rim of a test-tube or flask, or it may be inserted through a cork having the usual groove cut in the side to allow escape of gas (*cf.* Fig. 37).

The heating of the vessels is accomplished by means of a small bath or a micro-Bunsen burner. The vessel can be clamped at such a distance from the burner that the contained liquid boils gently under reflux. Smooth boiling is ensured by the addition of 1–2 minute pieces of unglazed porcelain, or of a short piece of melting-point tubing open at both ends.

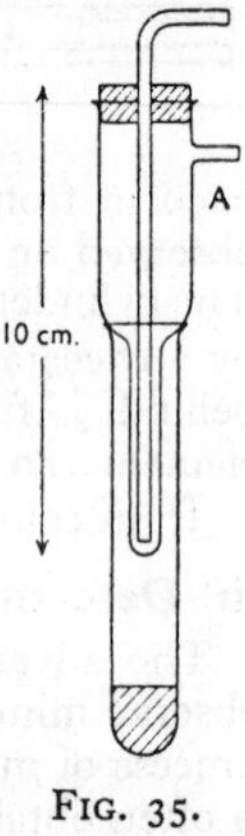

Stirring. In semi-micro work stirring is not often necessary as manual agitation usually suffices. When prolonged stirring is required, a small glass stirrer attached to a motor is recommended for reactions taking place in open flasks. For closed systems a small spring disc is available* which fits snugly into the neck of the flask. The disc contains a hole, centrally placed, through which a small glass stirrer can be pushed. The stirrer should be

FIG. 35.

smeared with a very small amount of silicone grease where it passes through the spring disc. A relatively powerful motor is required for this apparatus.

A magnetic stirrer is also recommended for semi-micro work. A small bar of glass-covered steel† is placed in the liquid contained

* Supplied by Messrs. Geo. Angus Ltd., Coast Road, Wallsend, Northumberland.

† Alternatively, the steel bar may be encased in Tevlon plastic, which preferably has a small ridge of the plastic around its middle to prevent it lying flat in the flask.

in a small flat-bottomed flask which is placed over a motor containing a horizontally-rotating magnet.

Distillation. This process is carried out in the apparatus shown in Figs. 36, 37 and 38. The distillation apparatus (Fig. 36) is of very general application and is made in one piece.

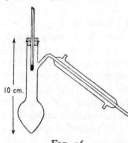

FIG. 36.

Distillations on the semi-micro scale can also be carried out in the simple pear-shaped distilling flask **A** (Fig. 37). The distillate is collected in the 'centrifuge-tube' **B** placed in the bottom of the vessel **C**. The latter is a boiling tube with a side-arm fused on at 45°. This arm is connected to that of the flask by a cork. A "cold finger" **D** serves to condense the vapour issuing from the side-arm of the flask. Distillation in this apparatus must be performed very slowly to ensure efficient condensation and collection of the distillate in **B**. This type of apparatus is particularly suitable for liquids of high boiling-point and especially for substances that solidify on cooling. As the side-arm of **A** is not cooled, condensation is not usually likely to take place before the distillate reaches **B**. As this apparatus is virtually closed except for the groove in the cork of **C**, it is also convenient for the distillation of pungent and lachrymatory materials (*e.g.*, benzyl chloride).

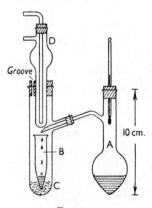

FIG. 37.

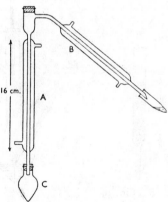

FIG. 38.

All thermometers for semi-micro preparations must have very small bulbs. They may often be inserted into flasks through a short "collar" of rubber tubing in place of the customary corks.

Distillation Technique. With all distillations on a semi-micro scale it is essential to heat the liquid so slowly that a "cushion" of its vapour envelopes the bulb of the thermometer for a sufficiently long time to enable the thermometer to register the correct temperature. It is for this reason that the side-arm of the flask proceeds upwards before passing downwards. By this device a "cushion" of vapour can be maintained round the bulb of the thermometer before the required fraction is distilled.

Reflux Distillation Unit. The apparatus shown in Fig. 38 is a specially designed distillation-unit that can be used for boiling liquids under reflux, followed by distillation. The unit consists of a vertical water-condenser **A**, the top of which is fused to the side-arm condenser **B**. The flask **C** is attached by a cork to **A**. This apparatus is particularly suitable for the hydrolysis of esters (p. 99) and anilides (p. 109), on a small scale. For example an ester is heated under reflux with sodium hydroxide solution while water is passed through the vertical condenser; water is then run out of the vertical condenser and passed through the inclined condenser. The rate of heating is increased and any volatile product will then distil over.

Fractional Distillation. Fractional distillation on a semi-micro scale can be carried out satisfactorily with the fractionating column shown in Fig. 39. The column is 10 cm. long and is filled with pieces

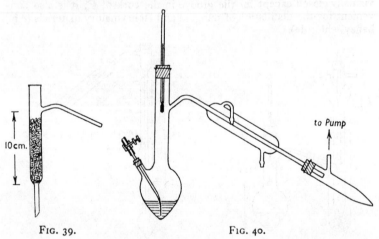

10cm.

to Pump

FIG. 39.   FIG. 40.

(3–4 mm. long) of very narrow glass tubing. As in all fractionations the distillation must be carried out very slowly and in this connection, particular use is made of the "upward" bend of the side-arm so as to record the maximum temperature of the issuing vapour.

The apparatus shown in Fig. 38 can also be used for fractionation by placing a secure plug of glass wool at the base of the vertical condenser and then filling it with short pieces of glass tubing.

Distillation under reduced pressure. The student should first read details of this operation on a macro-scale (p. 28). For micro-scale work the apparatus shown in Fig. 40 is very convenient. A small pear-

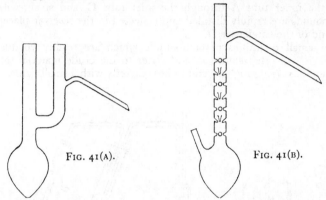

FIG. 41(A).   FIG. 41(B).

shaped flask of 5 ml. capacity is fitted with a small side-tube through which a piece of glass tubing can be passed. The latter is held in position by a rubber bung,* and is drawn out into a fine capillary tube to act as an air-leak. The upper end of the tubing is fitted with pressure tubing and a screw-clip to regulate the flow of air. Distilling flasks of alternative design are shown in Figs. 41(A) and 41(B).

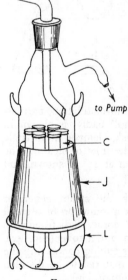

to Pump

C

J

L

FIG. 42.

With a single receiver tube as shown in Fig. 40 it is necessary to interrupt the distillation each time the receiver is changed. For more precise work a multiple receiver as shown in Fig. 42 should be used. The lower part **L** of this apparatus contains 6 small collecting tubes **C**, each† supported in a wire hoop attached to a fixed vertical glass rod. The receptacle **L** is attached to the upper part of the apparatus by a ground-in glass joint, **J**, carefully lubricated by silicone grease. By gently rotating the receptacle **L** about the ground-glass joint **J**, it is possible to collect the different fractions in the separate tubes without stopping the distillation, and hence without alteration of pressure.

* The type of apparatus shown in Fig. 40 can be obtained with ground-in glass joints thus obviating the use of rubber bungs.

† Each tube **C** should have an identification mark, so that the b.p./pressure of the contents of each can be recorded during the distillation.

Steam Distillation. A compact and efficient apparatus is shown in Fig. 43. The liquid to be steam-distilled is placed in the tube **A** and water is placed in the outer flask **B**. On heating **B**, steam passes into the inner tube **A** through the inlet tube **C**, and steam-volatile compounds are rapidly distilled and collected in the receiver placed at the end of the condenser **D**.

For small quantities of compounds which are readily volatile in steam, it will often suffice to add water to the crude material in the reaction flask (*e.g.*, Fig. 36) and to heat directly with a small flame.

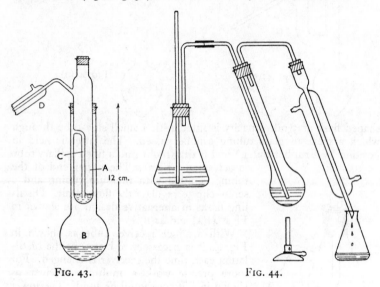

FIG. 43.   FIG. 44.

A very suitable apparatus for semi-micro steam-distillation, particularly for suspensions that are likely to "bump" badly, is shown in Fig. 44. This consists of a 50 ml. Kjeldahl flask, clamped at an angle of 45°, and fitted with a long glass tube for the inlet of steam. The outlet-tube is bent twice, first at 135° and then at 45° as shown, and fitted into a small water-condenser.

Steam generator. For small scale work the steam generator (**D**, Fig. 15, p. 33) is too cumbersome for the production of a small amount of steam. It is preferable to use a 250 ml. conical flask fitted with cork containing a vertical safety tube and an outlet-tube (Fig. 44). Care should be taken that the length of rubber tubing connecting the steam outlet tube to the flask containing the material to be distilled should be as short as possible and should not contain kinks.

Crystallisation and Filtration. Crystallisation is carried out in apparatus of conventional type but reduced in size. Glass rods should be about 10 cm. long and 2 mm. in diameter. It is advisable to use solvents in which the solute is sparingly soluble, so that larger volumes of liquid can be employed. Light petroleum and cyclohexane are often satisfactory for this purpose.

Choice of Solvent. In general, a higher boiling solvent is preferable to a low-boiling solvent, as evaporation is then considerably less.

When the correct solvent for recrystallisation is not known a procedure similar to that given on pp. 15-16 should be followed, but on the semi-micro scale not more than 10 mg. of the solid should be placed in the tapered-end test-tube (Fig. 29(B)) and about 0·1 ml. of the solvent should be added from the calibrated dropping-pipette (Fig. 30(B)). If the compound dissolves readily in the cold, the solvent is unsuitable, but the solution should not be discarded. [In this case recourse should be had to the use of mixed solvents (p. 18). For example if the substance is very soluble in ethanol, water should be added from a calibrated pipette with shaking to determine whether crystallisation will now take place, indicated by a "cloudiness" or by the separation of solid.]

If the solid does not dissolve in the cold solvent gently heat the mixture over a micro-Bunsen burner or in a small water-bath until the liquid boils. Continue to add 0·1 ml. portions of solvent until the solid dissolves. [If more than about 1 ml. of solvent is required, the solvent is considered unsatisfactory.] If a clear solution is obtained, cool the tube and scratch it below the surface of the solution with a *very fine* glass rod and proceed as suggested on p. 16. In general, the products from the "choice of solvent" investigation are not discarded but added to the main bulk of the crude product for recrystallisation.

The filtration of crystals is carried out using a small conical Buchner funnel (**C**, Fig. 4, p. 10) or a funnel of similar design but having a sintered filtration plate. Alternatively an ordinary conical funnel in which is placed a circular perforated plate can be used.

The complete filtration apparatus is shown in Fig. 5, p. 11. A simpler and cheaper apparatus is shown in Fig. 45. This consists of a boiling-tube **A** having a side-arm for connection to the pump: the tube **A** is conveniently held in a wooden or cork block **B** or in a clamp. The funnel **F** may be fitted into **A** through a pliable rubber disc **D**: the latter is more useful than a cork since it covers tubes of various diameters. The filtrate is collected in the centrifuge-tube **T**.

For the filtration of very small quantities of crystals, the simple apparatus shown in Fig. 46 is often used. It consists of a fine glass rod (sometimes termed a "filtration nail") which is flattened at one end, the flattened surface being preferably roughened. It fits as shown into a small funnel which replaces **F** (Fig. 45). A circular piece of filter-paper is cut (*e.g.*, with a *clean* sharp cork-borer) so as to fit completely and snugly over the flat end. After draining, the "nail" is raised and the filter-paper and crystals are removed with forceps and dried.

The filtration of hot or boiling liquids requires care, as rapid evaporation is likely to occur. Evaporation is minimised by the use of a

cylindrical tube **T** (Fig. 47) furnished with a filter-plate or sinter.
The tube **T** can be fitted into an adaptor **B** (Fig. 47), or it may be
inserted directly through the disc **D** (Fig. 45) so that the filtrate collects
in a suitable tube placed in the receiver **A** (Fig. 45). Adaptors such as
B (Fig. 47) are of considerable use in many kinds of micro-chemical work.

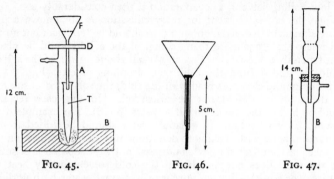

FIG. 45.   FIG. 46.   FIG. 47.

Drying of crystals. Whenever possible crystals should be dried
in a small vacuum desiccator containing a suitable desiccant. The
latter depends upon the nature of the solvent used (*cf.* p. 19). However
for most purposes anhydrous calcium chloride is satisfactory. If a
hydrocarbon has been used in the recrystallisation, a few thin fresh
shavings of paraffin wax are efficacious.

For more efficient drying at
elevated temperatures, the
vacuum apparatus (Fig. 48(A)) is
often used. The sample to be
dried is placed in an inner tube
surrounded by a heating jacket.
The latter is connected above to
a water-condenser and below to
a flask which contains a liquid of
appropriate boiling-point. The
inner tube is connected to a
water-pump. A more satisfactory
'pistol' (Fig. 48(B)) consists
of a wide glass tube **A** closed at
each end by ground-glass caps.
The tube is fitted with a two-
way tap, so that **B** can be
used for evacuating the tube,

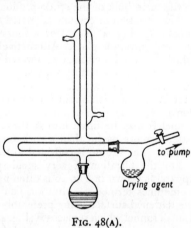

FIG. 48(A).

and the capillary tube **C** for the subsequent re-entrance of air. The
boat **D** contains the drying-agent (*e.g.*, P_4O_{10}), and a pad of glass-wool
E is held in position as shown. The material to be dried (usually in an
open specimen tube) is placed in the smaller boat **F**. Air should be

admitted into the evacuated tube only through the capillary tube **C** to ensure a gentle stream of air: the pad **E** provides an extra safeguard against material in **D** being swept towards **F**. The heating-element **G** allows the tube to be heated electrically to any required thermostatically-controlled temperature. This 'drying pistol' has obvious advantages over that in Fig. 48(A).

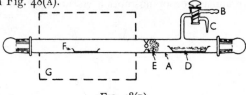

FIG. 48(B).

Evaporation. Very small evaporating basins of the conventional type may be used. Such a procedure, however, often results in the condensation of moisture. A more efficient method consists in drawing a stream of dry air over the surface of the liquid (Fig. 49), or alternatively in blowing air from the compressed air mains over the liquid.

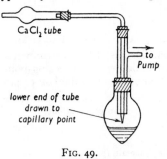

CaCl₂ tube

to Pump

lower end of tube drawn to capillary point

FIG. 49.

Sublimation. This is a most useful process for small-scale work as the losses are comparatively small. This can be performed: (a) In a long narrow tube sealed at one end. The material is shaken to the closed end of the tube, which is then inserted horizontally in a metal-heating block (Fig. 50); (b) In the "cold-finger" device (Fig. 35, p. 62).

Identification of Gases. The apparatus (Fig. 51(A)) consists of a glass bulb **B** with drawn-out open ends, and fitting snugly on to the rim of a test-tube. Before testing for a gas, a drop of the reagent is drawn into the lower end of the bulb, which is then placed on the tube in which the gas is being evolved. On removing the bulb and examining the reagent against a suitable background, significant colour changes or the formation of a precipitate in the reagent can be detected.

Vapours which can be readily condensed (*e.g.*, chloroform, aniline, nitro-benzene, *etc.*) are readily detected by the device shown in Fig. 51(B). It is essentially a "cold finger" with a deep indentation or well at the lower end. In this way two or three drops of liquid can easily be collected and removed by a capillary tube for qualitative tests.

Weighing and measurements. The rough balances used for macro-scale preparative work are not adequate for semi-micro preparations. For the latter purpose, ordinary analytical balances should be used. Small nickel spatulas of suitable size and design are now available for small-scale work. Small forceps are also almost indispensable.

The greatest quantitative errors in semi-micro work arise in connection with the measurement of liquids. For this reason the use of microburettes and graduated dropping-tubes is essential (*cf.* pp. 59-60).

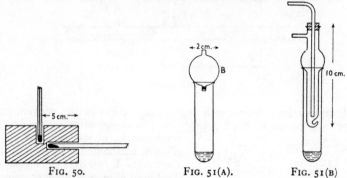

FIG. 50.   FIG. 51(A).   FIG. 51(B)

Molecular Weight Determinations. Details of the determination of molecular weights on a semi-micro scale by the Freezing-point method are given on p. 436, and by the Boiling-point method on p. 440.

PREPARATIONS. By employing suitable apparatus as described above, the student is enabled to carry out the following semi-micro preparations.

Copper acetate (p. 75)
Iodoform (p. 92)
Ethyl acetate (p. 97) and Hydrolysis of Ethyl acetate (p. 100)
Acetanilide (p. 107) and Hydrolysis of Acetanilide (p. 108)
2-Naphthyl acetate (p. 110)
Oxamide (p. 118)
Benzamide (p. 119)
Mercury benzamide (p. 120)
Glucosazone (p. 137)
Nitrobenzene (p. 157)
m-Dinitrobenzene (p. 158, $\frac{1}{10}$th scale given)
Aniline (p. 164)
m-Nitroaniline (p. 168, $\frac{1}{8}$th scale given)
p-Bromoacetanilide (p. 166)
p-Nitroacetanilide (p. 167, $\frac{1}{5}$th scale given)
p-Nitroaniline (p. 168, $\frac{1}{6}$th scale given)
Chlorobenzene (p. 189, $\frac{1}{5}$th scale given)
Sulphanilamide (p. 181, $\frac{1}{10}$th scale given)
Diphenylnitrosoamine (p. 203)
Benzeneazo-2-naphthol (p. 210, $\frac{1}{20}$th scale given)
Benzaldehyde phenylhydrazone (p. 229)
Benzylidene-aniline (p. 230)

Dibenzal-acetone (p. 231)

Benzoin (p. 233, $\frac{1}{10}$th scale given)

Benzil (p. 234), $\frac{1}{10}$th scale given)

Benzil osazone (p. 234)

Phenyl benzoate (p. 244) and Hydrolysis of phenyl benzoate (p. 244)

Benzanilide (p. 245) and Hydrolysis of benzanilide (p. 246)

Benzyl *p*-nitrobenzoate (p. 246)

Methyl 3,5-dinitrobenzoate (p. 247)

Phenyl toluene-*p*-sulphonate (p. 249)

Acetophenone (p. 255)

Acetophenone phenylhydrazone (p. 257)

Acetophenone semicarbazone (p. 258)

Anthraquinone (p. 259)

Triphenyl carbinol (p. 285)

The preparations of all the derivatives, and all the hydrolyses of esters, anilides, *etc.*, described in Part III, provide excellent practice in semi-micro manipulation.

The semi-micro scale is particularly suitable for students who wish to carry out a succession of syntheses from one starting material. For this purpose the following conversions are recommended.

(*a*) Benzene→nitrobenzene→aniline→acetanilide|→*p*-acetamidobenzenesulphonyl chloride→*p*-acetamidobenzenesulphonamide→sulphanilamide.

(*b*) Benzene→acetanilide (as in (*a*))→*p*-nitroacetanilide→*p*-nitroaniline.

(*c*) Benzene→aniline (as in (*a*))→benzenediazonium chloride→benzeneazo-2-naphthol.

(*d*) Benzene→benzenediazonium chloride (as in (*c*))→chlorobenzene.

(*e*) Benzoic acid→3,5-dinitrobenzoic acid→3,5-dinitrobenzoyl chloride.

(*f*) Benzene→aniline (as in (*a*))→2,4,6-tribromoaniline→1,3,5-tribromobenzene.

In each set of reactions, it is of course necessary to employ sufficient of the starting material to ensure that the final product will be not less than 0·1 g. for a solid and 1 ml. for a liquid.

STANDARD SEMI-MICRO EQUIPMENT. The authors have found, during many years, that a student provided with the following basic semi-micro equipment will be enabled to carry out the majority of the small preparations described in this book.

Apparatus contained in a 14″ × 5″ × 3¾″ *box*

1 × 50 ml. Round-bottomed flask.

1 × 10 and 1 × 5 ml. Conical flasks.

1 × 15 ml. Pear-shaped flask. (Fig. 29(A).)

1 × 15 ml. Pear-shaped distillation flask with condenser attached. (Fig. 36.)

1 × 15 ml. Pear-shaped distillation flask. (Fig. 37.)

1 × 7″ Liebig type condenser. (*Cf.* Fig. 3(B).)

1 × 4″ "Cold finger" type condenser. (Fig. 35.)

1 × 4″ Filter tube. (Fig. 45.)

2 × 1″ Analytical funnels. (Fig. 46.)

1 × 5″ Cylindrical separating funnel with tap. (Fig. 16(A).)

1 × 2 ml. Graduated pipette with rubber filler. (Fig. 30(A).)

1 × 5½″ Glass tube receiver with sloping side arm. (As in Fig. 37.)

1 × 2½″ Receiving tube. (Fig. 29(B).)

1 × Glass "filtration nail". (Fig. 46.)

1 × Hirsch funnel (2″ diameter). (C, Fig. 4, p. 10.)

2 × Glass stirring rods.

2 × Semi-micro clamps.

1 × Semi-micro Bunsen burner.

1 × Glass bulb for gas identification tests. (Fig. 51(A).)

In addition each student will require a lightweight 14″ retort stand.

The following apparatus is desirable but not essential.

1 × 50 ml. Kjeldahl flask. (Fig. 44.)

1 × Liebig type condenser with side condenser attached. (Fig. 38.)

PART II

PREPARATIONS*

The Oxidation of Ethanol.

Ethanol, being a typical primary alcohol containing the $-CH_2OH$ group, gives on oxidation first acetaldehyde and then acetic acid. This process, when carried out by an aqueous oxidising agent, probably consists in the direct

$$CH_3CH_2OH \xrightarrow{\;\;O\;\;} CH_3CH(OH)_2 \xrightarrow{\;-2H\;} CH_3COOH$$
Ethanol. $\qquad\qquad\qquad \downarrow -H_2O \qquad\qquad$ Acetic Acid.
$$CH_3CHO$$
Acetaldehyde.

addition of oxygen to the ethanol to give the dihydroxy-derivative, $CH_3CH(OH)_2$; the latter is unstable and readily loses water, *e.g.*, on warming, to give acetaldehyde, while in the presence of an excess of the oxidising agent it loses two atoms of hydrogen to give acetic acid. It is known that acetaldehyde, when dissolved in water, partly reforms the dihydroxy-compound, a process which occurs very readily with chloral or trichloro-acetaldehyde, CCl_3CHO, which forms a stable "hydrate," $CCl_3CH(OH)_2$.

The oxidising agent used for the preparation of both acetaldehyde and acetic acid is a mixture of sodium dichromate and sulphuric acid, but the conditions of the experiment are changed according to the product required. For the preparation of acetaldehyde, a mixture of aqueous sodium dichromate and ethanol is added gradually to hot dilute sulphuric acid: just sufficient of the dichromate-sulphuric acid mixture is thus produced to oxidise the added ethanol to acetaldehyde, which is rapidly distilled off from the reaction mixture. Acetaldehyde is thus produced in moderate yield, although in spite of the above precautions part of the aldehyde undergoes further oxidation to acetic acid. A further loss is occasioned by the condensation of some of the aldehyde with the unchanged ethanol under the influence of the sulphuric acid to give acetal: this loss is small,

$$CH_3CHO + 2HOC_2H_5 \rightarrow CH_3CH(OC_2H_5)_2 + H_2O$$

however, as the reaction reaches an equilibrium and much of the regenerated aldehyde escapes by volatilisation.

Pure acetaldehyde is extremely volatile, having b.p. 21°, and its isolation is therefore difficult: hence only the preparation of an aqueous solution is described below.

To prepare acetic acid, aqueous ethanol is added gradually to a hot mixture of aqueous sodium dichromate and sulphuric acid. The oxidising mixture is now always in excess, and therefore the oxidation proceeds as far as possible; moreover, the reaction is carried out under reflux, so that any acetaldehyde which volatilises is returned to the oxidising mixture. Hence the final product contains only a small amount of acetaldehyde.

* In most of these preparations, the corks or rubber-bungs can be replaced by ground-glass joints (pp. 42–47).

73

To prepare pure acetic acid (glacial acetic acid), the crude aqueous product is converted into the sodium salt, the latter dehydrated by fusion† and then heated with concentrated sulphuric acid: anhydrous acetic acid, b.p. 118°, distils over. Only the preparation of aqueous acetic acid and of crystalline copper acetate is described below.

Technically, acetaldehyde is mainly made by the oxidation of ethylene using a $CuCl_2/PdCl_2$ catalyst system. Although some acetic acid is still prepared by the catalytic oxidation of acetaldehyde, the main process is the catalytic oxidation of paraffins, usually n-butane.

Acetaldehyde, CH_3CHO, in Aqueous Solution.

Required: Ethanol, 40 ml.; sodium dichromate, 50 g.; sulphuric acid, 17 ml.

Fit a 500 ml. bolt-head flask **F** with a well-fitting cork which is free from flaws, and which carries a dropping-funnel **D** and a delivery tube (or "knee-tube") **T**, the latter being connected to a water-condenser **C** (Fig. 52). Attach an adaptor **A** to the lower end of the condenser. (Alternatively, use a ground-glass flask (Fig. 22(A), p. 43) with a distillation-head (Fig. 22(F)): the dropping-funnel can be fitted into the distillation-head, the side-arm of which is connected to a condenser as in Fig. 23(D), p. 45.)

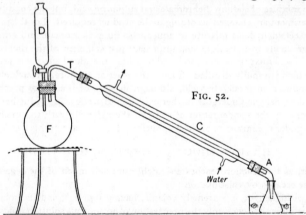

FIG. 52.

Place 50 ml. of water in the flask **F**, and then add slowly with shaking 17 ml. (31·5 g.) of concentrated sulphuric acid: finally add some fragments of unglazed porcelain, and replace the flask. Dissolve 50 g. of coarsely crushed sodium dichromate* in

* Sodium dichromate is used instead of the potassium salt because it is far more soluble in water, and is not precipitated from its aqueous solution by addition of the ethanol. It is also cheaper than the potassium salt, but has the disadvantage of being deliquescent.

† Cf. p. 117.

50 ml. water contained in a small beaker, add 40 ml. (32·5 g.) of ethanol, and then place the well-stirred mixture in the dropping-funnel. Ensure that a rapid stream of cold water is passing through the condenser and that the adaptor **A** dips into a 100 ml. conical flask which is surrounded with ice-water. Now heat the dilute acid in the flask until it starts to boil gently, and then remove the flame and run the dichromate solution very slowly into the flask. Directly the ethanolic dichromate solution enters the hot acid, a vigorous reaction occurs, and a mixture of acetaldehyde and water, containing a little acetic acid, begins to distil over: meanwhile the reaction mixture becomes green owing to reduction of the dichromate. The addition of the dichromate solution should take about 20 minutes: towards the end of this time it will be necessary to replace the flame under the flask to maintain *gentle* boiling. When the addition of the dichromate solution is complete, a moderately concentrated aqueous solution of acetaldehyde will have collected in the conical receiver.

Note cautiously the characteristic odour of acetaldehyde which this solution possesses. Then with the solution carry out the following general tests for aldehydes described on p. 341: Test No. 1 (Schiff's reagent), No. 3 (Action of sodium hydroxide), No. 4 (Reduction of ammoniacal silver nitrate). Finally perform the two special tests for acetaldehyde given on p. 344 (Nitroprusside test and the Iodoform reaction).

Pure acetaldehyde is a colourless volatile liquid, of b.p. 21°: freely soluble in water, ethanol and ether.

It should be emphasised that the above experiment serves solely to illustrate the oxidation of ethanol to acetaldehyde: the yield is never high, although it may be increased by blowing carbon dioxide through the solution during the oxidation in order to remove the acetaldehyde as fast as it is formed. For an efficient production of acetaldehyde from ethanol the latter is catalytically dehydrogenated by passing it over copper at 250–300° in an apparatus designed so that unchanged ethanol is separated from the aldehyde and circulated again over the catalyst.

Acetic Acid, CH_3COOH, in Aqueous Solution, and crystalline Cupric Acetate, $(CH_3COO)_2Cu,H_2O$. (Semi-micro scale).

Required: Sulphuric acid, 3·3 ml.; sodium dichromate, 3·5 g.; ethanol, 1·5 ml.; copper carbonate, 1·5 g.

Fit a 50 ml. bolt-head flask **F** (Fig. 53) with a reflux water-condenser **C**, to the top of which a dropping-funnel **D** is fixed by means of a cork having a vertical V-shaped groove **G** cut or filed in the side to allow subsequent escape of air. Place 5 ml. of water in the flask and then add 3·3 ml. (6·1 g.) of concentrated sulphuric acid slowly with shaking: finally add 3·5 g. of coarsely crushed sodium dichromate and *some fragments* of unglazed porcelain. The dichromate rapidly dissolves in the acid, which has become hot during the preliminary dilution. Place in the dropping-funnel a mixture of 1·5 ml. (1·2 g.) of ethanol and 6 ml. of water, and allow it to fall slowly drop by drop down the condenser into the oxidation mixture. A vigorous reaction occurs and the mixture becomes green owing to the formation of chromic sulphate, $Cr_2(SO_4)_3$. At *frequent* intervals* during the addition of the ethanol, mix the contents of the flask by vigorous shaking. When the addition is complete and the reaction has subsided, heat the flask on a boiling water-bath for 15 minutes. Then detach and reverse the condenser, and reconnect it to the flask through a knee-tube for direct distillation, as shown in Fig. 60, p. 101, or Fig. 23(D), p. 45. Distil the mixture, by direct heating over a gauze, until about 8 ml. of distillate have been collected. Acetic acid is volatile in steam and an aqueous solution of the acid, containing, however, some acetaldehyde, is thus obtained. With a very small portion of this solution, perform the tests for acetic acid given on p. 347.

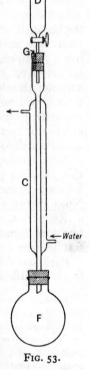

FIG. 53.

Place all but 0·5 ml. of the remainder of the distillate in a moderately large evaporating-basin, add about 2 ml. of water (to keep the copper acetate subsequently in solution) and then heat gently on a sand-bath until the solution just begins to boil: then without delay add 1·5 g. of powdered copper carbonate cautiously, in small quantities at a time, to the well-stirred hot solution until no further evolution of carbon dioxide occurs. Filter the mixture at the pump, using a Buchner funnel and flask which have been preheated by the filtration of some boiling distilled water: finally wash the residue of excess carbonate on the filter with about 1 ml. of hot water, allowing the wash-water to join the clear blue filtrate. Transfer the latter to an evaporating-basin, and add the 0·5 ml. of original distillate which has been kept in reserve: this prevents the subsequent formation of basic copper acetate. Now evaporate the solution on a water-bath† until crystals begin to appear on the surface. If the solution is now chilled in ice-water, a crop of small crystals of copper acetate is rapidly obtained: if, however, the

* If the contents of the flask are not *thoroughly* mixed at this stage, an explosion may occur during the subsequent distillation.

† The solution must not be concentrated by direct boiling, since copper acetate in these circumstances undergoes hydrolysis and gives a precipitate of cupric oxide.

solution is allowed to cool slowly (and preferably allowed to stand overnight), a crop of large, well-formed and very beautiful crystals results. In either case, filter off the crystals at the pump, wash rapidly with a *small* quantity of distilled water, drain thoroughly, and dry in an atmospheric calcium chloride desiccator to avoid dehydration of the crystals. By further evaporation of the filtrate, a second but less pure crop of crystals may be obtained.

For reactions of acetic acid and acetates, see p. 347.

The Interaction of Ethanol and Sulphuric Acid.

Three compounds may be formed by the interaction of ethanol and sulphuric acid, according to the experimental conditions:

(1) When concentrated sulphuric acid is added to ethanol, the mixture becomes hot owing to the formation of ethyl hydrogen sulphate, the yield of which is increased if the mixture is then gently boiled under reflux:

$$C_2H_5OH + H_2SO_4 \rightarrow C_2H_5HSO_4 + H_2O$$

(2) If the mixture contains an excess of ethanol, and is heated to 140°, the ethyl hydrogen sulphate reacts with the ethanol, giving diethyl ether and regenerating the sulphuric acid:

$$C_2H_5HSO_4 + HOC_2H_5 \rightarrow C_2H_5OC_2H_5 + H_2SO_4$$

(3) If the mixture contains a considerable excess of sulphuric acid and is heated to 160–170°, the ethyl hydrogen sulphate breaks down, giving ethylene and again regenerating the sulphuric acid.

$$C_2H_5HSO_4 = C_2H_4 + H_2SO_4$$

The mechanism of the formation of these three compounds is based on the initial reaction between ethanol and a strong acid such as sulphuric acid, which involves protonation of the ethanolic oxygen to form the ion (I).

$$CH_3CH_2OH + H_2SO_4 \rightarrow CH_3CH_2 \cdot \overset{+}{O}H + HSO_4$$
$$(I) \qquad \overset{\cdot}{H}$$

This ion (I) can react in three ways, according to the conditions.

(*a*) reaction with the $\overset{-}{HSO_4}$ may give ethyl hydrogen sulphate

$$CH_3CH \cdot \overset{+}{O}H + \overset{-}{HSO_4} \rightarrow CH_3CH_2OSO_3H + H_2O \cdot$$
$$\overset{\cdot}{H}$$

(*b*) reaction with ethanol gives diethyl ether

$$CH_3CH_2 \cdot \overset{+\cdot}{O}H + CH_3CH_2OH \rightarrow CH_3CH_2OCH_2CH_3 + H_2O + \overset{+}{H}$$
$$\overset{\cdot}{H}$$

(*c*) dehydration gives ethylene

$$CH_3CH_2 \cdot \overset{+}{O}H \rightarrow CH_2 = CH_2 + H_2O + \overset{+}{H}$$
$$\overset{\cdot}{H}$$

Potassium Ethyl Sulphate. $KC_2H_5SO_4$.

Pure ethyl hydrogen sulphate is difficult to prepare, as it is an oily liquid, very soluble in water, and easily hydrolysed. It is therefore usually isolated as the potassium salt, since potassium ethyl sulphate crystallises well from water, and is not readily hydrolysed in neutral or weakly alkaline solution.

To prepare the potassium salt, the mixture of ethanol and sulphuric acid is boiled under reflux, cooled, and treated with an excess of calcium carbonate.

$$2C_2H_5HSO_4 + CaCO_3 = Ca(C_2H_5SO_4)_2 + CO_2 + H_2O$$

The ethyl hydrogen sulphate is thus converted into the soluble calcium ethyl sulphate, whilst the excess of sulphuric acid is removed as insoluble calcium sulphate. The aqueous filtrate is then mixed with just sufficient potassium carbonate to give potassium ethyl sulphate, the insoluble calcium carbonate being now filtered off.

$$Ca(C_2H_5SO_4)_2 + K_2CO_3 = 2KC_2H_5SO_4 + CaCO_3.$$

The solution of potassium ethyl sulphate can be concentrated on the water-bath without appreciable hydrolysis, and the sulphate finally crystallised out.

Required: Rectified spirit, 20 ml.; sulphuric acid, 8 ml. (15 g.); calcium carbonate, 12 g.

Place 20 ml. (16 g.) of rectified spirit in a 100 ml. round-bottomed flask, and slowly add* 8 ml. (15 g.) of concentrated sulphuric acid, keeping the liquid in the flask well shaken throughout the addition to ensure thorough mixing. Fit a reflux water-condenser to the flask, and heat the latter on a gauze so that the mixture boils gently for 45 minutes. Then cool the product and pour it into 100 ml. of cold water contained in a large (6-inch) evaporating-basin or in a shallow earthenware dish. Now add 12g. of finely powdered calcium carbonate with stirring to the acid solution. *It is essential to add the calcium carbonate as a fine stream of powder, and to stir the latter immediately into the bulk of the solution:* for this purpose, it is best to sift the carbonate through a fine sieve directly into the liquid, or alternatively to add it from a spatula, tapping the latter gently over the liquid to ensure steady addition of the finely powdered chalk. If the carbonate is added carelessly several grams at a time, it becomes rapidly covered with insoluble calcium sulphate, which protects it from further reaction: in these circumstances, at least 10 times the theoretical quantity of the carbonate may be required and the evolution of carbon dioxide may continue for several hours.

The addition of the calcium carbonate should take about 20

---

* The mixture of ethanol and concentrated sulphuric acid required in this and several subsequent preparations should always be prepared by adding the heavy acid to the ethanol. If the ethanol is added to the acid, it will tend to float on the surface of the acid, and the heat generated at the interface may blow the upper liquid out of the flask.

minutes, and the well-stirred mixture should finally be neutral to litmus-paper. Now heat the mixture on a water-bath, using a thermometer as a stirrer, until the temperature reaches 60°, and then filter at the pump through a wide Buchner funnel: at this temperature, filtration should be rapid. Finally wash the residue of calcium sulphate on the filter with a small quantity of hot water, adding the wash-water to the main filtrate. In order to convert the calcium ethyl sulphate to potassium ethyl sulphate, add a concentrated aqueous solution of potassium carbonate cautiously *drop by drop* to the well-stirred filtrate until a drop of the latter withdrawn on a glass rod is *just* sufficiently alkaline to turn red litmus-paper blue. Then filter the solution at the pump, and wash the residual calcium carbonate again with a small quantity of water. Evaporate the filtrate on a water-bath until a drop withdrawn on a rod crystallises on cooling: then allow the solution to stand until almost cold, and finally chill it thoroughly in ice-water. (If the ice-water cooling is omitted, large well-developed colourless crystals of potassium ethyl sulphate will finally separate.) Filter off the crystals at the pump, drain, and dry over calcium chloride in a desiccator.

Yield, about 6g. To obtain a second (but necessarily less pure) crop of the sulphate, evaporate the filtrate further on the water-bath, and cool as before.

Hydrolysis of Potassium Ethyl Sulphate. Dissolve about 1 g. of the crystals in about 4 ml. of cold distilled water, and divide the solution into two portions. (*a*) To one portion, add barium chloride solution. If *pure* potassium ethyl sulphate were used, no precipitate should now form, as barium ethyl sulphate is soluble in water. Actually however, almost all samples of potassium ethyl sulphate contain traces of potassium hydrogen sulphate formed by slight hydrolysis of the ethyl compound during the evaporation of its solution, and barium chloride almost invariably gives a faint precipitate of barium sulphate. (*b*) To the second portion, add 2–3 drops of concentrated hydrochloric acid, and boil the mixture *gently* for about one minute. Cool, add distilled water if necessary until the solution has its former volume, and then add barium chloride as before. A markedly heavier precipitate of barium sulphate separates. The hydrolysis of the potassium ethyl sulphate is hastened considerably by the presence of the free acid: caustic alkalis have a similar, but not quite so rapid an effect.

Diethyl Ether.* $(C_2H_5)_2O$.

Required: Rectified spirit or ethanol, 95 ml.; sulphuric acid, 40 ml.

Assemble the apparatus shown in Fig. 54. Into the neck of

* The preparation of ether is described here because this is chemically its logical position. It is advisable, however, for students to defer its preparation

the distilling- flask **A** (of about 450 ml. capacity) are fitted a thistle-funnel **F** and a thermometer **T**, both reaching down to the bottom of **A**. The dropping-funnel **D** is then securely fitted by a cork into the mouth of the thistle-funnel as shown, so that the ethanol subsequently dropping from **D** can be clearly seen. To the flask **A** is fitted a *double-surface* condenser **C**, and to the latter in turn a Buchner flask **B** to act as receiver. To the side-arm of **B** is fitted a length of rubber tubing leading well below the level of the bench, so that any ether vapour escaping condensation cannot return to the neighbourhood of **A**. (Alternatively, use a ground-glass flask (Fig. 22(A), p. 43) carrying a three-necked adaptor (Fig. 22(J)). The thermometer can then be fitted through the central neck, the dropping-funnel through the left-hand neck, and the condenser joined through an adaptor (Fig. 22 (E)) to the right-hand neck.)

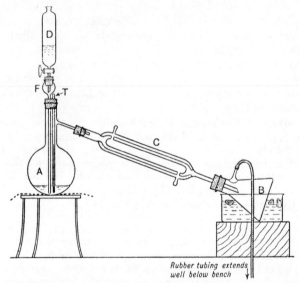

Rubber tubing extends
well below bench

Fig. 54.

First place about 5 g. of clean *dry* sand in **A**, and then 45 ml. (36 g.) of rectified spirit: cool the flask in ice-water and *cautiously* add 40 ml. (74 g.) of concentrated sulphuric acid, shaking the mixture thoroughly during the addition to ensure a

---

until they have had some experience in the manipulation, and particularly the distillation, of ether, such as its use for the extraction of aniline (p. 163), where full details and precautions are given.

homogeneous product. Then reassemble the apparatus, taking care that the lower end of the thistle-funnel **F** now reaches down to the bottom of the liquid in the flask and that the bulb of the thermometer is completely immersed. Place 50 ml. (40 g.) of rectified spirit in the funnel **D**, and cool the receiver **B** in a pan of ice-water. Heat the flask **A** over a gauze by means of a *small* Bunsen flame until the temperature of the liquid reaches 140–145°: owing to the presence of the sand steady boiling now occurs, and ether begins to distil over. Now allow the ethanol in **D** to fall drop by drop into the thistle-funnel **F** at approximately the same speed as that at which the crude ether distils over: in this way the total addition of the ethanol from **D** should take about 1 hour. Then continue heating **A** (still maintaining the temperature at 140–145°) until no more ether distils over, *i.e.*, for about a further 15 minutes. Turn out the gas, and then pour the distillate into a separating-funnel and shake it with about 25 ml. of 10% aqueous sodium hydroxide solution: this removes both sulphur dioxide and some of the unchanged ethanol from the ether. Run off and reject the lower aqueous layer, and then repeat the extraction with a fresh quantity of sodium hydroxide solution. Again run off the alkaline layer, transfer the ether to a small conical flask and dry it with an ample quantity of granular calcium chloride for at least 30 minutes. (The calcium chloride removes both water and any residual ethanol.)

Now filter the ether through a fluted filter-paper directly into a 100 ml. distilling-flask, and then equip the latter with a 100° thermometer and a double-surface condenser: to the end of the latter attach a receiver with a rubber delivery-tube *precisely as before*. Place the flask cautiously in a water-bath, the contents of which have previously been heated to about 60° at some distance from the apparatus: arrange the depth of the flask in the water-bath so that the ether distils slowly over. Collect the fraction boiling between 34–39°. Yield, 25 g. (35 ml.). Not more than a very small residue of ethanol should remain in the flask.

Diethyl ether is a mobile, colourless liquid having b.p. 35° and *d*, 0·720. It has a characteristic odour, and a burning taste. It is used chiefly as a solvent, and was formerly widely used as an anaesthetic; owing to its chemical non-reactivity, it is very seldom used actually as a reagent, except in the preparation of Grignard reagents (p. 280) where probably its chemical properties reinforce its solvent action.

Very great care should always be taken when manipulating

ether, particularly when it is being distilled. The liquid itself is very readily inflammable, and in addition the vapour forms with air a heavy and highly explosive mixture, which may roll along the laboratory bench for surprising distances, and still be capable of exploding when it comes in contact with a flame, the explosion at once travelling back towards the origin of the vapour.

For Williamson's Method for the preparation of ethers, see p. 103.

Pure Ether. Pure ether (entirely free in particular from water) is frequently required in the laboratory, and especially for the preparation and use of Grignard reagents. It is best prepared in quantity for classes by adding an ample quantity of granular calcium chloride to a "Winchester" bottle of technical ether, and allowing the mixture to stand for at least 24 hours, preferably with occasional shaking. The greater part of the water and ethanol present in the ether is thus removed. The ether should now be filtered through a large fluted filter-paper into another clean dry Winchester bottle. About 25 g. of sodium are now pressed as fine wire directly into the ether. For this purpose, a sodium press is used (Fig. 55). This consists essentially of a heavy iron stand **S** carrying a plunger **P**, which can be screwed down so that its end fits snugly into an iron cup **C**, which has a small hole at its base. (A number of cups, having holes of different diameters, is usually available for alternative use.) The cup **C** is nearly filled with lumps of sodium, and the plunger is then screwed steadily down, while (in this case) the Winchester bottle of ether is held immediately below **C**: the sodium is thus forced as fine wire directly into the ether, and exposure to the air reduced to a minimum.

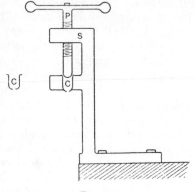

FIG. 55.

The Winchester bottle should then be closed by a rubber stopper carrying a calcium chloride tube (to allow escape of hydrogen) and the ether allowed to stand for a further 24 hours. It should then be decanted into a large distilling-flask, a few small pieces of freshly cut sodium preferably added, and the flask connected with a double-surface water-condenser having a receiver cooled in ice-water. Ether in these quantities should always be distilled in a fume-cupboard having an efficient draught, so that there is no possibility of any uncondensed vapour escaping into the laboratory. The flask itself should be heated by steam. If steam is not laid on in the fume-cupboard, it should be generated *outside* the cupboard in the usual steam-can (Fig. 15, p. 33) and then led into the cupboard through a length of soft metal "compo" tubing. The flask is supported on the usual concentric metal rings over an empty water-bath: a hole is punched in one of the outer rings, and then the compo tubing is led down throught this hole into the bath, and the extreme end of the tubing turned up so that the jet of steam strikes directly upwards on to the base of the flask. If the fume-cupboard has a vigorous draught induced by an electric motor, large quantities of the ether can thus be safely distilled, and an ordinary bottle can be used as a receiver, the end of the condenser being fitted into the neck of the bottle and held firmly in position by a plug of cotton-wool. If a large Buchner flask is used as a receiver, the rubber delivery tube (as shown in Fig. 54, p. 80, and in Fig. 23(E), p. 45) is of course required.

In very hot weather, the condenser water should first be chilled by passing it through a tall spiral of soft metal "compo" tubing immersed in a bucket of ice-water.

Ether so obtained is anhydrous, and almost entirely free from other impurities. On standing, however, it undergoes slight atmospheric oxidation, with the formation of traces of diethyl peroxide, $(C_2H_5)_2O_2$.* The formation of this peroxide can be largely checked, however, by storing the distilled ether over fresh sodium wire, preferably in the dark.

Ethylene. C_2H_4.

Required: Rectified spirit, 20 ml.; sulphuric acid, 40 ml.

Assemble the apparatus shown in Fig. 56. F is a 200 ml. flat-bottomed flask supported on a sand-bath and connected by a glass delivery-tube to the wash-bottle B, which is about two-thirds full of 10 % aqueous sodium hydroxide solution. A second delivery-tube leads from B into a beehive stand (or between two earthenware tiles placed side by side) in a pneumatic trough T containing water.

Place 20 ml. (16 g.) of rectified spirit in F, and add slowly, with cooling and shaking, 40 ml. (74 g.) of concentrated sulphuric acid. Then add about 2–3 g. of clean dry sand, to ensure a steady evolution of ethylene subsequently. Connect up the apparatus and heat F over the sand-bath as shown.

---

* Consequently traces of these unstable peroxides are present in samples of all the lower aliphatic ethers unless the samples have been freshly distilled. If these ethers when being distilled are heated on, for example, an electric heater, the final residue of peroxide may become sufficiently hot to explode violently. The use of a water-bath for heating, as described above, decreases considerably both the risk of the ether catching fire and of the peroxide exploding.

Peroxides can usually be completely removed from a sample of ether by thorough shaking with aqueous potassium permanganate solution.

The liquid becomes progressively darker in colour, and then effervesces gently as ethylene is evolved. Allow the gas to escape from the delivery-tube in **T** for several minutes in order to sweep out the air in **F** and **B**. Now fill a test-tube with water, close it with the finger, and invert the tube in the water in **T** over the delivery-tube so that a sample of the gas collects in the tube. Close the tube again with the finger, and then light the gas at a Bunsen burner at a safe distance from the apparatus. If the tube contains pure ethylene, the latter burns with a clear pale blue (almost invisible) flame: if the ethylene still contains air, the mixture in the test-tube ignites with a sharp report. Allow the

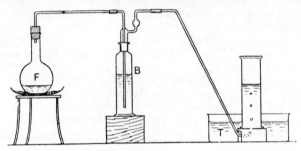

FIG. 56.

gas to escape from the delivery-tube in **T** until a sample tested in this way proves to be pure ethylene. Then collect 3–4 gas-jars of ethylene, closing each one under water with a slightly greased glass plate. Since appreciable quantities of sulphur dioxide are evolved in **F** during the later stages of the reaction, disconnect the delivery-tube joining **F** to **B**, and *then* turn out the gas. Carry out the following tests with the jars of ethylene.

(1) *Odour.* Smell the contents of one of the jars. The ethylene has a characteristic sweetish odour.

Ethylene when deeply inhaled produces temporary anaesthesia which is almost devoid of unpleasant after-effects; hence it has been used for dental surgery, minor operations, *etc.*

(2) *Bromine.* Slip slightly to one side the glass plate covering one jar of ethylene, add 2–3 ml. of bromine water (preparation, p. 525), restore the glass plate in position, and then shake the jar vigorously. The colour of the bromine rapidly disappears as 1,2-dibromoethane is formed. Note that owing to the absorption

$$C_2H_4 + Br_2 = C_2H_4Br_2$$

of ethylene, a partial vacuum now exists in the jar.

(3) *Alkaline Potassium Permanganate.* Add similarly to a second jar 1–2 ml. of *very dilute* aqueous potassium permanganate solution to which an equal volume of sodium carbonate solution has previously been added. On shaking as before, the purple colour of the permanganate is replaced by the green colour of potassium manganate, K_2MnO_4; further reduction ultimately causes the green manganate to be replaced by a brown precipitate of manganese dioxide. Note that a partial vacuum again exists owing to the absorption of ethylene.

In this reaction the ethylene is oxidised to ethylene glycol, $C_2H_4(OH)_2$.

$$C_2H_4 + H_2O + O = C_2H_4(OH)_2$$

If a solution of potassium permanganate containing dilute sulphuric acid is used, the purple colour disappears and the solution ultimately becomes

$$2KMnO_4 + 3H_2SO_4 = K_2SO_4 + 2MnSO_4 + 3H_2O + 5O$$

colourless. The use of the sodium carbonate solution, and the consequent change in colour first to the green manganate and then to the brown manganese dioxide, make the reagent more sensitive to observation.

Tests for Unsaturation. The above reactions are used as the general tests for the presence of double or triple bonds joining carbon atoms in an organic compound.

(1) The bromine test is applied first. The organic compound, if a liquid, is treated with 2–3 drops of liquid bromine or (preferably) a solution of bromine in carbon tetrachloride: if the organic compound is a solid, it should first be dissolved in cold carbon tetrachloride or chloroform. The rapid absorption of the bromine (and consequent disappearance of the red colour) is a strong indication that the compound is unsaturated, and is therefore undergoing direct addition of the bromine.

Since, however, some compounds, such as aniline (p. 164), react very rapidly with bromine *by substitution*, the bromine test should whenever possible be confirmed by the alkaline permanganate test.

(2) If the compound is soluble in cold water, its aqueous solution (after neutralisation, if acidic) is shaken with a dilute solution of potassium permanganate containing sodium carbonate as before. The conversion of the purple permanganate to the green manganate or (more frequently) directly to manganese dioxide confirms the result of the bromine test, since the alkaline permanganate is unaffected by possible substitution reactions.

Note that many readily oxidisable compounds (e.g., aldehydes) will also decolorise alkaline potassium permanganate in the cold.

Acetylene. C_2H_2.

Acetylene can be readily obtained by the action of water on calcium carbide: since, however, commercial calcium carbide contains traces of calcium

$$CaC_2 + 2HOH = Ca(OH)_2 + C_2H_2$$

sulphide, phosphide and nitride, the acetylene should be purified before use. If a specially pure sample of acetylene is required, it should be obtained by the action of alcoholic potassium or sodium hydroxide on 1,2-dibromoethane: this reaction should be compared with that of *aqueous* potassium or sodium hydroxide, which merely hydrolyses 1,2-dibromoethane to ethylene glycol.

$$C_2H_4Br_2 + 2KOH \text{ (ethanolic)} = C_2H_2 + 2KBr + 2H_2O$$
$$C_2H_4Br_2 + 2KOH \text{ (aqueous)} = C_2H_4(OH)_2 + 2KBr$$

If acetylene is required either in large quantities or in a steady regular current for several hours, it should be obtained from a cylinder, in which the acetylene is compressed in acetone solution. The cylinders can be purchased and when empty can then be exchanged for refilled ones. The acetylene in these cylinders is generated from calcium carbide, but is considerably purified before storage in the cylinder. The acetylene before use should, however, be passed through two wash-bottles containing water to eliminate acetone vapour: acetylene of high purity is then obtained.

(A) FROM CALCIUM CARBIDE. Place some small lumps of calcium carbide (about 15 g.) in a 150 ml. distilling-flask (or in a Buchner flask of similar capacity), and fit into the neck of the flask a tall dropping-funnel the stem of which has been drawn off to a fine point: the stem should pass well down below the side-arm of the flask. Connect this side-arm to a wash-bottle containing 10% aqueous copper sulphate solution: the tall dropping-funnel is thus required in order to give a sufficient "head" of water in the funnel to force the acetylene through the wash-bottle. Then fit to the wash-bottle a delivery-tube which passes into a pneumatic trough precisely as that in Fig. 56 (p. 84).

Fill the dropping-funnel with water, and allow the latter to fall drop by drop on to the calcium carbide: acetylene is at once generated, and on passing through the copper sulphate solution is freed from hydrogen sulphide, *etc.* Allow the gas to escape from the delivery-tube in the pneumatic trough until the issuing gas smells markedly of acetylene. Then collect a sample of the gas in a *small* test-tube precisely as described for ethylene (p. 84). Ignite the sample at a burner placed as before at a safe distance from the apparatus. If the air in the apparatus has not yet been completely displaced, the sample of gas will explode with a sharp report: if, however, the acetylene is free from air, it will burn quietly with a very smoky flame depositing carbon in the tube, in marked contrast to the clear flame of burning ethylene.

Then collect 5–6 gas-jars filled with the acetylene, and carry out the following tests.

(1) *Odour.* The gas collected in this way has a somewhat onion-like odour, which is much less pronounced than that of the crude gas given off directly from the carbide without subsequent purification. Absolutely pure acetylene, however, is almost odourless.

(2) *Bromine.* Slip the glass cover of a jar momentarily aside, add 2–3 ml. of bromine water, replace the cover and shake the contents of the jar vigorously. Note that the bromine is absorbed only very slowly, in marked contrast to the rapid absorption by ethylene. This slow reaction with bromine water is also in marked contrast to the action of chlorine water, which unites with acetylene with explosive violence. (Therefore do not attempt this test with chlorine or chlorine water.)

(3) *Alkaline Permanganate.* To another jar add similarly 2–3 ml. of very dilute potassium permanganate solution containing sodium carbonate. On shaking the jar the permanganate is reduced to green manganate, although the colour of the latter is only transient and is moreover obscured by the manganese dioxide formed.

(4) *Metallic Derivatives.* (*a*) *Cuprous Acetylide.* Cu_2C_2. Prepare an ammoniacal solution of cuprous chloride by first adding dilute ammonia to 2–3 ml. of dilute copper sulphate solution until the initial precipitate just redissolves and a clear deep-blue solution is obtained: now add an aqueous solution of hydroxylamine hydrochloride drop by drop with shaking until the solution becomes first green and then completely colourless, the cupric salt being thus reduced to the cuprous derivative.

Now add this solution to a jar of acetylene as before and shake vigorously. A chocolate-red precipitate of cuprous acetylide is at once formed.

(*b*) *Silver Acetylide.* Ag_2C_2. Add dilute ammonia drop by drop with shaking to 2–3 ml. of silver nitrate solution until the initial precipitate of silver oxide just redissolves.

Now add this solution to a jar of acetylene and shake. A yellow-white precipitate of silver acetylide at once forms.

The cuprous and silver acetylides are both explosive when dry. Therefore when these tests are completed, wash out the gas-jars thoroughly with water.

(B) FROM 1,2-DIBROMOETHANE. *Required:* Powdered potassium hydroxide, 25 g.; rectified spirit, 100 ml.; ethylene dibromide, 15 ml. (33 g.).

To prepare pure acetylene, assemble the apparatus shown in Fig. 57. **F** is a wide-necked 300 ml. bolt-head flask, to which is fitted a double-surface reflux water-condenser **C** and the dropping-funnel **D**. From the top of **C**, a delivery-tube leads down to the pneumatic trough **T**, where the gas can be collected in jars in the usual way. (Alternatively, use the apparatus shown in Fig. 23(A),

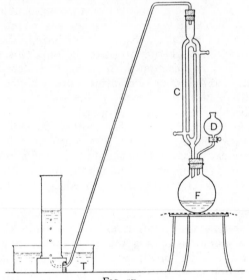

Fig. 57.

p. 45.) Place 100 ml. of rectified spirit and 25 g. of powdered potassium hydroxide in **F**, and boil the mixture gently under reflux until the potash is almost entirely dissolved. Then place 15 ml. (33 g.) of 1,2-dibromoethane in **D**, and allow the dibromide to fall drop by drop into the boiling solution in **F**. A rapid reaction occurs, acetylene being generated and potassium bromide precipitated. Test the gas issuing from the delivery-tube in the usual way to ensure that all air has been displaced by acetylene. Then collect the pure acetylene in gas-jars. Note that this acetylene is almost odourless.

Ethylene can be similarly prepared by the action of ethanolic potash on ethyl bromide, but the yield is usually very low.

Absolute Ethanol. Supplies of absolute ethanol, which is frequently required in organic chemical work, are now freely available commercially as a result of azeotropic distillation methods. If however it should be necessary to dehydrate rectified spirit, the process can be carried out most reliably by the use of quick-lime. The quick-lime should preferably be prepared in the laboratory by heating lumps of marble *strongly* in a good muffle-furnace for about 3 hours; the product, directly it cools, must be stored in a tightly stoppered tin or bottle, although whenever possible it should be used for dehydration immediately after its preparation. If the lime is obtained from a dealer, it should preferably be reheated immediately before use.

The preparation of absolute ethanol in moderate quantity for classes may be carried out as follows. Pour 3 Winchester bottles (*i.e.*, 7–8 litres) of rectified spirit into a 3-gallon (14–15 litre) can **C** (Fig. 58), add about 600 g. of the

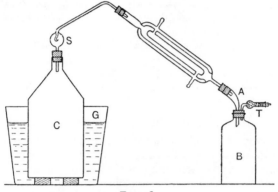

FIG. 58.

quick-lime, and fit a double-surface reflux condenser by means of a rubber stopper, the top of the condenser being closed with a calcium chloride tube. Place the can in a large galvanised iron bath **G** about half-full of water, supporting the can in the bath on some earthenware tiles. Heat the water-bath over a gas-ring so that the ethanol boils gently under reflux for 6 hours. Now (preferably) allow the apparatus to cool and stand overnight. Next day, add a further 100 g. of quick-lime to the ethanol, and fit to the can a still-head **S** as shown (Fig. 58). Reverse the condenser for distillation, and connect it to an adaptor **A**, which fits directly into the bottle **B** in which the absolute ethanol will subsequently be stored. Rubber stoppers must be used throughout the apparatus: that which fits into the receiving bottle **B** carries a calcium chloride tube **T** as shown. Now reheat the water-bath so that the ethanol distils over steadily: no "bumping" should occur in the can. Stop the distillation when about 500 ml. of ethanol still remain in the can.

The absolute ethanol obtained in this way should have $d^{15°}_{4°}$, 0·794. It is very hygroscopic, and the bottle in which it is stored should preferably have a well-fitting ground-glass stopper: alternatively, the bottle can be closed with a tightly fitting rubber stopper but *not* with a cork, as corks contain appreciable quantities of water.

Absolute methanol can be similarly prepared, and then has $d^{15°}_{4°}$, 0·796.

Chloroform. CHCl₃.

When chlorine is passed into boiling ethanol, both chlorination of the methyl group and oxidation of the primary alcohol group to an aldehyde occur, giving trichloro-acetaldehyde or chloral:

$$CH_3CH_2OH + 4Cl_2 \rightarrow CCl_3CHO + 5HCl$$

When chloral is treated with caustic alkali, fission of the C–C linkage occurs, giving chloroform and a formate:

$$CCl_3CHO + KOH \rightarrow CHCl_3 + HCOOK$$

Acetaldehyde and also many ketones, such as acetone, containing the CH_3CO- group behave similarly when treated with bleaching powder, chlorination of the CH_3CO- group being immediately followed by fission of the molecule by the alkali present in the bleaching powder:

$$CH_3COCH_3 + 3Cl_2 \rightarrow CCl_3COCH_3 + CHCl_3$$

$$2CCl_3COCH_3 + Ca(OH)_2 \rightarrow 2CHCl_3 + (CH_3COO)_2Ca$$

The acetone method clearly gives a much cheaper product than the ethanol method.

Required: Bleaching powder, 100 g.; acetone, 44 ml.

Place 100 g. of bleaching powder in a mortar and add 250 ml. of water in small quantities at a time: between each addition grind the mixture of bleaching powder and water well together and decant the cream-like suspension through a funnel into a 1-litre flat-bottomed flask. Finally, when all the water has thus been used, only a gritty residue remains in the mortar. Fit the flask with an efficient reflux water-condenser, pour 44 ml. (35 g.) of acetone in small quantities, at a time, down the condenser and mix by thorough shaking after each addition. The reaction usually starts spontaneously after a few minutes, and a bath of cold water should be available into which the flask may be dipped if necessary to moderate the reaction. Should the reaction show no signs of starting within 5 minutes of the addition of the acetone, warm the flask *cautiously* on a boiling water-bath until the reaction starts, and then remove it immediately. When the vigorous boiling has subsided, heat the flask on a boiling water-bath for a further 5–10 minutes (not more) to complete the reaction. Cool the flask in cold water (to prevent loss of chloroform vapour whilst the apparatus is being re-arranged) and then fit the flask with a fairly wide delivery-tube and reverse the water-condenser for distillation (as in Fig. 59, p. 100, or in Fig. 23(D), p. 45). Heat the flask on a water-bath until distillation of the chloroform is complete.

The chloroform thus obtained is usually acidic. Therefore

shake it thoroughly with *dilute* sodium hydroxide solution in a separating-funnel. (If the chloroform tends to float on the alkaline solution, it still contains appreciable quantities of acetone: in this case the sodium hydroxide solution should be run out of the funnel and the chloroform shaken with water to extract the acetone. The extraction with the sodium hydroxide solution can then be performed after the water has been removed.) Carefully run off the heavy lower layer of chloroform into a small conical flask, dry it over calcium chloride for 15–10 minutes, and then filter it directly into a 75 ml. distilling-flask fitted with a clean dry water-condenser. Distil the chloroform, collecting the fraction of b.p. 60–63°. Yield, 30 g. (20 ml.)

Chloroform is a colourless liquid, of b.p. 61° and d, 1·50. It has a characteristic sweetish smell, and is frequently used as a solvent in organic chemistry.

For reactions of chloroform, see p. 392.

Chloroform was formerly used in medicine as an anaesthetic. One disadvantage for this purpose is the ready oxidation which chloroform undergoes on exposure to light and air, generating the poisonous phosgene, or carbonyl chloride, $COCl_2$. This is counteracted by storing the liquid in dark amber-

$$CHCl_3 + O = COCl_2 + HCl.$$

coloured bottles, and also by the addition of about 2% of ethanol: the latter converts the phosgene into harmless diethyl carbonate:

$$2C_2H_5OH + COCl_2 = (C_2H_5O)_2CO + 2HCl$$

In addition to chloroform, many other compounds containing the trichloro-methyl group, Cl_3C-, show marked physiological action. Thus trichloro-acetaldehyde or *chloral hydrate*, $Cl_3C \cdot CH(OH)_2$ (p. 342), and trichloro-tertiary-butanol or *chloretone*, $Cl_3C \cdot C(CH_3)_2OH$, are both hypnotics. Similarly, tribromo-ethanol or *avertin*, $Br_3C \cdot CH_2OH$, has strong anaesthetic properties.

Iodoform. CHI_3.

The preparation of iodoform is similar to that of chloroform, of which it is the iodine analogue. Many substances which contain either the $CH_3CH(OH)-$ group or the CH_3CO-C group when treated with potassium iodide and sodium hypochlorite readily yield iodoform, and its formation can thus frequently be used as a test for these groups.* Among the compounds which contain the $CH_3CH(OH)-$ group and give iodoform are ethanol, CH_3CH_2OH, isopropanol, $CH_3CH(OH)CH_3$, lactic acid, $CH_3CH(OH)COOH$, and also acetaldehyde, which exists in aqueous solution partly as the hydrated form, $CH_3CH(OH)_2$: similar compounds containing the CH_3CO-C group are acetone, CH_3CO-CH_3, pyruvic acid, $CH_3CO-COOH$, and acetophenone, $CH_3CO-C_6H_5$. Methanol

* For other types of compounds which give the iodoform reaction, see H. Booth and B. C. Saunders, *Chem. and Industry*, 1950, 824.

does not give iodoform in these circumstances and can thus be distinguished from ethanol.

The reactions involved are similar in both cases, and closely parallel to those which give rise to chloroform. The sodium hypochlorite probably first oxidises the potassium iodide to potassium hypoiodite, which then oxidises the ethanol to acetaldehyde and then iodinates the latter to tri-iodo-

$$CH_3CH_2OH \longrightarrow CH_3CHO \longrightarrow CI_3CHO$$

acetaldehyde or iodal. Aqueous sodium hypochlorite always contains sodium hydroxide, which converts the tri-iodo-acetaldehyde to iodoform and sodium formate.

$$CI_3CHO + NaOH \rightarrow CHI_3 + HCOONa$$

If acetone is used there is no initial oxidation: tri-iodo-acetone is first formed and is then converted by the sodium hydroxide to iodoform and

$$CI_3COCH_3 + NaOH \rightarrow CHI_3 + CH_3COONa$$

sodium acetate. Iodoform is obtained more readily and in greater yield from acetone and acetaldehyde than from ethanol, possibly because no initial oxidation is required.

Iodoform is a disinfectant and can be used as an external antiseptic.

IODOFORM FROM ACETONE. (Semi-micro Scale.) *Required:* Acetone, 0·5 ml.; 10% potassium iodide solution, 20 ml.; 10% sodium hydroxide solution, 8 ml.; 2M sodium hypochlorite solution, 20 ml.

Place 0·5 ml. of acetone, 20 ml. of 10% aqueous potassium iodide solution and 8 ml. of 10% aqueous sodium hydroxide solution in a 50 ml. conical flask, and then add 20 ml. of a freshly prepared molar solution* of sodium hypochlorite. Well mix the contents of the flask, when the yellow iodoform will begin to separate almost immediately: allow the mixture to stand at room temperature for 10 minutes, and then filter at the pump, wash with cold water, and drain thoroughly. Yield of crude material, 1·4 g. Recrystallise the crude iodoform from methylated spirit. For this purpose, place the crude material in a 50 ml. round-bottomed flask fitted with a reflux water-condenser, add a small quantity of methylated spirit, and heat to boiling on a water-bath: then add more methylated spirit cautiously down the condenser until all the iodoform has dissolved. Filter the hot solution through a fluted filter-paper directly into a small beaker or conical flask, and then cool in ice-water. The iodoform rapidly·crystallises. Filter at the pump, drain thoroughly and dry.

* For preparation of 2M sodium hypochlorite solution, see p. 525.

Iodoform forms yellow crystals, of m.p. 120°, and has a characteristic odour.

For reactions of iodoform, see pp. 390–392.

Oximes.

Both aldehydes and ketones usually condense readily with free hydroxylamine, $HONH_2$, to give crystalline *oximes*:

$$CH_3CHO + H_2NOH \quad \rightarrow \quad CH_3CH:NOH + H_2O$$

Acetaldehyde   Acetaldoxime

$$(CH_3)_2CO + H_2NOH \quad \rightarrow \quad (CH_3)_2C:NOH + H_2O$$

Acetone   Acetoxime

Since hydroxylamine is usually available only in the form of its salts, *e.g.*, the hydrochloride or sulphate, the aqueous solution of these salts is treated with sodium acetate or hydroxide to liberate the base before treatment with the aldehyde or ketone. Most oximes are weakly amphoteric in character, and may dissolve in aqueous sodium hydroxide as the sodium salt, from which they can be liberated by the addition of a weak acid, *e.g.*, acetic acid.

Oximes have four important uses:

(1) Being crystalline compounds which usually have sharp melting-points, they are used to characterise the parent aldehydes and ketones.

(2) Impure aldehydes and ketones are sometimes purified by conversion into the corresponding oximes, and the latter after recrystallisation are then hydrolysed by boiling with dilute sulphuric acid:

$$(CH_3)_2C:NOH + H_2O + H_2SO_4 = (CH_3)_2CO + HONH_2,H_2SO_4$$

The acid, by neutralising the hydroxylamine, prevents the reverse reaction and thus causes rapid and complete hydrolysis: distillation of the final solution then drives over the aldehyde or ketone, the hydroxylamine sulphate remaining behind. This method must be used with care, however, as the acid may cause the Beckmann rearrangement to occur (p. 227).

(3) Reduction gives pure primary amines:

$$CH_3CH:NOH + 4H \quad = \quad CH_3CH_2NH_2 + H_2O$$
Monoethylamine

$$(CH_3)_2C:NOH + 4H \quad = \quad (CH_3)_2CHNH_2 + H_2O$$
Isopropylamine

(4) When treated with certain reagents, the ketoximes in particular undergo the Beckmann rearrangement to isomeric acid amides (p. 227).

For the further identification of aldehydes and ketones by phenylhydrazone formation, see pp. 229, 257, 341, 345; by 2,4-dinitrophenylhydrazone formation, see pp. 262, 342, 346; by semicarbazone formation, see pp. 258, 342, 346.

Acetoxime. $(CH_3)_2C:NOH.$

Required: Hydroxylamine hydrochloride, 12·5 g.; sodium hydroxide, 7 g.; dry acetone, 12 ml.

(NOTE. The sodium hydroxide must be accurately weighed out, for an excess will dissolve the oxime as the sodium derivative.)

Prepare a solution of 12·5 g. of hydroxylamine hydrochloride in 20 ml. of water contained in a 100 ml. conical flask. Dissolve 7 g. of powdered sodium hydroxide in 20 ml. of water, cool the solution in ice-water, and then add it to that of the hydroxylamine hydrochloride. Place a thermometer in the mixed solution, and chill the flask in ice-water until the temperature of the solution is between 5° and 10°. Now add 12 ml. (9·5 g.) of dry acetone (preferably from a burette to ensure accuracy) in small quantities so that, when the mixture is gently shaken in the ice-water during the addition, the temperature does not rise above 15°. The acetoxime usually starts to crystallise when about half the acetone has been added. When the addition is complete, allow the mixture to stand in ice-water for 15 minutes, and then filter off the crude acetoxime at the pump, drain well and finally dry by pressing repeatedly between several layers of drying-paper. The acetoxime so obtained contains sodium chloride, but is otherwise almost pure. Yield of crude dry material, 12–13 g.

The oxime is freely soluble in water and in most organic liquids. Recrystallise the crude *dry* product from a minimum of 60–80° petrol or (less suitably) cyclohexane: for this purpose first determine approximately, by means of a small-scale test-tube experiment, the minimum proportion of the hot solvent required to dissolve the oxime from about 0·5 g. of the crude material. Then place the bulk of the crude product in a small (100 ml.) round-bottomed or conical flask fitted with a reflux water-condenser, add the required amount of the solvent and boil the mixture on a water-bath. Then turn out the gas, and quickly filter the hot mixture through a fluted filter-paper into a conical flask: the sodium chloride remains on the filter, whilst the filtrate on cooling in ice-water deposits the acetoxime as colourless crystals. These, when filtered and dried (either by pressing between drying-paper or by placing in an *atmospheric* desiccator) have m.p. 60°. Acetoxime sublimes rather readily when exposed to the air, and rapidly when warmed or when placed in a vacuum. Hence the necessity for an atmospheric desiccator for drying purposes.

Hydrolysis of Acetoxime. Place about 1 g. of the recrystallised oxime in a small distilling-flask (50 ml.), add 10 ml. of dilute H_2SO_4, and heat *gently* until about half the solution has distilled over. Test (a) the aqueous distillate for acetone by the iodoform reaction (p. 346), (b) the residual solution in the distilling-flask for hydroxylamine by cooling, making strongly alkaline, and treating with Fehling's solution. A deep yellow precipitate of cuprous oxide results:

$$2HONH_2 + 4CuO = 2Cu_2O + N_2O + 3H_2O$$

Esters.

Esters may be prepared by the following methods:

(1) Directly from the corresponding acid and alcohol, in the presence of a dehydrating agent. Thus when ethanol and acetic acid are mixed, ethyl acetate and water are formed, but in addition an equilibrium is established.

$$CH_3COOH + HOC_2H_5 \to CH_3COOC_2H_5 + H_2O$$

If, however, concentrated sulphuric acid is present, the water is absorbed, the back reaction prevented, and a high yield of ethyl acetate is obtained. In practice the reaction is not so simple. It was formerly supposed that, since the sulphuric acid is usually added to the alcohol, ethyl hydrogen sulphate and water are formed, the latter being absorbed by the excess of sulphuric acid. A mixture of ethanol and acetic acid is then added to the ethyl hydrogen sulphate,

$$C_2H_5OH + H_2SO_4 \to C_2H_5HSO_4 + H_2O$$

whereupon the latter reacts with the organic acid to give the required ester, liberating the sulphuric acid which at once reacts with the free alcohol, the cycle

$$C_2H_5HSO_4 + CH_3COOH = CH_3COOC_2H_5 + H_2SO_4$$

of operations then recurring. The process can thus continue until the sulphuric acid becomes too dilute to furnish more ethyl hydrogen sulphate.

This method has the disadvantage that the corresponding ether is usually

$$C_2H_5HSO_4 + HOC_2H_5 \to (C_2H_5)_2O + H_2SO_4$$

formed as a by-product by the interaction of the alkyl hydrogen sulphate and unchanged alcohol.

The mechanism of esterification of an alcohol in the presence of a mineral acid is now considered to involve the following steps.

(1) Protonation of the carbonyl oxygen of the acid (I) to give (II), which is attacked by the lone pair on the oxygen atom of the alcohol to give the intermediate (III);

(2) This is followed by proton transfer to give the intermediate (IV).

(3) Loss of water now gives the protonated form (V) of the ester (VI).

$$\text{(III)} \;\rightleftharpoons\; R - \overset{\overset{\textstyle OH}{|}}{\underset{\underset{\textstyle +O}{|}}{C}} - OEt \;\rightleftharpoons\; R - \overset{\overset{\textstyle OH}{|}}{\underset{+}{C}} - OEt \;\overset{-H^{+}}{\rightleftharpoons}\; R - \overset{\overset{\textstyle O}{\|}}{C} - OEt$$

$$\overset{H \quad H}{\diagup \diagdown}$$

$$\text{(IV)} \qquad\qquad\qquad \text{(V)} \qquad\qquad \text{(VI)}$$

A series of equilibria is thus established, the constituents of the mixture depending on the local conditions.

(2) *The Fischer-Speier Method.* In certain cases of esterification sulphuric acid cannot be used. Thus if the alcohol or the organic acid is unsaturated, the sulphuric acid may add on at the unsaturated group. If the alcohol or the acid is aromatic in type, considerable sulphonation of the benzene ring may result. Finally, if an amino-acid, such as glycine or amino-acetic acid, NH_2CH_2COOH, is to be esterified, the amino group would also undergo salt formation, and thus the hydrogen sulphate of aminoacetic ethyl ester, $H_2SO_4,NH_2CH_2COOC_2H_5$, would result, and would be very difficult to isolate from the excess of sulphuric acid. These difficulties are overcome by the *Fischer-Speier* method, in which a mixture of the alcohol and the organic acid is gently boiled under reflux whilst a stream of dry hydrogen chloride gas is passed in, a high yield of the ester being thus obtained. The function of the hydrogen chloride is protonating and catalytic, since Fischer found that 5% of hydrogen chloride in the reaction mixture gave efficient esterification. The advantages of the Fischer-Speier method are that the hydrogen chloride does not usually add on to unsaturated groupings, it does not affect aromatic groups, and finally with amino-acids gives the hydrochloride of the ester, from which excess of hydrogen chloride can be readily removed by direct evaporation. A further advantage is that the corresponding ether is not formed as a by-product. The method is also suitable for the preparation of esters of hydroxy-acids, *e.g.*, lactic acid.

(3) Esters can also be prepared by the action of alcohols on acid chlorides and anhydrides.

$$CH_3CO\,Cl + H\,OC_2H_5 \rightarrow CH_3COOC_2H_5 + HCl$$
Acetyl chloride

$$CH_3CO\cdot O\cdot COCH_3 + H\,OC_2H_5 \rightarrow CH_3COOC_2H_5 + CH_3COOH$$
Acetic anhydride

(4) By the action of alkyl halides on the silver salt of the acid.

$$CH_3COO\,Ag + I\,C_2H_5 \rightarrow CH_3COOC_2H_5 + AgI$$

This method is to be recommended when only a small quantity of the acid is available, since both the conversion of the acid into its silver salt (p. 445) and of the latter to the ester give almost quantitative yields.

(5) Esters of the binary halogen acids (HCl, *etc.*) can be prepared by the

action of the corresponding phosphorus tri- or penta-halide. The reaction is often indicated by the equation:

$$3C_2H_5OH + PCl_3 = 3C_2H_5Cl + P(OH)_3$$

Ethyl chloride Phosphorous acid

It is however more complicated, esters of phosphorous acid* being also formed (*cf.* p. 308). Iodides are usually prepared by a modification of this method, the ethanol being mixed with red phosphorus, and iodine added. The phosphorus iodide is thus formed *in situ*, and at once reacts with ethanol to give the corresponding iodide.

For reactions of esters, see p. 354.

Ethyl Acetate. $CH_3COOC_2H_5$. (Method 1.)

Required: Ethanol, 50 ml.; sulphuric acid, 10 ml.; acetic acid, 50 ml.; calcium chloride, 25 g.

Mix 50 ml. (40 g.) of ethanol and 50 ml. (52 g.) of glacial acetic acid thoroughly in a 250 ml. round-bottomed flask, and add slowly, with cooling and shaking, 10 ml. (18·5 g.) of concentrated sulphuric acid. Ensure that the liquid is homogeneous, then fit the flask with a reflux water-condenser (Fig. 8, p. 17) and boil the mixture gently over a wire gauze for 10 minutes. Now alter the position of the condenser (Fig. 59, p. 100, or Fig. 23(D), p. 45) and distil off about two-thirds of the mixture and then transfer the distillate to a separating-funnel.† Add about 25 ml. of 30% sodium carbonate solution, cork the funnel and shake carefully in order to neutralise and remove the free acetic and sulphurous acids present in the crude ethyl acetate: much carbon dioxide is evolved during the shaking, therefore release the pressure in the funnel at frequent intervals by cautiously removing the cork, or alternatively by inverting the securely corked funnel and momentarily opening the tap. Now allow the two layers to separate, and carefully run off and reject the lower aqueous layer, ensuring that the sodium carbonate solution is removed as completely as possible. Then prepare a solution of 25 g. of anhydrous calcium chloride in 25 ml. of water, add it to the ethyl acetate in the funnel, and again shake vigorously. The calcium chloride solution removes any unchanged ethanol present in the ethyl acetate. Allow the mixture to separate, and again run off the lower aqueous layer as completely as possible. Then run the ethyl acetate into a small conical flask, add a few lumps of

---

* See also Saunders *et al.*, *J. Chem. Soc.*, 1945, 380.

† If a separating-funnel of only 100 ml. capacity is available, divide the distillate into two portions, and work up each separately as far as the drying stage.

granular calcium chloride, and shake occasionally.

After about 20 minutes, when the liquid should be dry, filter it through a small fluted filter-paper into a 100 ml. distilling-flask attached to a water-condenser. Add some fragments of unglazed porcelain to the ethyl acetate, fit a 100° thermometer to the flask, and place the latter on a cold water-bath, which is then brought to the boil. Some ether is always formed as a by-product with the ethyl acetate, and by these means is carefully distilled off as a preliminary and separate fraction, boiling at 35–40°: if the distilling-flask is rapidly heated on a previously boiling water-bath, however, the ether does not distil as a definite fraction, and the boiling-point of the distillate steadily rises without a perceptible break to that of the ethyl acetate itself. Collect the portion of the distillate boiling between 74° and 79°, rejecting a small fraction boiling immediately below this range. Yield 50 g. Ethyl acetate is a colourless liquid having b.p. 77° and d, 0·92; it has a pleasant apple-like odour, and is only slightly soluble in water.

Ethyl Acetate. (Semi-micro scale)

Required: Ethanol, 5 ml.; acetic acid, 5 ml.; sulphuric acid, 1 ml.; calcium chloride, 2·5 g.

Use the apparatus shown in Fig. 38, p. 63, using a thermometer reading to 100° and with water running through the vertical condenser. Place in the 25 ml. pear-shaped flask 5 ml. of ethanol, 5 ml. of glacial acetic acid and add carefully with shaking 1 ml. of concentrated sulphuric acid. Attach the flask to the reflux condenser and boil the mixture gently for 10 minutes.

Now run the water out of the vertical condenser and pass water through the inclined condenser. Continue to heat the mixture so that everything distilling up to 82° is collected. Transfer the distillate to a 25 ml. separating funnel and add 3 ml. of 30% sodium carbonate solution. Cork the funnel and shake carefully to remove acids, taking all the precautions mentioned in the macro preparation above. Run off and reject the lower layer. Dissolve 2·5 g. of anhydrous $CaCl_2$ in 2·5 ml. of water, and add it to the ethyl acetate in the funnel and shake vigorously. Again run off the lower layer and then add one or two *small* pieces of granular $CaCl_2$ to the liquid while *still* in the separating funnel. Shake the liquid which will become clear in a few minutes.

Now decant the dried liquid into a small distilling flask of about 10 ml. capacity (Fig. 36, p. 63). Distil the liquid and collect the fraction b.p. 74–79°. Yield, 3 g.

Calculation of Yield. The yield of a compound obtained in an organic preparation, in addition to being stated in grams, should also be calculated as a percentage of the yield theoretically possible from the weight of the original compounds taken. Thus in the preparation of ethyl acetate, the equation shows that 60 g. of acetic acid and 46 g. of ethanol react to give 88 g. of ethyl

$$CH_3COOH + C_2H_5OH = CH_3COOC_2H_5 + H_2O$$
$$60 46 88$$

acetate. If equimolecular quantities of acid and alcohol had been taken in the preparation, the percentage yield of the ethyl acetate would clearly be the same if calculated on the basis of either reagent. Actually, however, an excess of ethanol was used and the yield can therefore be calculated on the basis either of the ethanol or of the acid. Thus

46 g. of ethanol should give 88 g. of ethyl acetate

∴ 40 g. ,,　,,　　,,　　,, 76 g. ,, ,,　　,,

Actually 50 g. of ester were obtained. Hence yield of ethyl acetate

$$= \frac{50 \times 100}{76} = 66\%.$$

Similarly, since 60 g. of acetic acid should theoretically give 88 g. of ethyl acetate, 52 g. should give 77 g. of the ester, and hence the yield,

calculated on the acetic acid, is $\frac{50 \times 100}{77} = 65\%.$

(The yield of ester based on the ethanol taken is actually higher than the above value, as the rectified spirit used contains only 96% of ethanol.)

Hydrolysis of Ethyl Acetate.

When esters such as ethyl acetate are shaken with water, hydrolysis slowly occurs, and ultimately an equilibrium is attained:

$$CH_3COOC_2H_5 + HOH \rightleftharpoons CH_3COOH + C_2H_5OH$$

Complete hydrolysis can be rapidly obtained, however, if the ester is boiled under reflux with a dilute aqueous solution of either a caustic alkali, such as sodium hydroxide, or of a strong inorganic acid, such as sulphuric or hydrochloric acid. In the former case, the sodium hydroxide neutralises the acetic acid as fast as it is formed, and so promotes the hydrolysis: in the latter case, the dilute inorganic acid catalyses the hydrolysis, which in the presence of a large excess of water goes practically to completion. Since the sodium salts of some of the higher fatty acids are soaps, the general process of alkaline hydrolysis of esters (by which the soaps are obtained) is frequently called *saponification*.

Place 5 ml. of ethyl acetate in a 100 ml. round-bottomed flask, and add about 50 ml. of 10% sodium hydroxide solution, together with some fragments of unglazed porcelain. Fit the flask with a reflux water-condenser, and boil the mixture gently over a wire gauze for 30 minutes. Now disconnect the condenser, and fit it by means of a bent delivery-tube (or "knee-tube") to the flask for direct distillation (Fig. 59, or Fig. 23(D), p. 45). Reheat the liquid, and collect the first 10 ml. of distillate, which will consist of a dilute aqueous solution of ethanol. Confirm the presence of ethanol by the iodoform test (Test 3, p. 336).

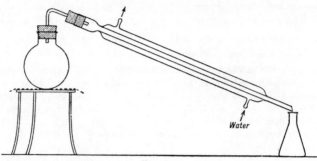

FIG. 59.

The residual liquid in the flask is a dilute alkaline solution of sodium acetate. To liberate the acetic acid, add dilute sulphuric acid until the solution is definitely acid to litmus, and then distil off about 20 ml. Perform on this aqueous distillate the tests for acetic acid given on p. 347.

Hydrolysis of Ethyl Acetate (Semi-Micro Scale)

The hydrolysis of as little as 0·5 ml. of the ester can be carried out in the combined "reflux-distillation" apparatus shown in Fig. 38 (p. 63). Pass a stream of cold water through the vertical condenser. Place in the 10 ml. pear-shaped flask 0·5 ml. of the ester, 5 ml. of 10% NaOH solution and one or two minute fragments of unglazed porcelain and heat the mixture gently for 15 minutes so that the vapours do not rise more than about half-way up the vertical water-condenser. Now run the water out of the vertical condenser, insert a thermometer at the top, and pass water through the inclined condenser. Heat the flask sufficiently strongly to collect 1–2 ml. of distillate. This is dilute ethanol.

Add dil. H_2SO_4 to the residue in the flask until definitely acid to litmus. Distil off 1–2 ml., and perform tests on this aqueous distillate for acetic acid.

Ethyl Bromide. C_2H_5Br. (Method 1, p. 95.)

Ethyl bromide is an example of an ester formed from an alcohol and an inorganic acid. Since hydrogen bromide is a gas, it is generated actually in the reaction mixture, where it is rapidly esterified without appreciable loss. For this purpose, a solution of ethyl hydrogen sulphate is prepared by adding sulphuric acid to an excess of ethanol. Sodium bromide is then added, and the liberated hydrogen bromide reacts with the ethyl hydrogen sulphate, giving

$$C_2H_5 HSO_4 + H Br \rightarrow C_2H_5Br + H_2SO_4$$

ethyl bromide. The excess of ethanol ensures that the sulphuric acid liberated in this reaction is reconverted into ethyl hydrogen sulphate, and that the excess of the latter in turn effects maximum conversion of the costly hydrogen bromide to ethyl bromide.

Required: Ethanol, 37 ml.; sulphuric acid, 40 ml.; sodium bromide ($NaBr,2H_2O$), 35 g.

Assemble the apparatus shown in Fig. 60. **A** is a 500 ml. bolt-head flask connected by a "knee-tube" **B** to a water-condenser **C**, to the lower end of which is fitted the adaptor **D**. In view of the low boiling-point of the ethyl bromide, it is essential that the various portions of the apparatus are connected together by well-bored, tightly fitting corks. (For this reason, the apparatus shown in Fig. 23(D), p. 45, is preferable.)

Arrange the adaptor **D** so that the end dips below the surface of about 50 ml. of water contained in a small conical flask, or beaker, which is in turn surrounded by a mixture of ice and water. Place 37 ml. (30 g.) of ethanol and 25 ml. of water in the flask **A**, and then add slowly 40 ml. (74 g.) of concentrated sulphuric acid, shaking the mixture gently around and cooling meanwhile. Now add 35 g. of coarsely powdered sodium bromide ($2H_2O$), reconnect the flask to the tube **B** without delay, and then heat the flask gently on a sand-bath, at the same time ensuring that an ample supply of cold water is passing through the condenser **C**.

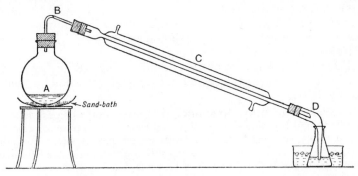

FIG. 60.

Ethyl bromide soon distils over, and collects as heavy oily drops under the water in the receiving flask, evaporation of the very volatile distillate being thus prevented. If the mixture in the flask **A** froths badly, moderate the heating of the sand-bath. When no more oily drops of ethyl bromide come over, pour the contents of the receiving flask into a separating-funnel, and carefully run off the heavy lower layer of ethyl bromide. Discard the upper aqueous layer, and return the ethyl bromide to the funnel. Add an equal volume of 10% sodium carbonate solution, cork the funnel securely and shake cautiously. Owing to the presence of hydrobromic and sulphurous acids in the crude ethyl bromide, a brisk evolution of carbon dioxide occurs: therefore release the pressure in the funnel at frequent intervals (as in the preparation of ethyl acetate, p. 97). Allow the two liquids to separate, and again run off the lower layer of ethyl bromide. Discard the upper layer, return the ethyl bromide to the funnel, and shake it with an equal volume of water to remove traces of sodium carbonate. Allow the two liquids to separate, and finally run the lower layer of ethyl bromide carefully into a small conical flask: add a few pieces of calcium chloride, securely cork the flask and then occasionally shake the mixture gently, protecting the liquid as much as possible from the heat of the hand. The liquid should become quite clear (and therefore dry) in about 20 minutes.

Then filter the ethyl bromide through a *small* fluted filter-paper directly into a 60 ml. distilling-flask. Fit the flask with a 100° thermometer, and a water-condenser having as before an ample supply of cold water: then arrange the condenser so that its lower end enters the neck of a small dry weighed conical flask, supporting the latter in line with the condenser, and chilling it externally by a mixture of ice and water. Distil the ethyl bromide slowly from a water-bath, and collect the fraction boiling between 35° and 40°. Average yield, 23 g. In view of the low boiling-point of the ethyl bromide, it should be preserved in a sealed glass specimen tube (see Fig. 21, p. 41).

Ethyl bromide is a colourless liquid, of b.p. 38° and d, 1·45, insoluble in water: as prepared above, it always contains some diethyl ether.

Hydrolysis of Ethyl Bromide. Add a few drops of pure freshly distilled ethyl bromide to 2–3 ml. of aqueous silver nitrate solution in a test-tube and shake. Only a faint opalescence of silver bromide should be formed. Now *carefully* warm the mixture in a small Bunsen flame, with gentle shaking: silver bromide soon appears as a white suspension which rapidly increases in quantity and becomes a heavy precipitate. The ethyl bromide is thus moderately stable in cold water, but rapidly hydrolysed by hot water.

n-Butyl Bromide. C_4H_9Br. (Method 1, p. 95.)

The preparation of *n*-butyl bromide as an example of ester formation by Method 1 (p. 95) has certain advantages over the above preparation of ethyl bromide. *n*-Butanol is free from Excise restrictions, and the *n*-butyl bromide is of course less volatile and therefore more readily manipulated without loss than ethyl bromide: furthermore, the *n*-butyl bromide boils *ca.* 40° below *n*-butyl ether, and traces of the latter formed in the reaction can therefore be readily eliminated by fractional distillation.

Required: Sodium bromide, 35 g.; *n*-butanol, 25 ml.

Place 30 ml. of water, 35 g. of powdered sodium bromide and

25 ml. (20 g.) of *n*-butanol in a 250 ml. round-bottomed flask, and then fit a dropping-funnel to the flask through a cork which has a groove cut or filed in the side (as **F** in Fig. 1(B), p. 3) to allow escape of air. Place 25 ml. of concentrated sulphuric acid in the funnel, and then allow the acid to fall slowly dropwise into the flask, keeping the contents well shaken meanwhile and cooled occasionally in an ice-water bath. When the addition is complete, replace the funnel with a reflux water-condenser, and then gently boil the mixture over a sand-bath for *ca.* 45 minutes, shaking the flask gently from time to time. Then remove the reflux condenser, and fit a "knee-tube" and condenser to the flask as shown in Fig. 59, p. 100 or Fig. 23(D), p. 45, and distil off the crude *n*-butyl bromide (*ca.* 30 ml.). Purify the distillate by first shaking it with water in a separating-funnel: run off the lower layer of bromide, reject the aqueous layer, and then return the bromide to the funnel and shake it with about half its volume of concentrated sulphuric acid; now run off the lower layer of acid, and shake the bromide layer in the funnel cautiously with dilute sodium carbonate solution, taking care to release the pressure in the funnel at frequent intervals.

Run off the lower layer of bromide, dry it with calcium chloride (as in the above preparation of ethyl bromide) and finally distil the filtered bromide from a small flask, preferably through a short column. Collect the *n*-butyl bromide as a colourless liquid of b.p. 99–102°. Yield, 30 g. A small residue of di-*n*-butyl ether, b.p. 142°, remains in the flask.

The Alkyl Halides.   Ethyl bromide and iodide (see below) are typical alkyl halides. Compounds of this class are of very great importance in synthetic work, owing to the reactivity of the halogen atom. This is illustrated by the following *general* reactions:

(1) Reduction gives the corresponding hydrocarbon.

$$C_2H_5Br + H_2 \rightarrow HBr + C_2H_6 \text{ (ethane)}.$$

(2) Elimination of halogen by sodium (Wurtz's reaction) gives a higher hydrocarbon.

$$C_2H_5Br + 2Na + BrC_2H_5 \rightarrow 2NaBr + C_4H_{10} \text{ (normal butane)}.$$

(3) (*a*) *Aqueous* potassium hydroxide gives the alcohol.

$$C_2H_5Br + KOH \rightarrow KBr + C_2H_5OH \text{ (ethanol)}.$$

(*b*) *Alcoholic* potassium hydroxide gives an unsaturated hydrocarbon, often however in only low yield with the earlier members of the series.

$$C_2H_5Br + KOH \rightarrow H_2O + KBr + C_2H_4 \text{ (ethylene)}.$$

(4) Sodium ethoxide gives an ether (Williamson's reaction).

$$C_2H_5Br + NaOC_2H_5 \rightarrow NaBr + C_2H_5OC_2H_5 \text{ (diethyl ether)}.$$

(5) (*a*) Potassium cyanide gives an alkyl cyanide or nitrile.

$$C_2H_5Br + KCN \rightarrow KBr + C_2H_5CN \text{ (ethyl cyanide or propionitrile)}$$

(*b*) Silver cyanide gives an alkyl *iso*cyanide or *iso*nitrile.

$$C_2H_5Br + AgCN \rightarrow AgBr + C_2H_5NC \text{ (ethyl } iso\text{cyanide).}$$

(6) Silver nitrite gives a mixture of ethyl nitrite and nitro-ethane (p. 131).

$$C_2H_5Br + AgNO_2 \begin{cases} \nearrow C_2H_5 \cdot O \cdot NO \text{ (ethyl nitrite)} \\ \searrow C_2H_5NO_2 \text{ (nitro-ethane).} \end{cases}$$

(7) Ammonia gives the corresponding amine (see however p. 127).

$$C_2H_5Br + HNH_2 \rightarrow HBr + C_2H_5NH_2 \text{ (monoethylamine).}$$

(8) The alkyl halides are also of great importance in synthetic operations (e.g.) using Grignard reagents (p. 280), acetoacetic ester (p. 269) and malonic ester (p. 275).

Ethyl Benzoate. $C_6H_5COOC_2H_5$. (Method 2; The Fischer-Speier Method, p. 96.)

As a general rule esterification by the Fischer-Speier method should be carried out using absolute ethanol: in the following preparation of ethyl benzoate, however, the yield is not sensibly affected by the use of the cheaper rectified spirit.

Required: Benzoic acid, 20 g.; rectified spirit, 20 ml.

Assemble in a fume-cupboard the apparatus shown in Fig. 61. **A** is a wide-necked round-bottomed 100 ml. flask to which the reflux water-condenser **B** is fitted by means of a *rubber* stopper. The latter carries also an inlet tube **C** (which should not be too narrow in diameter), by means of which a current of hydrogen chloride, dried by passage through the sulphuric acid wash-bottle **D**, can be passed down to the bottom of **A**. The hydrogen chloride is best generated by means of a Kipp's apparatus charged with solid ammonuim chloride and concentrated sulphuric acid. The top of the condenser **B** is fitted with a calcium chloride tube* **R**, preferably bent downwards as shown: drops of water tend to collect in the end of **E** as hydrogen chloride steadily escapes during the experiment, and are thus prevented from running back and so fouling the calcium chloride. (Alternatively, the flask, condenser and inlet-tube can be replaced by the apparatus shown in Fig. 23(B), p. 45.)

Place 20 g. of benzoic acid and 20 ml. (16 g.) of ethanol in **A**, connect up the apparatus, and then heat the flask on a sand-bath so that the solution in the flask boils gently. At the same time, pass a brisk current of hydrogen chloride into the reaction

* In all experiments in which an apparatus is closed by means of a calcium chloride tube, great care should be taken to ensure before the experiment that there is a free air-passage through the tube. This applies particularly when the tube has not been freshly charged, or in experiments where the heating has to be stopped during the night and started again next day: in both cases an air-tight crust of hydrated calcium chloride may have formed on the surface of the anhydrous material. The small uniformly sized pellets of the calcium chloride are best held in position by loose plugs of glass wool at each end of the tube.

mixture. The speed with which the hydrogen chloride enters the flask **A** must be carefully watched during the first few minutes of the experiment, and any tendency of the solution to suck back along the tube **C** (owing to the high solubility of hydrogen chloride in ethanol) should be checked by increasing the current: when once the boiling solution is saturated, however, the current of hydrogen chloride can be cut down until only a gentle stream of bubbles is passing through **D**.

When the solution has been boiling for $1\frac{1}{2}$ hours, remove **A**, cool the contents, and then pour the ethanolic solution of the ester into a separating-funnel containing about 200 ml. of water, finally rinsing out the flask with a few ml. of water which are also doured into the funnel. Since the pensity of ethyl benzoate is only

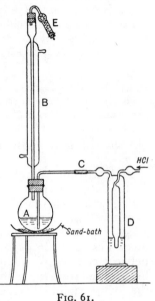

FIG. 61.

slightly greater than that of water, a sharp separation of the ester is not usually obtained. It is advisable at this stage therefore to add about 10 ml. of carbon tetrachloride, and then to shake the mixture in the funnel vigorously: on standing, the heavy solution of the ethyl benzoate in the carbon tetrachloride separates sharply and rapidly at the bottom of the funnel. Run off the ethyl benzoate solution carefully, reject the upper aqueous layer, and then return the ethyl benzoate to the flask and shake it with a very dilute solution of sodium carbonate until all free acid is removed and no further evolution of carbon dioxide occurs. Run off the lower layer into a small conical flask, and dry by the addition of a few pieces of granular calcium chloride. Cork the flask and allow to stand for about 20 minutes with occasional shaking. Then filter the ethyl benzoate solution through a small fluted filter-paper directly into a 50 ml. distilling-flask containing a few pieces of unglazed porcelain. Fit the flask with a 360° thermometer and an air-condenser: in view of the small quantity of carbon tetrachloride present, a water-condenser during the early stages of the distillation is not necessary. By direct heating over a gauze, distil first the carbon tetrachloride *slowly*, and then the ethyl benzoate, collecting the latter as a fraction of b.p. 210–214°. Yield, 19–20 g.

Ethyl benzoate is a colourless liquid, of b.p. 213° and d, 1·05; almost insoluble in water: it has a characteristic odour.

For a further example of the Fischer-Speier method, see Ethyl cinnamate, p. 235.

Ethyl Iodide. C_2H_5I. (Method 5, p. 96.)

This is a modification of Method 5, iodine being added to a mixture of red phosphorus and ethanol: phosphorus tri-iodide is thus formed *in situ*, and readily reacts with the ethanol, giving ethyl iodide and phosphorous acid (p. 96).

Required: Red phosphorus, 2·5 g.; ethanol, 25 ml.; iodine, 25 g.

Fit a 250 ml. round-bottomed flask securely by means of a tightly fitting, well-bored cork to a reflux condenser capable of taking an ample supply of water. Place in the flask 2·5 g. of *red* phosphorus, and then 25 ml. (20 g.) of ethanol. Well powder 25 g. of iodine, and add it to the contents of the flask in small quantities of about 3–4 g. at a time, allowing about two minutes between consecutive additions: for this purpose, the flask should be detached from the condenser *immediately* before each addition, the iodine rapidly dropped into the flask and the latter at once returned to the condenser. A moderate evolution of heat occurs, but if the addition of the powdered iodine is carefully performed, the contents of the flask should not actually boil. When all the iodine has been added, allow the product to stand for 10 minutes, and then heat on a boiling water-bath for 1 hour. Then change the position of the condenser for direct distillation, attaching it by means of a knee-tube to the flask, as shown in Fig. 59, p. 100, or Fig. 23(D), p. 45. Reheat the flask on a boiling water-bath, and collect the distillate, which consists of ethyl iodide and unchanged ethanol, usually coloured by traces of free iodine. When the distillation ceases, transfer the distillate to a separating-funnel, and shake with an equal volume of 10% aqueous sodium carbonate solution. Run off the lower layer of ethyl iodide, and discard the upper aqueous layer. Return the ethyl iodide to the separating-funnel, and shake it with an equal volume of water to remove traces of sodium carbonate solution. Run off the lower layer of ethyl iodide into a small conical flask, making the separation of the iodide from the upper aqueous layer as sharp and complete as possible. Add some pieces of granular calcium chloride, cork the flask and allow to stand for 15–20 minutes, occasionally shaking the contents gently. Then filter the ethyl iodide through a *small* fluted filter-paper directly into a 60 ml. distilling-flask.

Fit the flask with a 100° thermometer and a water-condenser, and distil the ethyl iodide carefully from a water-bath, collecting the fraction which distils between 68° and 73°. Yield, about 24 g.

Ethyl iodide is a heavy liquid, of b.p. 72° and of d, 1·94; insoluble in water. When freshly distilled it is colourless, but on prolonged exposure to light it darkens in colour owing to the liberation of free iodine. Its chemical properties are almost identical with those of ethyl bromide given on pp. 102 and 103.

Acetylation.

Compounds of the type ROH (alcohols and phenols), and also compounds of the type RNH_2 and R_2NH (primary and secondary amines) can be directly acetylated, the reactive H atom being replaced by the acetyl radical, $-COCH_3$. The acetylation of alcohols and phenols is really a special case of esterification, since the acetyl derivative, $ROCOCH_3$, is clearly an ester of acetic acid. Primary and secondary amines similarly give acetyl derivatives of the type $RNHCOCH_3$ and R_2NCOCH_3 respectively, which can be regarded as mono-and di-substituted derivatives of acetamide, H_2NCOCH_3.

The two chief methods of acetylation are:

(1) *Heating with a mixture of acetic anhydride and acetic acid.*

If a primary or secondary amine is heated with glacial acetic acid, the

$$RNH\ H + HOOCCH_3\ \rightarrow NHCOCH_3 + H_2O$$

corresponding acetyl derivative is produced, but the process is often extremely slow. If, however, the acetic acid is mixed with acetic anhydride, rapid acetylation usually results.

$$RNH\ H + CH_3CO\cdot O\cdot COCH_3\ \rightarrow RNHCOCH_3 + CH_3COOH$$

One disadvantage of using acetic anhydride is that with primary amines, traces of the diacetyl compound, $RN(COCH_3)_2$, may be formed: the chances of this secondary acetylation are, however, usually remote, and recrystallisation from an aqueous solvent will generally hydrolyse the diacetyl derivative rapidly back to the mono-acetyl compound.

For complete acetylation of polyhydric compounds, such as glucose (p. 141) and mannitol (p. 142), even undiluted acetic anhydride is insufficient, and a catalyst must also be employed. In such cases, the addition of zinc chloride or anhydrous sodium acetate to the acetic anhydride usually induces complete acetylation.*

(2) *Treatment with acetyl chloride.*

Acetylation will proceed particularly smoothly with acetyl chloride if pyridine is present to absorb the hydrogen chloride as fast as it is formed.

$$RO\ H + Cl\ COCH_3\ \rightarrow ROCOCH_3 + HCl$$

Acetylation has two chief uses: (1) to characterise and identify hydroxy

---

* Some amines, e.g., aniline, can on the other hand be readily acetylated by dissolving them in cold dil. acetic acid and adding acetic anhydride: the method is not however general.

compounds and primary and secondary amines, by obtaining crystalline acetyl derivatives. This applies particularly to aromatic compounds, since aliphatic compounds are often liquid, and frequently soluble in water; (2) to protect a primary or secondary amino group during a chemical reaction, as in the preparation of *p*-nitro-aniline by the nitration of acetanilide, followed by hydrolysis (p. 167), and in the preparation of sulphanilamide (p. 181).

Acetanilide. $C_6H_5NHCOCH_3$. (Method 1.)

Required: Acetic acid/anhydride mixture, 20 ml.; aniline, 10 ml.

Add 20 ml. of a mixture of equal volumes of acetic anhydride and glacial acetic acid to 10 ml. (10·3 g.) of aniline contained in a 150 ml. conical flask. Fit a reflux water-condenser to the flask, and boil the mixture gently for 10 minutes. Then pour the hot liquid into 200 ml. of cold water, stirring the latter well

$$C_6H_5NH_2 + O(OCCH_3)_2 = C_6H_5NHCOCH_3 + CH_3COOH$$

during the addition. The acetanilide rapidly crystallises. Filter at the pump, and wash the crude acetanilide well with water. Recrystallise from about 60 ml. of a mixture of one volume of acetic acid and two volumes of water: filter off the colourless crystals at the pump, again wash thoroughly with water, drain, and dry. M.p. 113°; yield, 10 g. Alternatively, the crude acetanilide may be recrystallised from boiling water, but in this case a much greater volume (about 300 ml.) of the solvent will be required.

Acetanilide (Semi-micro Scale) (1/40 of above scale).

Run into a test-tube from a micro-burette 0·25 ml. of aniline and 0·5 ml. of the 1:1 acetic acid-acetic anhydride mixture. Insert a "cold finger" (Fig. 35, p. 62) into the lip of the test-tube, without using a cork. Circulate the water through the finger and gently boil the mixture for 5 minutes. Cool, add about 5 ml. of cold water, stir well with a thin glass rod and filter off the precipitated acetanilide using the apparatus shown in Figs. 45 or 46 (p. 68). Use the filtrate to effect the *complete* transfer of all the solid from the test-tube to the filter funnel, and then wash the solid with about 1 ml. of ice-cold water and drain thoroughly. Recrystallise from boiling water (about 8 ml.). Filter if necessary while hot through a very small fluted filter paper (or using the apparatus shown in Fig. 47, p. 68) into a small conical flask or test-tube. When quite cold filter off the purified acetanilide, again using the apparatus shown in Figs. 45 or 46. Yield, 0·2 g.

Hydrolysis of Acetanilide. Anilides in general, such as acetanilide and benzanilide (p. 245), may be hydrolysed by caustic alkalis or by acids. Alkaline hydrolysis, however, is usually very slow, and therefore acid hydrolysis should always be used for anilides. For this purpose, a 70% solution of sulphuric acid, prepared by adding 40 ml. (74 g.) of the concentrated acid *cautiously* to 30 ml. of water with cooling and stirring, gives the most satisfactory results.

Place 1 g. of acetanilide and 10 ml. of the 70% sulphuric acid in a small flask fitted with a reflux water-condenser, and boil the mixture gently for 15 minutes, when the hot solution will smell perceptibly of free acetic acid. Dilute the solution with about 5 ml. of water,

$$C_6H_5NHCOCH_3 + H_2O + H_2SO_4 = C_6H_5NH_2,H_2SO_4 + CH_3COOH$$

transfer it to a small distilling-flask, and distil off about 1–2 ml. Acetic acid is volatile in steam: therefore apply to this distillate the tests for free acetic acid given on p. 347. Cool the residual liquid, which contains aniline sulphate dissolved in excess of dilute sulphuric acid, and apply the tests for aniline given on p. 373.

Alternatively the semi-micro apparatus shown in Fig. 38 (p. 63) may be used. Heat the anilide and sulphuric acid under reflux for 15 minutes in such a manner that the vapour does not rise higher than half-way up the vertical condenser through which water is passed. Then dilute the solution in the flask with 5 ml. of water. Empty the vertical condenser and run cold water through the inclined condenser. Now increase the rate of heating and distil off 1–2 ml. of aqueous acetic acid.

Phenyl Acetate. $CH_3COOC_6H_5$. (Method 1 modified.)

Although the acetylation of alcohols and amines by acetic anhydride is almost invariably carried out under anhydrous conditions owing to the ready hydrolysis of the anhydride, it has been shown by Chattaway (1931) that phenols, when dissolved in aqueous sodium hydroxide solution and shaken with acetic anhydride, undergo rapid and almost quantitative acetylation if ice is present to keep the temperature low throughout the reaction. The success of this method is due primarily to the acidic nature of the phenols, which enables them to form soluble sodium derivatives, capable of reacting with the acetic

$$CH_3CO·O·COCH_3 + NaOC_6H_5 \rightarrow CH_3COOC_6H_5 + CH_3COONa$$

anhydride before the latter undergoes appreciable hydrolysis. The general conditions of the acetylation are thus similar to those used in the Schotten-Baumann method for benzoylation (p. 243).

When the phenol contains a carboxylic acid group, *e.g.*, *m*- or *p*-hydroxy-benzoic acid, the acetylated derivative will of course remain in solution as the sodium salt, but is precipitated when the solution is subsequently acidified. Salicylic acid, however, cannot be acetylated under these conditions.

Some amino-acids, *e.g.*, glycine, can also be acetylated by this method.

Required: Phenol, 15 g.; acetic anhydride, 22 ml.

Dissolve 15 g. of phenol in 105 ml. (1.6 mols.) of 10% aqueous sodium hydroxide solution contained in a stout-walled bottle, and add about 150 g. of crushed ice. Then add 22 ml. (24 g., 1.5 mols.) of acetic anhydride, cork the bottle securely, and shake the contents vigorously for about 5 minutes, by which time the reaction will be complete and an emulsion of phenyl acetate obtained.

Pour the mixture into a separating-funnel. Owing to the density of the acetate being only slightly greater than that of water, a sharp separation is usually not rapidly obtained. It is advisable therefore to add about 8 ml. of carbon tetrachloride, when, after shaking, a sharp and rapid separation of the heavy solution of the phenyl acetate in the tetrachloride is obtained. Run off this solution, reject the upper aqueous layer, return the solution to the funnel, and shake again with about 80 ml. of very dilute sodium carbonate solution in order to remove traces of acetic acid or anhydride. Run off the lower layer into a small conical flask, dry over granular calcium chloride for 20–30 minutes and then filter through a small fluted filter-paper directly into a 50 ml. distilling-flask. Fit the latter with a 360° thermometer and an air-condenser and distil the contents *slowly* by heating over a gauze. (The quantity of carbon tetrachloride present is too small to make the preliminary use of a water-condenser necessary.) The boiling-point of the mixture rises slowly but steadily to about 170° before the distillation of the carbon tetrachloride is complete, and then rises rapidly to about 193°. Collect the phenyl acetate as the fraction of b.p. 193–197°. Yield, 20 g.

Phenyl acetate is a colourless liquid, of b.p. 196° and d, 1·08, almost insoluble in water and almost odourless.

2-Naphthyl Acetate. $CH_3COOC_{10}H_7$. Dissolve 1 g. of pure 2-naphthol in 5 ml. (1·8 mols.) of 10% sodium hydroxide solution as before, add 10 g. of crushed ice, and 1·1 ml. (1·14 g., 1·5 mols.) of acetic anhydride. Shake the mixture vigorously for about 10–15 minutes; the 2-naphthyl acetate separates as colourless crystals. Filter at the pump, wash with water, drain, and dry thoroughly. Yield of crude material, 1·4 g. (theoretical). Recrystallise from petroleum (b.p. 60–80°), from which, on cooling and scratching, the 2-naphthyl acetate separates as colourless crystals, m.p. 71°: yield, 1·0 g.

Acetylsalicylic Acid (Aspirin). $C_6H_4{<}^{O.COCH_3}_{COOH}$ (Method 2)

Required: Salicylic acid, 10 g.; pyridine, 7 ml.; acetyl chloride, 7·5 ml.

Dissolve 10 g. of salicylic acid (*o*-hydroxybenzoic acid) in 7 ml. of *dry* pyridine contained in a 100 ml. conical flask. Then without delay (since this solution if allowed to stand tends to become a semi-solid mass) run in 7·5 ml. (8·3 g.) of acetyl chloride, adding about 1 ml. of the chloride at a time, and shaking the mixture continuously during the addition. The heat of the reaction causes the temperature of the mixture to rise rapidly:

therefore maintain the latter between 50° and 60° throughout the addition, cooling the flask occasionally in cold water if necessary. Finally heat the mixture on a boiling water-bath for 5 minutes,

$$CH_3COCl + HOC_6H_4COOH = CH_3COOC_6H_4COOH + HCl$$
$$\text{Salicylic Acid} \qquad\qquad \text{Aspirin}$$

and then, after cooling in cold water, pour it in a thin stream into about 300 ml. of cold water, stirring the mixture vigorously meanwhile. The crude acetylsalicylic acid either solidifies at once, or separates as an oil which rapidly crystallises as the stirring proceeds. Filter the solid product at the pump, wash thoroughly with water and drain. Recrystallise from a mixture of equal volumes of water and acetic acid: yield, 11 g. (Alternatively, press the crude product between several sheets of drying-paper until *quite dry*, and then recrystallise from benzene: a sticky product will result, however, if traces of water still remain.) The acetylsalicylic acid is obtained as colourless crystals, m.p. 136–137°.

It should be emphasised that salicylic acid can be readily acetylated by Method 1, and that the above preparation of acetylsalicyclic acid is given solely as an illustration of Method 2. To employ Method 1, add 10 g. of salicylic acid to 20 ml. of a mixture of equal volumes of acetic anhydride and acetic acid, and boil gently under reflux for 30 minutes. Then pour into about 200 ml. of cold water in order to precipitate the acetylsalicylic acid (11 g.) and finally recrystallise as above. Method 2, however, gives the purer product.

Acetylsalicylic acid is largely used in medicine as an analgesic (*i.e.*, for removing pain) and as an antipyretic (*i.e.*, for reducing the body temperature).

Reactions of Aspirin. (1) *Distinction from Salicylic acid.* Shake up with water in two clean test-tubes a few crystals of (a) salicylic acid, (b) aspirin, a very dilute aqueous solution of each substance being thus obtained. Note that the addition of 1 drop of ferric chloride solution to (a) gives an immediate purple coloration, due to the free −OH group, whereas (b) gives no coloration if the aspirin is pure.

(2) *Hydrolysis of Aspirin.* Gently boil a mixture of 1 g. of aspirin and 15 ml. of 10% sodium hydroxide solution in a 50 ml. conical flask under reflux for 20 minutes. Then cool the solution thoroughly and add dilute sulphuric acid until the precipitation of the

$$CH_3COOC_6H_4COOH + 2NaOH = CH_3COONa + HOC_6H_4COONa + H_2O$$

salicylic acid is complete. Filter off the salicylic acid, recrystallise it from hot water, and confirm its identity by reaction (1) above. M.p. 156°.

The original filtrate still contains the acetic acid which is the other product of the hydrolysis. Therefore place this filtrate (which must be distinctly acid to litmus-paper) in a distilling-flask and distil off about 5 ml. through a water-condenser. Then apply to the filtrate the tests for acetic acid given on p. 347.

Oxalic Acid. $\dfrac{\text{COOH}}{\text{COOH}}$, 2H₂O.

Certain aliphatic compounds are oxidised by concentrated nitric acid, the carbon atoms being split off in pairs, with the formation of oxalic acid. This disruptive oxidation is shown by many carbohydrates, e.g., cane sugar, where the chains of secondary alcohol groups, –CH(OH)·CH(OH)·CH(OH)·CH(OH)–, present in the molecule break down particularly readily to give oxalic acid.

It should be noted that aliphatic compounds (except the paraffins) are *usually* oxidised by concentrated nitric acid, whereas aromatic compounds (including the hydrocarbons) are usually nitrated by the concentrated acid (in the presence of sulphuric acid) and oxidised by the dilute acid. As an example of the latter, benzaldehyde, C_6H_5CHO, when treated with concentrated nitric acid gives *m*-nitrobenzaldehyde, $NO_2C_6H_4CHO$, but with dilute nitric acid gives benzoic acid, C_6H_5COOH.

Required: Cane sugar, 20 g.; nitric acid, 100 ml.

Owing to the copious evolution of nitrous fumes, this preparation must be carried out in a fume-cupboard having an *efficient draught*. Place 20 g. of coarsely powdered cane sugar (sucrose) in a 750 ml. flat-bottomed flask, add 100 ml. of concentrated nitric acid and heat the flask on a boiling water-bath. As the mixture becomes warm, the greater part of the sugar dissolves and a vigorous but harmless reaction, accompanied by a tremendous evolution of nitrous fumes, takes place. Immediately the evolution of gas starts, remove the flask from the water-bath and place it on a wooden block or some similar non-conducting surface. When the reaction subsides (after about 15 minutes) pour the hot solution into an evaporating-basin, wash out the flask with about 20 ml. of concentrated nitric acid, and then evaporate the acid solution on the water-bath until it has a volume of about 20 ml. Some oxidation continues in the solution during the evaporation, which is comparatively rapid. Now add about 40 ml. of water to the solution, and again evaporate to about 20 ml. Cool the solution thoroughly in ice-water; oxalic acid rapidly crystallises. When crystallisation is complete, filter at the pump, and then recrystallise from a small quantity of hot water. Dry by pressing between pads of drying-paper, or in an atmospheric desiccator, but not in an oven where partial loss of water of crystallisation may occur. Yield, 7 g. The hydrated acid has m.p. 101°; the anhydrous acid decomposes on heating. Oxalic acid is poisonous.

For reactions of oxalic acid, see p. 351.

Formic Acid, HCOOH (in aqueous solution), and Lead Formate, $(HCOO)_2Pb$.

When a mixture of anhydrous glycerol and crystalline oxalic acid, $(COOH)_2, 2H_2O$, is heated the glycerol undergoes esterification, giving first glyceryl monoxalate (A): the latter, however, decomposes as the temperature

$$CH_2(OH) \cdot CH(OH) \cdot CH_2(OH) + (COOH)_2$$
$$\rightarrow H_2O + CH_2(OH) \cdot CH(OH) \cdot CH_2O \cdot CO \cdot COOH \quad (A)$$
$$CH_2(OH) \cdot CH(OH) \cdot CH_2 \cdot OCO \cdot COOH$$
$$\rightarrow CO_2 + CH_2(OH) \cdot CH(OH) \cdot CH_2O \cdot CO \cdot H \quad (B)$$
$$CH_2(OH) \cdot CH(OH) \cdot CH_2O \cdot CO \cdot H + H_2O$$
$$\rightarrow CH_2(OH) \cdot CH(OH) \cdot CH_2(OH) + HCOOH$$

reaches about 100°, losing carbon dioxide and giving glyceryl monoformate (B). On further heating, particularly if more oxalic acid is added, the monoformate is hydrolysed (the necessary water being provided both by the oxalic acid and by the first reaction), and consequently a distillate of aqueous formic acid is obtained.

Required: Glycerol, 70 ml.; oxalic acid, 40 g.; lead carbonate.

Since glycerol is a very hygroscopic substance, it may be necessary to ensure that the sample used is anhydrous. For this purpose, place about 70 ml. in a porcelain evaporating-basin, and heat it carefully over a gauze (preferably in a fume-cupboard), stirring it steadily with a thermometer until the temperature is 175–180°: then maintain this temperature for a further 5 minutes. Allow the glycerol to cool, but while it is still warm (*i.e.*, before it becomes viscous) pour 50 ml. (63 g.) into a 250 ml. distilling-flask containing 40 g. of powdered crystalline oxalic acid. Fit a thermometer in the flask so that the bulb is completely immersed in the glycerol mixture, and then fit a water-condenser to the flask. Heat the mixture carefully over a gauze so that the temperature rises to 110–120°, and then adjust the heating so that the temperature remains within these limits. A vigorous effervescence of carbon dioxide occurs, and the aqueous formic acid begins slowly to distil over. When the effervescence tends to subside, remove the Bunsen flame and allow the temperature to fall to 70–80°: then add a further 40 g. of powdered oxalic acid, and continue the heating as before. Ultimately 25–30 ml. of distillate are obtained, the total period of heating being about 1 hour. While the distillation is proceeding, withdraw a few ml. of the distillate and apply Tests 2, 3 and 4 for formic acid given on p. 350–351.

To obtain lead formate, add about 100 ml. of water to the distillate and then stir powdered lead carbonate into the gently heated solution until no further effervescence of carbon dioxide occurs. Then boil the mixture vigorously and filter at the pump, using a Buchner funnel. Evaporate the clear filtrate by direct boiling in a beaker until crystals appear on the surface, and then allow to cool, finally chilling in ice-water. The lead formate separates as colourless crystals; filter off, wash with a small quantity of cold water, and dry. Yield, about 6 g.

A considerable amount of the formic acid, however, still remains behind in the distilling-flask as the unhydrolysed monoformate. Therefore, if time allows, dilute the residue in the flask with about an equal volume of water, and then steam-distil, the monoformate ester being thus completely hydrolysed and the formic acid then driven over in the steam. Collect about 400 ml. of distillate. Add this distillate to that obtained by direct heating of the reaction mixture and then treat with lead carbonate as described above. Total yield of lead formate is now about 40 g.

Lead formate is only slightly soluble in cold water, and insoluble in hot absolute ethanol: it can therefore be readily distinguished from lead acetate or "sugar of lead" because, quite apart from chemical tests, the acetate is readily soluble in cold water and moderately soluble in ethanol.

Lead formate separates from aqueous solution without water of crystallisation. It can therefore be used for the preparation of anhydrous formic acid. For this purpose, the powdered lead formate is placed in the inner tube of an ordinary jacketed condenser, and there held loosely in position by plugs of glass-wool. The condenser is then clamped in an oblique position and the lower end fitted into a receiver closed with a calcium chloride tube. A current of dry hydrogen sulphide is passed down the inner tube of the condenser, whilst steam is passed through the jacket. The formic acid which is liberated

$$(HCOO)_2Pb + H_2S \rightarrow 2HCOOH + PbS.$$

collects in the receiver, and is then purified from dissolved hydrogen sulphide by redistillation over a further quantity of lead formate.

For reactions of formic acid and formates, see p. 350–351.

If the reaction mixture used in the above preparation of formic acid is heated to 190–200°, the glyceryl monoformate which has escaped hydrolysis undergoes decomposition, with the loss of carbon dioxide and water, and the

$$CH_2(OH) \cdot CH(OH) \cdot CH_2O \cdot CO \cdot H \rightarrow CH_2 : CH \cdot CH_2OH + CO_2 + H_2O$$

formation of allyl alcohol.

The neutral glyceryl oxalate (C), which is also formed in the reaction mixture, loses carbon dioxide at the higher temperature and thus also gives allyl alcohol.

$$CH_2OH \cdot CH \underset{\substack{| \\ O - C - C - O \\ \| \ \| \\ O \ O}}{\rule{2cm}{0.4pt}} CH_2$$

Potassium Antimonyl Tartrate (Tartar Emetic). $C_4H_4O_6KSbO, \frac{1}{2}H_2O$.

Tartaric acid is noteworthy for (a) the excellent way in which the majority of its salts crystallise, and (b) the frequent occurrence of salts having mixed cations. Examples of the latter are sodium potassium tartrate (or Rochelle salt), $C_4H_4O_6NaK$, used for the preparation of Fehling's solution (p. 525), sodium ammonium tartrate, $C_4H_4O_6NaNH_4$, used by Pasteur for his early optical resolution experiments, and potassium antimonyl tartrate (or Tartar Emetic), $C_4H_4O_6K(SbO)$. The latter is prepared by boiling a solution of potassium hydrogen tartrate (or "cream of tartar") with antimony trioxide,

$$2\ \begin{array}{l} CH(OH)\cdot COOK \\ | \\ CH(OH)\cdot COOH \end{array} + Sb_2O_3 \ \rightarrow\ 2\ \begin{array}{l} CH(OH)\cdot COOK \\ | \\ CH(OH)\cdot COO(SbO) \end{array} + H_2O$$

when the acidic hydrogen atom is replaced by the monovalent antimonyl (Sb:O) radical.*

Required : Potassium hydrogen tartrate, 5 g.; antimony trioxide, 5 g.

Add 5 g. of potassium hydrogen tartrate and 5 g. of antimony trioxide (each being finely powdered) to 30 ml. of water contained in a small flask, and boil the mixture under a reflux water-condenser for 15 minutes. Then filter hot, using a Buchner funnel and flask which have been preheated by the filtration of some boiling distilled water. Pour the clear filtrate into a beaker and allow to cool. Potassium antimonyl tartrate separates as colourless crystals. Filter, drain and dry. Yield, 5 g. The product can be recrystallised from hot water, but this is usually not necessary.

Tartar emetic, as its name indicates, can be used medicinally to cause vomiting. For the preparation of tartar emetic intended for medicinal use, pure antimony trioxide, free (in particular) from traces of arsenic, must of course be employed.

Acetic Anhydride. $CH_3CO\cdot O\cdot COCH_3$

Although some dibasic acids, *e.g.*, succinic acid and phthalic acid, readily lose water on heating with the formation of cyclic anhydrides, most monobasic

$$\begin{array}{l} CH_2COOH \\ | \\ CH_2COOH \\ \text{Succinic acid.} \end{array} \xrightarrow[\longrightarrow]{\text{Heat}} \begin{array}{l} CH_2CO \\ | \quad\ \ >O + H_2O \\ CH_2CO \\ \text{Succinic anhydride.} \end{array}$$

carboxylic acids when heated merely distil unchanged. Their anhydrides can however be prepared by the interaction of the acid chloride with a metallic salt of

* This is a simplified formula for tartar emetic, for X-ray crystal analysis and infrared studies indicate that the Sb is a part of the antimonate anion $[Sb(OH)_4]^-$ and forms part of a cyclic system.

the acid itself. Thus acetyl chloride and sodium acetate readily interact with

$$CH_3CO\ Cl + Na\ OOCCH_3 \rightarrow CH_3CO\cdot O\cdot COCH_3 + NaCl$$

the formation of acetic anhydride.

It should be emphasised that whereas the interaction of a sodium salt and an acid chloride is a convenient general laboratory method for preparing all classes of anhydrides, acetic anhydride is prepared on a large scale by other and cheaper methods. Industrial processes are based on reactions indicated by the equations:

(1) $CH_3COONa + S + 6Cl_2 \rightarrow 4(CH_3CO)_2O + 6NaCl + Na_2SO_4$

(2) $CH_2 : C : O + CH_3COOH \rightarrow (CH_3CO)_2O$
     ketene

Required: Anhydrous sodium acetate, 21 g.; acetyl chloride, 15 ml.

Place 21 g. (a 20% excess) of powdered anhydrous sodium acetate* in a 100 ml. round-bottomed flask fitted with a reflux water-condenser, and cool the flask in ice-water. Place 15 ml. (16·5 g.) of acetyl chloride in a dropping-funnel fitted into the top of the condenser by means of a grooved cork (*cf.* Fig. 53, p. 76, or Fig. 23(A), p. 45). Now allow the acetyl chloride to run slowly down into the chilled sodium acetate, thoroughly mixing the contents by shaking as soon as the product becomes sufficiently liquid. Then heat the flask on a boiling water-bath for 10 minutes to complete the reaction. Next disconnect the condenser and fit it by means of a "knee-tube" Fig. 59, p. 100, or Fig. 23(D), p. 45) to the flask for distillation. Heat the flask with a luminous smoky Bunsen flame (without a gauze), waving the flame around the base of the flask to ensure uniform heating and to minimise risk of cracking: continue heating until no more distillate passes over. Now fractionally distil the crude acetic anhydride *slowly* from a 40 ml. distilling-flask, preferably using an air-condenser. A small quantity passes over at 130–135° (due to traces of free acetic acid) and the major fraction at 135–140°. Yield, 18 g.

Add a few drops of the distillate to an aqueous silver nitrate solution containing some dilute nitric acid and warm gently: no silver chloride should be precipitated, indicating the complete absence of unchanged acetyl chloride.

Acetic anhydride is a colourless liquid, having b.p. 138° and

---

* For this preparation, it is particularly necessary that the sodium acetate should be free from traces of water. The anhydrous material can be prepared by gently heating the hydrated salt ($CH_3COONa,3H_2O$) in an evaporating-basin over a small Bunsen flame. The salt dissolves in its water of crystallisation and resolidifies as this water is driven off: further heating then causes the anhydrous material to melt. Stir the molten anhydrous material to avoid charring, and then allow it to cool in a desiccator. Powder the cold material rapidly in a mortar, and bottle without delay.

If a sample of the anhydrous salt is taken from stock, it should preferably be melted, allowed to cool, and then pulverised.

d, 1·08: it has a sharp pungent odour resembling that of acetic acid. It is used in organic chemistry chiefly as an acetylating agent, for which purpose it is frequently mixed with acetic acid, sodium acetate, *etc.*: for examples of such acetylations see pp. 107–112.

For reactions of acetic anhydride, see p. 364.

Acid Amides.

Acid amides may be prepared by the following methods:

(1) *Dehydration of the corresponding ammonium salt.* Thus ammonium acetate on heating loses water giving acetamide. An excess of acetic acid is

$$CH_3COONH_4 = CH_3CONH_2 + H_2O$$

usually added before heating, in order to suppress thermal dissociation of the ammonium acetate into ammonia and acetic acid.

(2) *By the action of Concentrated Aqueous Ammonia on:*

(*a*) *Esters*

$$\begin{array}{ccc} CO\,OC_2H_5 & H\,NH_2 & CONH_2 \\ | & + & \rightarrow | & + 2C_2H_5OH \\ CO\,OC_2H_5 & H\,NH_2 & CONH_2 \end{array}$$

Ethyl oxalate   Oxamide

(*b*) *Acid Chlorides* $C_6H_5CO\,Cl + H\,NH_2 \rightarrow C_6H_5CONH_2 + HCl$

Benzoyl Chloride   Benzamide

(*c*) *Acid Anhydrides*

$$CH_3CO\,O\cdot OCCH_3 + H\,NH_2 \rightarrow CH_3CONH_2 + CH_3COOH$$

Acetic anhydride   Acetamide

In reactions (*b*) and (*c*) the hydrochloric and acetic acids formed are of course at once neutralised by the excess of ammonia.

Method (1) is most frequently used for aliphatic acid amides, while Methods (2*a*), (2*b*) and (2*c*) are used most frequently for aromatic acid amides. Of the last three methods, the Acid Chloride Method (2*b*) is the most rapid and certain. The Ester Method (2*a*) is practicable only when the amide is insoluble in water, and even then is often very slow unless the ester itself is appreciably soluble in the aqueous ammonia solution.

For reactions of acid amides, see p. 560.

Acetamide. CH_3CONH_2. (Method 1.)

Required: Ammonium carbonate, 15 g.; acetic acid, 50 ml.

Add 15 g. of finely powdered ammonium carbonate gradually to 50 ml. of glacial acetic acid contained in a 150 ml. round-bottomed flask, shaking the mixture during the addition to ensure a steady evolution of carbon dioxide. When all the carbonate has dissolved and the evolution of carbon dioxide has ceased, fit a reflux air-condenser to the flask and boil the solution *gently* for 30 minutes, when the dehydration of the ammonium acetate will be complete. Now remove the condenser and fit a fractionating column to the flask: for this purpose a 4-pear column may be used, but far better results are obtained if a column of the type shown in Fig. 11(B) (p. 26), in which the glass sections themselves occupy a height of about 12 cm., is used. Fit a 360° thermometer in the column, and fit the air-condenser to the side-arm for distillation. Now distil the liquid through the column *very slowly* (to give about 1 drop of distillate every 3 seconds) until the temperature reaches 170°: it is very important that this operation should be carried out slowly in order to distil over as much water and excess of acetic acid as possible, and so to leave almost pure acetamide in the flask. Without delay, pour the hot molten acetamide into a small (50 ml.) distilling-flask, and attach the side-arm of the flask to a short glass tube (about 30 cms. long and 12 mm. internal diameter) to act as an air-condenser. Distil the acetamide carefully at such a rate that none escapes condensation, and that none crystallises while still in the condenser. Collect the fraction boiling between 215° and 225° directly into a weighed specimen-tube, where it should crystallise readily on cooling. Yield, 15 g.

Acetamide is thus obtained as a colourless crystalline solid, which has a characteristic odour of mice, stated to be due to the presence of small quantities of methylacetamide, $CH_3CONHCH_3$. The acetamide can be purified and rendered odourless by re-crystallisation from acetone, and then has m.p. 82°, b.p. 223°. If this recrystallisation is contemplated, the distilled material should be collected directly into a small weighed beaker or conical flask, so that the solidified acetamide can be readily broken up and removed.

Oxamide. $NH_2CO\cdot CONH_2$. (Method 2(a), p. 117.)

Required: Concentrated ammonia, 5 ml.; ethyl oxalate, 1 ml.

Oxamide differs from most aliphatic acid amides in being almost insoluble in water,* and therefore can be readily prepared from the diethyl ester by Method 2(a). Place a mixture of 5 ml. of concentrated (d, 0·880) ammonia solution and 5 ml. of water in a 25 ml. conical flask, for which a well-fitting cork is available. (The large excess of

---

* The very low solubility of oxamide is almost undoubtedly the result of the extensively hydrogen-bonded nature of the crystalline compound (cf. E. M. Ayerst and J. R. C. Duke, *Acta. Cryst.* (1954), **7**, 588).

ammonia solution is employed chiefly to prevent too great a rise in temperature during the reaction.) Now add 1 ml. (1·1 g.) of ethyl oxalate, cork the flask *securely* and shake vigorously: the mixture becomes perceptibly warm, and therefore throughout the shaking hold the cork tightly in position, with the flask pointing *away* from the operator (and from neighbouring students!). At intervals, release the pressure by cautiously removing the cork. The oxamide rapidly separates as a white powder and after 15 minutes' shaking the reaction is complete. Filter off the oxamide at the pump, wash it well with water and drain thoroughly. Dry by pressing between sheets of drying-paper, or in a desiccator. Yield 0·5 g. The low solubility of oxamide in most liquids makes recrystallisation very difficult: the product obtained in this preparation when dried is pure, however, and recrystallisation is therefore not necessary. Oxamide has no definite melting-point, as on heating it partly sublimes and partly decomposes.

Succinamide. $NH_2COCH_2 \cdot CH_2CONH_2$. (Method 2(a)). Add 5 ml. (5·8 g.) of dimethyl succinate to a mixture of 50 ml. of water and 25 ml. of concentrated (d, 0·880) aqueous ammonia solution in a 150 ml. conical flask. Cork the flask and shake the contents: the dimethyl succinate rapidly dissolves to give a clear solution. Allow the solution to stand; after about 1 hour the succinamide starts to crystallise, and then continues to separate for some time. Next day, filter off the succinamide at the pump, wash with cold water, and drain. Recrystallise from water, from which the succinamide separates as colourless crystals: the latter soften at 240° and melt at 254–255° with

$$\begin{array}{l} CH_2CONH_2 \\ | \\ CH_2CONH_2 \end{array} = \begin{array}{l} CH_2CO \\ | \quad \quad \rangle NH + NH_3 \\ CH_2CO \end{array}$$

considerable effervescence, as ammonia is liberated and succinimide formed by ring closure. Yield, 2·5 g.

Benzamide. $C_6H_5CONH_2$. (Method 2(b), p. 117.)

Required: Concentrated ammonia, 10 ml.; benzoyl chloride, 2 ml.

Carry out this preparation in precisely the same way as the above preparation of oxamide, using 2 ml. (2·4 g.) of benzoyl chloride instead of the ethyl oxalate, and *observing the same precautions*. Considerably more heat is generated in this reaction; therefore hold the cork very securely in position during the shaking. After vigorous shaking for 15 minutes, no trace of oily benzoyl chloride remains. Filter off the fine flakes of benzamide, wash with cold water, and then recrystallise from hot water: yield, 1·5 g. Colourless crystals, m.p. 130°.

Hydrolysis of Benzamide. When acid amides are hydrolysed, the corresponding acid and ammonia are formed. Consequently the hydrolysis, which is extremely slow with water alone, is hastened con-

$$C_6H_5CO\,NH_2 + H\,OH \rightarrow C_6H_5COOH + NH_3$$

siderably by the addition of either caustic alkalis (which give the alkali salt of the acid and liberate ammonia) or mineral acids (which neutralise the ammonia and liberate the organic acid). Caustic alkalis usually effect the more rapid hydrolysis, and their use is to be preferred.

Place 1 g. of benzamide and 15 ml. of 10% aqueous sodium hydroxide solution in a 100 ml. conical flask fitted with a reflux water-condenser, and boil the mixture gently for 30 minutes, during which period ammonia is freely evolved. Now cool the solution in ice-water, and add concentrated hydrochloric acid until the mixture is strongly acid. Benzoic acid immediately separates. Allow the mixture to stand in the ice-water for a few minutes, and then filter off the benzoic acid at the pump, wash with cold water, and drain. Recrystallise from hot water. The benzoic acid is obtained as colourless crystals, m.p. 121°, almost insoluble in cold water: yield, 0·8 g. (almost theoretical). Confirm the identity of the benzoic acid by the tests given on p. 347.

Mercury Benzamide. ($C_6H_5CONH)_2Hg$. (Semi-micro Scale.)

Acid amides have weakly amphoteric properties, and thus give salts such as $C_6H_5CONH_2,HCl$ with strong acids, and salts of the type $C_6H_5CONHNa$ with strong bases. These compounds have to be prepared at low temperatures to avoid hydrolysis, and are difficult to isolate. The *mercury* derivatives can, however, usually be readily prepared, because mercuric oxide is too feebly basic to cause hydrolysis of the amide, and the heavy mercuric derivatives crystallise well.

Required: Mercuric oxide, 1 g.; benzamide, 0·8 g.; ethanol, 10 ml.

Add 1 g. of *finely powdered* mercuric oxide and 0·8 g. of benzamide to 10 ml. of ethanol, and boil the mixture under a reflux water-condenser for 30 minutes. Now filter the hot solution through a fluted filter-

$$2C_6H_5CONH_2 + HgO = (C_6H_5CONH)_2Hg + H_2O$$

paper to remove unchanged mercuric oxide: if a fine suspension of the oxide passes through with the first portion of the filtrate, return the latter to the filter, when the remainder of the ethanolic solution will pass through as a clear filtrate. Cool the latter in ice-water, where-upon colourless crystals of mercury benzamide will separate. Finally filter the crystals at the pump, wash with a small quantity of ethanol, and then drain and dry. M.p. 222-223°: yield, 0·3 g. The mercury benzamide so obtained may be recrystallised from hot ethanol, but this is not necessary.

Nitriles (or Cyanides).

Aliphatic nitriles (or alkyl cyanides) can be prepared by the following methods:

(1) Dehydration of the corresponding acid amides. This process usually requires phosphorus pentoxide (correctly termed phosphoric anhydride) as a dehydrating agent.

$$CH_3CONH_2 - H_2O \rightarrow CH_3CN$$

Acetamide   Acetonitrile

(2) By the action of potassium cyanide on the corresponding alkyl halide.

$$CH_3 I + K CN \rightarrow CH_3CN + KI$$

NOTE.—*Silver* cyanide in these circumstances gives the isocyanide, CH_3NC.

(3) By the direct addition of hydrogen cyanide to aldehydes and ketones, giving cyanhydrins:

$$CH_3CHO + HCN = CH_3CH(OH)CN$$

Acetaldehyde cyanhydrin (Lactonitrile)

$$(CH_3)_2CO + HCN = (CH_3)_2C(OH)CN$$

Acetone cyanhydrin (α-Hydroxy-isobutyronitrile)

By this method, the nitrile of an α-hydroxy acid is necessarily obtained.

Aromatic nitriles (or aryl cyanides) can be obtained by methods (1) and (3), but not by method (2). In addition, aromatic nitriles can be prepared by two other methods, (a) from the corresponding diazo compound by Sandmeyer's Reaction (p. 189), (b) by fusing the corresponding sulphonic acid (or its salts)

$$C_6H_5 SO_3K + K CN \rightarrow C_6H_5CN + K_2SO_3$$

with potassium cyanide.

Acetonitrile (Methyl Cyanide). CH_3CN. (Method 1.)

Required: Acetamide, 20 g.; phosphorus pentoxide, 35 g.

In view of the great avidity of phosphorus pentoxide for water, the apparatus used in this experiment should be assembled before the pentoxide is weighed out. Fit a 500 ml. bolt-head flask to a water-condenser (see Fig. 59, p. 100). Disconnect the flask, then twist some glazed paper into the form of a cone, and push the narrow end of the latter (slightly opened) into the neck of the flask. Using a rough balance, weigh out on pieces of glazed paper first 20 g. of dry acetamide, and then (as quickly as possible) 35 g. of phosphorus pentoxide. With the aid of a spatula, tip the pentoxide without delay down the paper cylinder into the flask, then add the acetamide similarly, remove the paper, and at once cork the flask and mix the contents by gentle shaking. (Before throwing away the paper used for weighing the pentoxide, wet it thoroughly, otherwise residual pentoxide may cause it to smoulder and possibly inflame.) Now heat the flask by direct application of a Bunsen burner, using however a luminous smoky flame, and applying it uniformly over the bottom of the flask. The acetamide melts and then the mixture starts to effervesce gently. Adjust the heating so that the acetonitrile distils slowly over; use a small conical flask as a receiver, and continue heating until no more distillate can be readily obtained.

The crude acetonitrile contains as impurity chiefly acetic acid, arising from the action of phosphoric acid on the acetamide. Therefore add to the nitrile about half its volume of water, and then add powdered dry potassium carbonate until the well-shaken mixture is saturated. The potassium carbonate neutralises any acetic acid present, and at the same time "salts out" the otherwise water-soluble nitrile as a separate upper layer. Allow to stand for 20 minutes with further occasional shaking. Now decant the mixed liquids into a separating-funnel, run off the lower carbonate layer as completely as possible, and then pour off the acetonitrile into a 25 ml. distilling-flask into which about 3–4 g. of phosphorus pentoxide have been placed *immediately* before. Fit a thermometer and water-condenser to the flask and distil the acetonitrile slowly, collecting the fraction of b.p. 79–82°. Yield 9·5 g. (12 ml.).

Acetonitrile is a colourless liquid, of b.p. 82° and d, 0·790. It has a faint but pleasant odour: if a sample has a faint odour of mice, it indicates the presence of unchanged acetamide.

For reactions of acetonitrile, see p. 360.

Hydrolysis of Acetonitrile. Nitriles, like acid amides, undergo hydrolysis to give the corresponding carboxylic acid and ammonia. Consequently

$$CH_3CN + 2H_2O = CH_3COOH + NH_3$$

the hydrolysis (which is *extremely* slow with hot water alone) is hastened considerably by the presence of caustic alkalis or of mineral acids. The aliphatic nitriles, being soluble in water, are readily hydrolysed by sodium hydroxide or by hydrochloric acid. The aromatic nitriles (such as benzonitrile, C_6H_5CN) are almost insoluble in water and, although usually readily hydrolysed by alkalis, are only very slowly hydrolysed by hydrochloric acid: sulphuric acid (70%), however, causes rapid hydrolysis but there are practical objections to its use (p. 193). Consequently students are recommended to use 10% aqueous sodium hydroxide for hydrolysing nitriles generally, increasing the concentration of the hydroxide to 15 or 20% for very stable nitriles.

Boil a mixture of 5 ml. (4 g.) of acetonitrile and 75 ml. of 10% aqueous sodium hydroxide solution in a 200 ml. flask under a reflux water-condenser for 30 minutes, when hydrolysis will be complete. Detach the condenser and boil the solution in the open flask for a few minutes to drive off all free ammonia. Then cool the solution, and add dilute sulphuric acid (1 volume of concentrated acid: 2 volumes of water) until the solution is distinctly acid to litmus-paper. Fit the flask to a water-condenser by means of a bent delivery (or "knee") tube, and distil off about 10–15 ml. of the liquid. Confirm the presence of acetic acid in this distillate by the tests given on p. 347.

Urea (or Carbamide). $CO(NH_2)_2$.

Urea (the diamide of carbonic acid) can be prepared by the historic method of Wöhler. When an aqueous solution of ammonium cyanate is allowed to stand, the cyanate undergoes molecular rearrangement to urea, and an equilibrium mixture containing about 93% of urea is thus formed. Urea is

$$NH_4CNO \rightleftharpoons NH_2CONH_2$$

less soluble in water than ammonium cyanate; therefore if the solution is evaporated, urea begins to separate, and consequently the ammonium cyanate undergoes steady conversion to urea in order to maintain the above equilibrium. Ultimately, if the solution is evaporated to dryness, the conversion to urea becomes complete.

Ammonium cyanate, because of its instability in solution, is usually prepared

$$(NH_4)_2SO_4 + 2KCNO = 2NH_4CNO + K_2SO_4$$

by mixing aqueous solutions of ammonium sulphate and potassium cyanate. Complete evaporation then gives a mixture of potassium sulphate and urea, from which the urea may be extracted with hot absolute ethanol, in which potassium sulphate is insoluble.

Required: Ammonium sulphate, 10 g.; potassium cyanate, 12 g.

Add 10 g. of ammonium sulphate and 12 g. of potassium cyanate to 75 ml. of water contained in an evaporating-basin. Evaporate the mixed solution to dryness on a water-bath. During the evaporation, a crust of potassium sulphate crystals forms on the surface of the solution, and must be repeatedly broken by stirring with a glass rod, otherwise the evaporation, which even in favourable circumstances takes 4–5 hours, becomes extremely slow: the stirring also prevents any solid material from creeping over the edge of the basin. It is essential that the evaporation be continued until the solid residue is *completely* dry. Now transfer the residue to a 100 ml. flask fitted with a reflux water-condenser, add 40 ml. of absolute ethanol, and boil gently for 5–10 minutes in order to extract the urea. Filter the boiling solution through a small fluted filter-paper, and cool the filtrate in ice-water. Urea separates in colourless crystals, which when filtered at the pump, drained and dried, have m.p. 132°: yield, 4 g. A small second crop may be obtained by evaporating the ethanolic filtrate to about 10 ml., and again cooling in ice-water.

Urea is a monacidic base, and forms a characteristic **nitrate**, $CO(NH_2)_2,HNO_3$, and oxalate, $2CO(NH_2)_2,(COOH)_2,2H_2O$. To prepare the nitrate, dissolve 1 g. of urea in about 5 ml. of water, and add 2 ml. of concentrated nitric acid. White crystals of the nitrate separate almost immediately. Filter at the pump, drain thoroughly, reject the filtrate, and then wash with a few ml. of ethanol and ether in turn.

The oxalate is prepared in a similar way, using a solution of 1·2 g. of oxalic acid in about 15 ml. of water. On stirring the mixed solutions with a rod, the oxalate crystallises out.

The chief disadvantage of the above preparation of urea is the long time required for the complete evaporation of the mixed solutions, particularly as occasional stirring is required throughout this operation. A more rapid evaporation is obtained if ammonium chloride is used instead of the sulphate, as the potassium chloride formed is more soluble in water than potassium sulphate: the chloride is, however, slightly soluble in ethanol, and an impure sample of urea is thus obtained. The following preparation of monophenyl-urea (Method 1) may well be substituted for that of urea, as the reaction involved (molecular rearrangement of the cyanate of an amino compound) is the same, but since the monophenyl-urea is insoluble in cold water, the long evaporation is avoided.

For reactions of urea, see p. 362; for estimation, pp. 458, 520.

When the potassium cyanate used in the above preparation is replaced by potassium thiocyanate (or sulphocyanide), the ammonium thiocyanate formed undergoes partial rearrangement to thiourea (or sulpho-urea). Even above

$$NH_4CNS \rightleftharpoons NH_2CSNH_2$$

100°, however, the conversion into thiourea is incomplete, and the method does not readily give a satisfactory preparation of thiourea.

Monophenylurea. $C_6H_4NH \cdot CO \cdot NH_2$. (First Method.)

Mono-substituted and unsymmetrical di-substituted ureas may be prepared by a modification of Wöhler's urea synthesis, salts of primary or secondary amines being used instead of the ammonium salt for interaction with potassium cyanate. Thus when an aqueous solution containing both aniline hydrochloride and potassium cyanate is heated, aniline cyanate is first formed, and then

$$C_6H_5NH_2,HCl + KCNO = C_6H_5NH_2,HCNO + KCl$$
$$C_6H_5NH_2,HCNO = C_6H_5NHCONH_2$$

by the usual molecular rearrangement is converted into monophenyl-urea.

Required: Aniline hydrochloride, 5 g.; potassium cyanate, 4 g.

Dissolve 5 g. of aniline hydrochloride in 120 ml. of hot water contained in a 200 ml. conical flask and then add 4 g. of potassium cyanate. Heat the solution on a water-bath for 30 minutes, adding about 1–2 g. of animal charcoal towards the end of the heating if a slight turbidity has developed. Now bring the solution quickly to the boil over a gauze, and filter it at the pump, using a Buchner funnel and flask which have been pre-heated by the filtration of some boiling distilled water. The clear filtrate on cooling deposits fine colourless crystals of monophenyl-urea. Filter off at the pump and then recrystallise from hot water: slow cooling of the hot aqueous solution causes the monophenylurea to separate in large crystals. Yield, 3·0–3·5 g.; m.p. 147°.

Monophenyl- and Diphenyl-urea. (Second Method.)

These substances, having the formula $C_6H_5NHCONH_2$ and $OC(NHC_6H_5)_2$ respectively, are both formed when an aqueous solution of urea and aniline hydrochloride is heated. Their subsequent separation is based on the fact that diphenylurea is insoluble in boiling water, whereas monophenylurea is readily soluble. The formation of these compounds can be explained as follows. When urea is dissolved in water, a small proportion of it undergoes molecular rearrangement back to ammonium cyanate, an equilibrium thus being formed.

$$NH_2CONH_2 \rightleftharpoons NH_4CNO$$

The ammonium cyanate then reacts with the aniline hydrochloride giving aniline cyanate which, as in the previous preparation, gives in turn monophenyl-urea.

$$NH_4CNO + C_6H_5NH_2,HCl = NH_4Cl + C_6H_5NH_2,HCNO$$
$$C_6H_5NH_2,HCNO = C_6H_5NHCONH_2$$

A portion of the monophenylurea then reacts with the aniline (formed by the hydrolysis of the aniline hydrochloride or cyanate) to give diphenyl-urea and ammonia, a reaction which probably proceeds through the

$$C_6H_5NH·CO·NH_2 + H_2NC_6H_5 = C_6H_5NH·CO·NHC_6H_5 + NH_3$$

intermediate formation of an unstable addition product of the formula $C_6H_5NHC(OH)(NH_2)NHC_6H_5$. The relative amounts of the monophenyl- and the diphenylurea formed will therefore depend chiefly on the time during which the aqueous solution is heated.

Required: Aniline hydrochloride, 12 g.; urea, 6 g.

Dissolve 12 g. of aniline hydrochloride and 6 g. of urea in 50 ml. of warm water, and then filter the solution through a fluted filter to remove any suspended impurities which may have been introduced with the aniline hydrochloride. Transfer the clear filtrate to a 200 ml. conical flask, fit the latter with a reflux water-condenser, and boil the solution *gently* over a gauze for about 1½ hours. Crystals of diphenylurea usually start to separate after about 30–40 minutes' boiling. Occasionally however, the solution becomes supersaturated with the diphenyl-urea and therefore remains clear: in this case, if the solution is vigorously shaken after about 40 minutes' heating, a sudden separation of the crystalline diphenyl compound will usually occur. The further deposition of the crystals during the remainder of the heating may cause the solution to "bump": if this bumping becomes too vigorous, remove the flame for a few minutes to allow the solution to cool slightly and thus to ensure it is not superheated, then add some fragments of unglazed porcelain down the condenser, and continue the heating.

When the $1\frac{1}{2}$ hours' boiling is complete, preheat a Buchner funnel and flask by pouring some boiling water through the funnel with the filter-paper already in position, and then quickly filter the boiling solution. Transfer the filtrate to a beaker to cool, and then wash the insoluble residue of diphenylurea on the filter twice with hot water, and drain thoroughly. Cool the filtrate in ice-water; the monophenylurea separates as colourless needles. Filter at the pump and drain well. Recrystallise the crude product from boiling water, as in the previous preparation. Yield of monophenylurea, 2·5–3 g.; m.p. 147°.

The insoluble residue of diphenylurea from the original filtration is chemically almost pure. It may be recrystallised from hot rectified spirit or ethanol, a process which will be necessary if the material contains fragments of porcelain. When using either of these solvents, however, the hot solution should be filtered* at the pump using a *small* Buchner funnel and flask which again have been preheated by the filtration of some of the hot solvent, as the solution when cooled rapidly deposits the diphenylurea. *Sym*-Diphenylurea (or carbanilide) is thus obtained as fine colourless crystals, m.p. 237°; yield, 1–1·5 g.

Benzylthiouronium Chloride.

Thiourea, unlike urea, readily reacts in the tautomeric form (I) in the presence of suitable reagents, particularly alkyl halides: thus benzyl chloride reacts with

$$C_6H_5CH_2Cl + HS\cdot C{\overset{NH_2}{\underset{NH}{\Big\langle}}} \longrightarrow C_6H_5CH_2S\cdot C{\overset{NH_2}{\underset{NH_2}{\Big\langle}}} \overset{+}{} \overline{Cl}$$

(I)   (II)

thiourea in ethanolic solution to give benzylthiouronium chloride (II), sometimes known as S-benzylthiouronium chloride, a salt which is stabilised by resonance. Such salts on acid hydrolysis give the corresponding thiols, *e.g.*, $C_6H_5CH_2SH$, which can thus be readily prepared from the halides. Furthermore, the salt (II) is widely employed to identify carboxylic and other acids as their crystalline benzylthiouronium salts (pp. 349–353).

* Alternatively a preheated conical funnel and fluted filter may be used, and the filtrate collected directly in a conical flask.

Required: Benzyl chloride, 8·3 g.; thiourea, 5 g.

Add in turn benzyl chloride (8·3 g., 8·0 ml.) and powdered thiourea (5 gm.) to 10 ml. of 95 % ethanol in a 100 ml. flask fitted with a reflux condenser. Warm the mixture on the water-bath with gentle shaking until the reaction occurs and the effervescence subsides; then boil the mixture under reflux for 30 minutes. Cool the clear solution in ice-water, filter off the crystalline deposit of the benzylthiouronium chloride at the pump, wash it with ice-cold ethyl acetate, and dry in a desiccator. Yield, 11–12 g., m.p. 170–174°. The white product is sufficiently pure for use as a reagent. It is very soluble in cold water and ethanol, but can be recrystallised by adding ethanol *dropwise* to a boiling suspension in ethyl acetate or acetone until a clear solution is just obtained, and then rapidly cooling.

Hofmann's Primary Amine Synthesis.

The preparation of pure primary amines by the interaction of alkyl halides and ammonia is very difficult, because the primary amine which is formed reacts with unchanged alkyl halide to give the secondary amine: the latter

$$C_2H_5I + HNH_2 \rightarrow C_2H_5NH_2 + HI$$

$$C_2H_5I + HNC_2H_5 \rightarrow (C_2H_5)_2NH + HI$$

$$C_2H_5I + HN(C_2H_5)_2 \rightarrow (C_2H_5)_3N + HI$$

$$C_2H_5I + (C_2H_5)_3N \rightarrow (C_2H_5)_4NI$$

similarly gives the tertiary amine, which unites with unchanged alkyl halide to give the quaternary ammonium halide. The preparation of pure primary amines is carried out therefore by special methods, such as the reduction of oximes (p. 93) and of nitro-compounds (pp. 132, 161). A third method due to Hofmann is based on the action of bromine on acid amides, with subsequent alkaline hydrolysis. The reactions involved probably proceed as follows. Acetamide when treated with bromine forms acetbromoamide, $CH_3CONHBr$, which in NaOH solution gives the ionised sodium acetbromoamide, $CH_3CON\bar{N}Br$ + $\overset{+}{Na}$. The anion loses $\bar{Br}$ with simultaneous migration of the CH_3 group to the nitrogen, giving methyl isocyanate, which

$$\overset{CH_3}{\underset{\underset{Br}{\overset{|}{N}}}{\diagdown}}C{=}O \rightarrow CH_3\bar{N}\overset{+}{\underset{}{C}}{=}O \rightarrow CH_3N{=}C{=}O \rightarrow CH_3NH_2$$

undergoes hydrolysis to methylamine.

A certain amount of hydrolysis of the original acetamide to acid and ammonia always occurs, and the final amine always contains traces of ammonia. This is separated by extracting the mixed anhydrous hydrochlorides with absolute ethanol, which dissolves the amine hydrochloride but not the ammonium chloride: filtration of the hot ethanolic extract removes the ammonium chloride, whilst the amine hydrochloride crystallises readily from the filtrate on cooling.

Hofmann's amine synthesis can be applied to both aliphatic and aromatic carboxylic acid amides, benzamide, $C_6H_5CONH_2$, thus giving aniline, $C_6H_5NH_2$.

METHYLAMINE HYDROCHLORIDE. CH_3NH_2,HCl.

Required: Acetamide, 12 g.; bromine, 10·8 ml.; sodium hydroxide, 36 g.

Dissolve 36 g. of sodium hydroxide in 160 ml. of water contained in a 500 ml. conical flask, and chill the stirred solution to 0–5° in ice-water. Now add 10·8 ml. (32·4 g.) of bromine slowly to the stirred solution (*exercise care in manipulating liquid bromine!*): during this addition the temperature rises slightly, and it should again be reduced to 0–5°. Add a solution of 12 g. of acetamide in 20 ml. of water, in small portions, to the stirred hypobromite solution so that the temperature of the mixture does not exceed 20°: the sodium acet-bromoamide is thus obtained in the alkaline solution. Now remove the flask from the ice-water, and set it aside at room temperature for 30 minutes.

Meanwhile assemble the apparatus shown in Fig. 62, or that in Fig. 23(D), p. 45, having a distilling-flask of at least 500 ml. capacity in either case. If an ordinary condenser **C** (Fig. 62) is employed, fit the lower end of the condenser by means of a short piece of rubber tubing to a small inverted funnel. Arrange the latter so that its lip is just below the surface of 25 ml. of concentrated hydrochloric acid diluted with 75 ml. of water contained in a 250 ml. beaker **B**: the hydrochloric acid is thereby prevented from being sucked back into the condenser during the subsequent distillation. If the ground-glass apparatus shown in Fig. 23(D) is used, the inverted funnel can be similarly attached to the end of the adaptor.

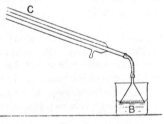

FIG. 62.

Transfer the solution into the flask, add some unglazed porcelain, and support the flask over an asbestos-covered gauze. Heat the solution cautiously with a Bunsen flame so that the temperature rises *slowly*. When a brisk effervescence occurs (at about 70–80°), remove the flame until the reaction subsides. Methylamine is evolved, and is absorbed by the hydrochloric acid in the beaker **B**. Then distil the solution in the flask carefully, keeping it boiling smoothly and uniformly so that no methylamine vapour escapes absorption in the hydrochloric acid, and at the same time so that the acid shows no marked tendency to rise in the funnel.

After boiling for 30 minutes, the distillation of the amine may be considered complete. Concentrate the hydrochloric acid solution by placing it in a 250 ml. distilling-flask connected with a water-condenser, and distilling carefully until about 30 ml. remain. Then transfer this residual solution to a small evaporating-basin, and evaporate to dryness on a boiling water-bath. (Yield of crude dry material, about 11 g.) Rapidly break up the *dry* solid (which consists of methylamine hydrochloride together with a small amount of ammonium chloride), and transfer it without delay to a 150 ml. round-bottomed flask fitted with a reflux water-condenser. Add about 60–70 ml. of *absolute* ethanol (in which ammonium chloride is insoluble), and boil the mixture for 5 minutes. Then pour the hot supernatant liquid quickly through a small fluted filter-paper into a conical flask. Again extract the undissolved residue with a further 20 ml. of absolute ethanol, and cool the united ethanolic filtrates: colourless crystals of methylamine hydrochloride separate out. Filter off the crystals at the pump, and, since they are deliquescent, transfer them *quickly* to a weighed bottle or specimen-tube: the methylamine hydrochloride may be finally dried by placing the tube in a desiccator. The yield of the recrystallised material should be about 5 g.; if the ethanolic filtrate from this first crop is concentrated by distillation to about 20 ml. and then cooled, a second crop of methylamine hydrochloride, weighing about 3 g., can be similarly isolated.

CAUTION.—If the ethanol used to extract the methylamine hydrochloride is not "absolute," *i.e.*, if it contains traces of water, considerably less than the above suggested quantity will be required for the extraction, because the solubility of the hydrochloride will be markedly increased by the water present. The recrystallised material will now, however, contain traces of ammonium chloride.

Glycine (Amino-acetic Acid). $NH_2 \cdot CH_2COOH$.

Glycine is the simplest member of a large and very important class of compounds, the α-amino-carboxylic acids. There are many different methods available for the synthesis of amino-acids, but glycine can be readily prepared by the action of an excess of ammonia on chloroacetic acid:

$$ClCH_2COOH + 2NH_3 = NH_2 \cdot CH_2COOH + NH_4Cl$$

(Note that although glycine is conveniently written as above, it is actually a

$zwitter$-ion, $\overset{+}{N}H_3{\cdot}CH_2\overset{-}{COO}$: consequently although the ammonium salt of glycine may be initially formed in the above reaction, it readily dissociates during the subsequent concentration of the solution to give the free glycine).

The glycine so formed has to be separated from the ammonium chloride, and the salt-like nature of the zwitterion precludes the use of most organic solvents for this purpose. The mixture can be treated with copper hydroxide (cf. p. 382) and the glycine precipitated as the insoluble non-ionic cupric complex (annexed formula): the latter can then be filtered off, washed and decomposed in aqueous suspension by hydrogen sulphide. The following more convenient method is based on the fact that glycine is much less soluble than ammonium chloride in methanol.

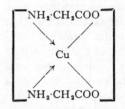

Note that the amino-acids, because of their salt-like nature, usually decompose on heating, and therefore seldom have sharp melting-points. Furthermore, all naturally occurring amino-acids are α-amino-acids, and consequently, with the exception of glycine, can exist in optically active forms.

Required: Chloroacetic acid, 15 g.; ammonia solution (d, 0·880), 300 ml.

Add 15 g. of chloroacetic acid to 300 ml. of aqueous ammonia solution (d, 0·880) contained in a 750 ml. conical flask. (The manipulation of the concentrated ammonia should preferably be carried out in a fume-cupboard, and great care taken to avoid ammonia fumes.) Cork the flask *loosely* and set aside overnight at room temperature. Now concentrate the solution to about 30 ml. by distillation under reduced pressure. For this purpose,* place the solution in a suitable distilling-flask with some fragments of unglazed porcelain, fit a capillary tube to the neck of the flask, and connect the flask through a water-condenser and receiver to a water-pump: then heat the flask carefully on a water-bath. Make the concentrated solution up to 40 ml. by the addition of water, filter, and then add 250 ml. of methanol. Cool the solution in ice-water, stir well, and set aside for *ca.* 1 hour, when the precipitation of the glycine will be complete.

Filter off the glycine through a Buchner funnel, and then transfer it to a beaker, add 80 ml. of methanol and stir the mixture well. Then filter again, wash the glycine on the filter with a small quantity of ether, drain and dry.

The glycine so obtained is almost pure. To remove traces of ammonium chloride, however, dissolve the glycine in 30 ml. of water, and then reprecipitate by the addition of 200 ml. of methanol. Cool the product in ice-water with stirring, and then

* Cf. p. 28.

filter again through a Buchner funnel. The glycine is obtained as a fine colourless crystalline powder, which has m.p. 230–231° (with decomposition) if it is placed in a bath preheated to *ca.* 210° and the temperature then increased fairly rapidly. Yield, 7·5–8·0 g.

Aliphatic Nitro-compounds.

Since aliphatic hydrocarbons (unlike aromatic hydrocarbons, p. 155) can be directly nitrated only under very special conditions, indirect methods are usually employed for the preparation of compounds such as nitroethane, $C_2H_5NO_2$. When ethyl iodide is heated with silver nitrite, two isomeric compounds are formed, and can be easily separated by fractional distillation. The first is the true ester, ethyl nitrite, C_2H_5ONO, of b.p. 17°: its identity is shown by the action of hot sodium hydroxide solution, which hydrolyses it, giving ethanol and

$$C_2H_5ONO + NaOH \rightarrow C_2H_5OH + NaNO_2$$

sodium nitrite. The second compound is nitroethane, $C_2H_5NO_2$, of b.p. 114°: its identity is clearly shown by the action of reducing agents, which convert it into ethylamine, $C_2H_5NH_2$, thus proving the presence of a nitrogen-carbon

$$C_2H_5NO_2 + 6H = C_2H_5NH_2 + 2H_2O$$

link in the nitro-ethane. This formation of the isomeric nitrite ester and nitro-paraffin is characteristic of the reaction of the lower alkyl halides with silver nitrite.

Nitromethane, CH_3NO_2, the first member of the homologous series, can, however, be readily prepared by a special reaction.* When equimolecular amounts of sodium nitrite and sodium monochloroacetate are heated together in aqueous solution, the chlorine in the monochloroacetate is replaced by the nitro group, and the sodium nitroacetate thus formed undergoes hydrolysis followed by decarboxylation:

$$NaNO_2 + ClCH_2COONa = NaCl + NO_2CH_2COONa$$
$$2NO_2CH_2COONa + H_2O = 2NO_2CH_3 + Na_2CO_3 + CO_2$$

The characteristic property of aliphatic nitro-compounds of the type RCH_2NO_2 and R_2CHNO_2 is that they are *pseudo-acids*, *i.e.*, whereas they are neutral in the normal form (A), they are able by tautomeric change under the influence of alkali to give the acidic hydroxy form (B) which thus in turn gives the sodium salt (C). When this sodium salt is treated with one equivalent of hydrochloric acid, the *acid* form (B) is at once regenerated, and then more slowly reverts to the more stable normal form (A).

$$CH_3CH_2 \cdot N{\overset{O}{\underset{O}{\diagup}}} \underset{\longleftarrow}{\overset{\longrightarrow}{}} CH_3CH{:}N{\overset{OH}{\underset{O}{\diagup}}} \underset{HCl}{\overset{NaOH}{\longrightarrow}} CH_3CH{:}N{\overset{ONa}{\underset{O}{\diagup}}}$$

(A)   (B)   (C)

* This reaction is general for α-chloro-carboxylic acids: of these, however only monochloroacetic acid is readily and cheaply obtainable, and it also gives the highest yield of the nitrohydrocarbon.

Nitromethane. CH_3NO_2.

Required: Monochloroacetic acid, 50 g.; anhydrous sodium carbonate, 30 g.; sodium nitrite, 36·5 g.

Dissolve 50 g. of monochloroacetic acid in 100 ml. of water contained in a 500 ml. round-bottomed bolt-head flask, and then neutralise the solution by the cautious addition of 30 g. of *finely powdered* anhydrous sodium carbonate. For this purpose, add the sodium carbonate in small quantities (about 1 g.) at a time, preferably with the aid of a spatula, and shake the solution gently around after each addition to facilitate the evolution of carbon dioxide: a clear solution is thus maintained throughout, whereas the rapid addition of large quantities of the carbonate produces lumps of material which are subsequently difficult to dissolve. Now dissolve 36·5 g. of sodium nitrite in 50 ml. of water with gentle heating, cool the solution thoroughly in ice-water, and then add it with shaking to that of the sodium mono-chloroacetate. Add some fragments of unglazed porcelain, and then fit the flask with a delivery-tube of moderately wide bore connected in turn to a water-condenser (as in Fig. 59, p. 100, or, better, in Fig. 23(D), p. 45). Support the flask over a gauze, and then heat it *gently* with a small Bunsen flame. The solution slowly becomes yellow in colour, then greenish and finally a yellowish-brown, when a vigorous effervescence starts: *at once* remove the Bunsen flame, and allow the reaction to proceed spontaneously, carbon dioxide being evolved and the solution boiling vigorously. When the reaction subsides, replace the Bunsen flame and maintain a steady boiling. Nitromethane distils over in the steam and separates as a colourless oil at the bottom of the distillate: since nitromethane is slightly soluble in water, stop the distillation as soon as drops of nitromethane can no longer be detected in the distillate leaving the condenser. Transfer the distillate to a separating-funnel, and carefully run off the lower layer of nitromethane and then dry it over anhydrous sodium sulphate for 30 minutes. Filter the dry nitromethane (preferably through a *small* dry Buchner funnel), transfer it to a 30 ml. distilling-flask fitted with a water-condenser, and then slowly distil, collecting the fraction of b.p. 100–102°.

In view of the small volume of nitromethane to be manipulated, the crude nitromethane may be extracted from the aqueous distillate with ether (30–40 ml.). Dry the ethereal extract over sodium sulphate, filter through a fluted filter-paper, and then distil off the ether on a water-bath with the usual precautions (Fig. 64, p. 163; Fig. 23(E), p. 45): finally distil the residual nitromethane.

Nitromethane is obtained as a colourless liquid, of b.p. 101°
and d, 1·16: yield, 10 g.

Reactions of Nitromethane. (1) Nitromethane, although only
slightly soluble in cold water, is freely soluble in sodium hydroxide
solution, the alkaline solution slowly becoming yellow in colour.

(2) Place a few drops of nitromethane in a test-tube, add about
3 times as much concentrated hydrochloric acid, and then a piece of
granulated tin. The tin dissolves in the acid and the nascent hydrogen
produced reduces the nitromethane to monomethylamine:

$$CH_3NO_2 + 6H = CH_3NH_2 + 2H_2O$$

Moderate the reaction if necessary by dipping the tube in cold water.
When the tin has completely dissolved, cool the solution thoroughly, and
make alkaline by the addition of concentrated (30%) sodium hydroxide
solution. A strong ammoniacal smell of monomethylamine is produced, and white fumes form when the open end of the tube is placed
near an open bottle of concentrated hydrochloric acid. This formation
of methylamine proves that in the original nitromethane the nitrogen
atom is joined directly to the carbon.

(3) Dissolve 0·5 g. of sodium in 10 ml. of anhydrous methanol
contained in a small conical flask: check the reaction at first by cooling
the flask in water to prevent evaporation of the methanol, but finally
warm the mixture gently to hasten the dissolution of the last traces
of sodium. Cool this solution of sodium methoxide, and then add
1 ml. of nitromethane, and mix thoroughly. A gelatinous precipitate
of sodium nitromethane rapidly appears. Cool the mixture in ice-
water for 5 minutes, and then filter off the sodium derivative at the
pump, using a *small* dry Buchner funnel; drain quickly, and then
wash with a *few drops* of methanol, to remove traces of excess sodium
methoxide, again draining the white sodium derivative as quickly as
possible. Perform the following tests with this sodium derivative
whilst it is still damp with methanol:

(*a*) Dissolve a small portion of the sodium derivative in a few ml. of
water in a test-tube, and add one drop of ferric chloride solution. A
deep red coloration is produced, but rapidly disappears as the iron is
precipitated as ferric hydroxide. The sodium derivative (A) of the
nitromethane when dissolved in water undergoes partial hydrolysis,

$$CH_2{:}N{\begin{matrix}ONa\\O\end{matrix}} + HOH \rightleftharpoons CH_2{:}N{\begin{matrix}OH\\O\end{matrix}} + NaOH$$

(A)   (B)

giving sodium hydroxide and the free acid (B): the latter, like many
hydroxy compounds (compare phenols, p. 338), gives a marked coloration with ferric chloride.

(*b*) Dissolve the remainder of the sodium derivative in about 50 ml.

of cold water in a clean beaker. Add a drop of phenolphthalein solution. A deep pink coloration is produced, owing to the free sodium hydroxide formed in the above hydrolysis. Now by means of a small pipette or a fine glass tube, add *very* dilute sulphuric acid *drop by drop* until the pink coloration is *just* discharged. In a few seconds the pink coloration becomes again perceptible, and rapidly deepens in tint. The sulphuric acid may again be added, and the process repeated several times.

The addition of the sulphuric acid first neutralises the sodium hydroxide, and then gives a weakly acidic and therefore colourless solution. The sodium derivative (A) then undergoes further partial hydrolysis in order to re-establish the original equilibrium, and the sodium hydroxide thus formed again produces the pink coloration, which increases in depth as the hydrolysis proceeds.

When the above tests have been completed, wash thoroughly with water all apparatus contaminated with the sodium derivative, since the latter, if allowed to dry, becomes very explosive.

(4) Dissolve a few drops of nitromethane in 10% sodium hydroxide solution. Add a few crystals of sodium nitrite and shake. Now add dilute sulphuric acid drop by drop. A brownish-red coloration develops, but fades again when an excess of acid is added. The sulphuric acid has thus liberated nitrous acid, which has in turn reacted with the nitromethane to give a *nitrolic acid*, the sodium salt of which is

$$CH_3NO_2 + ONOH = CH(NO_2){:}NOH + H_2O$$

reddish-brown in colour, probably owing to mesomeric ions of the type:

$$\overset{O}{O{\leftarrow}\ddot{N}{\cdot}CH{:}N{\cdot}\overset{}{O}} \longleftrightarrow \overset{O^-}{O{\leftarrow}\dot{N}{:}CH{\cdot}N{:}O}$$

An excess of sulphuric acid then converts the coloured sodium salt back to the almost colourless nitrolic acid.

NOTE.—A secondary nitro-paraffin, such as 2-nitropropane, $(CH_3)_2CHNO_2$, when similarly treated gives a *pseudo-nitrol*, which dissolves in chloroform,

$$(CH_3)_2CHNO_2 + HONO = (CH_3)_2C(NO)NO_2 + H_2O$$

producing a blue solution. A tertiary nitro-paraffin, such as trimethylnitromethane, $(CH_3)_3CNO_2$, gives no reaction with nitrous acid.

The Sugars (or Carbohydrates).

The only sugars which the student is likely to meet in the course of ordinary laboratory work are the two isomeric *monosaccharides* glucose (sometimes called dextrose or grape sugar) and fructose (laevulose or fruit sugar) of formula $C_6H_{12}O_6$, and the three isomeric *disaccharides* sucrose (cane sugar), lactose (milk sugar) and maltose (malt sugar) of formula $C_{12}H_{22}O_{11}$. It has been established that sugars possess ring structures (I, II, IV), but nevertheless under certain conditions the ring opens out to give a straight chain compound which may possess either a free – CHO group (aldoses, such as glucose, III) or a free >CO group (ketoses, such as fructose, V). Many of the characteristic reactions of sugars, particularly those of reduction and of osazone formation, are due to these groups.

$$
\begin{array}{cccccc}
& \underset{\displaystyle 1 \quad C}{\overset{\displaystyle H \quad OH}{\diagdown\diagup}} & \underset{\displaystyle C}{\overset{\displaystyle HO \quad H}{\diagdown\diagup}} & 1 \quad CHO & \underset{\displaystyle 1 \ HO \quad CH_2OH}{\overset{}{\diagdown\diagup}} & 1 \quad CH_2OH \\
\end{array}
$$

	α-Glucose	β-Glucose	Glucose	β-Fructose	Fructose
1	C — ⌐	C — ⌐	CHO	HO CH₂OH	CH₂OH
2	HCOH	HCOH	HCOH	C — ⌐	CO
3	HOCH	HOCH	HOCH	HOCH	HOCH
4	HCOH O	HCOH O	HCOH	HCOH O	HCOH
5	HC — ⌐	HC — ⌐	HCOH	HCOH	HCOH
6	CH₂OH	CH₂OH	CH₂OH	CH₂—	CH₂OH
	(I)*	(II)*	(III)	(IV)*	(V)

It will be seen that the ring form of glucose can exist in two isomeric forms α and β, which differ only with regard to the disposition of the H and the OH groups around carbon atom 1, since if the ring is regarded (for simplicity) as being in the plane of the paper, α-glucose (I) may have this H atom above, and the OH group below, the plane of the paper, whilst β-glucose (II) will have the H atom below, and the OH group above this plane. These ring structures for α and β-glucose can alternatively be represented by (VI) and (VII). α and

(VI)*   (VII)*

β-glucose, when dissolved in water, have different optical rotatory powers (although they are not of course optical enantiomorphs, as the above formulae show): the optical rotation of each solution changes slowly on standing, and the final value attained is identical in each case, *i.e.*. a mixture of both forms in equilibrium is ultimately obtained from either α or β-glucose. The difference between α- and β-glucose disappears in the straight chain form (III), and since it is in this form that glucose often appears to react, this difference between the α and β forms can often be ignored in practical work. Fructose exists similarly in two forms, determined by the disposition of the OH and

* Structures (I), (II) and (IV) are convenient projection formulæ; formulæ such as (IV) and (VII) are more realistic representations, but even these are only approximations as the rings are not flat.

the CH_2OH groups around carbon atom 2, this difference again disappearing in the straight chain form (V). It will be noted that carbon atom 1 in glucose is concerned with the formation of the ring, and that when the latter opens out, the free aldehyde group appears at this point. The grouping on carbon atom 1 may conveniently be called the "potential aldehyde group," and that on carbon atom 2 in the fructose molecule similarly the "potential ketone group."

For an elementary study of the sugars, it is not suggested that the student should remember the structure of the disaccharides: their chief and characteristic reactions will, however, be readily understood if the following facts are borne in mind.

Sucrose on hydrolysis with dilute acids, or with the enzyme *invertase* (or "*sucrase*," p. 514,) gives rise to one molecule of glucose and one molecule of fructose:

$$C_{12}H_{22}O_{11} + H_2O = C_6H_{12}O_6 + C_6H_{12}O_6$$
$$\text{sucrose} \qquad\qquad \text{glucose} \quad \text{fructose}$$

In the sucrose molecule, union takes place through carbon atom 1 of the glucose molecule and carbon atom 2 of the fructose molecule: hence sucrose is a non-reducing sugar, since neither the potential aldehyde nor the potential ketone grouping is now available for reaction. If glucose is represented as G-r, where r is the potential aldehyde group, and fructose as F-r, where r is the potential ketone group, then the sucrose molecule may be conveniently remembered as G-r-r-F, indicating clearly that both the reducing groups are concerned in the union of the two monosaccharide residues.

Maltose on hydrolysis with dilute acids or with the enzyme *maltase* gives rise to two molecules of glucose: only one of the potential aldehyde groups is concerned in the union of the glucose molecules, and the structure of maltose may therefore be represented as G-r-G-r. Maltose has thus one free potential aldehyde group, and is therefore a reducing sugar, differing in this respect from sucrose.

Lactose on hydrolysis gives glucose and an isomeric monosaccharide galactose, which may be given the symbol Ga-r. The lactose molecule may be represented as Ga-r-G-r, and it has therefore also a free potential aldehyde group and is a reducing sugar like maltose.

A very important method of identifying reducing sugars is by means of the *osazones* which they form with phenylhydrazine, $C_6H_5NHNH_2$. These osazones are bright yellow compounds, which exhibit characteristic crystalline forms under the microscope. To explain the formation of the osazones of glucose and fructose, the latter sugars are represented for simplicity by the straight chain formulae (III) and (V) respectively. When glucose is treated with an excess of phenylhydrazine (preferably in the presence of acetic acid), a soluble *phenylhydrazone* (IIIA) is first formed by the condensation of one molecule of phenylhydrazine with the – CHO group of the glucose. This is strictly analogous to the formation of benzaldehyde phenylhydrazone from benzaldehyde (p. 229).

$$\begin{array}{llll}
\text{(1) CHO} + \text{H}_2\text{NNHC}_6\text{H}_5 & \text{CH:NNHC}_6\text{H}_5 & \text{CH:NNHC}_6\text{H}_5 & \text{CH:NNHC}_6\text{H}_5 \\
| & | & | & | \\
\text{(2)CHOH} & \text{CHOH} & \text{CO} + \text{H}_2\text{NNHC}_6\text{H}_5 & \text{C:NNHC}_6\text{H}_5 \\
| & | \quad -2\text{H} & | & | \\
\text{(CHOH)}_3 \longrightarrow & \text{(CHOH)}_3 \longrightarrow & \text{(CHOH)}_3 \longrightarrow & \text{(CHOH)}_3 \\
| & | & | & | \\
\text{CH}_2\text{OH} & \text{CH}_2\text{OH} & \text{CH}_2\text{OH} & \text{CH}_2\text{OH} \\
\text{(III)} & \text{(IIIA)} & \text{(IIIB)} & \text{(IIIC)}
\end{array}$$

Now phenylhydrazine will readily act as an oxidising agent, since it can accept two hydrogen atoms from another compound, being itself reduced to aniline and ammonia, $\text{C}_6\text{H}_5\text{NHNH}_2 + 2\text{H} = \text{C}_6\text{H}_5\text{NH}_2 + \text{NH}_3$. The second molecule of phenylhydrazine therefore oxidises the secondary alcohol group (>CHOH) of carbon atom (2) to a ketone (>C:O) group by removal of two hydrogen atoms, giving the compound (IIIB). The free >C:O group of the latter compound now condenses with a third molecule of phenylhydrazine, giving the osazone of glucose, or *phenyl-glucosazone* (IIIC).

Fructose (V) under similar conditions gives first the *phenylhydrazone* (VA) by the direct condensation of the >C:O group of carbon atom 2 with one molecule of phenylhydrazine. The second molecule of phenylhydrazine then oxidises the primary alcohol group of carbon atom 1 to the -CHO group by removal of two atoms of hydrogen, which as before serve to reduce the phenylhydrazine to aniline and ammonia. The compound (VB) which is thus produced then undergoes direct condensation with the third molecule of phenylhydrazine, giving the osazone of fructose, or *fructosazone* (VC).

Now since the configuration of carbon atoms 3, 4 and 5 of glucose and fructose are identical, it follows that glucosazone and fructosazone are identical in all respects. The osazone is formed however more rapidly from fructose than from glucose, and this difference in rate of formation may be used to distinguish the two sugars, provided the reactions are carried out under strictly parallel conditions (pp. 138, 338).

$$\begin{array}{llll}
1 \; \text{CH}_2\text{OH} & \text{CH}_2\text{OH} & \text{CHO} + \text{H}_2\text{NNHC}_6\text{H}_5 & \text{CH:NNHC}_6\text{H}_5 \\
| & | & | & | \\
2 \; \text{CO} + \text{H}_2\text{NNHC}_6\text{H}_5 & \text{C:NNHC}_6\text{H}_5 & \text{C:NNHC}_6\text{H}_5 & \text{C:NNHC}_6\text{H}_5 \\
| & | \quad -2\text{H} & | & | \\
\text{(CHOH)}_3 \longrightarrow & \text{(CHOH)}_3 \longrightarrow & \text{(CHOH)}_3 \longrightarrow & \text{(CHOH)}_3 \\
| & | & | & | \\
\text{CH}_2\text{OH} & \text{CH}_2\text{OH} & \text{CH}_2\text{OH} & \text{CH}_2\text{OH} \\
\text{(V)} & \text{(VA)} & \text{(VB)} & \text{(VC)}
\end{array}$$

Both maltose and lactose, being reducing sugars, give osazones which differ from one another and from glucosazone in crystalline form. Sucrose (G-r-r-F), having no potential aldehyde or ketone grouping, does not form an osazone.

Glucosazone (Phenyl-glucosazone). $\text{C}_6\text{H}_{10}\text{O}_4(\text{N·NHC}_6\text{H}_5)_2$.

In the preparation of osazones (as in the preparation of phenylhydrazones,

p. 229) the free phenylhydrazine base may be used directly. Condensation occurs more readily and a cleaner product is obtained, however, if the reaction is carried out in weakly acidic solution—preferably at about pH 5 (see footnote, p. 509). The phenylhydrazine base should therefore always be dissolved in acetic acid for this purpose.

Phenylhydrazine is, however, frequently supplied in the form of its hydrochloride or sulphate, since these salts on exposure to light darken less rapidly than the free base. If these salts are used, however, osazone formation is unsatisfactory, partly because the mineral acid formed by hydrolysis of

$$C_6H_5NHNH_2,HCl \rightleftharpoons C_6H_5NHNH_2 + HCl$$

the salt hydrolyses the glucosazone to glucosone, $CHO \cdot CO \cdot (CHOH)_3CH_2OH$. Therefore if these salts are used, they should be mixed in solution with a small excess of sodium acetate, whereby the pH of the solution is raised to approximately the required value. On the other hand, care should be taken not to add too large an excess of sodium acetate, which by hydrolysis would make the solution too alkaline: this can if necessary be corrected by the addition of a few drops of acetic acid.

Required: Glucose, 1 g.; acetic acid, 2 ml.; phenylhydrazine, 2 ml.

Dissolve 1 g. of glucose (or fructose) in 5 ml. of water in a boiling-tube. In another tube dissolve 2 ml. of glacial acetic acid in 5 ml. of water, add 2 ml. of phenylhydrazine,* and shake until a solution of phenylhydrazine acetate is obtained. Add this solution (which is often opalescent) to the sugar solution, stir gently with a glass rod, and then place the tube in a boiling water-bath. The yellow osazone usually begins to crystallise out after about 15 minutes' heating. Continue the heating (with occasional stirring) for a total period of 45 minutes, then remove the tube and cool by immersion in cold water. Filter the product through a Buchner funnel, and wash it first with water and then with a few ml. of methylated spirit, and drain thoroughly. Yield of osazone from glucose, 1·5 g.† If fructose is used, only 30 minutes' heating is necessary, and the yield of osazone is 1·8 g., *i.e.*, almost theoretical.

Glucosazone is only slightly soluble in boiling ethanol or methylated spirit: for recrystallisation therefore it is sufficient to place about 0·5 g. of the crude material in a 150 ml. flask fitted

---

* If only the hydrochloride or sulphate of the base is available, dissolve 3 g. of crystalline sodium acetate (or 2 g. of the anhydrous acetate) in 12 ml. of water, add 3 g. of the phenylhydrazine salt, warm *gently* until dissolved, filter the solution if necessary, and then add to the sugar solution.

† If the reaction mixture is heated for 1½ hours, this yield is slightly increased. The increase is too small, however, to warrant the extra time expended.

PREPARATIONS

with a reflux condenser, then to add about 75 ml. of methylated spirit, and boil gently. The osazone dissolves slowly; filter the hot solution through a fluted filter-paper (or a preheated Buchner funnel), and allow the filtrate to cool slowly in order to ensure good crystal formation.

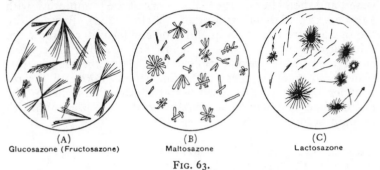

| (A) | (B) | (C) |
| Glucosazone (Fructosazone) | Maltosazone | Lactosazone |

Fig. 63.

If it is desired to observe the crystalline form of the osazone, draw up in a glass tube a few drops of the cold filtrate containing the fine crystals, and transfer to a microscope slide. Cover the drops with a slip and examine under the microscope: unless the filtrate has been cooled very slowly and thus given moderately-sized crystals, the high power of the microscope will probably be required. Note the fine yellow needles aggregated in the form of sheaves. Compare with Fig. 63(A).

Then filter the remainder of the product at the pump, drain and dry. The glucosazone is thus obtained as bright yellow crystals, m.p. 204° with decomposition.

Maltosazone (Phenyl-maltosazone).
$C_{12}H_{20}O_9(N \cdot NHC_6H_5)_2$.

Required: Maltose, 2 g.; acetic acid, 2 ml.; phenylhydrazine, 2 ml.

Proceed as in the preparation of glucosazone, using for the first solution 2 g. of maltose in 10 ml. of water, and for the second solution 2 ml. of phenylhydrazine dissolved in a mixture of 2 ml. of glacial acetic acid and 5 ml. of water. Heat in a boiling water-bath for 30 minutes. Maltosazone is much more soluble than glucosazone in hot water, and therefore does not separate whilst the boiling-tube is still in the boiling water-bath. When the heating is complete, either turn out the gas and allow the tube to cool slowly while still in the bath, or alternatively place the tube in a small beaker of boiling water and there let it cool: the maltosazone crystallises as the solution cools. (If the solution is cooled rapidly, the osazone separates as minute crystals, and subsequent filtration at the pump will be very slow.) Finally complete the cooling by immersing the boiling-tube in cold water, and then filter off the maltosazone at the pump, wash with a few ml. of cold water, and drain. (Yield, 1·2 g.). Recrystallise the osazone from a small quantity of boiling water. Allow the solution to cool very slowly as before, and examine the crystals as directed in the previous preparation. Note the long narrow plates, and compare them with Fig. 63(B). Filter off the remainder of the recrystallised material, drain and dry. The maltosazone is obtained as yellow crystals, m.p. 206°* with decomposition.

Lactosazone (Phenyl-lactosazone).
$C_{12}H_{20}O_9(N \cdot NHC_6H_5)_2$.

Proceed exactly as for maltosazone. When the heating is complete, however, remove the boiling-tube from the water-bath, and allow it to cool spontaneously in the air. (Lactosazone does not require the extremely slow cooling used for maltosazone in order to ensure rapid subsequent filtration.) Finally complete the cooling in cold water, and then filter at the pump, wash with cold water, and drain thoroughly. (Yield, 2 g.). Lactosazone is not so soluble as maltosazone in boiling water: for recrystallisation, therefore, boil a portion of the lactosazone with water, and then add ethanol drop by drop until a clear solution is obtained. Allow to cool slowly. Examine the crystals as before, and note the dense yellow clusters of very fine needles (sometimes referred to as "hedgehog" crystals): compare with Fig. 63(C). Filter off the remainder of the lactosazone, drain and dry. The pure lactosazone is obtained as yellow crystals, m.p. 208° with de-

---

* This is the value originally given by Fischer for the m.p. of maltosazone: it is a value obtained, however, only if the capillary tube containing the material is placed in a bath previously heated to about 180° and the temperature then rapidly increased. The m.p. of most samples of maltosazone, when determined in the usual way, is 190–192°.

The m.p. of lactosazone used to be given as 200°, but the pure samples of lactose now available give an osazone having the higher m.p. of 208° given above. In view of these variations in the m.p., and also of the fact that the m.p.s of all osazones of the commoner sugars lie very close together, the identification of an osazone should be based primarily on its crystal form: for this purpose it is frequently unnecessary to recrystallise the osazone, as the crystal form can often be observed excellently if a few drops of the original solution are used.

composition, the material darkening in colour immediately before melting.

α- and β-Pentacetylglucose. $C_6H_7O(O \cdot COCH_3)_5$.

When glucose is heated with an excess of acetic anhydride in the presence of a catalyst, all five hydroxyl groups are acetylated, and the resulting pen-tacetyl-glucose can clearly exist in two isomeric forms, corresponding to the α and β forms of glucose itself (see Formulae I and II, p. 135). When zinc chloride is used as a catalyst, the α-pentacetylglucose is formed, and when sodium acetate is used, the β-pentacetylglucose is produced. It is probable that the product in each case contains traces of the other isomeride, which however can be readily eliminated by recrystallisation.

(A) α-PENTACETYLGLUCOSE. *Required:* Zinc chloride, *ca.* 1 g.; acetic anhydride, 25 ml.; glucose, 5 g.

From a clean, dry stick of zinc chloride, break off a piece weighing roughly 1 g., crush it quickly into coarse fragments in a mortar, and then add it to 25 ml. of acetic anhydride contained in a 100 ml. round-bottomed or conical flask. (Owing to the very deliquescent nature of zinc chloride, this manipulation must be carried out *as rapidly as possible*: hence have both the acetic anhydride in the flask, and the mortar available near the balance, before the zinc chloride stick is withdrawn from the stock bottle.) Fit the flask with a reflux water-condenser and heat the mixture of zinc chloride and acetic anhydride on a vigorously boiling water-bath for about 5 minutes until the maximum temperature is reached and nearly all the chloride has dissolved. Now remove the condenser and add 5 g. of pow-dered glucose (anhydrous or monohydrate) cautiously to the acetic anhydride, shaking the mixture around occasionally during the addition, in order to control the vigorous reaction which follows. Finally replace the condenser and heat the mixture for 1 hour on the water-bath, and then pour the liquid into about 250 ml. of cold water. The latter should preferably be cooled exter-nally with ice-water, and be stirred vigorously during the addition of the acetylated product. A viscous oil separates at the bottom of the beaker, and if occasionally stirred will crystallise within about 10 minutes. After solidification of the oil, allow the mixture to stand for a further 15 minutes, and then filter at the pump. If any large lumps of the crude acetyl compound have formed, transfer them to a mortar, pulverise, and then wash them back into the Buchner funnel. Finally wash the product on the filter thoroughly with water, and drain. (Yield of crude material,

7·5–8·0 g.). Recrystallise the product from rectified spirit until the α-pentacetylglucose is obtained as colourless crystals melting sharply at 110–111°. Two recrystallisations are usually sufficient for this purpose.

(B) β-PENTACETYLGLUCOSE. *Required:* Anhydrous sodium acetate, 2·5 g.; acetic anhydride, 25 ml.; glucose, 5 g.

Carry out this preparation precisely as described for the α-compound, but instead of zinc chloride add 2·5 g. of anhydrous powdered sodium acetate (preparation, p. 116) to the acetic anhydride. When this mixture has been heated on the water-bath for 5 minutes, and the greater part of the acetate has dissolved, add the 5 g. of powdered glucose. After heating for 1 hour, pour into cold water as before. The viscous oil crystallises more readily than that obtained in the preparation of the α-compound. Filter the solid material at the pump, breaking up any lumps as before, wash thoroughly with water and drain. (Yield of crude product, 10·0–10·5 g.). Recrystallise from rectified spirit until the pure β-pentacetylglucose is obtained as colourless crystals, m.p. 130–131°: again two recrystallisations are usually sufficient for this purpose.

Conversion of β- into α-pentacetylglucose. The β-pentacetylglucose is readily converted into the α-isomeride by heating in acetic anhydride solution with zinc chloride. Add 0·5 g. of zinc chloride (rapidly crushed to coarse fragments as before) to 25 ml. of acetic anhydride and heat on a boiling water-bath for about 5 minutes in order to dissolve the zinc chloride. Then add 5 g. of pure β-pentacetylglucose, which will dissolve rapidly in the hot solution. Continue heating on the water-bath for 30 minutes, and then pour the hot solution, which will have acquired a pale brown colour, into 250 ml. of cold water, stirring vigorously. The oily drops rapidly solidify. Filter the solid product at the pump, wash, drain and recrystallise from rectified or methylated spirit. One recrystallisation is usually sufficient to give pure α-pentacetylglucose, m.p. 110–111°.

For the determination of the number of acetyl groups in pentacetyl-glucose, see p. 456.

Hexacetyl mannitol.
$$CH_2(O·COCH_3)(CH·O·COCH_3)_4CH_2(O·COCH_3).$$

Mannitol, $CH_2OH(CHOH)_4CH_2OH$, is a hexahydric alcohol obtained by the reduction of mannose. Since ring formation does not occur in mannitol, the hexacetyl derivative can exist in only one form, and therefore either zinc chloride or sodium acetate can be used as a catalyst for the acetylation.

Required: Mannitol, 5 g.; acetic anhydride, 30 ml.; zinc chloride, *ca.* 0·5 g.

Add 5 g. of finely powdered mannitol to 30 ml. of acetic anhydride contained in a 100 ml. round-bottomed or conical flask. Now break off a *small* fragment (not exceeding 0·5 g.) from a clean dry stick of zinc chloride, crush it quickly into coarse fragments in a mortar, and then add it to the acetic anhydride: this manipulation of the zinc chloride—as in the above preparation of α-pentacetyl-glucose—should be performed as rapidly as possible. (Alternatively, 4 g. of powdered anhydrous sodium acetate may be added in place of the zinc chloride.) Boil the mixture gently on a sand-bath under a reflux water-condenser for 30 minutes, a clear solution being rapidly obtained. Then pour the solution into 250 ml. of cold water, stirring the mixture vigorously for a few minutes until the oil which separates at first has solidified to a mass of fine colourless crystals. Allow to stand for 15 minutes, and then filter at the pump, wash thoroughly with water, and drain. Recrystallise the well-drained material (without drying) from a small quantity of methylated or rectified spirit, when the hexacetylmannitol will separate in colourless crystals, m.p. 120°: yield, 11·5 g. (almost theoretical).

For the determination of the number of acetyl groups in hexacetyl-mannitol, see p. 456.

α-**Methylglucoside.** $C_6H_7O(OH)_4(OCH_3)$.

When anhydrous glucose is boiled in methanol solution containing a small quantity of hydrogen chloride, condensation occurs between the methanol and the terminal (aldehydic) hydroxyl group of the glucose molecule, and a mixture of the isomeric α- and β-methylglucosides (A and B) is obtained: these correspond to α- and β-glucose respectively (compare formulae I and II, p. 135).

It should be noted that, since the hydroxyl group concerned in this condensation is derived from the terminal aldehydic group, the glucosides are similar in chemical nature to the acetals, *e.g.*, $CH_3CH(OC_2H_5)_2$, which are also formed by the condensation of an aldehyde with an alcohol. Consequently the methylglucosides can be readily hydrolysed back to methanol and glucose: if, on the other hand, the remaining hydroxyl groups in the glucose molecule are methylated, true ethers are obtained and these methyl groups cannot be readily hydrolysed.

```
 H   OCH₃  CH₃O   H
  \ /          \ /
   C ——         C ——
   |    |        |    |
  HCOH  |       HCOH  |
   |    |        |    |
  HOCH  O      HOCH  O
   |    |        |    |
  HCOH  |       HCOH  |
   |    |        |    |
  HC ——        HC ——
   |             |
  CH₂OH (A)    CH₂OH (B)
```

The following preparation works excellently if it is carried out in a laboratory which has become "inoculated" by the methylglucoside from previous preparations, or alternatively if some of the glucoside is available for "seeding" the solution of the crude material; otherwise there may be a considerable delay before crystallisation starts.

Required: Anhydrous glucose, 20 g.; methanol, 40 ml.

Add 20 g. of pure powdered anhydrous glucose to 40 ml. of anhydrous methanol (preparation, p. 88) contained in a flask fitted by means of a rubber stopper to a reflux water-condenser: close the top of the condenser with a calcium chloride tube. It is now required to add about 5% of dry hydrogen chloride to the methanol in the flask. For this purpose, fit a corked boiling-tube with two narrow delivery-tubes so that it can act as a wash-bottle: fit the inlet tube to a hydrogen chloride Kipp's apparatus (p. 104) through a concentrated sulphuric acid wash-bottle to ensure thorough drying of the gas, and fit the outlet tube with a calcium chloride tube. Place 2·5 ml. of anhydrous methanol in the boiling-tube, stand the latter in ice-water, and bubble hydrogen chloride through the chilled methanol until the latter is saturated. (The gas should be passed briskly through the methanol at first, to prevent the latter from "sucking back" through the inlet tube.) Then add this saturated methanol without delay to the contents of the flask, and mix well.

Boil the mixture *gently* on a sand-bath for 4 hours and then decant into a conical flask and cool. Seed the cold solution if necessary with a trace of α-methylglucoside. The glucoside separates as colourless crystals. When crystallisation ceases, filter the glucoside at the pump, drain, wash quickly with a *small* quantity of methanol, and then recrystallise from a minimum of methanol. For this purpose methanol of good quality, but not necessarily anhydrous, should be used. The α-methylglucoside is obtained as colourless crystals, m.p. 165°. Yield, 6–7 g.

If the mother-liquor from the crude product (together with the washings) is concentrated to nearly half its original volume by gentle distillation, and is then cooled and seeded with a trace of the first crop, a second and less pure crop of the α-methylglucoside is obtained. This should be purified by recrystallisation from the mother-liquor obtained from the recrystallisation of the first crop, and then if necessary recrystallised a second time from a small quantity of fresh methanol. Yield of second crop, about 2·5 g.

The crude concentrated mother-liquor still contains some

α-methylglucoside, together with the more soluble β-methyl-glucoside: the amount of the latter is too small, however, to warrant attempted isolation.

If difficulty is experienced in inducing the first crude crop of the α-glucoside to crystallise, place a few drops of the solution on a watch-glass and expose freely to the air, with occasional scratching: meanwhile keep the main volume of the solution securely corked in the conical flask. After an interval of varying length (possibly several days), partial crystallisation occurs in the material on the watch-glass. Then seed the solution with this material: crystallisation of the first main crop will rapidly follow.

α-Methylglucoside responds to General Tests 1 and 2 for carbohydrates given on p. 366 (blackening with sulphuric acid, and Molisch's test). Since, however, the glucoside does not contain a free aldehydic hydroxyl group, it does not possess the reducing properties of glucose itself. Confirm this by applying to pure α-methylglucoside Tests 1 and 2 for glucose (p. 367), *i.e.*, the reduction of ammoniacal silver nitrate and of Fehling's solution respectively. No reduction is obtained in either case, although prolonged warming in Test 1 and (in particular) prolonged boiling in Test 2 causes partial hydrolysis of the glucoside with consequent slight reduction.

Periodate Oxidation of 1,2-Diols.

Sodium *meta*periodate ($NaIO_4$) in cold aqueous solution readily oxidises 1,2-diols with splitting of the molecule and the consequent formation of aldehydes or ketones: thus ethylene glycol gives formaldehyde and pinacol gives acetone. In the case of a 1,2,3-triol, the central carbon atom of the triol

$$CH_2(OH) - CH_2(OH) \rightarrow 2CH_2O$$
$$(CH_3)_2C(OH) \cdot C(OH)(CH_3)_2 \rightarrow 2(CH_3)_2CO$$

system breaks off as formic acid, whereas the other two are oxidised as before to aldehydes or ketones, according to the terminal substituents: for example, glycerol gives two equivalents of formaldehyde and one of formic acid.

$$CH_2(OH) \cdot CH(OH) \cdot CH_2(OH) \rightarrow 2CH_2O + HCOOH$$

This selective oxidation has proved of great value in the investigation of sugar structures. For this purpose, a glycoside is frequently employed to protect

(I)   (II)   (III)   (IV)

the terminal group. It will be seen that a methyl aldopento-furanoside (I) will give solely the dialdehyde (II), whereas a methyl aldohexo-pyranose (III) will give the dialdehyde (IV) and one equivalent of formic acid, which may be estimated.

In the following examples, pinacol is oxidised to acetone, which is identified as its semicarbazone and its 2,4-dinitrophenylhydrazone, and glycerol is oxidised to formaldehyde and formic acid. The formaldehyde is readily detected by the condensation product which it gives with "dimedone," 5,5-dimethylcyclohexan-1,3-dione (p. 277).

For these experiments, prepare two solutions: (A) A solution of 2·5 g. of sodium metaperiodate in 50 ml. of water. A clear solution can be readily prepared by gentle warming, and then cooled.

(B) A solution of 1 g. of "dimedone" (preparation, p. 277) in 10 ml. of ethanol. This solution will be required only for the glycerol oxidation experiment.

OXIDATION OF PINACOL.

Dissolve 1 g. of pinacol (preparation, p. 148) in 20 ml. of water, and add 20 ml. of the 5% aqueous sodium periodate solution. After 15 minutes, distil the clear solution, collecting the first 5 ml. of distillate. Treat this distillate with 2,4-dinitrophenylhydrazine solution A (p. 263). Acetone 2,4-dinitrophenylhydrazone rapidly separates from the solution; when filtered off, washed with a small quantity of ethanol, and dried, it has m.p. 126–127°, and after recrystallisation from ethanol it has m.p. 128°.

OXIDATION OF GLYCEROL.

Dissolve 0·5 ml. of glycerol in 20 ml. of water, and add 20 ml. of the above 5% aqueous sodium periodate solution. After 15–20 minutes add 12 ml. of the above 10% ethanolic dimedone solution, and stir well at intervals for another 15 minutes. The addition of the dimedone solution may cause a rapid precipitation of some of the dimedone itself, which is only slightly soluble in water, whereas the formaldehyde-dimedone compound separates more slowly from the solution.

Filter the mixed product at the pump, and wash it well with ethanol to remove excess of dimedone, and then with water and again with ethanol. The dried white residual "methylene-dimedone", m.p. 186–188°, weighs 0·55–0·65 g. It may be recrystallised from ethanol containing about 10% of water, and then has m.p. 189°.

Selenium Dioxide Oxidations.

Selenium dioxide, SeO_2, is very poisonous (cf. p. 147), but is valuable particularly for the oxidation of methylene ($:CH_2$) groups to carbonyl ($:CO$) groups.

This oxidation proceeds readily if the methylene group is activated by linkage to (a) a carbonyl group, (b) an aromatic ring; (c) an olefine link also activates adjacent :CH$_2$ and ·CH: groups.

Examples. (a) CH$_3$COCH$_3$ →   CH$_3$COCHO
              Also cyclohexanone   →   cyclohexan-1,2-dione
         (b) C$_6$H$_5$CH$_2$C$_6$H$_5$ →   C$_6$H$_5$COC$_6$H$_5$
              C$_6$H$_5$CH$_2$CH$_2$C$_6$H$_5$ →   C$_6$H$_5$CO·COC$_6$H$_5$
         (c) CH$_3$CH:CH$_2$ →   CH$_3$COCHO.

Compounds containing olefine links may be oxidised to 1,2-diketones, as in C$_6$H$_5$CH:CHC$_6$H$_5$ → C$_6$H$_5$CO·COC$_6$H$_5$. Anthracene is readily oxidised to anthraquinone, but phenanthrene is almost unaffected.

In certain cases, selenium dioxide may act solely as a dehydrogenating agent, as in the examples:

C$_2$H$_5$OOC·CH$_2$·CH$_2$COOC$_2$H$_5$ →   C$_2$H$_5$OOC·CH:CH·COOC$_2$H$_5$
     Diethyl succinate   Diethyl fumarate
CH$_3$COCH$_2$·CH$_2$COCH$_3$ →   CH$_3$COCH:CHCOCH$_3$
     Acetonyl-acetone   Diacetyl-ethylene
(*n*-Hexan-2,5-dione)   (*n*-Hex-3-ene-2,5-dione)

The following oxidation of camphor to camphor-quinone illustrates the oxidising action of selenium dioxide, and readily gives a crystalline product.

CAUTION. The vapour of selenium dioxide is poisonous, and all operations involving the hot material, alone or in solution, should be performed in a fume-cupboard. If lumps of selenium dioxide have to be powdered in a mortar, the latter should also be in a fume-cupboard, with the window lowered as far as possible, to avoid inhaling the fine dust. (cf. p. 191)

Camphorquinone from Camphor

When camphor (I) is heated with selenium dioxide in acetic acid, the methylene group next to the carbonyl group is oxidised also to a carbonyl group, to form camphorquinone (II). Note that the compound (II) is not a true quinone but a 1,2-diketone:

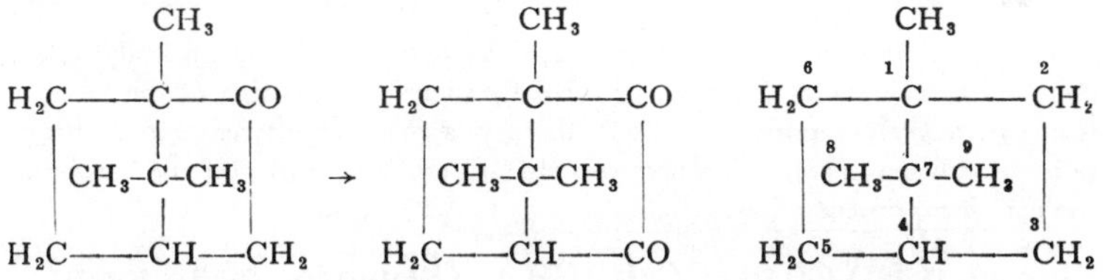

it has the characteristic yellow colour of such diketones, whereas camphor is colourless. The systematic name of camphorquinone should therefore be 2, 3-dioxocamphane, derived from the parent hydrocarbon camphane (III).

Required: Camphor, 5 g.; selenium dioxide, 6 g.; acetic anhydride, 5 ml.

In this preparation, the (+) or dextro-rotatory (natural) camphor or the (±) or racemic (synthetic) camphor can be used. *Perform the oxidation in a fume-cupboard.*

Place a mixture of 5 g. of camphor, 6 g. of powdered selenium dioxide and 5 ml. of acetic anhydride in flask fitted with a reflux water-condenser. Heat the flask in an oil-bath for 3 hours at 140–150° so that gentle boiling occurs: shake the mixture from time to time.

Then cool the reaction-mixture, filter it at the pump, leaving a black residue of selenium, and wash out the flask twice with 2 × 5 ml. of acetic acid, passing the washings also through the filter. Dilute the united filtrates with water, and make the solution alkaline with 10% aqueous sodium hydroxide, which precipitates the camphorquinone. Cool, filter off the yellow camphorquinone at the pump, wash with water and drain thoroughly.

The camphorquinone can be purified in either of two ways. (i) To save time, the drained but still damp material can be recrystallised from water containing 10% of acetic acid, the hot filtered solution being cooled and vigorously stirred. The quinone separates as brilliant yellow crystals (yield, 2·5 g.), m.p. 192–194°, increased to 196–197° by a second recrystallisation. (ii) The crude camphorquinone can be dried in a vacuum desiccator (weight of dry quinone, 5 g.), and then recrystallised from petroleum (b.p. 100–120°), the hot solution being filtered through a fluted paper in a pre-heated funnel. The quinone separates in beautiful crystals, m.p. 196–197°, 2·8 g.

The m.p. of the quinone obtained from the optically inactive camphor is almost identical with the above values, obtained from dextro-camphor.

The melting-points of the *dextro* and *laevo* forms of any optically active compound may, as in this case, be virtually identical with that of the racemic form: in many compounds however there is a marked difference in melting-point, and often in solubility, between the (+) and (−) forms on one hand and the (±) form on the other.

Pinacol. $(CH_3)_2C(OH)\cdot C(OH)(CH_3)_2$. (Reduction of Acetone)

Acetone when treated in ethanol with sodium undergoes reduction mainly to isopropanol. By modifying the conditions, however, acetone may be induced to undergo a bimolecular reduction to pinacol.

$$2(CH_3)_2CO \rightarrow (CH_3)_2C - C(CH_3)_2$$
$$\quad\quad\quad\quad\quad\quad\quad\quad\quad OH \quad OH$$

Aromatic ketones undergo this type of reduction particularly readily.

Two methods of preparing pinacol from acetone are given below. In Method (A) sodium is added to acetone which is floating on 30% aqueous potassium hydroxide and which therefore contains a strictly limited amount of water. The method is simple and reasonably rapid but gives a low yield of pinacol. In Method (B), a modified method due to R. Adams, magnesium is treated with mercuric chloride and thus activated by the formation of a film of magnesium amalgam. It therefore reacts with acetone to give the magnesium derivative of pinacol, which on hydrolysis furnishes the free pinacol. The scale

$$2(CH_3)_2CO + Mg \rightarrow (CH_3)_2C\text{-----}C(CH_3)_2 \rightarrow (CH_3)_2C\text{----}C(CH_3)_2$$

of this preparation can readily be increased above that given below.

METHOD (A)

Required: Acetone, 60 ml.; 30% aqueous potassium hydroxide, 90 ml.; sodium, 17 g.

Fit a 250 ml. round-bottomed flask with a reflux water-condenser down which pieces of sodium may be dropped: alternatively, use a flask having a short straight stoppered side-arm for this purpose.

Place 90 ml. of 30% aqueous potassium hydroxide and 60 ml. of acetone in the flask. Weigh out 17 g. of sodium, cut it into small lumps or strips, and store these in a short wide-necked corked bottle for protection from the atmosphere. Now add the sodium, withdrawn one piece at a time with tongs or a pointed glass rod, to the mixture: the sodium floats on the upper layer of acetone as it reacts. Occasionally swirl the mixture *gently* around, taking *great care* that the sodium does not come in contact with the lower solution of potash, otherwise local over-heating and charring will occur. (If the sodium should stick in the condenser during the addition, push it down with a glass rod having at its upper end either a right-angle bend, or a cork firmly affixed, so that the lower end of the rod can project only just beyond the bottom of the condenser: if it slips from the fingers, it cannot therefore smash the base of the flask.)

As the reaction of the pieces of sodium becomes steadily slower, add water in small quantities from time to time very cautiously.

When the sodium has completely dissolved, pour the reaction-mixture into a separating-funnel, run off the strongly alkaline lower layer, and dry the upper layer over sodium sulphate (*not* calcium chloride). Then fractionally distil the dried liquid up a short column, and collect the fraction of b.p. 150–180° (mainly at 170–172°).

Work up the product by method (*a*) or (*b*): method (*b*) affords the anhydrous pinacol.

(*a*) Cool the fraction of b.p. 150–180° in ice-water, and add water (*ca.* 5 ml.) dropwise with stirring. The crystalline hexahydrate of pinacol is formed with considerable heat evolution: directly the product becomes solid, stop adding water, for an excess will redissolve the hexahydrate. Transfer the hexahydrate (yield 10–11 g.) on to a pad consisting of several thicknesses of drying-paper, and press it with another pad to remove all moisture, transferring the hydrate if necessary to a fresh pad to complete the drying. Then store it in a bottle having a well-fitting stopper. The sample may be recrystallised from water (*ca.* 10 ml.) before drying: yield of pure hexahydrate, 9 g.

(*b*) Add about 60 ml. of petroleum (b.p. 60–80°) with stirring to the fraction of b.p. 150–180°, thus precipitating the pure anhydrous pinacol (2·5–3 g.). Filter this off, and then shake the filtrate with *ca.* 4 ml. of water: the remaining pinacol now separates as the hexahydrate (5 g.). The two crops may be united and recrystallised from *ca.* 10 ml. of water (total yield of hexahydrate, 8–9 g.). Dry and bottle the product rapidly as described in (*a*).

The anhydrous white crystalline pinacol has m.p. 42°, b.p. 172°, and has a strong odour of camphor: the hexahydrate has m.p. 46°.

Both forms sublime very readily, even at room temperature: a small sample on exposure to the air will completely volatilise in a short time, particularly on a warm day or if the sample is exposed to a gentle current of air. Hence the above method for rapid drying. A sample confined in an atmospheric desiccator over calcium chloride rapidly disappears as the vapour is adsorbed by the calcium chloride. A sample of the hexahydrate similarly confined over sodium hydroxide undergoes steady dehydration with initial liquefaction, for the m.p. of the hydrated-anhydrous mixture is below room temperature: as the dehydration proceeds to completion, complete resolidification occurs.

METHOD (B)

Required: Magnesium, 8·0 g.; mercuric chloride, 9·0 g.; dry benzene, 150 ml.; dry acetone, 75 ml.

The acetone employed should be dried over calcium chloride for 2–3 days before use. The benzene should be similarly dried although a shorter period is sufficient. The apparatus must also be thoroughly dry.

Fit a 500 ml. round-bottomed flask with a dropping-funnel, and with an efficient reflux water-condenser having a calcium chloride guard-tube at the top.

Place 8·0 g. of magnesium turnings or ribbon and 80 ml. of the dry benzene in the flask. Prepare a solution of 9·0 g. of mercuric chloride in 50 ml. of the dry acetone, transfer it to the dropping-funnel, and then allow it to enter the flask slowly at first, and then more rapidly, so that the addition takes about 3–5 minutes. The reaction usually starts shortly after the initial addition of the mercuric chloride solution: if it is delayed, it may then start vigorously, and the flask may have to be cooled in water to prevent escape of acetone through the condenser.

As the reaction beings to subside, run in from the dropping-funnel without delay a mixture of 25 ml. of acetone and 20 ml. of benzene, in order to maintain a brisk and continuous reaction. When the reaction finally subsides, heat the mixture on a boiling water-bath for 45 minutes with occasional shaking. If the shaking does not break up the spongy mass of magnesium pinacolate, cool the flask at the end of this period, remove it from the condenser, and then cork and shake it vigorously to disintegrate the reaction product. Replace the condenser and heat the mixture for a further 30 minutes.

Now add 20 ml. of water from the funnel and continue heating for 30 minutes, with occasional shaking. Then allow the mixture to cool to about 50°, and filter it at the pump. Return the collected solid to the flask, add 50 ml. of benzene, and heat as before for 10 minutes to extract any remaining pinacol, and again filter. Unite the filtrates and concentrate them by distillation to about half the original volume in order to remove any unchanged acetone. Add 30 ml. of water to the concentrated benzene solution, and cool the stirred mixture to 10–12°. After 10 minutes, filter off the pinacol hydrate at the pump, wash it with a small quantity of benzene, and after draining, recrystallise it from water, adding charcoal if the crude pinacol hydrate was discoloured. Yield of pinacol hydrate, 35 g.

The pinacol hydrate may be used (i) for conversion to pinacolone (see below), and (ii) to illustrate the oxidation of 1,2-diols to aldehydes or ketones by periodic acid (p. 145).

Tetraphenylethylene Glycol. This preparation illustrates the mild conditions under which aryl ketones may undergo bimolecular reduction to compounds of the pinacol type.

Dissolve 1 g. of powdered benzophenone in 6–7 ml. of cold isopropanol with shaking, add 1 drop of glacial acetic acid, and then confine the solution either in a glass receiver having a ground-glass stopper, or in a tube which is sealed

$$2(C_6H_5)_2CO \rightarrow (C_6H_5)_2C(OH) \cdot C(OH)(C_6H_5)_2$$

or closed with a tightly fitting rubber bung. Place the container on a window-ledge in full daylight and (if possible!) in sunlight. Within a few days in summer (and 2–3 weeks in winter), crystals of tetraphenylethylene glycol separate. Filter these off, and recrystallise from ethanol. M.p. 189°.

Pinacolone. $(CH_3)_3C \cdot CO \cdot CH_3$ The Pinacol-Pinacolone Rearrangement.

When pinacol is warmed with acids, it undergoes rearrangement to pina-colone, with an over-all loss of one molecule of water.

This rearrangement is general for 1,2-diols of the type $R_2C(OH) \cdot C(OH) \cdot R_2$ where the groups R may be alike or different, and may be alkyl or aryl groups.

(I)   (II)   (III)   (IV)

The probable mechanism of this change is first proton addition to one oxygen atom of the pinacol to give (I), which loses water to give the carbonium ion (II). The group R then migrates to give the isomeric ion (III), which loses a proton, giving the pinacolone (IV).

Required: Pinacol hexahydrate, 10 g.; concentrated sulphuric acid, 15 ml. (28 g.).

Add cautiously 15 ml. of concentrated sulphuric acid to 50 ml. of water in a 100 ml. distilling-flask, and then add 10 g. of pinacol hydrate. Distil the solution *slowly*. When about 40 ml. of distillate (consisting of pinacolone and water) have been collected, and no more pinacolone comes over, extract the distillate with ether. Dry the extract over sodium sulphate. Distil the dry filtered extract carefully, with the normal precautions for ether distillation (p. 164). When the ether has been removed, continue the distillation slowly, rejecting any fraction coming over below 100°. Collect the pinacolone, b.p. 106°, as a colourless liquid having a peppermint odour. Yield, 4·5–5·0 g. A small quantity of higher-boiling material remains in the flask.

Benzhydrol (Diphenylcarbinol), $(C_6H_5)_2CH \cdot OH$, from Benzo-phenone. The Meerwein-Ponndorf-Verley Reductions.

When aldehydes or ketones are heated with an excess of isopropanol in the presence of aluminium isopropoxide, Al ⫶[OCH(CH$_3$)$_2$]$_3$, the overall reaction may be represented as a reduction of the carbonyl group of the aldehyde or ketone, with oxidation of the isopropanol to acetone:

$$R \cdot CHO + HO \cdot CH(CH_3)_2 \rightarrow RCH_2OH + OC(CH_3)_2$$
$$R_2CO + HO \cdot CH(CH_3)_2 \rightarrow R_2CHOH + OC(CH_3)_2$$

In view of the boiling-points of acetone (57°) and isopropanol (82°), the acetone can be steadily distilled off from the reaction-mixture, and the reduction ultimately becomes virtually complete.

This type of reduction has the advantage of requiring only mild conditions, and also of leaving unaffected various groups such as olefine groups, nitro groups, and halogen atoms in aliphatic compounds, which might be affected by other more vigorous reagents. For example, bromal under the above conditions gives tribromoethanol (or avertin): $CBr_3 \cdot CHO \rightarrow CBr_3 \cdot CH_2OH$. The immunity of olefine groups has made this type of reduction of particular value in steroid investigations.

In the following preparation to illustrate the Meerwein-Ponndorf-Verley reduction, a solution of benzophenone in isopropanol is rapidly reduced in the presence of aluminium isopropoxide to benzhydrol: $(C_6H_5)_2CO \rightarrow (C_6H_5)_2CH \cdot OH$. It is clear that the aluminium isopropoxide must take some essential part in this reaction, for benzophenone when dissolved even in cold isopropanol with a trace of acetic acid is reduced to tetraphenylethyleneglycol (p. 150).

The mechanism of the reduction remains uncertain. The work of E. D. Williams, K. A. Krieger and A. R. Day (1953)* using deuterium-labelled aluminium isopropoxide, shows that hydrogen atoms are transferred predominantly from the central carbon atom of an isopropoxide group to the carbon atom of the carbonyl group undergoing reduction, the process probably involving a cyclic complex:

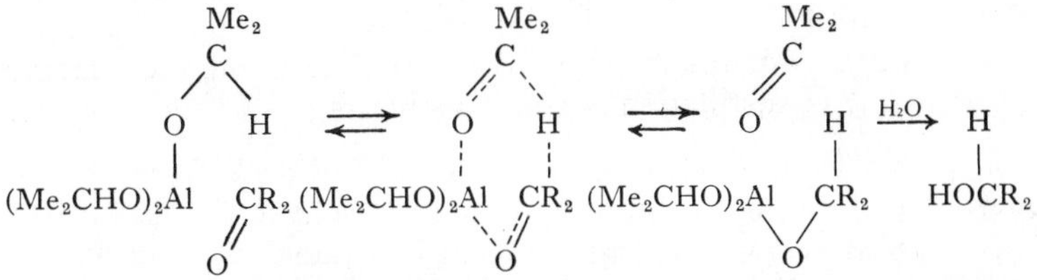

Aluminium isopropoxide can be obtained as a fine powder from technical sources. When the bottle has once been opened however, the stopper should be firmly replaced and covered with wax: more conveniently, the stoppered bottle can be kept in an atmospheric desiccator over calcium chloride or sodium hydroxide, preferably in the dark.

It is advisable in any case before an experiment to place the weighed aluminium isopropoxide overnight in a shallow dish in a vacuum desiccator over sodium hydroxide. The isopropanol should be dried over anhydrous sodium sulphate, and the clear liquid decanted off before use.

* *J. Amer. Chem. Soc.*, **75**, 2404 (1953).

Required : Benzophenone, 2 g.; aluminium isopropoxide, 2·5 g.; isopropanol, 20 ml.

The powdered isopropoxide and the isopropanol must be dried as described above.

This experiment requires a 50 ml. flask attached by a ground-glass neck or a rubber bung (*not* a cork) to an efficient fraction-ating column. This may be of the type shown in Fig. 11(B) (p. 26) with at least 4 inches of column packed with glass rings, and without external lagging: or a less efficient type of column, for example, one similar to that shown in the micro-model, Fig. 39 (p. 64), in which the column is 6–8 inches high. A water-condenser is fitted to the column.

Place in the flask 2 g. of benzophenone, 15 ml. of isopropanol and 2·5 g. of aluminium isopropoxide. This mixture has now to be heated *gently* under reflux so that the temperature regis-tered by the thermometer in the column does not exceed 80°, i.e., so that only acetone distils. For this purpose, the flask should preferably be heated in an oil-bath: direct heating, even over an asbestos sheet, may cause local overheating and decompo-sition; the use of a water-bath on the other hand may make the column undesirably damp.

Adjust the temperature so that acetone distils *very slowly*. After about 1 hour the distillation should be complete: confirm by testing a drop of the distillate with 2,4-dinitrophenylhydrazine solution. Now add an extra 5 ml. of isopropanol, and continue the slow distillation until the boiling-point of the distillate reaches 82°, *i.e.*, until isopropanol begins to distil: continue the distilla-tion until the distillate gives a negative reaction for acetone. (Total time of distillation is about $1\frac{1}{2}$ hours.)

Disconnect the column, and remove the flask from the oil-bath. Add 25 ml. of dilute hydrochloric acid to the flask, shake the contents vigorously, and chill in ice-water, when crystals of benzhydrol will separate. (Occasionally the hydrol will separate initially as an oil, which crystallises on vigorous stirring.)

Filter the crystals at the pump, wash them with water, and drain well. To save time, the product may be recrystallised directly from an ethanol-water mixture (1:2 by vol.), and obtained as colourless crystals, m.p. 68°. Alternatively, the crude product can be dried in a desiccator (yield of dry product, 1·9–2·0 g., m.p. 65–67°) and recrystallised from petroleum (b.p. 60–80°), and obtained as needles, m.p. 68°.

Lithium Aluminium Hydride Reductions.

Lithium aluminium hydride, $LiAlH_4$, is a very active reducing agent, and is used particularly for the ready reduction of carboxylic acids (or their esters) to primary alcohols: $R \cdot COOH \rightarrow R \cdot CH_2OH$.

It will also reduce acid chlorides, acid anhydrides and aldehydes to primary alcohols, ketones to secondary alcohols, and amides to the corresponding amines: $R \cdot CONH_2 \rightarrow R \cdot CH_2NH_2$. Nitro-hydrocarbons if aromatic are usually reduced to azo-compounds, and if aliphatic to primary amines. The C:C bond in aliphatic compounds is usually unaffected, but in aromatic compounds the bond may be hydrogenated if it is directly linked to the aromatic nucleus: thus cinnamic acid gives 3-phenylpropan-1-ol: $C_6H_5CH{:}CH \cdot COOH$ $\rightarrow C_6H_5CH_2CH_2CH_2OH$. The C∶C bond, unless strongly activated by neighbouring groups, is also usually unaffected.

Lithium aluminium hydride if carelessly manipulated may be dangerous for two distinct reasons. The material is caustic, and should not be allowed to touch the skin: it is particularly important that the finely divided material should be kept away from the lips, nostrils and eyes, and consequently pulverisation in a mortar must be carried out with the mortar in a fume-cupboard, and with the window drawn down as far as possible in front of the operator. This danger from handling has however been greatly reduced, for the hydride is now sold in stated amounts as a coarse powder enclosed in a polythene bag in a metal container: this powder dissolves readily in ether, and preliminary pulverisation is unnecessary.

The second danger may arise from the careless treatment of the hydride in a glass vessel with water or acid: a significant volume of hydrogen may be evolved, and a fragment of the hydride may ignite and so cause an explosion. These conditions should never arise in the course of careful work.

In an experiment, a slight excess of the hydride is employed to ensure the complete reduction: the unused hydride must then be destroyed. This can be done by the cautious addition of (a) water, or (b) ordinary undried ether, which will ensure that the supply of water is both small and gradual, or (c) an ester such as ethyl acetate, which will be reduced to ethanol. The first of these methods, namely the addition of water, is hazardous and should be avoided.

In the following experiment, salicylic acid is reduced to o-hydroxybenzyl alcohol (or saligenin), which being crystalline is readily isolated: the excess of hydride is destroyed by the addition of undried ether, and the aluminium hydroxide then brought into solution by the addition of sulphuric acid.

o-Hydroxybenzyl Alcohol (Saligenin) $C_6H_4(OH) \cdot CH_2OH$ from Salicylic Acid.

The student should read the above directions for the safe manipulation of the hydride before starting this experiment.

Required: Salicylic acid, 6·0 g.; lithium aluminium hydride, 2·5 g.; dry ether, 165 ml.

Assemble in a fume-cupboard a 3-necked flask fitted with a stirrer, a reflux condenser, and a dropping-funnel, the apparatus being thoroughly dry, and the condenser and funnel closed by calcium chloride tubes (Fig. 23(G), p. 46).

Run 90 ml. of *dry* ether into the flask and start the stirring. Weigh out 2·5 g. of lithium aluminium hydride, and then divide 0·5 g. of this amount *into very small portions*: add these portions in turn cautiously to the stirred ether to remove any traces of water which in spite of the above precautions may be present in the reaction flask. Then add the remaining 2·0 g. of the hydride more rapidly. When the addition is complete, continue stirring the mixture for 15 minutes; the hydride should dissolve in the ether except for a slight grey suspension. (If at the end of this period the larger particles of the hydride have not disintegrated, boil the stirred mixture under reflux on a water-bath for a further 15 minutes.)

Now cool the mixture thoroughly in ice-water, and run in over a period of 45 minutes a solution of 6·0 g. of dry salicylic acid in 75 ml. of dry ether. When the addition of the acid to the stirred solution is complete, heat the mixture under reflux on the water-bath for 15 minutes to ensure completion of the reduction. Then thoroughly chill the mixture in ice-water, and hydrolyse any unused hydride by the *slow* addition of 50 ml. of ordinary undried ether, followed similarly by 75 ml. of dilute sulphuric acid.

Transfer the reaction-mixture to a separating-funnel, run off the aqueous layer, and collect the ethereal layer. Extract the aqueous layer twice with ether (2 × 25 ml.), add the extracts to the main ethereal solution and dry over sodium sulphate.

Distil the filtered ethereal solution, using a 100 ml. flask fitted with a dropping-funnel and a side-arm for the condenser: observe all the normal precautions for ether distillation (p. 162) and run the ethereal solution into the flask as fast as the ether distils over. When all the ether has distilled off, detach and cool the flask, when the oily colourless residue of saligenin will rapidly crystallise. Weight of product, 5·0 g.; m.p. 75–82°. Recrystallise either from a mixture of benzene and petroleum (b.p. 60–80°), or from a minimum of water, allowing the stirred aqueous solution to cool to 65–70° before chilling. The dry crystalline saligenin has m.p. 85–86°.

Saligenin readily sublimes when heated above its m.p., and consequently cannot be distilled.

Nitration.

One of the chief differences between aliphatic and aromatic hydrocarbons is that the latter when treated with nitric acid (in the presence of sulphuric acid) undergo direct *nitration*, benzene being thus converted to nitrobenzene:

$$C_6H_5H + HONO_2 \xrightarrow{H_2SO_4} C_6H_5NO_2 + H_2O.$$

A similar reaction occurs only very rarely with aliphatic hydrocarbons.

It is found experimentally, however, that if benzene is treated with concentrated nitric acid alone, the yield of nitrobenzene is small. If, however, the nitric acid is first mixed with concentrated sulphuric acid, a high yield of nitrobenzene results.

Ingold and co-workers have shown that nitration is caused by the nitronium ion, $\overset{+}{N}O_2$. The overall reaction is: $C_6H_6 + \overset{+}{N}O_2 \longrightarrow C_6H_5NO_2 + \overset{+}{H}$

It is considered that the $\overset{+}{N}O_2$ ion is produced in the mixture of nitric and sulphuric acids by changes such as:

$$H_2SO_4 + HNO_3 \longrightarrow H\overset{-}{S}O_4 + H_2\overset{+}{N}O_3$$
$$H_2\overset{+}{N}O_3 + H_2SO_4 \longrightarrow H\overset{-}{S}O_4 + H_3\overset{+}{O} + \overset{+}{N}O_2$$

Nitrobenzene. $C_6H_5NO_2$.

Required: Nitric acid, 35 ml.; sulphuric acid, 40 ml.; benzene, 29 ml. (25 g.).

The conversion of benzene to nitrobenzene has to be performed with care in order to avoid the further nitration of the nitrobenzene to *m*-dinitrobenzene. Place 35 ml. of concentrated nitric acid in a 500 ml. flask, and add slowly 40 ml. (74 g.) of concentrated sulphuric acid, keeping the mixture cool during the addition by immersing the flask in cold water. Place a thermometer in this nitrating mixture, and then add *very slowly* 29 ml. (25 g.) of benzene. The benzene should be added about 3 ml. at a time, and the contents of the flask *thoroughly* mixed after each addition: the temperature of the mixture must not be allowed to rise above 50°, and should be kept under control if necessary by cooling the flask in cold water. When all the benzene has been added, fit a reflux water-condenser to the flask, and place the latter *in* a water-bath, which is then maintained at 60° for 45 minutes. During this period the flask should be withdrawn from the bath from time to time and vigorously shaken in order to break up the nitrobenzene layer which would otherwise float on the dense acid layer below.

After the 45 minutes' heating, pour the contents of the flask into a large excess of cold water (about 300 ml.), in which the nitrobenzene, being heavier than water, sinks to the bottom. Stir the mixture vigorously in order to wash out as much acid as possible from the nitrobenzene. Decant off as much as possible of the supernatant aqueous layer,* and then transfer the residual liquid to a separating-funnel. Run off the lower layer of nitrobenzene, rejecting the upper aqueous layer, and then return the nitrobenzene to the separating-funnel, and shake it vigorously with an equal volume of cold water. Allow the nitrobenzene to separate again, and then run it off and repeat the washing using dilute sodium carbonate solution. The nitrobenzene should be shaken with increasing quantities of the carbonate solution until the cessation of evolution of carbon dioxide shows that all free acid has been neutralised.

The nitrobenzene ought now to be separated and again washed with water to remove traces of sodium carbonate solution: washing with water at this stage, however, frequently gives an emulsion of nitrobenzene and water and takes a very long time to separate again into two well-defined layers. It is best therefore to omit this final washing with water, and to separate the nitrobenzene *as completely as possible* from the sodium carbonate solution. Then transfer the nitrobenzene to a small flask, add some granular calcium chloride, and shake the mixture occasionally until the liquid is quite clear (usually about 20 minutes). Filter the nitrobenzene through a small fluted filter-paper directly into a 60 ml. distilling-flask fitted to an air-condenser. Distil the nitrobenzene carefully, collecting the fraction which boils between 207° and 211°. Yield, 35 g.

Nitrobenzene is a pale yellow liquid, having a b.p. 210°, and *d*, 1·20. It has an odour which is similar to that of almonds, and which is therefore often confused with that of benzaldehyde. Nitrobenzene is used chiefly for the preparation of aniline.

Nitrobenzene. (Semi-micro scale). (1/10 of above scale.)

Place 3·5 ml. of conc. HNO_3 in a 50 ml. round-bottomed flask and add slowly with cooling 4 ml. of conc. H_2SO_4. (Measure the acids from a burette or 5 ml. measuring cylinder.) Add slowly from a burette 2·9 ml. of benzene, shaking the mixture well during the addition: the temperature must be kept at 45–50°. Fit a small reflux water-condenser to the flask and heat in a water-bath maintained at 60° for 10 minutes. During this period, shake the flask vigorously from time to time, and then pour the mixture into 30 ml. of cold water. (If emulsification occurs, add about 5 ml. of chloroform to extract the nitrobenzene.) Proceed as in the larger-scale experiment above as far as the drying stage. Use only 2–3 small pieces of granular calcium chloride, and dry for 10 minutes. If a clear liquid is obtained, omit the filtration, and decant carefully into the flask shown

* This is done so that a small separating-funnel of about 100 ml. capacity may be used for the subsequent washing of the nitrobenzene.

in Fig. 36 (p. 63). Distil without water in the condenser (after removal of chloroform). Keep the hot vapour of the nitrobenzene around the bulb of the thermometer (which has a considerable heat-capacity) for one minute without actually distilling, so that the true temperature can be recorded, and then collect the fraction of b.p. 207–211°. Yield, 2.7 g.

For reactions of nitrobenzene, see pp. 384, 385.

Aromatic Substitution.

The student when preparing disubstituted benzenes should bear in mind Vorländer's Rules of aromatic substitution, which form the most convenient modification of Crum Brown's earlier rules. Vorländer stated that if a substance C_6H_5Q be converted into a substance C_6H_4QR, where Q and R are any substituents, then

(1) The nature of C_6H_4QR depends solely on Q, and is independent of R.

(2) The product C_6H_4QR is either

    (a) the *meta* isomeride,

    or (b) a mixture of the *ortho* and *para* isomerides.

(3) If the group Q contains a double or triple bond, then C_6H_4QR will be the *meta* isomeride: otherwise, C_6H_4QR will be a mixture of *ortho* and *para* isomerides.

The chief *meta* directing groups are therefore:

    $-CHO$, $-COOH$, $-CONH_2$, $-CN$, $-NO_2$, $-SO_3H$,

and the chief *ortho* and *para* directing groups are:

    $-Cl$, $-Br$, $-I$, $-OH$, $-OCH_3$, $-NH_2$, $-CH_3$ and other alkyl groups.

It must be emphasised that the above are empirical rules, and not scientific laws, and are not always accurate. The only common exceptions are the $-NHCOCH_3$ group, which, like the parent $-NH_2$ group, directs *ortho* and *para*, the $-CH{:}CHCOOH$ group (as in cinnamic acid) which also directs *ortho* and *para*, and the $-CCl_3$ group, which directs *meta*. Moreover, many reactions which give the *meta* isomeride (*e.g.*, *m*-dinitrobenzene, p. 161) also give traces of the *ortho* and *para* isomerides, and *vice-versa*.

It is also to be noted that *ortho* and *para* substitution often occur together in the same molecule, so that the group R enters the *para* and also both the *ortho* positions: thus both aniline and phenol on bromination readily give symmetric (2,4,6) tribromo-compounds (p. 165), while both toluene and phenol on nitration readily give the symmetric trinitro-derivatives (p. 170).

The course of aromatic substitution has been placed on a more scientific basis by the following rules of Hammick and Illingworth (*Jour. Chem. Soc.*, 1930, 2358). If a monosubstituted benzene derivative has the formula C_6H_5XY, where X is the atom joined to the benzene ring and Y is an atom or group of atoms attached to X, then:—

XY is *meta* directing:

    (a) if Y is in a higher group in the Periodic Classification than X,

    (b) if Y is in the same group as X, but is of lower atomic weight.

XY is *ortho* and *para* directing:

(c) if Y is in a lower group than X,

(d) if X and Y are atoms of the same element,

(e) if the group XY consists of 1 atom alone.

To apply those rules, only the elements given in the accompanying Table need usually be considered. Hydrogen is considered as being in Group I: if Y consists solely of hydrogen atoms, the latter obey the above rule; if, however, Y consists partly of hydrogen and partly of another element, both attached to X (as in $-CHO$), then the influence of the hydrogen can usually be ignored and the rules applied to the remaining element alone.

Group I	IV	V	VI	VII
H	C	N	O	F
			S	Cl
				Br
				I

Examples of the above classes are:

Meta directing:

    (a) $-CHO$, $-COOH$, $-CN$, $-CCl_3$, $-NO_2$.

    (b) $-SO_2OH$.

Ortho and *para* directing:

    (c) $-CH_3$, $-OH$, $-OCH_3$, $-NH_2$, $-NHCOCH_3$, $-SCN$.

    (d) $-CH_2 \cdot CH_3$ (X and Y being the C·C atoms).

        $-CH:CHCOOH$ (X and Y being the C:C atoms).

        $-N:N-$ (X and Y being the N:N atoms).

    (e) $-Cl$, $-Br$, $-I$.

The student should remember that *para* compounds have almost invariably higher melting-points than the corresponding *ortho* and *meta* isomerides, as the following examples show:

Melting-points of Disubstituted Benzenes

		Ortho	Meta	Para
Dichloro-benzene	$C_6H_4Cl_2$	−17	−25	53
Chloro-bromo-benzene	C_6H_4ClBr	12	−21	67
Dibromo-benzene	$C_6H_4Br_2$	6	−7	89
Chloro-aniline	$C_6H_4ClNH_2$	−2	−10	70
Bromo-aniline	$C_6H_4BrNH_2$	31	18	66
Nitro-aniline	$C_6H_4(NO_2)NH_2$	72	114	148
Bromo-phenol	$C_6H_4Br(OH)$	5	32	63
Nitro-phenol	$C_6H_4(NO_2)OH$	46	97	114
Bromo-toluene	$C_6H_4BrCH_3$	−26	−40	28
Nitro-toluene	$C_6H_4(CH_3)NO_2$	−4	16	52
Toluene sulphonylchloride	$C_6H_4(CH_3)SO_2Cl$	10	12	66

It will be seen that the *para* compound is frequently the only isomeride which is solid at room temperature, a fact which should be borne in mind when identifying organic compounds.

m-Dinitrobenzene. $C_6H_4(NO_2)_2$.

Required: Fuming nitric acid, 15 ml.; sulphuric acid, 20 ml.; nitrobenzene, 12 ml.

This preparation must be performed in a fume-cupboard, because nitrous fumes are evolved during the nitration. A ground-glass flask and air condenser (Fig. 22(A) and (C), p. 43) should preferably be used.

Place 15 ml. of fuming nitric acid (d, 1·5) in a 150 ml. flask and add carefully with shaking 20 ml. (37 g.) of concentrated sulphuric acid and then *some fragments of unglazed porcelain*. Fit a reflux air-condenser securely to the flask, and then add slowly down the condenser 12 ml. (14·5 g.) of nitrobenzene: do not add more than 3 ml. of the nitrobenzene at a time, and after each addition *shake the flask to ensure thorough mixing of the contents*. Now heat the flask on a boiling water-bath for 1 hour, both the flask and the condenser being securely clamped in position if joined by a cork, which the acid fumes evolved may attack and weaken. Shake the flask vigorously from time to time throughout this period of heating. Finally pour the mixture carefully with stirring into an excess of cold water (about 300 ml.), whereupon the heavy oily dinitrobenzene will rapidly solidify. Filter the crystalline material at the pump, wash *thoroughly* with water to remove all acid, and then drain as completely as possible.

To purify the crude dinitrobenzene, transfer it to a 200 ml. conical flask fitted with a reflux water-condenser, add about 100 ml. of rectified spirit, and heat on a water-bath until the crystalline material dissolves completely. If the solution so obtained is not quite clear, filter it through a fluted filter-paper in a heated funnel or a Buchner funnel which has been pre-heated by the filtration of some boiling solvent. The solution on cooling deposits m-dinitrobenzene as colourless crystals: yield, 14–15 g. A second recrystallisation is, however, usually necessary in order to eliminate traces of o- and p-dinitrobenzene, and thus obtain pure m-dinitrobenzene, m.p. 90°.

For reactions of m-dinitrobenzene, see p. 384, 385.

Aniline. $C_6H_5NH_2$.

Both aliphatic and aromatic nitro-compounds can be readily reduced in acid solution to the corresponding primary amine. Thus when a mixture of nitro-benzene and tin is treated with hydrochloric acid, the tin dissolves to give stannous chloride, $SnCl_2$, which in these circumstances then reacts with more acid to give stannic chloride, $SnCl_4$, and the nascent hydrogen produced from

$$Sn + 2HCl = SnCl_2 + 2H \qquad SnCl_2 + 2HCl = SnCl_4 + 2H$$
$$C_6H_5NO_2 + 6H = C_6H_5NH_2 + 2H_2O$$

these sources reduces the nitrobenzene to aniline. The stannic chloride combines with the excess of hydrochloric acid to give the complex chlorostannic acid,

H_2SnCl_6, with which the aniline forms a salt, aniline chlorostannate $(C_6H_5NH_2)_2,H_2SnCl_6$, similar in type to aniline chloroplatinate (p. 448). The crude product is therefore made strongly alkaline with sodium hydroxide, which liberates the base with the formation of sodium stannate, and the aniline can

$$(C_6H_5NH_2)_2H_2SnCl_6 + 8NaOH = 2C_6H_5NH_2 + Na_2SnO_3 + 6NaCl + 5H_2O$$

then be removed by steam-distillation.

Required: Nitrobenzene, 21 ml.; tin, 50 g.; hydrochloric acid, 100 ml.; sodium hydroxide, 75 g.; common salt, *ca.* 30 g.

Place 21 ml. (25 g.) of nitrobenzene and 50 g. of granulated tin in a 600 ml. bolt-head flask fitted with a reflux water-condenser. Now pour about 20 ml. of concentrated hydrochloric acid down the condenser, and shake the contents of the flask steadily. If the heat of the reaction causes the mixture to boil too vigorously, moderate the action by immersing the flask temporarily in cold water. Then as the reaction slackens, pour another 20 ml. of hydrochloric acid down the condenser, and shake the flask to ensure good mixing, again cooling the flask if the action becomes too violent. Continue in this way ·until a total of 100 ml. of hydrochloric acid has been added. Then heat the flask on a briskly boiling water-bath for 20 minutes. By these means the reduction is completed by the stannous chloride present: at the end of this time, therefore, the odour of the nitro-benzene should be barely perceptible. Now cool the flask in water, and slowly add a solution of 75 g. of sodium hydroxide in 100 ml. of water, thus making the solution strongly alkaline and liberating the aniline. Equip the flask for steam-distillation as shown in Fig. 15, p. 33, and steam-distil the mixture until about 175 ml. of distillate have been collected. The aniline is only moderately soluble in cold water (giving an approximately 3% solution), and the greater part therefore separates as oily drops in the aqueous distillate: in order to reduce further the solubility of the aniline in the water, add about 30 g. of powdered salt to the entire distillate and shake thoroughly until all the salt has dissolved. In spite of the decreased solubility of the aniline in the aqueous distillate, an ether extraction is still advisable to ensure efficient isolation of the aniline. Therefore transfer the distillate to a separating-funnel,* add about 40 ml. of ether, and shake vigorously, occasionally relieving the pressure of the ether vapour within the funnel by momentarily lifting the stopper. Allow the

---

* If only 100 ml. separating-funnels are available, the distillate must be divided into two portions and each extracted with ether as described, the final ether extracts being united for drying with potassium hydroxide.

two layers to separate, and then run off the lower aqueous layer, finally pouring off the remaining ethereal layer through the mouth of the funnel (to avoid contamination with adherent drops of the aqueous layer) into a 200 ml. conical flask. Replace the aqueous solution in the funnel, and again extract with a further 40 ml. of ether. Proceed as before, and transfer the ethereal layer to the conical flask. Now add some coarsely powdered potassium hydroxide to the combined ethereal extracts, and allow the securely corked flask to stand (preferably overnight) until the ethereal solution is clear and dry.

Owing to the volatility of ether, and the explosive inflammability of its vapour when mixed with air, special precautions must be taken when distilling off this solvent. Fit up the apparatus as shown in Fig. 64 (or in Fig. 23 (E), p. 45). A is a 60 ml. distilling-flask fitted with a dropping-funnel B, so that the bottom of the stem of the funnel passes well below the side-arm of the flask. The latter is then connected to a water-condenser C, through which an ample supply of water can be passed. The lower end of C is then securely fitted into a Buchner flask D of about 300 ml. capacity. A long piece of rubber tubing is attached to the side-arm of D as shown, so that the rubber tubing reaches well below the level of the bench: should any of the heavy ether vapour escape condensation during distillation, it will thus be carried away well below the apparatus. Place some fragments of unglazed porcelain in A, and extinguish all flames near the apparatus. Now decant

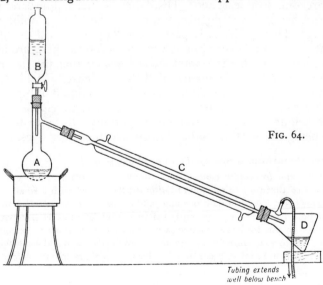

Fig. 64.

Tubing extends
well below bench

the dried ethereal solution carefully into a small fluted filter-paper, so that it filters directly into the funnel **B**. It is probable that the water extracted from the ether during drying will have dissolved some of the potassium hydroxide, and that a mixture of solid potash and saturated aqueous potash solution will have collected at the bottom of the ether. If some of this aqueous potash solution should pass into the filter during the decantation of the ether, it will not pass through the filter-paper whilst the latter is saturated with the non-miscible ether, but will merely collect at the bottom of the fluted paper.

When the filtration is complete, run about 25 ml. of the ether solution into **A**, and place under the latter a water-bath which has been brought to the boil at some considerable distance from the apparatus. (With large classes, or in crowded laboratories, the water-baths may well be heated in fume-cupboards, which are usually at a safe distance for this purpose from the working benches.) As the ether distils off from **A**, run in more of the solution from **B**, and thus continue until it appears that all the ether has been distilled off, and only aniline remains in **A**. To complete the latter stages of the distillation, it may be necessary to reheat the water-bath: this should be done as before at a safe distance from the apparatus. Now detach the Buchner flask **D**, pour the contents into an ether residue bottle, and then replace **C** by an air-condenser: finally replace the funnel **B** by a thermometer reading to at least 200°. Distil the residual aniline carefully by direct heating over a gauze, and collect the fraction boiling at 180–185°. During the early part of distillation, a small quantity of ether may come over although the recorded temperature may be well above its boiling-point: hence ensure that the flame is kept well away from the open end of the condenser. Yield, 17 g.

Aniline when freshly distilled is a colourless liquid of b.p. 184° and d, 1·025: on exposure to air and light, it develops a deep brown colour. It is an extremely important substance technically, being the starting point of many azo and other dyes.

Aniline. (Semi-micro Scale). (1/10 of above scale.)

Place 2·1 ml. (measured from a micro-burette) of nitro-benzene and 5 g. of granulated tin in a 150 ml. round-bottomed flask fitted with a small reflux water-condenser. (A large flask is employed because the mixture when subsequently boiled may "bump" violently.) Pour 10 ml. of conc. HCl down the condenser: on this scale the reaction is not sufficiently vigorous to get out of control. Heat over a gauze for 15 minutes. Cool the flask and add a solution of 7·5 g. of NaOH in 10 ml. of water to redissolve the initial precipitate. Add about

15 ml. of water and fit the flask with a small knee-tube and water-condenser (Fig. 59, p. 100). Heat over a gauze and collect the distillate in a small flask: the aniline distils rapidly in the steam, and the distillate suddenly becomes clear when about 18 ml. have been collected. Add 3 g. of powdered salt to the distillate, shake to dissolve and extract twice with about 4 ml. of ether each time. Dry the ethereal extracts in a 20 ml. conical flask with a few small pieces of solid KOH: the solution will be dry in about 15 minutes. Carefully decant the ethereal solution into the flask shown in Fig. 36 (p. 63), taking care that no adhering moisture or solid falls into the flask; add a small piece of unglazed porcelain or a few granules of carborundum (which does not absorb the liquid) and place the flask in a beaker containing hot water. Distil off *all* the ether with water running through the condenser, and away from all flames. Then run the water out of the condenser and heat the flask with a small flame. Attempt to keep the vapour of the hot aniline around the bulb of the thermometer for about one minute before actually distilling over the aniline. This is done in order to allow the bulb to reach the true temperature of the vapour. Collect the fraction of b.p. 180–185°. Using the pear-shaped flask shown in Fig. 36, it is usually possible to distil almost to the last drop. Yield, 1·5 g.

For reactions of aniline, see pp. 372–373.

2,4,6-Tribromoaniline. $C_6H_2(NH_2)Br_3$.

Aniline undergoes very ready nuclear substitution by bromine even in the cold, the bromine atoms entering the two *ortho* positions and the *para* position with the formation of symmetric or 2,4,6-tribromoaniline. The presence

$$C_6H_5NH_2 + 3Br_2 = C_6H_2(NH_2)Br_3 + 3HBr$$

of the bromine atoms in tribromoaniline reduces considerably the basic properties of the amino group, and salts even with strong acids are almost completely hydrolysed in the presence of water, although they can be prepared in the presence of solvents such as benzene (p. 203).

It should be noted that phenol also reacts very readily with bromine to give the corresponding 2,4,6-tribromophenol, $C_6H_2(OH)Br_3$.

Required: Aniline, 4 ml.; bromine, 6·4 ml.

Assemble the apparatus shown in Fig. 65. A 500 ml. Buchner flask **A** is fitted with a cork through which passes a glass delivery-tube **B** reaching nearly to the bottom of **A**. **B** is then connected by a short piece of rubber tubing to the side-arm of a 150 ml. distilling-flask **C**, care being taken to ensure that the two glass tubes touch one another inside the rubber connection. A narrow glass tube **D** is then fitted as shown so that it reaches within 2–3 cm. of the bottom of **C**.

Dissolve 4 ml. of aniline in 10 ml. of dilute hydrochloric acid in **A**, and then dilute the solution with 200 ml. of water. Now

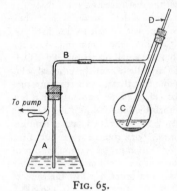

FIG. 65.

place 6·4 ml. (20·5 g.) of bromine (*care!*) in **C**, and cover it with about 40 ml. of cold water. Adjust the position of the tube **D** until it nearly touches the surface of the bromine layer. Connect **A** to a suction water-pump, so that a steady stream of bromine vapour is carried over from **C** into **A**, where the greyish-white tribromoaniline soon begins to separate. Shake the contents of **A** from time to time to ensure an even distribution of the tribromoaniline. When the evap-oration of the bromine has caused the water in **C** to become almost colourless (about 40 minutes), stop the current of air, and filter off the tribromoaniline at the pump, wash well with water and drain. Recrystallise from rectified spirit, using animal charcoal: the tribromoaniline is obtained as colourless crystals, m.p. 120°. Yield, 8·5 g.

For the elimination of the amino group from tribromoaniline, see p. 202.

p-Bromoacetanilide.   BrC$_6$H$_4$NHCOCH$_3$.   (Semi-micro scale.)

Acetanilide also undergoes ready bromination, with the formation of a mixture of *o*- and *p*-bromoacetanilide. The *ortho* compound is formed in only

$$C_6H_5NHCOCH_3 + Br_2 = BrC_6H_4NHCOCH_3 + HBr$$

small amount, however, and being more soluble in ethanol than the *para* compound, can be readily eliminated by recrystallisation.

Required: Acetanilide, 1 g.; bromine, 0·42 ml.

Dissolve 1 g. of finely powdered acetanilide in 5 ml. of cold glacial acetic acid contained in a 25 ml. conical flask. Then in another small flask prepare a solution* of 0·42 ml. (1·34 g.) of bromine (*care!*) in 6 ml. of glacial acetic acid, and add this solution *slowly* to the acetanilide solution, shaking the latter throughout the addition to ensure thorough mixing. Allow the final mixture to stand at room temperature for 15 minutes. Then

* For class work it is convenient to make up a single bromine solution by dissolving 7 ml. of bromine in 100 ml. of glacial acetic acid, and using 6·5 ml. of this solution for each preparation.

pour the pale reddish-orange solution, which may already contain some crystals of *p*-bromoacetanilide, into a large excess (about 60 ml.) of cold water, whereupon the *p*-bromoacetanilide will rapidly crystallise out. Stir these crystals thoroughly with the water to eliminate acetic acid, unchanged bromine, *etc.*, and then filter at the pump, wash well with cold water, drain, and finally re-crystallise from rectified spirit. The *p*-bromoacetanilide is obtained as colourless crystals, m.p. 167°. Yield, 1·0 g.

p-Nitroacetanilide, $NO_2C_6H_4NHCOCH_3$, and p-Nitro-aniline, $NO_2C_6H_4NH_2$.

Aniline cannot be directly nitrated with the usual nitrating mixture of nitric and sulphuric acid, because considerable charring and oxidation of the aniline occurs. The difficulty may be overcome either by using a very large excess of sulphuric acid, or (better) by protecting the reactive amino group by acetylation, since the acetylamido group, $CH_3CONH -$, has the same *ortho* and *para* directing influence as the $NH_2 -$ group itself. Acetanilide undergoes ready nitration, giving chiefly the colourless *p*-nitroacetanilide, mixed, however, with a much smaller proportion of the yellow *o*-nitroacetanilide. Re-crystallisation from ethanol readily removes the more soluble *ortho* compound, and the pure *p*-nitroacetanilide which separates can then be hydrolysed to *p*-nitroaniline.

Required: Acetanilide, 10 g.; acetic acid, 10 ml.; sulphuric acid, 20 ml.; fuming nitric acid, 4 ml.

Add 10 g. of powdered acetanilide to 10 ml. (10·6 g.) of glacial acetic acid contained in a 100 ml. beaker, and then to the well-stirred mixture add 20 ml. (37 g.) of concentrated sulphuric acid. The mixture becomes hot and a clear solution is rapidly obtained. Place the beaker in an intimate mixture of salt and crushed ice until the temperature of the reaction-mixture falls to about 0–5°. Now, whilst stirring the viscous mixture continuously with the thermometer, add 4 ml. of ordinary fuming nitric acid (*d*, 1·5) cautiously drop by drop from a burette (preferably in a fume-cupboard), so that the temperature of the mixture does not rise above 25°: this operation should take 10–15 minutes. Then remove the beaker from the freezing mixture, allow it to stand for 30 minutes at room temperature, and pour the contents on to about 100 g. of crushed ice, whereby the crude nitro-acetanilide is at once precipitated: finally rinse out the beaker with 50 ml. of water containing a few fragments of ice, adding the solution to the main bulk of the product. Allow the mixture to stand for about 20 minutes, and then filter at the pump, wash *thoroughly* with cold water to remove acid, and drain.

Yield of crude product, 14 g., the high value being due to traces of polynitro-derivatives.

Recrystallise the crude pale yellow product from methylated spirit, filter at the pump, wash quickly with a few ml. of fresh spirit, and then drain and dry. The yellow *o*-nitroacetanilide remains in the filtrate, whilst the *p*-nitroacetanilide is obtained as colourless crystals, m.p. 214°. A second recrystallisation of the *para* compound should not be necessary. Yield of pure product, 8 g.

Hydrolysis to *p*-Nitroaniline. For this purpose use 70% sulphuric acid, the usual reagent employed for the hydrolysis of anilides (p. 108). Add 5 g. of the recrystallised *p*-nitro-acetanilide to 30 ml. of 70% sulphuric acid, and boil the mixture gently under a reflux water-condenser for 20 minutes. Then pour the clear hot solution into about 150 ml. of cold water, and finally add an excess of sodium hydroxide solution until precipitation of the yellow *p*-nitroaniline is complete. Cool the mixture in ice-water if necessary, and then filter at the pump, wash well with water, and drain thoroughly. The *p*-nitroaniline is thus obtained as a dark yellow powder, which has m.p. 147–148° and therefore, in spite of the dark colour, is practically pure. Yield, 3·5 g. (almost theoretical). Recrystallise from a mixture of equal volumes of rectified spirit and water, boiling the solution gently with a small quantity of animal charcoal for 3–4 minutes, and then filtering the hot solution through a Buchner funnel preheated by the filtration of some boiling solvent. The *p*-nitroaniline separates in bright yellow crystals, m.p. 148°.

For reactions of *p*-nitroaniline, see p. 387.

m-Nitroaniline. $C_6H_4(NO_2)NH_2$.

m-Nitroaniline, unlike *o*- and *p*-nitroaniline, clearly cannot be prepared by the direct nitration of aniline or of acetanilide. It has therefore to be prepared by reducing only one of the nitro groups in the readily accessible *m*-dinitroben-zene. The earlier method for this purpose consists in boiling an ethanolic solution of the dinitrobenzene with ammonium sulphide. The latter undergoes dissociation giving hydrogen sulphide, which reduces the dinitrobenzene to

$$C_6H_4(NO_2)_2 + 3H_2S = C_6H_4(NO_2)NH_2 + 2H_2O + 3S$$

m-nitroaniline with liberation of sulphur. The method however is long and tedious, primarily because the hot ethanolic solution has to be repeatedly cooled and resaturated with hydrogen sulphide to ensure efficient reduction. Very much better results are obtained by boiling an aqueous suspension of *m*-dinitro-benzene with sodium disulphide solution, prepared by the direct addition of sulphur to sodium sulphide. In these circumstances the dinitrobenzene is

$$Na_2S + S = Na_2S_2$$
$$C_6H_4(NO_2)_2 + Na_2S_2 + H_2O = C_6H_4(NO_2)NH_2 + Na_2S_2O_3$$

readily reduced to *m*-nitroaniline, the sodium disulphide being oxidised mainly to sodium thiosulphate.

Required: Sulphur, 4·2 g.; sodium sulphide, 16 g.; *m*-dinitrobenzene, 10 g.

The crystalline sodium sulphide ($Na_2S,9H_2O$) used to prepare the disulphide is very deliquescent, and only a sample which has been kept in a well-stoppered bottle and therefore reasonably dry should be used. A sample from a badly-stoppered bottle may contain, in addition to the crystals, a certain amount of aqueous solution, in which hydrolysis and partial decomposition will have occurred: such a sample should therefore be rejected. Add 4·2 g. of finely powdered sulphur to a solution of 16 g. of the crystalline sodium sulphide in 60 ml. of water, and boil the mixture gently for a few minutes until a clear solution of the disulphide is obtained.

Heat a mixture of 10 g. of pure *m*-dinitrobenzene and 450 ml. of water in a 750 ml. beaker on a sand-bath until the water boils gently. Transfer the sodium disulphide solution to a small dropping-funnel, and clamp the funnel in position so that the end of the stem is immediately above the beaker. Now allow the disulphide solution to fall drop by drop into the boiling water at such a rate that the total addition takes 10–15 minutes: *throughout this period* keep the molten *m*-dinitrobenzene vigorously stirred by means of a glass rod (having the lower end covered by a short length of rubber tubing) so that the dinitrobenzene is kept continuously dispersed as fine drops and not allowed to settle to the bottom. (On a larger scale a mechanical stirrer can be advantageously used at this stage, but with the above quantities hand-stirring gives excellent results.) When the addition of the disulphide is complete, boil the solution gently for a further 20 minutes. Then add sufficient hot water to restore the total volume to at least 500 ml., boil vigorously for a few moments and quickly filter the solution, using a Buchner funnel and flask which have been preheated by the filtration of much boiling water: a small quantity of elementary sulphur remains on the filter. The pale brown filtrate rapidly deposits yellow crystals of the *m*-nitroaniline. Chill in ice-water, and then filter at the pump, wash with cold water, and drain. (Yield, 6·5–7·0 g.) Recrystallise from much hot water (about 80 ml. per g. of nitroaniline, to allow filtration through a preheated funnel without premature crystallisation). *m*-Nitroaniline is thus obtained as bright yellow crystals, m.p. 114°.

If an impure and discoloured sample of *m*-dinitrobenzene is used in the above preparation, add some animal charcoal to the solution immediately prior to the 20 minutes' boiling: the use of charcoal is to be avoided when possible, however, as it is liable to absorb an appreciable quantity of the *m*-nitroaniline.

For reactions of *m*-nitroaniline, see p. 387.

The Nitration of Phenol.

One of the characteristic properties of phenol is the ease with which it gives substitution products, this property being particularly well shown by the ready nitration, sulphonation and bromination which the benzene ring in the phenol molecule undergoes.

If phenol is treated even with dilute nitric acid at room temperature, nitration readily occurs with the simultaneous formation of the yellow *o*-nitrophenol and the white *p*-nitrophenol. These compounds can be readily separated, because the former is volatile, and the latter non-volatile, in steam. (This nitration probably does not involve the $\overset{+}{N}O_2$ ion, which is present in a mixture of concentrated nitric and sulphuric acids.)

If phenol is heated with more concentrated nitric acid (in the presence of sulphuric acid), nitration occurs ultimately at the *para* and at both the *ortho* positions, giving picric acid or 2,4,6-trinitrophenol. To prepare picric acid, however, it is more convenient first to heat the phenol with sulphuric acid, whereby a mixture of *o*- and *p*-phenol sulphonic acids is readily obtained. If this mixture is now heated with concentrated nitric acid, nitration occurs at the

$$HOC_6H_4H + HOSO_3H \rightarrow HOC_6H_4SO_3H + H_2O$$

two positions *meta* to the $-SO_3H$ group in each compound, and finally the $-SO_3H$ group in each of the dinitrophenol sulphonic acids is replaced by a

$$HOC_6H_4SO_3H + 2HONO_2 = HOC_6H_2(NO_2)_2SO_3H + 2H_2O$$
$$HOC_6H_2(NO_2)_2SO_3H + HONO_2 = HOC_6H_2(NO_2)_3 + H_2SO_4$$

third nitro group, giving picric acid in both cases.

o- and *p*-Nitrophenols. $NO_2C_6H_4OH$.

Required: Nitric acid, 25 ml.; phenol, 20 g.

Prepare a mixture of 25 ml. of concentrated nitric acid and 80 ml. of water in a 750 ml. flat-bottomed flask for which a steam-distillation fitting is available for subsequent use. Warm a mixture of 20 g. of phenol and 15 ml. of water *gently* in a small conical flask until the phenol is molten: on shaking the mixture vigorously an emulsion of the phenol in the water is thus obtained. Now place a thermometer in the dilute nitric acid, cool the latter in ice-water, and add the phenol emulsion in small quantities at a time so that the temperature of the well-shaken mixture does not rise above 30°. When the addition of the phenol is complete, remove the flask from the ice-water and allow the mixture to stand for at least 2 hours—and preferably overnight. During the first hour of this period of standing, retain the thermometer in the liquid and occasionally shake the latter vigorously to ensure thorough mixing: the temperature will spontaneously rise slowly to 50–55° but should not be allowed to rise above this upper limit. If the mixture is allowed to stand for only 2 hours, chill it thoroughly in ice-water at the *end* of this period in order to coagulate and partly harden the black syrupy insoluble residue and so obtain a sharp separation between this heavy residue and the aqueous layer above. (If the mixture is allowed to stand overnight, a complete separation will occur spontaneously.)

Then add 100 ml. of water, shake well to extract excess of acid, and allow the black oily drops to settle. Then decant the clear reddish-brown aqueous solution from the heavy black residual oil: this can readily be done if the nitration mixture has been set aside overnight, as the oily drops then rapidly sink and collect at the bottom of the aqueous layer, but if the mixture has been allowed to stand for only 2 hours, care must be taken that any oily drops still floating on the surface of the solution are not poured away with the aqueous solution. Now add 200 ml. of water, repeat the shaking, when the heavy oil will become semi-solid and the aqueous layer can readily be poured off. Add 300 ml. of water to the residue in the flask, fit the latter with the steam-distillation inlet and outlet tubes, and assemble the complete apparatus for steam-distillation (Fig. 15, p. 33), using a single-surface glass-jacketed condenser of wide bore. Steam-distil the mixture until about 250 ml. of distillate have been collected, the receiver being meanwhile cooled in ice-water. The o-nitrophenol readily passes over in the steam and crystallises in the cold distillate. If the nitrophenol crystallises in the condenser, run out the condenser-water for a few moments: the nitrophenol will then soon melt and pass on into the distillate. When the distillation is complete (*i.e.*, when a few ml. of the distillate collected in a test-tube give no crystalline deposit on thorough cooling), cool the distillate in ice-water for a further few minutes to ensure complete solidification of the o-nitrophenol, and then filter the latter at the pump, and drain thoroughly. Yield, 7 g. The o-nitrophenol so obtained is practically pure. It may be further purified if desired either by steam-distilling a second time, or by recrystallisation.

For the latter purpose, dissolve the crystals in hot ethanol, and then add water drop by drop to the well-stirred solution until a fine emulsion *just* appears: then add more ethanol, also drop by drop, until the emulsion just redissolves. Now allow the solution to cool spontaneously: if the emulsion reappears, add a few drops of ethanol from time to time in order to keep the solution clear. Finally the o-nitrophenol separates in crystals, and the well-stirred mixture may now be cooled in ice-water until crystallisation is complete. Filter, drain and dry either in an atmospheric desiccator, or by pressing between drying-paper.

The o-nitrophenol is obtained as bright yellow crystals, m.p. 46°, possessing an odour which resembles both that of phenol and of nitrobenzene.

Meanwhile to obtain the p-nitrophenol, chill the crude residue in the steam-distillation flask thoroughly in ice-water for about 20 minutes.* The black tar becomes almost solid, and crystals of crude p-nitrophenol separate. Filter off the complete solid product at the pump, wash it with water, and transfer it to a beaker. Extract the p-nitrophenol by boiling this residue with about 150 ml. of water, finally decanting off the aqueous solution and filtering it through a fluted filter-paper directly into a 800 ml. beaker. Repeat the extraction with a further 150 ml. of boiling water, and finally a third time with a boiling mixture of 150 ml. of water and 50 ml. of concentrated hydrochloric acid. Finally add about 3 g. of animal charcoal to the united filtrate, and then boil the latter in the open beaker until the volume is reduced to about 100 ml. Then filter through a small Buchner funnel which has been preheated by the filtration of some boiling distilled water. The filtrate on cooling, and finally chilling in ice-water, deposits the p-nitrophenol as pale brownish-white crystals: filter at the pump, wash with a *small* quantity of water and drain. Yield, 4 g. The p-nitrophenol can be recrystallised with very little loss from a mixture of equal volumes of water and concentrated hydrochloric acid, and is thus obtained as colourless odourless crystals, m.p. 114°. (If the p-nitrophenol is re-

---

* The preparation can be shortened by omitting this stage and extracting the black residue by boiling it first with the water already present in the flask. In this case the yield of p-nitrophenol is increased somewhat, but the product is usually very dark in colour.

crystallised from hot water alone, it almost invariably separates
first as a fine emulsion, which subsequently crystallises.)

For properties and reactions of *o*- and *p*-nitrophenols, see p. 386.

Picric Acid (2,4,6-Trinitrophenol).

$$
\begin{array}{c}
\text{OH} \\
\text{NO}_2 \diagup\hspace{-0.3em}\diagdown \text{NO}_2 \\
\text{NO}_2
\end{array}
$$

Required: Phenol, 8 g.; sulphuric acid, 10 ml.; nitric acid
30 ml.

Weigh out 8 g. of phenol into a *dry* 750 ml. flat-bottomed
flask, add 10 ml. (18·5 g.) of concentrated sulphuric acid, and
shake the mixture, which becomes warm. Now heat the flask
on a briskly boiling water-bath for 30 minutes to complete the
formation of the phenol-sulphonic acid, and then chill the flask
thoroughly in an ice-water mixture. Place the flask on a wooden
block (or on some similar non-conducting surface) in an efficient
fume-cupboard, and without delay, *i.e.*, whilst the phenol-
sulphonic acid is still a cold viscous syrup, add 30 ml. of concentrated nitric acid and *at once* thoroughly mix the liquids by shaking
for a few seconds. Then allow the mixture to stand undisturbed.
Usually within one minute a vigorous (but harmless) reaction
occurs, and red fumes pour out of the flask. When the action
subsides, heat the flask on a boiling water-bath for 1½ hours, with
occasional shaking. During this period the heavy oil, which is
present at the beginning, ultimately forms a mass of crystals.
When the heating is complete, add 100 ml. of cold water, mix
well and then chill thoroughly in ice-water. Filter the yellow
crystals at the pump, wash *thoroughly* with water to eliminate all
inorganic acid and drain. Recrystallise from a mixture of 1
volume of ethanol and 2 volumes of water, about 90 ml. of the
mixed solvent being required. Picric acid is obtained in pale
yellow leaflets, m.p. 122°. Dry by pressing between sheets of
drying-paper, or in a desiccator. Yield of recrystallised material,
13 g.

Picric acid if stored in bulk should, for safety, first be damped.
Smaller quantities may be safely kept whilst dry, but should be
stored in bottles having cork or rubber stoppers: glass stoppers
should never be used for potentially explosive substances, because
on replacing the stopper some of the material may be ground
between the neck of the flask and the stopper, and so caused to
explode.

REACTIONS OF PICRIC ACID. (1) The presence of the three nitro groups in picric acid considerably increases the acidic properties of the phenolic group and therefore picric acid, unlike most phenols, will evolve carbon dioxide from sodium carbonate solution. Show this by boiling picric acid with sodium carbonate solution, using the method described in Section 5, p. 330. The reaction is not readily shown by a cold saturated aqueous solution of picric acid, because the latter is so dilute that the sodium carbonate is largely converted into sodium bicarbonate without loss of carbon dioxide.

(2) To a cold aqueous solution of picric acid, add about an equal volume of dilute potassium cyanide solution. An orange coloration develops and rapidly darkens to a deep red.

USES OF PICRIC ACID. The following further reactions of picric acid are used for analytical purposes in the laboratory.

(3) *Identification of Aromatic Hydrocarbons.* Picric acid combines with many aromatic hydrocarbons, giving addition products of definite m.p. Thus with naphthalene it gives yellow naphthalene picrate, $C_{10}H_8,(NO_2)_3C_6H_2OH$, m.p. 152°, and with anthracene it gives red anthracene picrate, $C_{14}H_{10},(NO_2)_3C_6H_2OH$, m.p. 138°. For practical details, see p. 394.

(4) *Identification of Amines.* Picric acid combines with many amines to give crystalline picrates, of general formula $B,(NO_2)_3C_6H_2OH$, where B is a molecule of a monacidic base. These picrates have usually sharp melting- or decomposition-points, and serve to characterise the amines concerned. They may be formed either by (a) direct union of the acid and the base in a suitable solvent, or (b) by the interaction of sodium picrate and a salt of the amine in aqueous solution.

(a) Dissolve 3-4 drops of pyridine in about 3 ml. of ethanol and add a cold ethanolic solution of picric acid. A yellow precipitate of pyridine picrate, $C_5H_5N,(NO_2)_3C_6H_2OH$, at once separates. It may be filtered off, and recrystallised from ethanol, m.p. 167°. Quinoline similarly gives quinoline picrate, $C_9H_7N,(NO_2)_3C_6H_2OH$, m.p. 203°.

(b) If an ethanolic solution of picric acid is similarly added to one of aniline, no precipitation occurs, owing to the high solubility of aniline picrate in ethanol. If, however, a cold aqueous solution of aniline hydro-chloride is added to a similar solution of sodium picrate and the mixture shaken, yellow crystals of aniline picrate, m.p. 165°, soon separate.

(5) *Detection of Potassium in the presence of Sodium.* Add a cold saturated aqueous solution of sodium picrate to a solution of potassium chloride. A rapid precipitation of the less soluble potassium picrate occurs, even from a 1% solution of potassium chloride.

Picric acid is used on a large scale as a high explosive, but for this purpose requires a detonator. If a *few small* crystals of the pure acid are heated on a crucible lid, they first melt, and ultimately burn harmlessly with a smoky flame. Metallic salts of picric acid are much less stable than the free acid, and should always be stored damp.

Bromobenzene. C_6H_5Br.

If cold benzene is treated with bromine in the absence of sunlight, very little reaction occurs; if, however, a "halogen carrier," such as iron, iodine, pyridine, *etc.*, is also present, a rapid reaction by substitution occurs, forming first

$$C_6H_6 + Br_2 = C_6H_5Br + HBr$$

bromobenzene, and then mainly *p*-dibromobenzene.

The reaction must be carried out in the absence of direct sunlight, since sunlight causes the bromine to add directly on to benzene, particularly if the

$$C_6H_6 + 3Br_2 = C_6H_6Br_6$$

latter is warm, to give benzene hexabromide.

Bromination of the aromatic nucleus is now regarded as replacement of a hydrogen atom of the intact nucleus as a result of an attack by a polarised complex with a positive end. Iron acts as a "carrier" by forming $FeBr_3$, which as a Lewis acid forms a polarised complex with one mol. of Br_2:

Required: Purified benzene, 34 ml.; pyridine, 0·5 ml.; bromine, 24 ml.

The benzene used in this preparation should be reasonably free from toluene: therefore use a sample of benzene supplied by dealers as "crystallisable benzene," *i.e.*, one which crystallises readily when cooled in ice-water. It should preferably be dried over calcium chloride and, immediately before use, filtered through a fluted filter-paper. The pyridine should also preferably be dried over solid potassium hydroxide and redistilled.

Place 0·5 ml. of the pyridine in a 200 ml. round- or flat-bottomed flask and add 34 ml. (30 g.) of benzene. Fit the flask with a reflux water-condenser, and then place it *in* a cold water-bath. If the experiment is conducted in a fume-cupboard, the top of the condenser can be closed with a calcium chloride tube bent downwards (as in Fig. 61, p. 105; or in Fig. 23(A), p. 45, where the outlet-tube **A** will carry the calcium chloride tube) and the hydrogen bromide subsequently allowed to escape: if, however, the experiment is performed in the open laboratory, fit to the top of the condenser (or to the outlet-tube **A**) a glass delivery-tube which leads through a piece of rubber tubing to an inverted glass funnel, the rim of which dips just below the surface of some water in a beaker, so that the hydrogen bromide may be absorbed without risk of "sucking back." Ensure that the apparatus is not standing in the direct rays of the sun.

Now pour 24 ml. (76 g.) of bromine (*care in manipulation!*) down the condenser, and *at once* replace the calcium chloride tube or the delivery-tube, as a vigorous reaction occurs when the bromine dissolves in the benzene. When the initial evolution of hydrogen bromide slackens, heat the water-bath to 25–30° for one hour, occasionally shaking the contents of the flask: finally raise the temperature of the bath to 65–70° for a further 45 minutes. Now transfer the dark-coloured liquid to a separating-funnel and shake with an *excess* of 10% aqueous sodium hydroxide solution: the heavy lower layer of crude bromobenzene becomes almost colourless at this stage. Run off the bromobenzene, shake it again with water to ensure absence of alkali, and then dry with calcium chloride for 20–30 minutes. Filter through a small fluted filter-paper directly into a 50 ml. distilling-flask fitted with an air-condenser. Now distil the crude bromobenzene *slowly*, rejecting the fraction boiling up to 150°, and collecting that of b.p. 150–160°. Yield, 28–29 g. (about 19 ml.). A small quantity of crude *p*-dibromobenzene remains in the flask.

Carefully refractionate the liquid of b.p. 150–160°, either by direct distillation from a small distilling-flask or (preferably) by using a short fractionating column, of the type shown in Fig. 11(B), p. 26. Almost pure bromobenzene is thus obtained, of b.p. 155–156° if a column is used. Yield in either case, about 22 g. (14–15 ml.).

Bromobenzene is a colourless liquid of b.p. 156°, and *d*, 1·50: it has a faint agreeable odour. The bromine atom, being directly joined to the benzene ring, is very inert, and the only common reactions in which it is split off from the ring are the Fittig reaction (p. 288) and the Grignard reagent (pp. 280-284).

For reactions of bromobenzene, see p. 390.

The *p*-dibromobenzene formed as a by-product in the above reaction usually solidifies when the undistilled residue obtained in the first distillation is chilled. It may then be isolated by adding about 10 ml. of methylated spirit and some animal charcoal to the flask, boiling for a few minutes, and filtering hot. On cooling the filtrate in ice-water, crystals of *p*-dibromobenzene, m.p. 89°, separate: recrystallise a second time if necessary to obtain colourless crystals.

Ethyl γ-Bromocrotonate. $BrCH_2CH:CH\cdot COOC_2H_5$.
(Using *N*-Bromosuccinimide.)

N-Bromosuccinimide (prepared by the action of bromine on succinimide at 0° in the presence of sodium hydroxide) is a valuable specific reagent for brominating olefines in the α-methylene position to the double bond without simultaneously adding bromine to this bond. For example, if *N*-bromosuccinimide is represented by $(C_4H_4O_2)NBr$:—

$$(C_4H_4O_2)NBr + CH_3\cdot CH:CH\cdot COOEt \rightarrow (C_4H_4O_2)NH + BrCH_2\cdot CH:CH\cdot COOEt$$

The reaction was formerly considered to involve a radical mechanism initiated by the non-ionic fission of the very weak N-Br bond.

$$\begin{array}{ccc} H_2C\cdot CO & & H_2C\cdot CO \\ | \quad \rangle NBr & \rightarrow & | \quad \rangle \overset{\bullet}{N} + \overset{\bullet}{Br} \\ H_2C\cdot CO & & H_2C\cdot CO \end{array}$$

$$\begin{array}{cc} H_2C\cdot CO & H_2C\cdot CO \\ | \quad \rangle \overset{\bullet}{N} + CH_3\cdot CH:CH\cdot COOEt \rightarrow & | \quad \rangle NH + \overset{\bullet}{C}H_2\cdot CH:CH\cdot COOEt \\ H_2C\cdot CO & H_2C\cdot CO \end{array}$$

$$\begin{array}{cc} & H_2C\cdot CO & & H_2C\cdot CO \\ \overset{\bullet}{C}H_2\cdot CH:CH\cdot COOEt + | \quad \rangle NBr \rightarrow BrCH_2\cdot CH:CH\cdot COOEt + & | \quad \rangle \overset{\bullet}{N} \\ & H_2C\cdot CO & & H_2C\cdot CO \end{array}$$

Such a mechanism is supported by the fact that the reaction is accelerated by benzoyl peroxide and other radical-producing agents. It is now however considered that the function of the *N*-bromosuccinimide is to provide a constant, very low concentration of molecular bromine (Tedder *et al.*).

The substitution is best carried out by boiling *N*-bromosuccinimide with the olefine in carbon tetrachloride. Succinimide crystallises out from the carbon tetrachloride on cooling whereas the brominated product remains dissolved in the carbon tetrachloride.

Required: Ethyl crotonate, 22·8 g.; *N*-bromosuccinimide, 35·6 g.; carbon tetrachloride, 40 ml.

Dissolve 22·8 g. of ethyl crotonate in 40 ml. of dry carbon tetrachloride and add 35·6 g. of *N*-bromosuccinimide.* Heat the mixture under reflux for three hours. Cool to 0° and filter off the succinimide which is insoluble in cold carbon tetrachloride. Now shake the filtrate with water in a separating funnel, separate and dry the carbon tetrachloride layer with sodium sulphate. Filter through a fluted filter-paper into a Claisen flask and distil

*Add 0·2 g. of benzoyl peroxide to accelerate reaction.

off the carbon tetrachloride (b.p. 77°) at atmospheric pressure. Distil the residue at water-pump pressure. The fraction coming over below about 58°/14 m.m. is unchanged ethyl crotonate. Collect the fraction boiling at 98–99°/14 m.m. This is pure ethyl γ-bromocrotonate, a colourless, mobile liquid having a strong pleasant odour. Yield, 25 g.

Sulphonation.

A further difference between aliphatic and aromatic hydrocarbons is that only the latter are capable of direct *sulphonation*. Thus benzene when heated with concentrated sulphuric acid gives benzenesulphonic acid, a reaction which proceeds more readily, however, if chlorosulphonic acid is used instead of sulphuric acid: an excess of chlorosulphonic acid however may convert the sulphonic acid into the sulphonyl chloride (*cf.* p. 181).

$$C_6H_5H + HOSO_3H \rightarrow C_6H_5SO_3H + H_2O$$

$$C_6H_5H + ClSO_3H \rightarrow C_6H_5SO_3H + HCl$$

Aromatic sulphonic acids are frequently difficult to obtain pure, since they almost invariably decompose on attempted distillation, and many are very soluble in water: such aqueous solutions on being concentrated often give syrupy solutions from which the sulphonic acid crystallises with difficulty.

Toluene however sulphonates readily, and the following preparation illustrates the rapid formation of toluene-*p*-sulphonic acid mixed with a small proportion of the deliquescent *o*-sulphonic acid, and the isolation of the pure crystalline *para*-isomer.

The mechanism of aromatic sulphonation is complex and may vary, *e.g.* with the concentration of water or oleum in the acid, the temperature, and the hydrocarbon. One active agent is SO_3, and one simplified route may be:

This direct sulphonation should be compared with the indirect methods for the preparation of aliphatic sulphonic acids, *e.g.*, oxidation of a thiol (RSH → RSO₃H), and interaction of an alkyl halide with sodium sulphite to give the sodium sulphonate (RBr + Na₂SO₃ → RSO₃Na + NaBr).

Toluene-*p*-sulphonic Acid. $CH_3 \cdot C_6H_4 \cdot SO_3H$.

Required: Pure toluene, 30 ml. (26 g.); concentrated sulphuric acid, 6 ml. (11 g.).

Place 30 ml. of pure toluene and 6ml. of concentrated sulphuric acid in a 100 ml. conical flask fitted with a reflux water-condenser. Boil the mixture gently over a gauze for 5 minutes, with frequent and thorough shaking to mix the two layers. Now cool the mixture (whilst still in the flask) in ice-water, when the lower layer of the crude sulphonic acid will solidify. Decant off and discard the upper layer of toluene. Now add 25 ml. of concentrated hydrochloric acid, attach the condenser, and heat the mixture gently until a clear solution is *just* obtained, and then cool as before. (If the boiling is prolonged, and the concentration of the hydrochloric acid thus reduced, the sulphonic acid will subsequently remain dissolved.) The toluene-*p*-sulphonic acid separates as white crystals, which are contaminated with the deliquescent *o*-sulphonic acid. Therefore filter off the crystals using a small Buchner funnel, drain *quickly*, and return the crystals to the flask. Now add 15 ml. of concentrated hydrochloric acid and repeat the recrystallisation as before. The crystalline toluene-*p*-sulphonic acid can now be drained more thoroughly at the pump, and should then be dried in a vacuum desiccator. Yield, 6·3 g. M.p. 103–105°.

A further crystallisation from 15 ml. of hydrochloric acid gives the sulphonic acid, 5·5 g., m.p. 105°, almost devoid of deliquescent properties.

On a larger scale, the acid may be purified by dissolving it in a minimum of cold water, and then saturating the solution with hydrogen chloride, when the acid will crystallise.

For the preparation of the benzylthiouronium salt, m.p. 182° see p. 353.

Sulphanilic Acid (*p*-Aminobenzenesulphonic Acid). $NH_2C_6H_4SO_3H,2H_2O$

A second preparation to illustrate sulphonation is that of sulphanilic acid, $NH_2C_6H_4SO_3H$, a highly crystalline substance which, having a low solubility in cold water, can be readily isolated. If aniline is treated with an excess of concentrated sulphuric acid, aniline hydrogen sulphate is first formed, and then on heating is converted into sulphanilic acid. This conversion into the sulphanilic acid is, however, very slow with concentrated sulphuric acid: if

$$C_6H_5NH_2 + H_2SO_4 = C_6H_5NH_2,H_2SO_4$$
$$C_6H_5NH_2,H_2SO_4 = NH_2C_6H_4SO_3H + H_2O$$

fuming sulphuric acid is used, the sulphonation proceeds much more rapidly, but the aniline undergoes a certain amount of charring and decomposition on the addition of the stronger acid. It is best, therefore, first to add concentrated sulphuric acid to the aniline, and then to add fuming sulphuric acid to the more resistant aniline hydrogen sulphate so formed: under these conditions little decomposition occurs, and sulphonation proceeds readily on heating.

Required: Aniline, 10 ml.; sulphuric acid, 20 ml.; fuming

sulphuric acid (10%), 20 ml.

Place 10 ml. (10·3 g.) of aniline in a 150 ml. conical flask, and add slowly 20 ml. (37 g.) of concentrated sulphuric acid; shake the mixture gently during the addition, and keep it cool by immersing the flask occasionally in cold water. White lumps of aniline hydrogen sulphate separate. Add cautiously 20 ml. of 10% fuming sulphuric acid (*i.e.*, concentrated sulphuric acid containing 10% of dissolved sulphur trioxide), and then heat the mixture in an oil-bath at 180–190° for 1 hour, preferably in a fume-cupboard. Allow the product to cool, and pour it carefully into about 200 ml. of cold water, stirring the mixture vigorously during the addition. Allow to stand for about 5 minutes, and then filter off at the pump the sulphanilic acid which has crystallised out, wash it well with water, and drain. The crystals so obtained should be almost colourless. Purify by recrystallising from about 250 ml. of boiling water: filter the hot solution through a Buchner funnel and flask which have been preheated by the filtration of boiling distilled water. If, however, the temperature of the reaction mixture has been allowed to rise above 190°, the crude sulphanilic acid may be greyish-brown in colour: in this case, boil the aqueous solution obtained during the recrystallisation with about 2 g. of animal charcoal for 10–15 minutes (see p. 23), and then filter the hot solution through the preheated Buchner funnel. The sulphanilic acid rapidly separates from the filtrate in colourless crystals: when the filtrate is quite cold, filter off the crystals at the pump, wash with a small quantity of cold water and drain thoroughly. Dry the crystals by pressing between sheets of drying-paper, or by placing in an atmospheric calcium chloride desiccator. In a vacuum desiccator the sulphanilic acid loses its water of crystallisation, and hence its crystalline form. Yield, about 10 g.

Sulphanilic acid has no melting-point, as it decomposes on being heated. It is only slightly soluble in cold water, but easily soluble in boiling water. The strongly acid sulphonic group suppresses considerably the basic properties of the amino-group: consequently although the substance will act as an acid, forming salts with alkalis, it will not usually act as a base to form salts with acids. It is probable that sulphanilic acid exists as a doubly charged ion, $H_3\overset{+}{N}C_6H_4S\overset{-}{O}_3$.

For reactions of sulphanilic acid, see p. 384.

One of the chief uses of sulphanilic acid is in the preparation of coloured derivatives of the methyl-orange type (p. 214).

Sulphanilamide (*p*-Aminobenzenesulphonamide). NH₂·C₆H₄·SO₂NH₂.

Sulphanilamide, the simplest member of a large series of bacteriostatic drugs, can readily be prepared by the following reactions. Acetanilide, when treated with an excess of chlorosulphonic acid, gives *p*-acetamidobenzenesulphonyl chloride (Reaction A), which readily reacts with ammonia to give *p*-acetamidobenzenesulphonamide (Reaction B). The acetamido-group in the latter

$$CH_3CO·NHC_6H_5 + HOSO_2Cl = CH_3CO·NH·C_6H_4·SO_2Cl + H_2O \quad (A)$$
$$CH_3CO·NH·C_6H_4·SO_2Cl + 2NH_3 = CH_3CO·NH·C_6H_4·SO_2NH_2 + NH_4Cl \quad (B)$$
$$CH_3CO·NH·C_6H_4·SO_2NH_2 + H_2O = NH_2·C_6H_4·SO_2NH_2 + CH_3COOH \quad (C)$$

compound can be readily hydrolysed under conditions which leave the sulphonamido group unaffected, and sulphanilamide can thus be obtained (Reaction C).

Note that *p*-acetamidobenzenesulphonyl chloride will similarly react with primary and secondary amines, and the products, after hydrolysis of the acetyl group, may furnish notable drugs: *e.g.*, the condensation products with 2-amino-pyridine and 2-aminothiazole, after removal of the acetyl groups, provide the drugs commonly known as sulphapyridine (M & B 693) and sulphathiazole respectively.

Required: Acetanilide, 25 g.; chlorosulphonic acid, 63 ml.; aqueous ammonia (*d*, 0·880), 120 ml.

p-ACETAMIDOBENZENESULPHONYL CHLORIDE. (Reaction A.) Carefully add 25 g. of dry powdered acetanilide, with occasional shaking, to 63 ml. (110 g., *i.e.*, 5 molecular equivalents) of chlorosulphonic acid* contained in a 250 ml. conical flask (fume-cupboard), and then heat the solution to 60–70° for 2 hours. Cool the mixture and pour it *carefully* on to about 500 g. of crushed ice, whereupon the sulphonyl chloride separates as a white solid. Filter off the sulphonyl chloride at the pump, wash it thoroughly with water, and drain. This crude product (weight when dry, *ca.* 38 g.) is sufficiently pure to use directly in the next stage. A small sample may be dried and recrystallised from chloroform, and is finally obtained as colourless crystals, m.p. 149–150°.

p-ACETAMIDOBENZENESULPHONAMIDE. (Reaction B.) Place the above crude damp sulphonyl chloride in a

* The chlorosulphonic acid should be handled *with great care*, and always in a fume-cupboard. The technical acid is usually pure enough for the above preparation. If it is dark in colour, it can be further purified by *careful* distillation (preferably in an all-glass apparatus) and the fraction of b.p. 149–152° collected for use.

500 ml. conical flask and *cautiously* add 120 ml. of concentrated ammonia solution (d, 0·880) (fume-cupboard): a vigorous reaction with evolution of heat will follow. Stir the mixture until a smooth thin paste is obtained, and then heat at 70° for 30 minutes with occasional stirring. Cool the mixture and make it *just* acid with dilute sulphuric acid. Filter off the precipitated *p*-acetamidobenzenesulphonamide at the pump, wash it well with cold water, and drain it thoroughly. (Yield almost theoretical.) Again, this material is pure enough for the next stage: a sample may be recrystallised from hot water and the pure sulphonamide obtained as colourless crystals, m.p. 219°.

SULPHANILAMIDE. (Reaction C.) Add 15 g. of the above thoroughly drained sulphonamide to 10 ml. of concentrated hydrochloric acid diluted with 20 ml. water, and boil the mixture gently under reflux for 1 hour. Then add 30 ml. of water and heat the mixture again to boiling, with the addition of a small quantity of animal charcoal. Filter the boiling solution, and add powdered sodium carbonate in small quantities to the filtrate with stirring until all effervescence ceases and the sulphanilamide is precipitated as a white powder. Cool the mixture thoroughly and filter off the sulphanilamide at the pump, wash with water and dry. Yield, *ca.* 10 g.

Purify by recrystallisation from hot water: the sulphanilamide is obtained as colourless crystals, m.p. 163°.

Diazotisation.

Aromatic primary amines differ markedly from aliphatic amines in their reaction with nitrous acid. Thus a cold aqueous solution of mono-ethylamine hydrochloride reacts with nitrous acid to give mainly the corresponding primary alcohol:

$$C_2H_5NH_2,HCl + HONO = C_2H_5OH + H_2O + N_2 + HCl.$$

Aniline hydrochloride under similar conditions gives, however, benzenediazonium chloride, sometimes called diazo-benzene chloride:

$$C_6H_5NH_2,HCl + HONO = C_6H_5 \overset{+}{N}Cl^- + 2H_2O$$
$$\underset{N}{\overset{|||}{}}$$

Diazonium compounds are usually very soluble in water, and cannot be readily isolated, since on warming their aqueous solutions, decomposition occurs with the formation of a phenol:

$$C_6H_5 \overset{+}{N}Cl^- + HOH = C_6H_5OH + N_2 + HCl$$
$$\underset{N}{\overset{|||}{}}$$

When an aqueous solution of benzenediazonium chloride is added to a cold concentrated solution of potassium hydroxide, the unstable potassium diazotate, $C_6H_5N:NOK$, is formed, and this when heated with alkali to 130° changes to the isomeric but far more stable potassium isodiazotate: it is probable that these compounds have the structures (A) and (B) respectively.

$$
\text{(A)} \quad
\begin{array}{c}
C_6H_5N \\
\| \\
KON
\end{array}
\longrightarrow
\begin{array}{c}
C_6H_5N \\
\| \\
NOK
\end{array}
\quad \text{(B)}
$$

In preparing an aqueous solution of a diazonium salt, such as benzene-diazonium chloride, it is usual to dissolve the amine in a slight excess (about 2·2 molecular equivalents) of dilute hydrochloric acid (or alternatively to dissolve the crystalline amine hydrochloride in 1·2 equivalents of the acid) and then add an aqueous solution of a metallic nitrite. Nitrous acid is thus generated *in situ*, and reacts with the amine salt to give the diazonium compound. For a successful preparation of an aqueous solution of the diazonium salt, however, two conditions must always be observed:

(1) The solution of the aniline hydrochloride should be cooled to 5°C., and this temperature maintained throughout the addition of the sodium nitrite solution. External cooling has to be maintained, otherwise the heat of the reaction would cause the temperature to rise, with the consequent decomposition of the diazonium chloride and the production of phenol. If, on the other hand, the temperature is reduced to about 0°, diazotisation becomes extremely slow and unchanged nitrous acid may remain in the solution for an impracticably long time.

(2) Sufficient sodium nitrite must be added to diazotise all the aniline present, otherwise the unchanged aniline will react with the diazonium chloride to give diazoaminobenzene (p. 187):

$$C_6H_5N_2Cl + HNHC_6H_5 \rightarrow C_6H_5N_2NHC_6H_5 + HCl.$$

To ensure the presence of a slight excess of nitrous acid, potassium iodide-starch paper is sometimes used as an external indicator, a drop of the solution being removed from time to time during the addition of the sodium nitrite, and then dropped on to the paper. When an excess of nitrous acid is present, iodine is liberated, and gives the familiar

$$2HNO_2 + 2HCl + 2KI = 2NO + 2KCl + I_2 + 2H_2O$$

blue colour with starch. In actual practice, however, it is found that long before the addition of the theoretical quantity of sodium nitrite is complete, the solution will give a blue coloration (presumably by atmospheric oxidation) within a few seconds of being placed on the KI-starch paper. If this indicator is used, therefore, it should be noted that an excess of nitrous acid is not present until an *immediate* blue colour is obtained when a drop of the solution is placed on the paper.

The use of KI-starch paper is definitely not recommended, however:

it is better to use sodium nitrite* of good quality and to add an amount which is about 10% in excess of that theoretically required.

The student is recommended to carry out the preparation of iodobenzene in order to gain experience in the preparation of aqueous solutions of diazonium compounds, and then to prepare a solution of benzenediazonium hydrogen sulphate with which to carry out the chief reactions that diazonium compounds undergo.

Iodobenzene. C_6H_5I.

When potassium iodide or hydrogen iodide is added to an aqueous solution of a diazonium salt, nitrogen is readily evolved (no catalyst being necessary) and the corresponding iodo-compound is formed. Iodo-compounds can thus

$$C_6H_5N_2Cl + KI = C_6H_5I + N_2 + KCl$$

be readily obtained from aromatic primary amines.

Required: Aniline, 15 ml.; hydrochloric acid, 40 ml.; sodium nitrite, 12·5 g.; potassium iodide, 35 g.

Dissolve 15 ml. (15·4 g.) of aniline in a mixture of 40 ml. of concentrated hydrochloric acid and 40 ml. of water contained in a 250 ml. conical flask. Place a thermometer in the solution, immerse the flask in a mixture of ice and water, and cool until the temperature of the stirred solution reaches 5°. Dissolve 12·5 g. of powdered sodium nitrite in 30 ml. of water, and add this solution in small quantities (about 2–3 ml. at a time) to the cold aniline hydrochloride solution, meanwhile keeping the latter well stirred by means of a thermometer. Heat is evolved by the reaction, and therefore a short interval should be allowed between consecutive additions of the sodium nitrite, partly to allow the temperature to fall again to 5°, and partly to ensure that the nitrous acid formed reacts as completely as possible with the aniline. The temperature must not be allowed to rise above 10°, otherwise appreciable decomposition of the diazonium compound to phenol will occur: on the other hand, the temperature should not be allowed to fall as low as 0°, as at this temperature diazotisation becomes very slow, and free nitrous acid may remain in the solution for a considerable time.

When all the sodium nitrite has been added and diazotisation is complete, transfer the cold solution to a 600 ml. round-bottomed bolt-head flask. Dissolve 35 g. of potassium iodide in 50 ml. of water, and add this solution slowly with shaking to the cold

---

* Hence all the following preparations involving diazotisation are based on the use of "Sodium Nitrite Recryst." and not "Sodium Nitrite Technical" or "Commercial."

diazo solution. A vigorous reaction occurs, nitrogen being freely evolved, and some iodine being liberated owing to the slight excess of nitrous acid present. Allow the complete mixture to stand for 10 minutes with occasional shaking, and then heat it on a boiling water-bath for a further 20 minutes to complete the reaction: the crude iodobenzene separates as a heavy dark oil at the bottom of the flask. Add 10% sodium hydroxide solution to the mixture until the latter is definitely alkaline, *i.e.*, until a drop withdrawn on a glass rod imparts a definite blue colour to red litmus-paper: this converts any phenol which may have been formed into sodium phenoxide which (unlike phenol itself) is not volatile in steam. Now equip the flask for steam-distillation (Fig. 15, p. 33), and steam-distil the mixture until no more oily drops of iodobenzene come over with the aqueous distillate. Transfer the distillate to a separating-funnel, and carefully run off the heavy lower layer of iodobenzene into a small conical flask, rejecting the upper aqueous layer. (The iodobenzene should now have a pale yellow colour. If it is dark in colour, return it to the funnel, and shake it vigorously with a dilute aqueous solution of sodium thiosulphate until a pale yellow colour is obtained: then run off the heavy lower layer as before.) Add a few pieces of granular calcium chloride to the liquid in the conical flask, and shake for about 10 minutes until the liquid is clear and dry. Filter through a small fluted filter-paper directly into a 60 ml. distilling-flask. Fit the flask with a thermometer reading up to at least 200°, and with a short air-condenser about 12 inches long. Distil the liquid slowly, and collect the fraction boiling at 185–190°. Yield, about 28 gms. (15–16 ml.).

Iodobenzene, as usually prepared, is a very pale yellow liquid of b.p. 188°, and d, 1·83. The freshly distilled pure liquid is colourless, but soon redevelops the yellow colour on exposure to light. Iodobenzene is insoluble in water.

The iodine atom in iodobenzene (unlike that in the corresponding aliphatic compounds) is very resistant to the action of alkalis, potassium cyanide, silver nitrite, *etc*. This firm attachment of the iodine atom to the benzene ring is typical of aromatic halides generally, although in suitably substituted nitro-compounds, such as chloro-2,4-dinitrobenzene, the halogen atom does possess an increased reactivity (p. 262).

Iodobenzene Dichloride $C_6H_5ICl_2$, Iodosobenzene, C_6H_5IO, and Iodoxybenzene, $C_6H_5IO_2$.

When iodobenzene in chloroform solution is treated with chlorine, the iodine becomes trivalent by the addition of chlorine, and iodobenzene dichloride is formed. The latter can be regarded as a salt of the basic iodosobenzene, which can be readily obtained by treating the dichloride with sodium hydroxide.

$$C_6H_5ICl_2 + 2NaOH = C_6H_5IO + 2NaCl + H_2O$$

Iodosobenzene forms similar salts with other acids; dilute nitric acid gives the dinitrate, $C_6H_5I(NO_3)_2$, and acetic acid the diacetate, $C_6H_5I(OOCCH_3)_2$.

When iodosobenzene is boiled with water, interaction occurs with the formation of one equivalent of iodobenzene and one of iodoxybenzene:

$$2C_6H_5IO = C_6H_5I + C_6H_5IO_2$$

the iodobenzene steam-distils off, whilst the iodoxy-benzene dissolves in the hot water and rapidly crystallises on cooling.

IODOBENZENE-DICHLORIDE. If a cylinder of chlorine is not available for this preparation, generate the chlorine by allowing concentrated hydrochloric acid to fall from a dropping-funnel which is fitted into the neck of a Buchner flask containing coarsely powdered potassium permanganate, aiding the reaction when necessary by gentle warming on a water-bath: purify the chlorine by passing it through wash-bottles containing water and sulphuric acid respectively. Chlorine from a cylinder may be used directly without washing.

Dissolve 5 ml. (9·2 g.) of iodobenzene in 35 ml. of chloroform contained in a wide boiling-tube or in a conical flask. Cool the latter in ice-water and then pass a steady stream of chlorine through the solution until no further precipitation of the yellow crystals of iodobenzene dichloride occurs. Then filter the latter at the pump, and wash with a small quantity of chloroform. Yield, 11–12 g. The dichloride slowly decomposes on standing, giving chiefly p-chloroiodobenzene and hydrogen chloride: $C_6H_5ICl_2 \rightarrow ClC_6H_4I + HCl$. Its melting-point is therefore uncertain, but a freshly prepared dry sample usually melts at 101–103° with decomposition.

IODOSOBENZENE. The hydrolysis of the dichloride may be carried out using either sodium hydroxide or pyridine: the former gives the better product.

(a) Add 4 g. of the *finely powdered* dichloride to 40 ml. of 10% sodium hydroxide solution contained in a conical flask and shake the mixture vigorously. A rapid reaction follows, and the yellow colour of the dichloride fades. Shake at intervals over a period of 20 minutes, and then filter at the pump, wash with 10% sodium hydroxide solution, then repeatedly with water, drain thoroughly and dry. Yield, theoretical (2·9 g.).

(b) Dissolve 4 g. of the dichloride in 12 ml. of pyridine, and then dilute the mixture by slowly adding 150 ml. of water, stirring vigorously throughout the addition. The iodosobenzene separates at first as a fine emulsion, which rapidly crystallises. Filter, wash with water, and dry. Yield, 2 g.

Melting-point determinations should not be attempted with iodosobenzene, as it explodes violently at about 220°.

IODOBENZENE DIACETATE. Add 2 g. of iodosobenzene to 6 ml. of glacial acetic acid, boil gently until a clear solution is obtained, and then cool. The diacetate is freely soluble in acetic acid, but not in ether. Therefore add ether (about 50 ml.) in order to precipitate the iodobenzene diacetate, which rapidly separates in colourless crystals, particularly on scratching with a rod. Filter, wash with ether, and dry. M.p. 157°. Yield, 2 g. The diacetate so obtained is pure, but may if desired be recrystallised from benzene. Unlike the dichloride, it is stable on being kept.

IODOXYBENZENE. Add 3 g. of iodosobenzene to about 100 ml. of water contained in a small flask, and steam-distil the mixture until iodobenzene ceases to come over and the distillate leaving the condenser is no longer turbid (usually about 20 minutes). The residual solution in the flask should now be clear: pour it quickly into a beaker and cool. (If the residual solution is not clear, it should be filtered rapidly, using a small Buchner funnel and flask preheated by the filtration of boiling distilled water, as the iodoxybenzene begins to separate very rapidly on cooling.) Filter off the colourless crystals of iodoxybenzene, wash with water, and dry. Yield, 1 g.

Alternatively, if it is not desired to collect the iodobenzene, the iodosobenzene can be added to about 150 ml. of water contained in an open beaker or conical flask, and the mixture *gently* boiled until a clear solution is obtained and the pale yellow colour has disappeared. On cooling the iodoxybenzene rapidly separates.

Iodoxybenzene on being heated explodes at 236–237°, and a m.p. determination should not be attempted.

Benzenediazonium Hydrogen Sulphate, $C_6H_5N_2HSO_4$, in aqueous solution.

Required: Aniline, 5 ml.; sodium nitrite, 4·5 g.

Dissolve 5 g. (5 ml.) of aniline in 50 ml. of warm dilute sulphuric acid in a conical flask and add 50 ml. of water. Place a thermometer in the solution, immerse the flask in a mixture of ice and water, and cool until the temperature of the stirred solution falls to 5°. Dissolve 4·5 g. of powdered sodium nitrite in 20 ml. of water, and add this solution in small quantities (about 2–3 ml. at a time) to the cold aniline sulphate solution. Keep the latter well shaken and maintain the temperature at about 5° (see p. 183). When all the sodium nitrite solution has been added, transfer about 5 ml. of the cold solution to a test-tube for each of the following reactions. The remainder of the diazonium hydrogen sulphate solution must be kept in ice-water until required, and then when all the reactions have been carried out, the solution should be poured down the sink.

(1) Boil the solution gently for 1–2 minutes. Nitrogen is rapidly evolved, and phenol is formed in solution. Cool the solution (which

$$C_6H_5N_2HSO_4 + HOH \rightarrow C_6H_5OH + N_2 + H_2SO_4$$

should smell of phenol) and test for phenol by adding bromine water.
A brownish-white precipitate of tribromophenol is produced (p. 339).

(2) To the cold solution, add about 2 ml. of 10% potassium iodide
solution. A brisk effervescence of nitrogen occurs, and iodobenzene
separates, usually as drops so small that in spite of their density they
float on the surface.

$$C_6H_5N_2HSO_4 + KI \rightarrow C_6H_5I + N_2 + KHSO_4$$

(3) (a) Dissolve about 0·5 g. of phenol in a considerable excess of
10% sodium hydroxide solution and cool in ice-water. Pour the diazonium solution into this sodium phenoxide solution and note the formation of an orange-yellow solution of the sodium derivative of benzeneazophenol.

$$C_6H_5N_2HSO_4 + HC_6H_4ONa \rightarrow C_6H_5N{:}NC_6H_4ONa + H_2SO_4$$

The sulphuric acid is of course neutralised at once by the alkaline
solution.

(b) Repeat, using 0·5 g. of 2-naphthol instead of the phenol. A
scarlet precipitate of benzeneazo-2-naphthol is similarly produced.

$$C_6H_5N_2HSO_4 + HC_{10}H_6OH \rightarrow C_6H_5N{:}NC_{10}H_6OH + H_2SO_4$$

The above condensations occur only in alkaline solution, hence the
need of an excess of sodium hydroxide in the phenol solutions.

(4) (a) To 1 ml. of the diazonium solution, add 0·5 ml. of aniline, and
shake vigorously. Diazoaminobenzene separates as a finely-divided
yellow solid.

$$C_6H_5N_2HSO_4 + HNHC_6H_5 \rightarrow C_6H_5N{:}NNHC_6H_5 + H_2SO_4$$

(b) Repeat, using 0·5 ml. of dimethylaniline in place of aniline. A
red solution of benzeneazo-p-dimethylaniline hydrochloride is produced on adding dil. hydrochloric acid. Add an excess of sodium

$$C_6H_5N_2HSO_4 + HC_6H_4N(CH_3)_2, HCl \rightarrow C_6H_5N_2C_6H_4N(CH_3)_2, HCl + H_2SO_4$$

hydroxide solution in order to liberate the free base, which is yellow.

(5) Add 2 ml. of ethanol to the solution, shake the mixture and
warm gently. Phenetole (ethyl phenyl ether) is the main product.

$$C_6H_5N_2HSO_4 + HOC_2H_5 \rightarrow C_6H_5OC_2H_5 + N_2 + H_2SO_4$$

At the same time, the ethanol reduces some of the diazonium compound
to benzene, the ethanol itself being oxidised to acetaldehyde, the odour

$$C_2H_5OH = CH_3CHO + 2H$$
$$C_6H_5N_2HSO_4 + 2H = C_6H_6 + N_2 + H_2SO_4$$

of which can sometimes be detected.

Chlorobenzene. C_6H_5Cl. (Sandmeyer's Method.)

Chlorobenzene may be obtained from an aqueous solution of benzenediazonium chloride by two methods:

(a) *Gattermann's Method*. The addition of finely divided copper powder to the benzenediazonium chloride solution has a catalytic action even at room

$$C_6H_5N_2Cl = C_6H_5Cl + N_2$$

temperature, causing the evolution of nitrogen and the formation of chlorobenzene.

(b) *Sandmeyer's Method*. If the aqueous solution of benzenediazonium chloride is added to a solution of cuprous chloride in hydrochloric acid and the mixture then warmed, a similar decomposition occurs, nitrogen and chlorobenzene being formed.

Required: Copper sulphate, 28 g.; sodium chloride, 9·5 g.; sodium bisulphite, 14 g.; hydrochloric acid, 70 ml.; aniline, 20 ml.; sodium nitrite, 17 g.

To prepare the solution of cuprous chloride, add 28 g. of crystalline copper sulphate and 9·5 g. of sodium chloride in turn to 100 ml. of water in a 250 ml. beaker, and warm the mixture to 55–60°, stirring it with a thermometer until a clear solution is obtained at this temperature. Now reduce this solution *either* by adding a solution of 14 g. of sodium bisulphite in 25 ml. of water, whereupon the mixed solutions will rapidly become green in colour, *or*, if a syphon of liquid sulphur dioxide is available, by passing a brisk current of sulphur dioxide into the solution. By either method, the cupric chloride formed by the interaction of the cupric sulphate and the sodium chloride is reduced to cuprous chloride, which separates as a white powder as the solution cools. Now place the beaker in cold water containing a *small quantity* of ice in order to cool the solution to about 10–15°, and thus to complete the separation of the cuprous chloride: it is important that the solution is not cooled below this temperature, otherwise crystals of sodium sulphate, *etc.*, may separate and contaminate the cuprous chloride. Allow the solution to stand in the cold water whilst the diazotisation of the aniline is being performed; then filter off the cuprous chloride rapidly through a Buchner funnel at the pump, wash it once with a few ml. of distilled water, and then, immediately it is well drained, transfer it to a mixture of 20 ml. of concentrated hydrochloric acid and 20 ml. of water in a 600 ml. round-bottomed flask. During the draining of the cuprous chloride on the filter, slight atmospheric oxidation may give the surface of the chloride a blue colour: the cuprous chloride will, however, dissolve in the hydrochloric acid to give a clear brownish-coloured solution. Attach a

reflux water-condenser to the flask, and in the top of the condenser fit a dropping-funnel securely by a cork which has a
shallow groove cut or filed vertically down the side, in order to
allow the subsequent escape of nitrogen. (Alternatively, use the
apparatus shown in Fig. 23(A), p. 45.)

Meanwhile, during the cooling of the cuprous chloride solution,
prepare a solution of benzenediazonium chloride by dissolving 20
ml. (20·5 g.) of aniline in a mixture of 50 ml. of concentrated
hydrochloric acid and 50 ml. of water, and after cooling to 5°,
adding slowly a solution of 17 g. of sodium nitrite in 40 ml. of
water. Observe carefully the general conditions for diazotisation
given in the preparation of iodobenzene (p. 184).

When the preparation of the cuprous chloride is complete, place
the diazonium solution in the dropping-funnel at the top of the
reflux condenser, and then heat the flask containing the cuprous
chloride on a boiling water-bath. When the cuprous chloride
solution has been thoroughly heated, remove the water-bath,
support the flask on a stand, and allow the diazonium solution to
run *slowly* drop by drop down the condenser, meanwhile shaking
the flask gently to ensure thorough mixing. As each drop of the
diazo solution enters the liquid in the flask, a momentary separation of a yellow addition product, $C_6H_5N_2Cl,Cu_2Cl_2$, occurs: this
compound then breaks down, giving nitrogen and chlorobenzene,
and the heat of the reaction maintains the temperature of the
solution well above 60°. When all the diazonium solution has
been added, allow the mixture to stand for 10 minutes, and then
replace the flask on the boiling water-bath for a further 15 minutes
in order to complete the reaction. Then detach the flask, equip it
for steam-distillation (Fig. 15, p. 33) and steam-distil the contents
until no more oily drops of chlorobenzene pass over. Place the
distillate in a separating-funnel, and run off the lower layer of
chlorobenzene into a small conical flask: add a few pieces of
granular calcium chloride, allow to stand for 15–20 minutes, and
then filter the dry chlorobenzene directly into a 60 ml. distilling-
flask. Fit the flask with an air-condenser, and distil the chlorobenzene, collecting the fraction which boils at 130–135°. Yield
18–19 g.

Chlorobenzene is a stable colourless liquid having b.p. 132°
and d, 1·11; it is insoluble in water.

For reactions of chlorobenzene, see p. 340.

Benzonitrile (Phenyl Cyanide). C_6H_5CN. (Sandmeyer's Method.)

Sandmeyer's method for the preparation of chlorobenzene can similarly be extendéd to the preparation of bromobenzene and of cyanobenzene or benzo-nitrile. Thus an aqueous solution of benzenediazonium chloride on treatment with a solution of cuprous bromide in hydrobromic acid gives nitrogen and bromobenzene: alternatively, on treatment with a solution of potassium cupro-cyanide, $K_3[Cu(CN)_4]$, it gives nitrogen and cyanobenzene (or benzonitrile), C_6H_5CN. No similar catalyst is required for the preparation of iodobenzene (p. 184).

Potassium cupro-cyanide is the most convenient form in which cuprous cyanide can be used in Sandmeyer's Reaction. It is prepared by adding an excess of potassium cyanide to copper sulphate solution, whereby the cupric cyanide which is formed immediately breaks down to give cuprous cyanide and cyanogen, and the cuprous cyanide then dissolves in the excess of potassium

$$CuSO_4 + 2KCN = Cu(CN)_2 + K_2SO_4 \qquad 2Cu(CN)_2 = Cu_2(CN)_2 + C_2N_2$$
$$6KCN + Cu_2(CN)_2 = 2K_3[Cu(CN)_4]$$

cyanide to give potassium cupro-cyanide.

Required: Aniline, 20 ml.; hydrochloric acid, 50 ml.; sodium nitrite, 17 g.; copper sulphate, 55 g.; potassium cyanide, 60 g.

Apart from the diazotisation, *the whole of the following prepara-tion up to the completion of the steam-distillation must be carried out in a fume-cupboard having a vigorous draught.*

Prepare a solution of benzenediazonium chloride from 20 ml. (20·5 g.) of aniline precisely as in the preparation of chloro-benzene (p. 189), *i.e.*, by dissolving the aniline in a mixture of 50 ml. of concentrated hydrochloric acid and 50 ml. of water, cooling to 5°, and then cautiously adding a solution of 17 g. of sodium nitrite in 40 ml. of water to the well-cooled and stirred aniline hydrochloride solution so that the temperature of the mixture remains between 5° and 10°.

Then, while the diazonium solution is standing in ice-water, dissolve 55 g. of powdered copper sulphate ($CuSO_4,5H_2O$) in 200 ml. of water contained in a 1500 ml. flat-bottomed flask, for which a steam-distillation fitting is available for subsequent use. Place a thermometer in the copper sulphate solution and warm the latter to 60–65°. Now cautiously add a solution of 60 g. of powdered potassium cyanide* in 100 ml. of water to the copper

* The "double salt," *i.e.*, potassium cyanide mixed with sodium cyanide, is best and cheapest for this purpose, and can be obtained already powdered, in which form, however, storage in an air-tight receptacle is particularly necessary. If only fused or lump cyanide is available, great care should be taken when powdering the material in a mortar, in order to prevent small fragments from flying up and adhering to the lips, nostrils, or eyes. This is best achieved by draping a duster tent-wise around the pestle and over the mortar, so that the cyanide is completely covered while it is being crushed.

sulphate solution, shaking the flask during the addition to facilitate the evolution and escape of the cyanogen—*take great care to avoid inhaling traces of the cyanogen.* During the addition of the cyanide solution the temperature of the mixture rises a few degrees (usually to about 75°), and finally a clear pale-brown solution of potassium cupro-cyanide is obtained.

Now add the diazonium solution to the potassium cupro-cyanide in small quantities at a time so that the temperature of the mixture remains between 60° and 70°: shake the mixture vigorously after each addition of the diazo solution. Then fit a reflux air- or water-condenser to the flask, and heat the latter on a boiling water-bath for 15 minutes to complete the reaction. Finally steam-distil the solution until no more oily benzonitrile passes over (usually until about 600 ml. of distillate have been collected).

Place the distillate in a separating-funnel and extract the benzonitrile twice, using about 30 ml. of ether for each extraction. Return the united ethereal extracts to the funnel and shake with 10% sodium hydroxide solution to eliminate traces of phenol formed by decomposition of the benzenediazonium chloride. Then run off the lower aqueous layer, and shake the ethereal solution with about an equal volume of dilute sulphuric acid to remove traces of foul-smelling phenyl isocyanide (C_6H_5NC) which are always present. Finally separate the sulphuric acid as completely as possible, and shake the ether with water to ensure absence of acid. Run off the water and dry the benzonitrile solution over granular calcium chloride for about 20 minutes.

Filter the dried ethereal solution, and then distil off the ether from a small flask, using precisely similar apparatus and the same method as those described in the preparation of aniline (Fig. 64, p. 163; see also Fig. 23(E), p. 45) and observing the same precautions. When the ether has been removed, fit the distilling-flask to a short air-condenser, and distil the benzonitrile, collecting the fraction boiling between 187° and 191°. Yield, 16·5 g. (16 ml.).

Benzonitrile is a colourless liquid, having b.p. 190° and *d*, 1·02: it is almost insoluble in water, and has an odour resembling that of nitrobenzene and of benzaldehyde.

Hydrolysis of Benzonitrile. Benzonitrile is moderately readily hydrolysed by 10% aqueous sodium hydroxide, but only slowly by hydrochloric acid (*cf.* p. 122). Ready hydrolysis is obtained by boiling the nitrile under reflux

$$C_6H_5CN + 2H_2O = C_6H_5COOH + NH_3$$

with 70% sulphuric acid (preparation, p. 109), but the benzoic acid volatilises in the steam and crystallises again in the reflux condenser, which may become choked with a hard deposit of the acid: moreover some aromatic nitriles are liable to undergo sulphonation as well as hydrolysis when boiled with such concentrated sulphuric acid. These disadvantages do not apply to hydrolysis by sodium hydroxide, as the benzoic acid remains in solution as sodium benzoate: furthermore, the completion of the hydrolysis is readily detected by the complete disappearance of oily drops of the insoluble nitrile.

Boil 5 ml. (5·1 g.) of benzonitrile and 75 ml. of 10% aqueous sodium hydroxide in a 200 ml. flask under a reflux water-condenser until no more oily drops of unchanged nitrile run down from the condenser (usually about 40 minutes). Then detach the condenser and boil the solution in the open flask for a few minutes to remove free ammonia. Cool the liquid, and add concentrated hydrochloric acid cautiously until precipitation of benzoic acid is complete. Cool the mixture again thoroughly, filter off the benzoic acid at the pump, and wash well with cold water. Yield, 5·8 g. (almost theoretical). Confirm the identity of the benzoic acid by the tests given on p. 347. The benzoic acid obtained in this way should be pure and have m.p. 121°: a portion may if desired be recrystallised from hot water.

Benzamide from Benzonitrile. (A) Although benzonitrile when boiled with 70% sulphuric acid undergoes ready hydrolysis to benzoic acid (see above), treatment with hot 90% sulphuric acid gives the intermediate benzamide. This difference arises partly from the difference in temperature employed, but also

$$C_6H_5 \cdot C \equiv N \rightarrow [C_6H_5 \cdot \overset{+}{C} = NH]HSO_4 \rightarrow [C_6H_5 \cdot \underset{OH}{\overset{+}{C}} = NH_2]HSO_4 \rightarrow C_6H_5 \cdot CO \cdot NH_2$$

from the fact that the speed of hydrolysis of a nitrile to an amide increases rapidly and steadily with the concentration of the acid, whereas the speed of hydrolysis of the amide to the acid rises to a maximum and then decreases.

(B). Many nitriles when treated with hydrogen peroxide in warm alkaline solution undergo hydrolysis to amides which can thus be readily obtained in high yield. Insoluble liquid nitriles can be treated directly in the aqueous suspension, but for insoluble solid nitriles the addition of a suitable organic solvent to give a complete solution may be desirable, although the completion of the hydrolysis may not then be so readily detected.

This method has the great advantage over method (A) in that it can be applied in particular to those aromatic nitriles in which the aryl group is readily sulphonated: clearly, it can also be applied to nitriles in which the alkyl or aryl portion contains groups which are in any other way affected by concentrated sulphuric acid, or by concentrated aqueous alkalis.

Method A. Prepare approximately 90% sulphuric acid by adding 25 ml. of the concentrated acid cautiously with gentle shaking to 5 ml. of water.

Add 2 g. (2 ml.) of benzonitrile to 20 ml. of 90% sulphuric acid in a conical flask: a clear solution is rapidly obtained. Heat the solution in an oil-bath at 120-130° for 20 minutes, and then cool the solution and pour it on to 50 g. of crushed ice. Filter the precipitated benzamide at the pump, wash it with water, and recrystallise it once (or twice) from water. The benzamide is obtained as white crystals, m.p. 128-130°. Yield, 1 g.

Method (B). Add 3 g. (3 ml.) of benzonitrile to 50 ml. of "10-volumes" hydrogen peroxide in a beaker, stir mechanically and add 1 ml. of 10% aqueous sodium hydroxide solution. Warm the stirred mixture at 40° until the oily suspension of the nitrile has been completely replaced by the crystalline benzamide (45-60 minutes). Cool the solution until crystallisation of the benzamide is complete, and then filter at the pump and recrystallise as above. One recrystallisation gives the pure benzamide, m.p. 129-130°; yield of purified material, 2-2·5 g.

p-Tolunitrile (*p*-Tolyl Cyanide). $CH_3C_6H_4CN$. (Sandmeyer's Method.)

Required: *p*-Toluidine, 24 g.; hydrochloric acid, 55 ml.; sodium nitrite, 17 g.

The preparation of *p*-tolunitrile illustrates the method employed for the diazotisation of amines the hydrochlorides of which are only moderately soluble in cold water. Dissolve 24 g. of powdered *p*-toluidine in a warm mixture of 55 ml. of concentrated hydrochloric acid and 180 ml. of water, and then chill the solution thoroughly in ice-water: during the cooling, stir the mixture continuously in order to ensure that the *p*-toluidine hydrochloride crystallises out as small feathery crystals which will subsequently redissolve readily during the diazotisation. Now continue precisely as in the above preparation of benzonitrile (p. 191), *observing the same precautions against inhaling cyanogen*, and using the same quantities of all the reagents, *i.e.*, diazotising with a solution of 17 g. of sodium nitrite in 40 ml. of water, and pouring the diazotised solution into the potassium cupro-cyanide solution prepared as before. During the addition of the diazotised solution, however, the potassium cupro-cyanide mixture must be occasionally warmed on a water-bath in the fume-cupboard in order to keep the temperature between 60° and 70°.

If during the steam-distillation the *p*-tolunitrile tends to crystallise in the condenser, it is usually sufficient to increase the amount of steam momentarily in order to melt and dislodge the nitrile: alternatively the condenser-water can be turned off for a few moments. Collect about 500 ml. of distillate to ensure complete distillation of the nitrile, and cool the receiver in ice-water during the distillation. The oily nitrile in the distillate readily solidifies, particularly on stirring. Then filter at the pump, and press and drain the solid nitrile thoroughly on the filter to remove liquid impurities. Dry in a desiccator, or by pressing between layers of drying-paper: in the latter case, take care that the nitrile does not melt under the warmth of the hand. *p*-Tolunitrile is thus obtained as a pale brown solid: yield, 19 g. Purify the dry material by direct distillation, preferably after mixing it with 1-2 g. of animal charcoal: use a *short* air-condenser, which will require gentle warming at the beginning of the distillation to prevent premature crystallisation. Collect the fraction having b.p. 214-218°. The distilled nitrile solidifies as colourless crystals, m.p. 29°, b.p. 218°.

Hydrolysis of *p*-Tolunitrile. As in the case of benzonitrile, alkaline hydrolysis is preferable to hydrolysis by 70% sulphuric acid. Boil a mixture of 5 g. of *p*-tolunitrile, 75 ml. of 10% aqueous sodium hydroxide solution and 15 ml. of ethanol under a reflux water-condenser. The ethanol is added partly to increase the speed of the hydrolysis, but in particular to prevent the nitrile (which volatilises in the steam) from actually crystallising in the condenser. The solution becomes clear after about 1 hour's heating, but the boiling should be continued for a total period of 1·5 hours to ensure complete hydrolysis. Then precipitate and isolate the *p*-toluic acid, $CH_3C_6H_4COOH$, in precisely the same way as the benzoic acid in the above hydrolysis of benzonitrile. Yield 5·5 g. (almost theoretical). The *p*-toluic acid has m.p. 178°, and may be recrystallised from a mixture of equal volumes of water and rectified spirit.

The methyl group in *p*-toluic acid may be oxidised to a –COOH group forming *p*-phthalic (or *tere*-phthalic) acid, $C_6H_4(COOH)_2$, but the oxidation is usually slow.

Phenol. C_6H_5OH.

When a diazonium salt in aqueous solution is gently warmed, it reacts with the water, liberating nitrogen and forming the corresponding phenol:

$$C_6H_5N_2HSO_4 + HOH \rightarrow C_6H_5OH + N_2 + H_2SO_4$$

The diazonium hydrogen sulphate is used for this reaction in preference to the diazonium chloride since the latter by direct decomposition always forms small quantities of the chloro-hydrocarbon as a by-product:

$$C_6H_5N_2Cl = C_6H_5Cl + N_2$$

For the preparation of phenol, the aqueous solution should be heated carefully to 50-55°, at which temperature the reaction proceeds smoothly: above this temperature, however, the reaction may rapidly become very vigorous, and the heat of reaction will then cause a marked rise in the temperature and the production of a large amount of tarry byproducts.

Required: Sulphuric acid, 27·5 ml.; aniline, 24 ml.; sodium nitrite, 20 g.; dry potassium carbonate, 3-4 g. (To ensure that the potassium carbonate is dry, it should be *gently* heated in an evaporating-basin over a small Bunsen flame for 4-5 minutes with stirring, and then allowed to cool in a desiccator.)

Add 27·5 ml. (50·5 g.) of concentrated sulphuric acid cautiously with shaking to 150 ml. of water, and to the hot solution so obtained, add 24 ml. (24·5 g.) of aniline. If all the aniline sulphate thus formed does not dissolve, warm the mixture gently until a clear solution is obtained. Now pour the solution into 200 ml. of cold water contained in a 600 ml. flask, and cool the mixture in ice-water until the temperature falls to 5°. (Some aniline sulphate may crystallise out again at this stage. This does not interfere with the reaction, however, because the sulphate separates as very fine crystals which rapidly redissolve as the reaction proceeds.) Dissolve 20 g. of sodium nitrite in 50 ml. of water, and add this cautiously to the aniline sulphate solution, carrying out the diazotisation with the precautions described in the preparation of iodobenzene (p. 184). When all the sodium nitrite solution has been added, allow the solution to stand at room temperature for 15 minutes to ensure complete diazotisation, and then place the flask *in* a water-bath and heat the latter until the temperature of the diazotised solution (recorded by a thermometer in the solution itself) reaches 50–55°. Continue the heating for a further 30 minutes, taking particular care that the temperature of the well-stirred solution does not rise above 55°. A vigorous evolution of nitrogen occurs meanwhile, and the liquid becomes dark in colour. Pour the contents of the flask into a 1-litre round-bottomed flask, and steam-distil, collecting about 500 ml. of distillate: the solution is apt to foam during the steam distillation, hence the necessity for the large flask.

Now transfer the cold distillate to a separating-funnel,* and shake vigorously with about 50–60 ml. of ether: run off the lower aqueous layer and then decant† the ethereal solution through the mouth of the funnel into a 200 ml. conical flask. Replace the aqueous layer in the funnel, and extract similarly twice more with ether, combining the ethereal extracts in the conical flask. Add 3–4 g. of *dry* powdered potassium carbonate to the ethereal solution, securely cork the flask and shake the contents gently. The ethereal solution of the phenol

* If only small separating-funnels are available, divide the distillate into portions, and extract each thoroughly with ether, uniting the ethereal extracts subsequently.

† The ethereal solution is decanted through the mouth of the funnel to prevent contamination by traces of water which, after running off the heavier aqueous layer, will always be present in the tap and the stem of the funnel. Traces of water will similarly still be present also in the body of the separating-funnel, but will remain adhering to the sides when the ethereal solution is carefully decanted through the mouth. This process should be generally adopted for removing a light liquid from a separating-funnel after a heavier liquid has been run off.

should now be allowed to remain in contact with the potassium carbonate for at least one hour, and preferably overnight. Then fit up the apparatus for ether distillation as shown in Fig. 64 (p. 163, or Fig. 23(E), p. 45). Filter the dry ethereal solution through a small fluted filter-paper directly into the dropping-funnel, run about 30 ml. into the distilling-flask, and finally continue running in the solution as fast as the ether distils over (as described in the preparation of aniline, p. 164). When all the ether has apparently distilled off, disconnect the flask, and fit it with a thermometer reading up to at least 200°, and also with an air-condenser about 12–14 inches long. Now heat the flask very cautiously, as some residual ether always comes over at first, although the temperature may rise rapidly above the boiling-point of ether itself: therefore keep flames away from the open end of the condenser, particularly during the early stages of the distillation. Distil the phenol at such a rate that none escapes condensation, and none crystallises in the condenser. Finally collect the fraction boiling at 178–184° directly into a small weighed specimen-tube, where it should crystallise on cooling. The phenol so obtained sometimes remains as a super-cooled liquid which does not readily crystallise: in such a case, chill the liquid in ice-water, and either scratch it with a glass rod, or seed it with a crystal of pure phenol, when crystallisation should rapidly occur. Yield, 14 g.

Pure phenol is a colourless crystalline substance, having m.p. 43°, and b.p. 182°: on exposure to air, it slowly sublimes, and on exposure to light, develops a pink colour. It has a characteristic odour, and a limited solubility in water. Phenol in dilute aqueous solution has strongly antiseptic properties, but the crystalline substance should not be allowed to come in contact with the skin, as it may cause severe blistering.

For reactions of phenol, see p. 337.

Phenylhydrazine. $C_6H_5NH\cdot NH_2$.

Benzenediazonium chloride reacts in solution with sodium sulphite to give benzenediazonium sodium sulphonate, which when treated with sulphurous acid undergoes reduction to phenylhydrazine sodium sulphonate. The latter readily hydrolyses in the presence of concentrated hydrochloric acid to give

$$C_6H_5N_2Cl + Na_2SO_3 = C_6H_5N_2SO_3Na + NaCl$$
$$C_6H_5N_2SO_3Na + 2H = C_6H_5NH\cdot NH\cdot SO_3Na$$
$$C_6H_5NH\cdot NH\cdot SO_3Na + HCl + H_2O = C_6H_5NH\cdot NH_2,HCl + NaHSO_4$$

phenylhydrazine hydrochloride, from which the free base can be isolated by the action of sodium hydroxide solution.

Benzenediazonium chloride also undergoes direct reduction to phenylhydrazine

$$C_6H_5N_2Cl + 2SnCl_2 + 4HCl = C_6H_5NH \cdot NH_2,HCl + 2SnCl_4$$

when treated with an *acid* solution of stannous chloride (*e.g.*, a solution in hydrochloric acid) but the yields are not as high as those obtained by the above sulphonate method.

Required: Aniline, 20 ml.; hydrochloric acid, 50 ml.; sodium nitrite, 17 g.; sodium carbonate (anhydrous) 17 g.; sodium sulphite $(7H_2O)$, 115 g

First prepare a solution of benzenediazonium chloride from 20 ml. (20·5 g.) of aniline precisely as described in the preparation of chlorobenzene (p. 189), adding a solution of 17 g. of sodium nitrite in 40 ml. of water to a solution of the aniline in 50 ml. of concentrated hydrochloric acid and 50 ml. of water, the temperature of the mixture being kept between 5° and 10°.

While this solution is standing, dissolve 17 g. of anhydrous sodium carbonate in 70 ml. of warm water in a 800 ml. beaker, and then add 115 g. of finely powdered crystalline sodium sulphite $(Na_2SO_3,7H_2O)$ and continue warming the solution at 40–50° for a few minutes, so that the greater part of the sulphite dissolves. Then cool the solution in ice-water until the temperature is between 5° and 10°, some of the sulphite meanwhile crystallising out again. Now add the diazonium solution *slowly* to the well-stirred sulphite solution: the mixture becomes red in colour, and a deep red oil separates and later solidifies as orange-coloured crystals (sometimes the orange crystals separate without the intermediate formation of the oil). When the addition of the diazo solution is complete, continue stirring the mixture for 5–10 minutes, and then warm it to 30° on a water-bath (in a fume-cupboard) and pass in a stream of sulphur dioxide from a syphon until the solution is saturated and no more gas is absorbed: the excess of sodium sulphite and the orange crystals dissolve up at this stage. Now heat the solution to 70° and add 150 ml. of concentrated hydrochloric acid with stirring. Within a few minutes, crystals of phenylhydrazine hydrochloride separate out: cool the mixture in ice-water for 15 minutes with occasional stirring and then filter at the pump and drain thoroughly.

Suspend the crude hydrochloride in some water in a separating-funnel and add 20% sodium hydroxide solution until the mixture is definitely alkaline and the crude phenylhydrazine base floats as a deep red oil on the surface. Now extract the phenylhydrazine twice with benzene (using about 30 ml. of benzene on each occasion) and dry the united benzene extracts with powdered anhydrous potassium carbonate. After the mixture has been allowed to stand for 20–30 minutes, filter at the pump, and wash the residual carbonate with a small quantity of dry benzene.

The benzene has now to be distilled off at atmospheric pressure and the residual phenylhydrazine at reduced pressure. For this purpose, fit a small dropping-funnel to the main neck of a 60 ml. Claisen flask, cork the other neck, and fit a water-condenser to the side-arm. Run about 30 ml. of the benzene solution into the flask, and heat the latter in an oil-bath, controlling the temperature of the bath so that the benzene distils gently over. Allow the remainder of the solution to run in from the dropping-funnel as fast as the benzene itself distils over. When the benzene has been almost entirely removed, fit a capillary tube and a thermometer into the necks of the flask, and then assemble the complete apparatus for vacuum distillation, using either the simple apparatus shown in Fig. 12(A) (p. 29) or a water-condenser fitted with a "pig" (Fig. 13, p. 31, or Fig. 23(F), p. 46). Distil the phenylhydrazine carefully from an oil-bath and collect a fraction boiling over a range of about 3°, e.g., at 127–130°/22 mm. The phenylhydrazine is thus obtained as a very pale yellow (almost colourless) oil, of d, 1·10: it has a characteristic odour and is only slightly soluble in water. Yield, 16–17 g. Pure phenylhydrazine has m.p. 23°; it boils at 242–243° at atmospheric pressure with partial decomposition.

Phenylhydrazine on exposure to light slowly darkens and eventually becomes deep red in colour: salts of the base share this property but to a lesser degree, the sulphate and acetate (of the common salts) being most stable to light. Phenylhydrazine is largely used in organic chemistry to characterise aldehydes and ketones as their phenylhydrazones (pp. 342, 345), and carbohydrates as their osazones (pp. 136–140). It is readily reduced: thus in the process of osazone formation some of the phenylhydrazine is reduced to aniline and ammonia. On the

$$C_6H_5NH\cdot NH_2 + 2H = C_6H_5NH_2 + NH_3$$
$$C_6H_5NH\cdot NH_2 + 2CuO = C_6H_6 + N_2 + Cu_2O + H_2O$$

other hand, Fehling's solution oxidises it to benzene and nitrogen.

Add 2–3 drops of phenylhydrazine to about 2 ml. of Fehling's solution in a test-tube and shake the mixture vigorously: nitrogen is evolved and reddish-brown cuprous oxide is precipitated. The reaction proceeds rapidly on gentle warming, more slowly in the cold.

Biphenic Acid.* $C_{12}H_8(COOH)_2$.

Many diazonium compounds when treated with an ammoniacal cuprous

---

* Formerly known as Diphenic acid.

solution undergo loss. of nitrogen with the formation of the corresponding biphenyl derivative. The yield depends largely on the diazotised amine employed, but anthranilic acid (I) gives biphenic acid (III) or (biphenyl-2,2'-dicarboxylic acid) in high yield. The reaction may often be promoted by

(I)　　　　　　　　(II)　　　　　　　　(III)

cuprous chloride, but this reagent tends to contaminate the product with the chloro-compound corresponding to the amine employed (Sandmeyer's reaction, p. 189).

Required: Anthranilic acid, 20 g. anhydrous sodium carbonate, 7·5 g.; sodium nitrite, 12 g.; concentrated hydrochloric acid, 190 ml.; crystalline copper sulphate, 50 g.; concentrated ammonia, 85 ml.; hydroxylamine hydrochloride, 14·5 g. (or hydroxylamine sulphate, 17·4 g.); acetic acid, 10–20 ml.

(A) *Diazotisation of Anthranilic Acid.* Dissolve 20 g. of anthranilic acid in a solution of 7·5 g. of anhydrous sodium carbonate in 200 ml. of water contained in a 400 ml. beaker. (The mixture may be warmed very gently with stirring to obtain a solution more rapidly, and then cooled.) Add slowly 12 g. of sodium nitrite and cool the stirred solution below 10°. Pour this cold solution slowly on to a vigorously stirred mixture of 40 ml. of concentrated hydrochloric acid and 120 g. of crushed ice in a 600 ml. beaker.

(B) *Preparation of the Cuprous Solution.* Add 85 ml. of concentrated ammonia solution (*d*, 0·088) to a solution of 50 g. of crystalline copper sulphate in 200 ml. of water, and cool to 10°. Dissolve 14·5 g. of hydroxylamine hydrochloride (or 17·4 g. of the sulphate) in 50 ml. of water, cool to 10°, and add a solution of 9 g. of sodium hydroxide in 30 ml. of water. *Without delay,* add this hydroxylamine solution with stirring to the copper solution, which will be immediately reduced, but will retain a blue colour.

Place the cuprous solution in a 1200 ml. beaker, and cool it in ice-water with (mechanical) stirring: run in the diazotised solution slowly from a dropping-funnel, keeping the temperature below 10° throughout. When the addition of the diazotised solution is complete, heat the reaction-mixture rapidly to boiling and then slowly add 150 ml. of concentrated hydrochloric acid. The biphenic acid separates as a pale brown crystalline deposit.

Set aside (preferably overnight), and then filter off the acid, wash it with water and dry. Yield of crude acid, 12 g.; m.p. 223–226°.

For purification, transfer the acid to a 150 ml. flask containing 60 ml. of water, boil the mixture under reflux, and then add acetic acid in 5 ml. portions down the condenser until almost all the solid has dissolved: avoid an excess of acetic acid by ensuring that the solvent action of each addition is complete before the next portion is added. A small suspension of insoluble impurity may remain. Add 2 g. of animal charcoal, boil the solution again for 10–15 minutes, and then filter it through a preheated Buchner funnel. Cool and stir the filtrate, which will deposit pale cream-coloured crystals of the acid. Collect as before and if necessary repeat the recrystallisation. Yield of pure acid, 9 g.; m.p. 227–229°.

4(or *p*)-Bromobiphenyl. $BrC_6H_4 \cdot C_6H_5$. (Gomberg Reaction.)

When an aqueous solution of a diazonium salt is added to an alkaline solution of a phenol, coupling occurs with formation of an azo-compound (p. 188). If however the aqueous solution of the diazonium salt, *e.g.*, *p*-bromobenzene diazonium chloride, is mixed with an excess of an aromatic hydrocarbon, and aqueous sodium hydroxide then added to the vigorously stirred mixture, the diazotate which is formed, *e.g.*, $BrC_6H_4N_2OH$, dissolves in the hydrocarbon and there undergoes decomposition with the formation of nitrogen and two free radicals. The aryl free radical then reacts with the hydrocarbon to give a biphenyl.

$$BrC_6H_4N_2OH \rightarrow Br\overset{\bullet}{C_6H_4} + N_2 + \overset{\bullet}{O}H$$

$$Br\overset{\bullet}{C_6H_4} + C_6H_6 + \overset{\bullet}{O}H \rightarrow BrC_6H_4 \cdot C_6H_5 + H_2O$$

The free radical mechanism is confirmed by the fact that if a substituted aromatic hydrocarbon is used in this reaction, the incoming group (derived from the diazotate) may not necessarily occupy the position in the benzene ring normally determined by the substituent present—a characteristic of free radical reactions.

Required: *p*-Bromoaniline, 20 g.; benzene, 150 ml.; sodium nitrite, 8·5 g.

Add 20 g. of *p*-bromoaniline to 20 ml. of water in a 250 ml. beaker, and warm the mixture until the amine melts. Now add 23 ml. of concentrated hydrochloric acid and without delay stir the mixture mechanically in an ice-water bath, so that a paste of fine *p*-bromoaniline hydrochloride crystals separates. Maintain the temperature of the stirred mixture at about 5° whilst slowly adding from a dropping-funnel a solution of 8·5 g. of sodium nitrite in 20 ml. of water: continue the stirring for 20 minutes after the complete addition of the nitrite.

Transfer the diazotised solution to a 600 ml. beaker, add 150 ml. of benzene, and stir the mixture vigorously to obtain an intimate mixture of the two liquids. Then again maintain the temperature at about 5° (by ice-salt cooling because of the heat evolved) whilst 27 ml. of 20% aqueous sodium hydroxide solution are added from a dropping-funnel during 40–50 minutes. When the addition of the alkali is complete, remove the ice-water bath, and allow the stirred mixture to reach room temperature.

Pour the mixture into a 500 ml. flask fitted with a steam-distillation head, and with a steam-inlet tube reaching almost to the bottom of the flask. First distil off the benzene in steam. Then place the flask in an oil-bath heated to 165–170°, and continue the steam-distillation (2–3 hours). The *p*-bromobiphenyl passes over and forms orange crystals in the water-condenser: therefore run the water out of the condenser for a short while from time to time to melt the orange deposit and allow it to run into the receiver containing the distilled water.

When the distillation is complete, filter off the crude orange solid (9 g.) at the pump, wash it with water and drain well. Recrystallise from methanol or from methylated spirits. The *p*-bromobiphenyl is obtained as colourless lustrous plates, m.p. 89–91°: yield, 7 g.

1,3,5-Tribromobenzene, $C_6H_3Br_3$, from 2,4,6-Tribromoaniline.

When a solution of a diazonium compound in absolute methanol is boiled, the chief product is the corresponding methyl ether, benzenediazonium hydrogen sulphate thus giving methyl phenyl ether or anisole:

$$C_6H_5N_2HSO_4 + HOCH_3 = C_6H_5OCH_3 + N_2 + H_2SO_4$$

In absolute ethanol solution, the ethyl ether and the corresponding hydrocarbon are formed, the latter by reduction of the diazonium compound by the ethanol, which is itself oxidised to acetaldehyde:

$$CH_3CH_2OH = CH_3CHO + 2H$$
$$C_6H_5N_2HSO_4 + 2H = C_6H_6 + N_2 + H_2SO_4$$

With higher alcohols, the formation of the ether becomes negligible, the reaction being limited almost entirely to reduction to the hydrocarbon.

This elimination of the diazonium group is therefore a very valuable reaction, as it affords almost the only method by which nitro and primary amino groups directly attached to the benzene ring can be eliminated.

A similar reaction occurs when an aqueous solution of a diazonium compound is made strongly alkaline and then warmed with an alkaline solution of stannous chloride. This reaction, however, involves the intermediate formation of the

$$C_6H_5N_2Cl \xrightarrow{KOH} C_6H_5N:NOK \xrightarrow{2H} C_6H_6 + N_2 + KOH$$

unstable alkali diazotate, which may explode even in cold aqueous solution.

2,4,6-Tribromoaniline (preparation, p. 165) is used to illustrate this elimination of the amino group, because the tribromobenzene so formed is solid, and small quantities can easily be purified by recrystallisation.

Required: 2,4,6-Tribromoaniline, 5 g.; absolute ethanol, 40 ml.; dry benzene, 10 ml.; sodium nitrite, 3 g.

Dissolve 5 g. of 2,4,6-tribromoaniline in a hot mixture of 40 ml. of absolute ethanol and 10 ml. of dry benzene contained in a 150 ml. wide-necked bolt-head flask. (The benzene is added to increase the solubility of the tribromoaniline.) Now add 2 ml. (3·9 g.) of concentrated sulphuric acid (preferably from a burette or a small pipette) to the hot solution, shaking the latter gently round. Attach the flask to a reflux water-condenser and heat on a water-bath until the clear solution boils. Now detach the flask, add 3 g. of dry powdered sodium nitrite, and return the flask to the condenser but not to the water-bath. Shake the flask vigorously: the heat of the reaction causes the solution to continue boiling for several minutes. When the boiling subsides, return the flask to the water-bath and boil the solution for 45 minutes with occasional vigorous shaking. Allow the solution to cool somewhat and then cool it thoroughly in ice-water. A mixture of tribromobenzene and sodium sulphate crystallises out. Filter at the pump, drain, wash once with a small quantity of methylated or rectified spirit and then repeatedly with water to remove all sodium suplhate.

Recrystallise from methylated spirit, using animal charcoal: for this purpose, use about twice the minimum quantity of methylated spirit required to obtain a clear solution, and filter through a funnel preheated by the filtration of some boiling solvent, as the tribromobenzene separates very rapidly as the solution cools. The 1,3,5-tribromobenzene is thus obtained as colourless crystals, m.p. 122°: yield, 3 g.

The tribromobenzene obtained in this way should be entirely free from unchanged tribromoaniline. To test its purity, dissolve a small quantity in hot dry benzene and pass in hydrogen chloride gas from a Kipp's apparatus: no trace of crystals of tribromoaniline hydrochloride should appear. Note also that although the m.p.s of the two compounds are almost identical, that of the recrystallised product from the above preparation is considerably depressed by admixture with tribromoaniline.

Diphenylnitrosoamine.* $(C_6H_5)_2N \cdot NO.$ (Semi-micro scale.)

Secondary amines of both the aliphatic and the aromatic series react similarly with nitrous acid, giving *nitrosamines*:

* Alternative name *N*-nitrosodiphenylamine.

$$R_2NH + HONO \rightarrow R_2N \cdot NO + H_2O$$

The nitrosamines are insoluble in water, and the lower members are liquid at ordinary temperatures. The separation of an oily liquid when an aqueous solution of an amine salt is treated with sodium nitrite is therefore strong evidence that the amine is secondary. Diphenylnitrosoamine is selected as a preparation because it is a crystalline substance and is thus easier to manipulate on a small scale than one of the lower liquid members. For this preparation, a fairly pure (and therefore almost colourless) sample of diphenylamine should be used. "Technical" diphenylamine, which is almost black in colour, should not be employed.

Required: Diphenylamine, 1 g.; ethanol, 8 ml.; sodium nitrite, 0·5 g.; hydrochloric acid, 0·8 ml.

Prepare two solutions, one containing 1 g. of diphenylamine in 8 ml. of warm ethanol, and the other containing 0·5 g. of sodium nitrite in 1 ml. of water, and cool each solution in ice-water until the temperature falls to 5°. Now add 0·8 ml. of concentrated hydrochloric acid steadily with stirring to the diphenylamine solution, and then *without delay* (otherwise diphenylamine hydrochloride may crystallise out) pour the sodium nitrite solution rapidly into the well-stirred mixture. The temperature rises at once and the diphenylnitrosoamine rapidly crystallises out. Allow the mixture to stand in the ice-water for 15 minutes, and then filter off the crystals at the pump, drain thoroughly, wash with water to remove sodium chloride, and then drain again. Recrystallise from methylated spirit. Diphenylnitrosoamine is thus obtained as very pale yellow crystals, m.p. 67–68°: yield, 0·9–1·0 g.

Reaction of Diphenylnitrosoamine. Carry out Liebermann's Nitroso Reaction as described for phenol (p. 340), but use about 0·05 g. of the nitrosamine instead of the one crystal of sodium nitrite, and finally add only 3–4 drops of sulphuric acid. The deep greenish-blue colour is obtained, becoming red on dilution and reverting to blue on being made alkaline.

p-Nitrosodimethylaniline.† $(CH_3)_2NC_6H_4NO$.

Nitrous acid does not react with aliphatic tertiary amines, such as triethylamine, $(C_2H_5)_3N$, nor does it usually react with aromatic tertiary amines such as triphenylamine, $(C_6H_5)_3N$, which contain three aryl groups.

If, however, a tertiary amine has two alkyl groups and also an aryl group having the *para* position unsubstituted, then the action of nitrous acid is to insert the nitroso group directly into this *para* position. Dimethylaniline, for example, when treated with nitrous acid readily gives *p*-nitrosodimethyl-

† Alternative name N,N'-dimethyl-*p*-nitrosoaniline.

$$(CH_3)_2NC_6H_5 + HONO \rightarrow (CH_3)_2NC_6H_4NO + H_2O$$

aniline. The salts of p-nitrosodimethylaniline, such as the hydrochloride, are yellow, whereas the free base is a beautiful green crystalline compound. The colour is presumably due to a strong contribution by the quinonoid form in which a charge separation has occurred within the molecule:

$$O{:}N{\cdot}C_6H_4{\cdot}N(CH_3)_2 \longleftrightarrow \bar{O}{\cdot}N{:}C_6H_4{:}\overset{+}{N}(CH_3)_2$$

This marked difference in colour between a base and its salts is also exemplified in the case of aminoazobenzene (p. 208).

Tertiary amines containing one alkyl and two aryl groups, such as monomethyldiphenylamine, $CH_3(C_6H_5)_2N$, are rarely encountered and are unimportant. They usually react with nitrous acid with the insertion of a nitroso group into only one of the two available *para* positions: monomethyl-diphenylamine thus gives monomethyl-mono-p-nitroso-diphenylamine, $CH_3(C_6H_5)NC_6H_4NO$, or N-methyl-p-nitrosodiphenylamine.

Required: Dimethylaniline, 15 ml.; hydrochloric acid, 50 ml.; sodium nitrite, 9 g.

Dissolve 15 ml. (14·3 g.) of dimethylaniline in a mixture of 50 ml. of concentrated hydrochloric acid and 50 ml. of water contained in a 300 ml. beaker, and then place the latter in a freezing-mixture consisting of finely crushed ice and salt. Stir the contents of the beaker with a thermometer until the temperature of the solution is between 0° and 2°. Dissolve 9 g. of sodium nitrite in 20 ml. of water and add this solution in small quantities (about 2 ml. at a time) to the dimethylaniline hydrochloride solution, keeping the mixture well stirred and taking care that the temperature recorded by the thermometer in the solution does not rise above 2°. When the addition of the sodium nitrite solution is complete, allow the product to remain in the freezing-mixture for a further 45 minutes, and then filter off the yellow crystalline nitrosodimethylaniline hydrochloride at the pump, wash it with dilute hydrochloric acid, and then drain thoroughly. Yield of crude hydrochloride, about 18 g. Recrystallise approximately half the hydrochloride by dissolving it in a minimum amount of boiling water, and adding about 0·5 ml. of concentrated hydrochloric acid: on cooling the solution, the hydrochloride crystallises out in yellow needles, m.p. 177°.

In order to prepare the free base, place the remaining half of the crude hydrochloride in a 200 ml. beaker, add 20 ml. of water, and then stir the mixture with a glass rod until a thin paste of uniform consistency (quite free from lumps) is obtained. Now add 10% aqueous sodium hydroxide solution with stirring until the whole mass has become bright green—the colour of the free base. Pour the contents of the beaker into a separating-funnel, and isolate the free base by one of the following alternative methods.

(a) Extract the free base by shaking the mixture in the separating-funnel with about 40 ml. of benzene, repeating the extraction to ensure that all the base has entered the benzene solution. Dry the combined benzene extracts by shaking with powdered anhydrous potassium carbonate for a few minutes, and then filter through a fluted filter-paper directly into a distilling-flask fitted with a water-condenser. Distil off about half the benzene over a sand-bath, and then pour the residual hot benzene solution into a small beaker. On cooling, the *p*-nitrosodimethylaniline crystallises out in brilliant deep green leaflets: when these are filtered off and dried, however, they usually decrepitate, giving a fine green crystalline powder, m.p. 85°.

(b) Extract the mixture with about 40 ml. of chloroform, in which the free base is very soluble. Run off the lower chloroform layer, dry it with potassium carbonate as in (a), and then add carbon tetrachloride slowly with stirring to the filtered chloroform solution until the base starts to crystallise out. Allow to stand for a short time (*i.e.*, until the deposition of crystals ceases) and then filter at the pump: as the crystals lose the last trace of solvent, they tend as before to break up into a fine powder, the deep green colour becoming paler in consequence.

A small quantity of the base may be recrystallised from hot ether, and magnificent deep green crystals obtained: the base is not sufficiently soluble in cold ether, however, to enable this solvent to be used advantageously in the above extractions.

Reactions. (1) *p*-Nitrosodimethylaniline does *not* give Liebermann's Nitroso Reaction with phenol and sulphuric acid (see footnote, p. 340).

(2) Place about 1 g. of the base in a test-tube, and cover with concentrated (about 20%) sodium hydroxide solution. Bring the mixture gently to the boil, keeping the test-tube lightly closed with the finger meanwhile to prevent undue escape of vapour. As the solution boils a strong fishy odour of dimethylamine is detected, and white fumes form when the test-tube is held near an open bottle of concentrated

$$NaOH + (CH_3)_2NC_6H_4NO \rightarrow (CH_3)_2NH + NaOC_6H_4NO$$

hydrochloric acid. The sodium hydroxide has hydrolysed the base, giving the volatile dimethylamine, whilst the sodium derivative of *p*-nitrosophenol remains in solution. The reaction affords an excellent method of preparing *pure* aliphatic secondary amines, particularly when required completely free from primary and tertiary amines.

Diazoaminobenzene. $C_6H_5 \cdot N{:}N \cdot NH \cdot C_6H_5$.

Diazonium salts couple readily with aromatic primary amines, giving diazo-amino compounds. If for instance an aqueous solution of aniline sulphate is diazotised with a deficiency of nitrous acid, only part of it is converted into benzenediazonium sulphate and the latter then couples with the unchanged aniline to give diazoaminobenzene. The reaction is carried out at the opti-

$$C_6H_5NH_2,H_2SO_4 + HONO = C_6H_5N_2HSO_4 + 2H_2O$$

$$C_6H_5N_2HSO_4 + HNHC_6H_5 \rightarrow C_6H_5 \cdot N{:}N \cdot NH \cdot C_6H_5 + H_2SO_4$$

mum temperature of 30°, for at this temperature coupling takes place readily, and the diazonium sulphate is used up before it has time to decompose.

Dissolve 2 ml. (3·7 g.) of concentrated sulphuric acid in 350 ml. of water contained in a 600 ml. beaker, and then add with stirring 12 ml. (12·3 g.) of aniline. Place the beaker *in* a water-bath and heat the latter gently until a thermometer in the solution records a temperature of 30°. Dissolve 4·5 g. of sodium nitrite in 15 ml. of water, and add about 1 ml. of this solution at half-minute intervals to the solution of aniline sulphate, keeping the mixture well stirred meanwhile. When the addition of the nitrite is complete, keep the mixture at 30° for a further 15 minutes: the diazo-aminobenzene rapidly begins to separate as a yellow crystal-line mass. Then remove the beaker from the bath, and allow it to stand for 30 minutes, with occasional stirring. Filter off the solid material at the pump, using a Buchner funnel, wash re-peatedly with water, and then drain thoroughly. Finally dry the diazoaminobenzene by pressing between several sheets of thick drying-paper. The sample so obtained is sufficiently pure for the following preparation of aminoazobenzene. Yield of crude material, 11–12 g. (almost theoretical).

The recrystallisation of diazoaminobenzene has to be performed with care, as the substance is freely soluble in most liquids and tends moreover to decompose if its solution is not rapidly cooled. Place 2 g. of the crude, freshly prepared, well-drained material in a boiling-tube, add about 15–20 ml. of ethanol and 1–2 drops of 10% aqueous sodium hydroxide solution, and then heat *rapidly* until boiling: if the solution should contain insoluble impurities, filter through a *small* fluted paper, and at once cool the filtrate in ice-water. The diazoaminobenzene should rapidly crystallise out from the cold and stirred solution: filter the crystals rapidly at the pump whilst the solution is still cold, as they tend to redissolve if the solution reaches room temperature. Diazoaminobenzene is thus obtained as yellow crystals, which melt at 98°, the molten material decomposing vigorously above this temperature: the crystalline material darkens on exposure to light and most specimens are therefore of a yellowish-brown colour.

Aminoazobenzene. $C_6H_5 \cdot N:N \cdot C_6H_4 \cdot NH_2$.

When diazoaminobenzene is added to a warm aqueous solution of hydrochloric acid, it tends to break up into its original components, *i.e.*, to benzenediazonium chloride and aniline, and an equilibrium is thus established. The diazonium chloride and the aniline, however, in addition to recombining to form diazoaminobenzene, also undergo direct condensation at the *p*-hydro-

$$C_6H_5N_2NHC_6H_5 + HCl \rightleftharpoons C_6H_5N_2Cl + H_2NC_6H_5 \rightarrow C_6H_5N:NC_6H_4NH_2 + HCl$$

gen atom of the aniline molecule, giving aminoazobenzene. Since this reaction is irreversible, whilst the former is freely reversible, the final result is the complete conversion of the diazoaminobenzene into the aminoazobenzene. (The intermediate formation of the benzenediazonium chloride can be demonstrated by adding dimethylaniline, with which the diazonium chloride couples preferentially, giving dimethylaminoazobenzene, $C_6H_5N:NC_6H_4N(CH_3)_2$.)

The conversion of the diazoaminobenzene into aminoazobenzene is promoted by the addition of aniline hydrochloride even more readily than by that of free hydrochloric acid. The aniline hydrochloride dissociates in solution giving hydrochloric acid and aniline: the former promotes the formation of the above equilibrium, and the latter by increasing the active mass of the free aniline further accelerates the condensation to aminoazobenzene.

Aminoazobenzene is a very weak base, and consequently it will not form salts with weak organic acids, such as acetic acid, although it will do so with the strong mineral acids, such as hydrochloric acid. Aminoazobenzene is a yellowish-brown compound, whilst the hydrochloride is steel blue. The colour of the latter is presumably due to the addition of the proton to the phenyl-N-atom, the cation thus having benzenoid and quinonoid forms:

$$\overset{+}{C_6H_5 \cdot NH:N \cdot C_6H_4 \cdot NH_2} \longleftrightarrow C_6H_5 \cdot NH \cdot N:C_6H_4:\overset{+}{NH_2}$$

Required: Aniline hydrochloride, 4 g.; aniline, 16 ml.; diazoaminobenzene, 8 g.; acetic acid, 20 ml.

Add 4 g. of aniline hydrochloride to 16 ml. of aniline contained in a 100 ml. conical flask, and then add 8 g. of diazoaminobenzene, both the solid components being finely powdered. Place the flask in a water-bath, and heat the latter carefully so that the well-stirred mixture is kept at 40° for 1 hour. Then remove the flask from the water-bath and allow it to stand overnight to ensure that the conversion is complete. Then add about 20 ml. of glacial acetic acid dissolved in the same volume of water, and stir the mixture well to extract the free aniline in the form of its soluble acetate. Allow the mixture to stand (with occasional stirring) for at least 10 minutes, and then filter at the pump and wash well with water.

Aminoazobenzene is freely soluble in methylated spirit, although insoluble in water. For recrystallisation, therefore, dissolve the crude substance in boiling methylated spirit, remove from the water-bath, and then add water drop by drop until the solution becomes just cloudy owing to the separation of the solute: replace the solution momentarily on the water-bath until the cloudiness disappears, and then at once remove the solution, and allow it to cool slowly. (Alternatively, the crude *dry* material can be recrystallised from carbon tetrachloride in the usual way.) Aminoazobenzene is thus obtained as yellowish-brown crystals, m.p. 126°: yield, 5 g.

To prepare the hydrochloride, add about 1 g. of amino-azobenzene to 200 ml. of dilute hydrochloric acid and boil until nearly all the solid material has dissolved. Filter hot and allow to cool slowly. Aminoazobenzene hydrochloride separates as beautiful steel-blue crystals: filter and dry. If a small quantity of the powdered hydrochloride is moistened with water and a few drops of ammonia added, the blue hydrochloride is converted back to the yellowish-brown base.

Azo-Compounds.

Aminoazobenzene is a member of the large class of azo-compounds, all of which contain the characteristic grouping, C·N:N·C. Azo-compounds are of considerable technical importance, as they are all coloured, and the majority possess considerable stability. They may be prepared by the following methods:

(1) By coupling a diazonium salt with:

(a) A primary amine to give the diazoamino compound, which is then converted into the isomeric aminoazo compound (as in the above preparation of aminoazobenzene).

$$C_6H_5N_2HSO_4 + HNHC_6H_5 \longrightarrow C_6H_5N_2NHC_6H_5 \longrightarrow C_6H_5N:NC_6H_4NH_2$$

(b) A tertiary amine, the azo-compound being directly formed. Thus benzenediazonium sulphate and dimethylaniline give dimethylamino-azobenzene (p. 188).

$$C_6H_5N_2HSO_4 + HC_6H_4N(CH_3)_2 \longrightarrow C_6H_5N:NC_6H_4N(CH_3)_2$$

(c) A phenol in alkaline solution. 2-Naphthol dissolved in sodium hydroxide solution this gives benzeneazo-2-naphthol, a scarlet dye.

(2) The alkaline reduction of an aromatic nitro-compound to give the azoxy

derivative, which is then further reduced to the azo-compound. Nitrobenzene thus gives first azoxybenzene, and then azobenzene.

$$2C_6H_5NO_2 \longrightarrow C_6H_5NO{:}NC_6H_5 \longrightarrow C_6H_5N{:}NC_6H_5$$

(3) By condensing nitroso derivatives with primary amines. Nitrosobenzene and aniline, for example, readily give azobenzene. This method is seldom used

$$C_6H_5NO + H_2NC_6H_5 \rightarrow C_6H_5N{:}NC_6H_5 + H_2O$$

but is of importance in that it establishes clearly the constitution of the azo grouping.

The most noteworthy reaction of azo-compounds is their behaviour on reduction. Prolonged reduction first saturates the azo group, giving the *hydrazo* derivative (C·NH·NH·C), and then breaks the NH·NH linkage, with the formation of two primary amine molecules. If method (1) has been employed to prepare the azo-compound, these two primary amines will therefore be respectively (a) the original amine from which the diazonium salt was prepared, and (b) the amino derivative of the amine or phenol with which the diazonium salt was coupled. For example, amino-azobenzene on complete reduction gives one equivalent of aniline, and one of p-phenylene diamine, $NH_2C_6H_4NH_2$; benzene-azo-2-naphthol similarly gives one equivalent of aniline and one of

$$C_6H_5N{:}N\text{—}\langle\text{HO}\rangle + 4H = C_6H_5NH_2 + H_2N\text{—}\langle\text{HO}\rangle$$

1-amino-2-naphthol, experimental details for this reduction being given below. The constitution of an azo-compound (and particularly the position of the azo group in the molecule) can thus often be determined by identifying the two primary amines formed on complete reduction.

Benzeneazo-2-naphthol.

$C_6H_5{\cdot}N{:}N{\cdot}C_{10}H_6OH$ [Method 1(c)].

Required: Aniline, 4·5 ml.; hydrochloric acid, 10· ml.; sodium nitrite, 4 g.; 2-naphthol, 7 g.

Dissolve 4·5 ml. of aniline in a mixture of 10 ml. of concentrated hydrochloric acid and 20 ml. of water: cool the solution to 5°, and diazotise by the addition of 4 g. of sodium nitrite dissolved in 20 ml. of water, observing the usual precautions given on page 181. Dissolve 7 g. of 2-naphthol in 60 ml. of 10% sodium hydroxide solution contained in a 200 ml. beaker, and cool this solution to 5° by external cooling, aided by the direct addition of about 20–30 g. of crushed ice. Now add the diazotised solution very slowly to the naphthol solution, keeping the latter well stirred meanwhile: the mixed solutions immediately develop a deep red colour, and the benzeneazonaphthol should rapidly separate as red crystals. If the diazonium solution is added too rapidly, the azo-compound may separate at first as a thick viscous mass, which, however, will crystallise later and may then be easily broken up with the stirrer. When the addition of the diazo solution is complete, allow the mixture to stand in an ice-salt mixture for 30 minutes, with occasional stirring, and then filter the solution through a Buchner funnel under gentle suction from the pump: if the above directions have been carefully followed, filtration should be rapid. Wash the benzeneazo-2-naphthol well with water, and then drain thoroughly, pressing the crystals well down on to the filter with a spatula. Recrystallise one-third of the product from glacial acetic acid, reserving the remainder for reduction to 1-amino-2-naphthol. (The azo-compound when dry is freely soluble. in acetic acid, but when moist is only moderately soluble: about 40 ml. of acetic acid are required for the portion recrystallised as above.) Filter the re-crystallised material at the pump, wash with a few ml. of ethanol or methylated spirit to eliminate acetic acid, and dry: yield, 3 g. Benzeneazo-2-naphthol is obtained as deep red crystals, m.p. 133°. Should further recrystallisation of the *dry* compound be required, ethanol is the best solvent.

Hydrochloride of 1-amino-2-naphthol (1-amino-2-hydroxynaphthalene). $C_{10}H_6(NH_2)OH,HCl$.

Required: Benzeneazo-naphthol from above experiment; methylated spirit, 100 ml.; stannous chloride, 22 g.; hydrochloric acid, 60 ml.

Add the reserved portion of the unrecrystallised benzeneazo-naphthol to 100 ml. of methylated spirit contained in a 350 ml. conical flask and boil gently under reflux until the greater part of the azo-compound has gone into solution. Meanwhile dissolve 22 g. of stannous chloride in 60 ml. of concentrated hydrochloric acid (warming gently, if necessary, to obtain a clear solution), add this solution to that of the azo-compound, and continue the boiling under reflux for 30 minutes. The azo-compound rapidly dissolves, and is reduced by the stannous chloride, and after about 20 minutes' boiling, the red colour disappears and the solution acquires a permanent very pale brown tint. (If the red colour, instead of disappearing, slowly darkens to a deep reddish-violet, the stannous chloride is at fault, as the violet colour usually develops if a stale sample of stannous chloride, particularly one which has been unduly exposed to the air, is employed.) When the boiling for 30 minutes is complete, decant the solution into a beaker, and cool in ice-water; the amino-naphthol hydrochloride separates as fine greyish-white crystals. Filter off at the pump, and wash the hydrochloride thoroughly with dilute hydrochloric acid, in which it is almost insoluble. Recrystallise from hot water containing a *few drops* of dilute hydrochloric acid; care must be taken that too much water is not used for this purpose, as the hydrochloride usually

contains traces of a sparingly soluble stannous impurity which should
be left undissolved and removed by filtration from the hot solution.
If the hydrochloride does not crystallise readily from the cold filtrate,
seed the latter with a minute quantity of the crude material, or add a
few more drops of dilute hydrochloric acid. 1-Amino-2-naphthol
hydrochloride is thus obtained as fine colourless crystals, which darken
in colour on exposure to light: yield, 3 g.

Azoxybenzene, $C_6H_5NO:NC_6H_5$, and Azobenzene, $C_6H_5N:NC_6H_5$. (Method 2, p. 208.)

When a solution of nitrobenzene in methanol is boiled with sodium hydroxide,
the nitrobenzene is reduced to azoxybenzene by the methanol, which is itself
oxidised to formic acid.

$$4C_6H_5NO_2 + 3CH_3OH + 3NaOH = 2C_6H_5NO:NC_6H_5 + 3HCOONa + 6H_2O$$

The azoxybenzene in turn, when heated with iron filings, readily undergoes

$$C_6H_5NO:NC_6H_5 + Fe = C_6H_5N:NC_6H_5 + FeO$$

further reduction to azobenzene.

AZOXYBENZENE. *Required:* Sodium hydroxide, 23 g.;
nitrobenzene, 15 ml.; methanol, 120 ml.

Add 23 g. of powdered (or "flake") sodium hydroxide to a
solution of 15 ml. (18 g.) of nitrobenzene in 120 ml. of methanol
contained in a 250 ml. short-necked bolt-head flask. Fix a
reflux water-condenser to the flask and boil the solution on a
water-bath for 3 hours, shaking the product vigorously at intervals to ensure thorough mixing. Then fit a bent delivery-tube to
the flask, and reverse the condenser for distillation, as in Fig. 59,
p. 100, or Fig. 23(D), p. 45). Place the flask *in* the boiling water-
bath (since methanol will not readily distil when heated on a
water-bath) and distil off as much methanol as possible. Then
pour the residual product with stirring into about 250 ml. of cold
water: wash out the flask with water, and then acidify the mixture
with hydrochloric acid. The crude azoxybenzene separates as a
heavy oil, which when thoroughly stirred soon solidifies, particularly if the mixture is cooled in ice-water.

Then filter off the solid azoxybenzene at the pump, wash it
thoroughly with water, and drain well. Recrystallise from a
minimum of methylated spirit, allowing the hot solution to cool
spontaneously (with occasional stirring) until crystallisation
starts, and then cool in ice-water. If crystallisation is delayed,
"seed" the solution with a trace of the crude product: if on the
other hand the azoxybenzene separates at first as an emulsion, add
methylated spirit, drop by drop, with stirring until the solution is
clear, and then allow the cooling to proceed as before. The

azoxybenzene is obtained as very pale yellow crystals, m.p. 36°. Yield of recrystallised material, 11 g.

The fact that a mixed azoxy-compound, such as p-toluene-azoxy-benzene, $CH_3C_6H_4NO:NC_6H_5$, exists in two isomeric forms, disproves the earlier symmetric formula (A) alloted to azoxybenzene, and confirms the formula (B), in which the oxygen is joined by a co-ordinate link to one nitrogen atom.

$$\begin{matrix} C_6H_5N \diagdown \\ & \Big\downarrow O \\ (A)\ C_6H_5N \diagup \end{matrix} \qquad \begin{matrix} C_6H_5N \rightarrow O \\ \| \\ C_6H_5N\ \ (B) \end{matrix}$$

AZOBENZENE. *Required*: Azoxybenzene, 8 g.; iron filings, 25 g.

Place 8 g. of the pure powdered azoxybenzene and 25 g. of iron filings (both reagents being quite dry) in a 75 ml. distilling-flask **F** and mix *thoroughly* by shaking. Cork the flask and fit to the side-arm a boiling-tube **B** to act as receiver (Fig. 66): cut or file a groove **G** in the boiling-tube cork to allow escape of air. Now heat the mixture directly with the Bunsen flame, waving the latter around the base of the flask to ensure uniform heating: heat gently at first and later more strongly. The red liquid azobenzene distils over smoothly and eventually solidifies in the receiver. When no more distillate passes over, detach the boiling-tube, and then, in

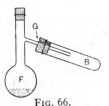

FIG. 66.

order to eliminate basic impurities which are formed as by-products in the reaction, add 20–30 ml. of dilute hydrochloric acid (1 vol. of concentrated acid : 2 vols. of water) which have been heated to about 70°: cork the tube securely and shake the mixture, so that impurities in the molten drops of azobenzene are thoroughly extracted by the acid, which usually becomes dark in colour. Now cool in water until the globules of azobenzene solidify, and then filter at the pump. Break up the azobenzene with a spatula on the filter, wash thoroughly with water, and drain. Recrystallise from a minimum of boiling methylated spirit, filtering the hot solution through a small fluted filter-paper. The azobenzene separates as reddish-orange crystals, m.p. 67–68°. Yield, 4 g. A second recrystallisation from methylated spirit may be necessary to obtain a satisfactory melting-point.

In order to save the cost of the distilling-flask (which after the above treatment is useless for further work), the mixture may be distilled from a small retort made by blowing a suitable bulb on the end of a rather thick-walled tube of about 8–10 mm. internal diameter: the tube is then bent through almost 90° a few cm. above the bulb, cut to a suitable length, and the open end fitted into the boiling-tube as before.

Methyl-orange (Sodium salt).
$NaO_3SC_6H_4N : NC_6H_4N(CH_3)_2$.

When hydrochloric acid is cautiously added to an aqueous solution containing both sodium nitrite and the sodium salt of sulphanilic acid, $NaO_3SC_6H_4NH_2$, the amino group of the latter undergoes normal diazotisation, giving the diazonium chloride (A). The latter, however, ionises in solution, giving sodium and chloride ions and the internal salt (B), which possesses two opposite charges and is therefore neutral: this internal salt is stable under

$$\text{(A) } NaO_3SC_6H_4N_2Cl \rightarrow \overset{+}{Na} + \overset{-}{Cl} + \overset{-}{O_3}SC_6H_4\overset{+}{N_2} \text{ (B)}$$

these conditions, and being only moderately soluble in water, will be largely precipitated unless the solution is very dilute. If now dimethylaniline hydrochloride is added to the solution, coupling will occur between the internal salt and the tertiary amine, with the formation of methyl-orange:

$$\bar{O}_3S \langle \bigcirc \rangle \overset{+}{N}_2 + H \langle \bigcirc \rangle N(CH_3)_2, HCl \rightarrow HO_3S \langle \bigcirc \rangle N:N \langle \bigcirc \rangle N(CH_3)_2 + HCl$$

On the addition of sodium hydroxide, the sparingly soluble sodium salt of methyl-orange, $NaO_3SC_6H_4N:NC_6H_4N(CH_3)_2$, will crystallise out.

It is important in this preparation to avoid an excess of nitrous acid before coupling occurs, otherwise the excess of nitrous acid will react directly with the dimethylaniline, and the deep green p-nitrosodimethylaniline so formed will contaminate the methyl-orange.

Required: Anhydrous sodium carbonate, 2 g.; sulphanilic acid, 7 g.; sodium nitrite, 2·2 g.; hydrochloric acid, 12 ml.; dimethylaniline, 4 ml.

Dissolve 2 g. of anhydrous sodium carbonate in 50 ml. of water contained in a 400 ml. beaker and add 7 g. of finely powdered crystalline sulphanilic acid ($2H_2O$), warming the mixture gently in order to obtain a clear solution. Add a solution of 2·2 g. of sodium nitrite in 10 ml. of water and then cool the mixture in ice-water until the temperature has fallen to 5°. Now add *very slowly* (drop by drop) with continual stirring a solution of 8 ml. of concentrated hydrochloric acid in 15 ml. of water: do not allow the temperature to rise above 10°. When all the acid has been added, allow the solution to stand in ice-water for 15 minutes to ensure complete diazotisation: during this period fine crystals of the internal salt separate from the pink solution. Dissolve 4 ml. of dimethylaniline in a mixture of 4 ml. of concentrated hydrochloric acid and 10 ml. of water, cool the solution in ice-water, and add it slowly to the cold well-stirred diazo solution: a pale red coloration is developed. Allow the mixture to stand for 5 minutes and then add *slowly with stirring* aqueous

10% NaOH solution until the mixture attains a uniform orange colour (about 50 ml. are required).

The sodium salt of methyl-orange separates as very fine particles, and filtration, if attempted directly, may be very slow. Therefore warm the mixture to 50–55°, stirring it meanwhile with a thermometer: when nearly all the methyl-orange has dissolved, add about 10 g. of finely powdered sodium chloride, and continue warming for a few minutes until the chloride itself has dissolved. Now allow the mixture to cool spontaneously for 10–15 minutes, and then cool in ice-water. Filter off the methyl-orange at the pump: filtration is now rapid, particularly if only gentle suction is employed, so that the particles of the methyl-orange are not dragged into the pores of the filter-paper. Drain thoroughly, and then recrystallise the methyl-orange from about 100 ml. of boiling water: filter the hot solution (if necessary) through a fluted filter-paper in a heated funnel, or a Buchner funnel which has been preheated by the filtration of some boiling water. The deep reddish-orange crystals of methyl-orange separate rapidly as the solution cools. Yield, 9 g.

The use of methyl-orange as an indicator is based on the fact that the sodium salt in aqueous solution furnishes a yellow anion, which when treated with acids (except weak acids such as H_2CO_3 and H_2SO_3) apparently gives rise to a red

$$\overset{+}{Na} + \overset{-}{SO_3}\langle\bigcirc\rangle N = N \langle\bigcirc\rangle N(CH_3)_2 \text{ (yellow)}$$

alkalis $\uparrow\downarrow$ acids (e.g. HCl)

$$\overset{+}{Na} + \overset{-}{SO_3}\langle\bigcirc\rangle NH-N=\langle\bigcirc\rangle=\overset{+}{N}(CH_3)_2 \text{ (red)} + \overset{-}{Cl}$$

quinonoid cation, the change being reversed by alkalis. It is possible, however, that there are additional factors governing these colour changes.

Benzidine or 4,4'-Diamino-biphenyl.*
$H_2N \cdot C_6H_4 \cdot C_6H_4 \cdot NH_2$.

When hydrazobenzene, or *sym*-diphenylhydrazine, is warmed with acids, it undergoes an intramolecular rearrangement, with the formation of benzidine,

$$C_6H_5 \cdot NH \cdot NH \cdot C_6H_5 \longrightarrow H_2N\langle\bigcirc{-}\bigcirc\rangle NH_2$$

or 4,4'-diamino-biphenyl. This reaction is of wide application and is known as the *Benzidine Transformation*.

Required: Hydrazobenzene, 10 g.; zinc dust, 10 g.

HYDRAZOBENZENE. The above preparation of benzidine

* See footnote, p. 216.

should be carried out with pure hydrazobenzene. This compound, however, when kept in store undergoes atmospheric oxidation to azobenzene (p. 212), and such samples are therefore usually orange-red in colour due to contamination with azobenzene. If the hydrazobenzene is coloured in this way, it should be purified by the following process, which reduces any azobenzene back to hydrazobenzene.

Add 10 g. of the crude hydrazobenzene to 80 ml. of ethanol contained in a flask fitted with a reflux water-condenser. Heat the mixture on a water-bath until the ethanol boils, and then add 10 g. of zinc dust and 30 ml. of 30% aqueous sodium hydroxide solution. Remove the flask from the water-bath and shake the contents vigorously from time to time. After about 10 minutes, replace the flask on the water-bath and boil the contents for 3–5 minutes. Filter the mixture at the pump, transfer the filtrate to a beaker and cool in ice-water with stirring. The hydrazobenzene separates as colourless crystals, which are filtered off at the pump and drained. A portion when dried in a desiccator has m.p. 124°.

BENZIDINE. Add 5 g. of the thoroughly drained (and almost dry) hydrazobenzene to a mixture of 15 ml. of concentrated hydrochloric acid and 100 ml. of distilled water contained in a 250 ml. conical flask. Warm the mixture to 25–30°, and then securely cork the flask and shake the contents vigorously. Occasionally withdraw the cork, and re-warm the mixture before shaking again. After about 15 minutes, heat the mixture carefully to 50° for about 5 minutes. If the original hydrazobenzene were pure, a clear solution should now be obtained. If any undissolved material remains, however, filter the solution, and precipitate the benzidine by the addition of aqueous sodium hydroxide solution to the cooled filtrate. Filter off the precipitated benzidine, and recrystallise from boiling water (in which it is only moderately soluble), adding some animal charcoal to the boiling solution if it is coloured.* The benzidine separates from the cooled filtrate as a monohydrate, which when placed in a vacuum desiccator readily gives the anhydrous benzidine as colourless crystals, m.p. 127°. A second recrystallisation from water is however sometimes necessary. Yield, 2·5 g. Alternatively, the crude precipitated benzidine can be recrystallised from ethanol, or it may be dried and recrystallised from benzene.

---

* *Care.* Benzidine is carcinogenic, and strict care should be taken not to absorb it either by inhalation or by contact with the skin.

N-Phenylanthranilic Acid, $C_6H_5 \cdot NH \cdot C_6H_4 \cdot COOH$.
(The Ullmann Condensation.)

A halogen atom directly attached to a benzene ring is usually unreactive, unless it is activated by the nature and position of certain other substituent groups. It has been shown by Ullmann, however, that halogen atoms normally of low reactivity will condense with aromatic amines in the presence of an alkali carbonate (to absorb the hydrogen halide formed) and a trace of copper powder or oxide to act as a catalyst. This reaction, known as the *Ullmann Condensation*, is frequently used to prepare substituted diphenylamines: it is exemplified

in the following condensation of o-chlorobenzoic acid with aniline to give N-phenylanthranilic acid or o-carboxydiphenylamine.

Required: Aniline, 30 ml.; o-chlorobenzoic acid, 8 g.; potassium carbonate, 8 g.; powdered copper oxide, 0·4 g.

Prepare a mixture of 30 ml. of aniline, 8 g. of o-chlorobenzoic acid, 8 g. of anhydrous potassium carbonate and 0·4 g. of copper oxide in a 500 ml. round-bottomed flask fitted with an air-condenser, and then boil the mixture under reflux for 1·5 hours: the mixture tends to foam during the earlier part of the heating owing to the evolution of carbon dioxide, and hence the large flask is used. When the heating has been completed, fit the flask with a steam-distillation head, and steam-distil the crude product until all the excess of aniline has been removed. The residual solution now contains the potassium N-phenylanthranilate: add *ca.* 2 g. of animal charcoal to this solution, boil for about 5 minutes, and filter hot. Add dilute hydrochloric acid (1:1 by volume) to the filtrate until no further precipitation occurs, and then cool in ice-water with stirring. Filter off the N-phenylanthranilic acid at the pump, wash with water, drain and dry. Yield, 9–9·5 g. The acid may be recrystallised from aqueous ethanol, or methylated spirit, with addition of charcoal if necessary, and is obtained as colourless crystals, m.p. 185–186°.

For the cyclisation of N-phenylanthranilic acid to acridone, see p. 303.

Methylation can be carried out by the following methods:

(1) *Williamson's Method*, more particularly for hydroxy- and thiol- (mercapto) compounds. The substance is treated either directly with sodium or (more usually) with a solution of sodium methoxide in methanol, to give the sodium derivative. The latter is then boiled with methyl iodide.

$$RONa + ICH_3 \rightarrow ROCH_3 + NaI$$

Note that this is only a particular case of Williamson's general method for the preparation of ethers.

(2) *Purdie's Method*, also chiefly for hydroxy-compounds. The substance is mixed with a small excess of dry silver oxide, and then shaken (or, if necessary, heated) with methyl iodide, a smooth methylation usually occurring.

$$2ROH + Ag_2O + 2CH_3I = 2ROCH_3 + 2AgI + H_2O$$

This method is used more particularly for hydroxy-compounds which also contain other groups (such as Cl atoms, *etc.*) which might be affected by the sodium hydroxide used in the following method.

(3) *Dimethyl Sulphate Method*, for hydroxy-compounds and for primary and secondary amines, acid amides, *etc.* The substance is dissolved or suspended in water, a small excess (above the theoretical) of sodium hydroxide added and then the theoretical quantity of dimethyl sulphate, the mixture being finally shaken without external warming. Methylation is usually rapid, the dimethyl sulphate being converted to methyl hydrogen sulphate

$$ROH + (CH_3)_2SO_4 + NaOH = ROCH_3 + CH_3NaSO_4 + H_2O$$
$$RNH_2 + (CH_3)_2SO_4 + NaOH = RNHCH_3 + CH_3NaSO_4 + H_2O$$

which dissolves in the alkali present. The general conditions are thus very similar to those used for the Schotten-Baumann reaction (p. 243) by which the same classes of compound (hydroxy-derivatives, primary and secondary amines) can be benzoylated, *etc.*

For the preparation of tertiary amines, the conditions must not be too vigorous, otherwise the tertiary amine may react further to form the quaternary methyl methosulphate.

For experimental details, see p. 220.

Dimethyl sulphate is poisonous, both when the hot vapour is inhaled and even when the cold liquid is spilt on the hands, and considerable care should be exercised in its use (*cf.* pp. 215, 218, 526).

(4) *Diazomethane Method.* Diazomethane readily methylates phenolic hydroxy-compounds, primary and secondary amines, and carboxylic acids,

$$ROH + N_2CH_2 = ROCH_3 + N_2$$

nitrogen being liberated. Since diazomethane is a gas, it is usually employed in ethereal solution. One advantage of this method of methylation is that it takes place in an almost neutral solution, *i.e.*, the addition of alkalis or acids is unnecessary. *Diazomethane is both poisonous and* (*in the gaseous state*) *explosive, and requires therefore careful manipulation.*

(5) *The Formaldehyde-Formic Acid Method.* This method applies to primary and secondary amines, which when boiled with a formalin-formic acid mixture undergo complete methylation to the corresponding tertiary amine. This method has the advantage over the dimethyl sulphate method in that quaternary salts clearly cannot be formed.

The mechanism of this methylation is probably that the primary amine

$$RNH_2 \rightarrow RN{:}CH_2 \rightarrow RNHCH_3 \rightarrow RN({\cdot}CH_2OH)CH_3 \rightarrow RN(CH_3)_2$$
$$\text{(I)} \qquad \text{(II)} \qquad \text{(IIA)} \qquad \text{(III)}$$

condenses with the formaldehyde to give a Schiff's base (I) [or an analogous compound RNH($\cdot$CH$_2$OH)], which is then reduced to the secondary amine (II) by the formic acid, which is itself oxidised to carbon dioxide. The secondary amine then undergoes a similar conversion through the intermediate (IIA) to the tertiary amine (III). For experimental details, see p. 226.

Methods (2) and (3) have been extensively used in the investigation of the structure of sugars.

Anisole (Methyl Phenyl Ether). C$_6$H$_5$OCH$_3$. (Method 1.)

Required: Sodium, 3·8 g.; methanol, 75 ml.; phenol, 15 g.; methyl iodide, 11 ml.

Weigh out 3·8 g. of metallic sodium, cut it into small pieces, and add it to 75 ml. of good-quality (preferably absolute) methanol contained in a 250 ml. bolt-head flask: at once attach the flask to an efficient reflux water-condenser. Considerable heat is evolved by the dissolution of the sodium, and the alcohol boils vigorously under reflux: no attempt should be made to cool the alcohol (unless the condenser tends to "choke"), otherwise a considerable time will elapse before the last traces of the sodium dissolve. Then cool the clear solution of sodium methoxide in ice-water, and add 15 g. of phenol,* which will rapidly dissolve to give sodium phenoxide (or phenate) when the mixture is gently shaken. Now add 11 ml. (25 g., 1·1 mols.) of methyl iodide and some fragments of unglazed porcelain, re-attach the flask to the reflux condenser, and boil the solution *gently* on a water-bath for one hour. Then remove the flask from the water-bath, and rearrange the condenser for direct distillation, connecting it through a "knee-tube" to the flask (as in Fig. 59, p. 100, or Fig. 23(D), p. 45). Replace the latter on the water-bath, and distil off the excess of methanol as completely as possible. Pour the residual liquid in the flask into 100 ml. of cold water contained in a separating-funnel, and wash out the flask with another 50 ml. of water, adding these washings also to the liquid in the funnel. Then extract the anisole by shaking with about 40–50 ml. of ether. Run off the lower aqueous layer, and shake the ethereal solution with an equal volume of 10 % aqueous sodium hydroxide solution: this removes unchanged phenol, and also any traces of free iodine present, leaving the ethereal solution quite colourless. Run off the sodium hydroxide solution as completely as possible, and shake the ethereal solution with an equal volume of water to remove the last traces of the sodium hydroxide. Separate the ethereal solution,

---

* The phenol should be weighed out *carefully* on a piece of glazed paper on the balance pan. If spilt crystals of phenol are allowed to remain on the balance pans, the latter may become corroded. If phenol is allowed to come in contact with the hands, it should be washed off without delay.

dry it with calcium chloride, and then distil off the ether from the filtered solution in a 50 ml. distilling-flask, using a similar apparatus and observing the same precautions as in the preparation of aniline (see Fig. 64, p. 163, or Fig. 23(E), p. 45). When all the ether has been distilled off, replace the water-condenser by an air-condenser, and distil the residual anisole slowly over a gauze. Collect the fraction distilling at 152°–156°. Yield, 9 g.

Anisole is a colourless and almost odourless liquid, having b.p. 154°, and d, 0·99. Like the aliphatic ethers, it is chemically inert, although of course the phenyl group shows the normal aromatic reactions.

Phenetole. (Ethyl Phenyl Ether.) $C_6H_5OC_2H_5$. (Method 1, p. 217.)

In view of the high cost of methyl iodide in the above preparation of anisole, and the fact that, unless absolute methanol is used, the ready hydrolysis of the methyl iodide may cause a low yield of the ether, the preparation of anisole may be advantageously replaced by that of phenetole. The reaction is not of course a methylation, but is nevertheless of the same type as that used in the preparation of anisole.

Required: Sodium, 3·8 g.; ethyl bromide, 13·2 ml. (19·1 g.); phenol, 15 g.

Dissolve 3·8 g. of sodium in 75 ml. of rectified spirit, using otherwise the same conditions as in the preparation of anisole. Then add 15 g. of phenol, and to the clear solution add 13·2 ml. (19·1 g., 1·1 mols.) of ethyl bromide. Continue precisely as in the preparation of anisole, shaking the ethereal extract with sodium hydroxide solution as before in order to eliminate any unchanged phenol. Finally collect the fraction boiling at 168–172°. Yield, 14 g.

Phenetole is a colourless liquid, having b.p. 171°, and d, 0·98.

Methyl 2-Naphthyl Ether. (Nerolin.) $C_{10}H_7OCH_3$. (Method 3, p. 218.)

Experiments involving the use of dimethyl sulphate should be carried out by students only under immediate supervision. Not only is the vapour of dimethyl sulphate highly poisonous, but the cold liquid itself is absorbed easily through the skin, with toxic results: individual susceptibility to dimethyl sulphate poisoning varies and may be very high. If the sulphate is splashed on to the hands, wash immediately with plenty of concentrated ammonia solution in order to hydrolyse the methyl sulphate before it can be absorbed through the skin (see p. 528).

Required: 2-Naphthol, 10 g.; dimethyl sulphate, 6·9 ml. (9·2 g.).

Dissolve 10 g. of pure 2-naphthol in 30 ml. of 10% sodium hydroxide solution (1·1 mols.) contained in a stout-walled wide-necked bottle of about 200 ml. capacity, and for which a well-fitting *rubber* stopper is available. Dilute the solution with 30 ml. of water in order to moderate the subsequent reaction, and then run in from a burette 6·9 ml. (9·2 g., 1·05 mols.) of dimethyl sulphate. Cork the bottle securely and shake the contents vigorously. As the reaction proceeds, the mixture becomes warm and the methyl naphthyl ether rapidly separates as a greyish-white powder: finally after about 20 minutes' shaking the reaction is complete and the mixture has again become almost cold. Filter the methyl naphthyl ether at the pump, wash with dilute (10%) sodium hydroxide to remove any traces of unchanged naphthol or methyl sulphate, and then wash thoroughly with water and drain.

Recrystallise from methylated spirit, from which the methyl 2-naphthyl ether separates readily as colourless crystals, m.p. 72°: yield, 9 g.

Nerolin, which has a faint but persistent odour, is used technically for scenting soaps, *etc.*

1-Naphthol, similarly methylated, gives the liquid methyl 1-naphthyl ether, b.p. 263°. Phenol gives anisole, the preparation of which by Method 1 has, however, already been described.

Toluene-*p*-sulphon-dimethylamide.*
$CH_3C_6H_4SO_2N(CH_3)_2$. (Method 3, p. 218.)

Toluene-*p*-sulphonamide can be similarly converted into the dimethylamide, but the methylation now occurs in two definite stages. First the sulphonamide dissolves in the sodium hydroxide to form the mono-sodium salt (see p. 252), which then reacts with the dimethyl sulphate to give the mono-

$$CH_3C_6H_4SO_2NHNa + (CH_3)_2SO_4 = CH_3C_6H_4SO_2NH(CH_3) + NaCH_3SO_4$$

methylamide: the latter, being still acidic, remains dissolved in the alkaline solution as the sodium salt, which then reacts with a second equivalent of

$$CH_3C_6H_4SO_2NNa(CH_3) + (CH_3)_2SO_4 = CH_3C_6H_4SO_2N(CH_3)_2 + NaCH_3SO_4$$

dimethyl sulphate to give the dimethylamide. The dimethylamide is neutral and therefore separates from solution.

Required: Toluene-*p*-sulphonamide, 10 g.; dimethyl sulphate, 12·7 ml. (17 g.).

Dissolve 10 g. of powdered toluene-*p*-sulphonamide in 60 ml. of 10% aqueous sodium hydroxide (2·5 mols.) diluted with 50 ml. of water to moderate the reaction. Then, using the same precautions as in the previous preparation, add 12·7 ml. (17 g., 2·3 mols.) of dimethyl sulphate and shake the mixture vigorously. The crystalline dimethylamide rapidly separates from the warm

* Alternative name: *N,N*-dimethyltoluene-*p*-sulphonamide.

solution. After 15–20 minutes' shaking, cool the mixture in ice-water, and filter off the dimethylamide. Wash with sodium hydroxide solution, then with water and drain. The product thus prepared is (when dry) almost pure, but can be readily re-crystallised from a mixture of equal volumes of water and glacial acetic acid: filter the recrystallised material at the pump, wash with water, drain and dry. Colourless crystals, m.p. 79°: yield, 8 g.

The toluene-*p*-sulphon-dimethylamide can be readily hydrolysed by boiling under reflux with 70% sulphuric acid (see p. 107). If the

$$CH_3C_6H_4SO_2N(CH_3)_2 + H_2O + H_2SO_4 \rightarrow CH_3C_6H_4SO_2OH + (CH_3)_2NH,H_2SO_4$$

clear solution so obtained is placed in a distilling-flask and made alkaline, the liberated dimethylamine may be driven over by heating, and then absorbed in hydrochloric acid. Evaporation of the hydrochloric acid solution gives the deliquescent crystalline dimethylamine hydrochloride, $(CH_3)_2NH,HCl$.

N-Methylanthranilic Acid. $CH_3 \cdot NH \cdot C_6H_4 \cdot COOH$.
(Method 3, p. 218.)

This preparation illustrates the use of dimethyl sulphate to convert a primary amino group into the secondary monomethylamino group, without the methylation proceeding to the tertiary dimethylamino stage. The methylation of anthranilic acid is arrested at the monomethylamino stage by using 1·1 molecular equivalents of sodium hydroxide and of dimethyl sulphate. The reactions can be considered as:

$$NH_2 \cdot C_6H_4 \cdot COOH + NaOH \rightarrow NH_2 \cdot C_6H_4 \cdot COONa + H_2O$$

$$NH_2 \cdot C_6H_4 \cdot COONa + (CH_3)_2SO_4 \rightarrow CH_3 \cdot NH \cdot C_6H_4 \cdot COOH + NaCH_3SO_4$$

The isolation of the *N*-methylanthranilic acid is greatly facilitated by the fact that in cold water it is appreciably less soluble than anthranilic acid, and very much less soluble than *NN*-dimethylanthranilic acid.

Required: Anthranilic acid, 2 g.; dimethyl sulphate, 1·6 ml. (2 g.).

A fresh sample of dimethyl sulphate should be employed: an old sample, or one that has been frequently exposed to the air, should be shaken with water, separated, dried over sodium sulphate, and distilled (b.p. 188°).

Dissolve 2 g. of anthranilic acid in 12·8 ml. of 5% aqueous sodium hydroxide, or in 16 ml. of *N*-NaOH solution in a 50 ml. conical flask. (It is essential that the concentration of the hydroxide solution is accurately known.) Add 1·6 ml. of dimethyl sulphate, and shake the securely-stoppered flask vigorously.

The *N*-methylanthranilic acid rapidly separates. Cool the mixture in ice-water, filter off the acid at the pump, wash thoroughly with water and drain. The crude acid if now dried weighs 1·5 g. and has m.p. 166–170°.

To save time, the well-drained acid may be recrystallised twice from ethanol, and the pure acid, m.p. 176–177°, thus obtained.

This recrystallised acid is "pure" in the normally accepted sense of the word, namely it has a sharp m.p. and gives on analysis excellent values for carbon, hydrogen and nitrogen. If however it is subjected to one-dimensional paper chromatography (p. 53), the presence of traces of unchanged anthranilic acid can be detected, and repeated recrystallisation is necessary to remove these traces.

1-Phenyl-ethylamine. $CH_3 \cdot CH(C_6H_5)NH_2$.
(The Leuckart Reaction.)

Aldehydes and ketones may be converted into the corresponding primary amines by reduction of their oximes or hydrazones (p. 93). A method of more limited application, known as the Leuckart Reaction, consists of heating the carbonyl compound with ammonium formate, whereby the formyl-amino derivative is formed, and can be readily hydrolysed by acids to the amine. Thus acetophenone gives the 1-phenylethylformamide, which without isolation can be hydrolysed to 1-phenylethylamine.

$$CH_3 \cdot CO + 2HCOONH_4 \rightarrow CH_3 \cdot CH \cdot NH \cdot CHO + CO_2 + NH_3 + 2H_2O$$
$$C_6H_5 C_6H_5$$

$$CH_3 \cdot CH \cdot NH \cdot CHO + H_2O \rightarrow CH_3 \cdot CH \cdot NH_2 + HCOOH$$
$$C_6H_5 C_6H_5$$

The reaction proceeds most readily with alkylaryl, dialkyl, and cyclic ketones, but the crude product may contain some secondary or tertiary amine.

Required: Acetophenone, 30 g.; ammonium formate, 50 g.; benzene, 30 ml.; hydrochloric acid, 30 ml.; ether, 100 ml., sodium hydroxide.

Fit a 100 ml. Claisen flask with a thermometer reaching almost to the bottom of the flask, and a water-condenser for distillation. Place in the flask 30 g. of acetophenone and 50 g. of dry ammonium formate (with some unglazed porcelain), and heat the mixture *gently* over a small flame. The mixture readily forms two layers and distillation begins: at 150–155° the reaction starts with moderate effervescence. Continue heating until the temperature of the mixture reaches 185°, and then allow to cool. The distillate has meanwhile separated into two layers, the upper layer being mainly unchanged acetophenone. Separate this upper layer, return it to the flask, and continue heating the mixture at 180–185° for 30–40 minutes.

Cool the reaction mixture, transfer it to a separating-funnel, and extract it with 40 ml. of water to remove ammonium formate and formamide. Run the lower layer of 1-phenylethylformamide back into the original flask, and extract the upper aqueous layer with 30 ml. of benzene. Discard the aqueous layer, and run the benzene extract also into the flask. Now add 30 ml. of concentrated hydrochloric acid and some porcelain, and distil off the benzene: then boil the residual liquid gently under reflux for 30 minutes. Cool the liquid, and extract it with 25 ml. of benzene to remove traces of acetophenone. Chill the aqueous layer thoroughly and then liberate the amine by slowly adding with stirring a solution of 25 g. of sodium hydroxide in 50 ml. of water. Extract the mixture twice with ether (50 ml. each time) and dry the united ethereal extracts over solid sodium hydroxide. Then distil off the ether from the filtered extract, and finally the 1-phenylethylamine, b.p. 185–188°. Yield, 12–13 g. The small higher-boiling residue is di-1-phenylethylamine, $(CH_3CH \cdot C_6H_5)_2NH$.

2-Dimethylamino-*n*-octane from *n*-Octan-2-ol.

This complete preparation entails four consecutive intermediate preparations each illustrating a standard reaction in organic chemistry.

n-Octan-2-ol (A), sometimes called *sec*.octyl alcohol, can be obtained, at a low price and of high purity, from technical sources. As a secondary alcohol, it can be readily oxidised by potassium dichromate-sulphuric acid to *n*-hexyl

$$(A) \quad CH_3(CH_2)_5 \cdot CH(OH) \cdot CH_3$$
$$\downarrow$$
$$(B) \quad CH_3(CH_2)_5 \cdot CO \cdot CH_3$$
$$\downarrow$$
$$(C) \quad CH_3(CH_2)_5 \cdot \overset{||}{\underset{NOH}{C}} \cdot CH_3$$
$$\downarrow$$
$$(D) \quad CH_3(CH_2)_5 \cdot \overset{}{\underset{NH_2}{CH}} \cdot CH_3$$
$$\downarrow$$
$$(E) \quad CH_3(CH_2)_5 \cdot \overset{}{\underset{N(CH_3)_2}{CH}} \cdot CH_3$$

methyl ketone (B). This ketone gives with hydroxylamine an oxime (C), which is purified by distillation under reduced pressure. The oxime is reduced by sodium and ethanol to 2-amino-*n*-octane (D). This primary amine, when boiled with a formaldehyde-formic acid mixture (p. 218), undergoes methylation to the tertiary amine 2-dimethylamino-*n*-octane (E).

Required: *n*-Octan-2-ol (redistilled), 61 ml. (50 g.); sodium dichromate dihydrate, 37·5 g.; hydroxylamine sulphate, 80 g. (or the hydrochloride, 68·5 g.); hydrated sodium acetate, 25 g.; sodium, 38 g.; 40% formalin solution, 50 ml.; formic acid, 80 ml.; ethanol, 250 ml.

(B) *n*-HEXYL METHYL KETONE. $CH_3(CH_2)_5 \cdot CO \cdot CH_3$.

Redistil technical *n*-octan-2-ol, and collect the fraction of b.p. 178–179°. Fit a three-necked round-bottomed flask of *ca.* 500 ml. capacity with a stirrer, dropping-funnel and reflux water-condenser (as in Fig. 23(G), p. 46). Place 250 ml. of water in the flask, cautiously add with stirring 27·5 ml. (50 g.) of concentrated sulphuric acid, and then add 37·5 g. of pulverised sodium dichromate dihydrate. To this stirred solution add 61 ml. (50 g.) of *n*-octan-2-ol from the dropping-funnel during 45 minutes. Then heat the reaction-mixture under reflux on a boiling water-bath for 1 hour. Transfer the solution to a steam-distillation apparatus (or fit a steam-distillation head to the original flask) and steam-distil the mixture until no more ketone passes over. Separate the insoluble ketone from the aqueous distillate, and dry it over calcium chloride. After filtration, distil the *n*-hexyl methyl ketone, b.p. 172–173°. Yield, 40 g.

(C) *n*-HEXYL METHYL KETOXIME.
$CH_3(CH_2)_5 C(:NOH) \cdot CH_3$.

Place 80 g. of hydroxylamine sulphate (or 68·5 g. of the hydrochloride), 25 g. of hydrated sodium acetate, and 100 ml. of water in a 500 ml. flask fitted with a stirrer and a reflux water-condenser, and heat the stirred solution to 55–60°. Run in 35 g. (42 ml.) of *n*-hexyl methyl ketone, and continue the heating and vigorous stirring for $1\frac{1}{2}$ hours. (The mixture can conveniently be set aside overnight after this stage.) Extract the oily oxime from the cold mixture twice with ether. Wash the united ethereal extract once with a small quantity of water, and dry it with sodium sulphate. Then distil off the ether from the filtered extract, preferably using a distillation flask of type shown in Fig. 41 (p. 65) and of *ca.* 50 ml. capacity, the extract being run in as fast as the ether distils, and then fractionally distil the oxime at water-pump pressure. Collect the liquid ketoxime, b.p. 110–111°/13 mm. Yield, 30–32 g.

(D) 2-AMINO-*n*-OCTANE. $CH_3(CH_2)_5 CH(\cdot NH_2) \cdot CH_3$.

For this reduction use preferably a 1 litre round-bottomed flask having 3 necks (Fig. 23(G), p. 46), the two necks at the flanks being straight (to avoid the obstruction, during the addition of sodium, which a curved neck might cause). Fit the central neck with a stirrer, one of the side necks with a reflux water-condenser, and the other with a glass or rubber stopper.

Place 25 g. (29 ml.) of the oxime and 100 ml. of ethanol in the flask, and heat the stirred solution under reflux on a boiling water-bath. Meanwhile cut up 38 g. of sodium into small pieces of convenient size for inserting through the third neck of the flask, and store them temporarily in a wide-necked bottle closed by a cork. Add the pieces of sodium in turn to the stirred boiling solution, removing each piece from the bottle by means of forceps or tongs: when the reaction appears to be subsiding add more ethanol (150–200 ml.) in small portions to maintain a vigorous reaction, and to complete the dissolution of the sodium (total time, $1\frac{1}{2}$–2 hours).

Discontinue the heating, and add 125 ml. of water *cautiously* from a dropping-funnel to the stirred hot solution. Then either pour the solution into a flask fitted for steam-distillation, or adapt the 3-necked flask by replacing the stirrer by a steam-head to which the reversed condenser can be fitted, the other two necks being closed unless the design of the steam-head necessitates the steam being led in through one of these necks. Collect about 750 ml. of distillate in a flask containing *ca.* 20 ml. of concentrated hydrochloric acid. Evaporate the acidic mixture to 30–40 ml. on a water-bath (to save time, start evaporating the first 50–100 ml. of distillate as soon as it is collected, and add the remainder in portions whilst the distillation is proceeding).

Chill the concentrated solution of the amine hydrochloride in ice-water, and then cautiously with stirring add an excess of 20% aqueous sodium hydroxide solution to liberate the amine. Pour the mixture into a separating-funnel, and rinse out the flask or basin with ether into the funnel. Extract the mixture twice with ether (2 × 25 ml.). Dry the united ether extracts over "flake" or powdered sodium hydroxide, preferably overnight. Distil the dry filtered extract from an apparatus similar to that used for the oxime: when the ether has been removed, distil the amine *slowly* under water-pump pressure, using a capillary tube having a soda-lime guard-tube to ensure that only dry air free from carbon dioxide passes through the liquid. Collect the amine, b.p. 59–61°/12 mm.: at atmospheric pressure it has b.p. 163–164°. Yield, 18 g.

To prepare a sample of the hydrochloride, add 0·5 ml. of the base to 10 ml. of dilute hydrochloric acid in an evaporating basin and evaporate to dryness, preferably in a vacuum desiccator. Recrystallise the dry residue from petroleum (b.p. 60–80°). The hydrochloride separates as white crystals, m.p. 90°.

(E) 2-DIMETHYLAMINO-*n*-OCTANE.

$$CH_3 \cdot (CH_2)_5 \cdot CH[\cdot N(CH_3)_2] \cdot CH_3.$$

Dissolve 12 g. of the amine in 50 ml. of fresh 40% formalin in a flask fitted with a reflux water-condenser. Cool the mixture,

add slowly 70 ml. of formic acid down the condenser, and then
boil the mixture under reflux for $1\frac{1}{2}$ hours, during which time
carbon dioxide is steadily evolved.

Cool the solution *thoroughly* in ice-water, and then make it
alkaline by the cautious addition (with stirring or shaking) of a
solution of 80 g. of sodium hydroxide in *ca.* 150 ml. of water.
Now isolate the free tertiary amine by steam-distillation into
hydrochloric acid, etc., precisely as for the primary amine in
Stage (D), but preferably using a smaller flask for the final distillation. Collect the 2-dimethylamino-*n*-octane, b.p. 76–78°/15
mm. Yield, 13–14 g. At atmospheric pressure the amine has
b.p. 187–188°.

The hydrochloride of the amine may be prepared precisely as that of the
primary amine. For recrystallisation, boil a suspension of the powdered salt in
petroleum (b.p. 60–80°), and then add acetone slowly in small drops until the
boiling suspension just becomes clear: allow the stirred solution to cool until
crystallisation starts, and then chill in ice-water before collecting the colourless
plates of the hydrochloride, which after drying in a vacuum desiccator have
m.p. 132–134°.

Both the primary amine (D) and the tertiary amine (E) are
reasonably strong bases, and will absorb carbon dioxide if
exposed to the air. They should therefore be stored in ground-
glass stoppered bottles or in sealed tubes.

Caprolactam. The Beckmann Rearrangement.

The oximes of ketones when treated with various acidic reagents undergo the
Beckmann Rearrangement, whereby, *e.g.*, the ·OH group in the oxime (I) can
be regarded as undergoing a *trans* exchange with the group R^1, followed by back
migration of the H atom, to give the substituted acid amide (II). This process

when applied to the oxime of an alicyclic ketone will therefore give a cyclic
lactam with ring enlargement: cyclohexanone-oxime (III) will thus give the
lactam (IV) of ε-amino-caproic acid, or caprolactam, which systematically is a
cyclic acid amide. In this example, 85% sulphuric acid is used as the reagent.

Required: Cyclohexanone, 20 g.; hydroxylamine hydrochloride, 17 g.; anhydrous sodium carbonate, 13 g.; concentrated sulphuric acid, 50 ml.; 25% aqueous potassium hydroxide solution, approx. 200 ml.; chloroform, 120 ml.

Cyclohexanone oxime. Add 20 g. (21 ml.) of cyclohexanone to a solution of 17 g. of hydroxylamine hydrochloride in 40 ml. of water, and cool the mixture in ice-water. Add a solution of 13 g. of anhydrous sodium carbonate in 40 ml. of water *slowly* to the mixture, stirring the latter with a 100° thermometer, and maintaining the temperature of the mixture at 20–25° meanwhile. The oxime rapidly separates. Stir the complete mixture at intervals, and after 10 minutes filter the oxime at the pump, drain thoroughly and dry it in a (vacuum) desiccator. Yield of crude oxime, 20 g. Recrystallise from petroleum (b.p. 100–120°) and dry over paraffin wax (p. 19). Yield of pure oxime, 16 g., m.p. 88°.

Beckmann Rearrangement. Prepare the 85% sulphuric acid by adding 50 ml. of the concentrated acid *cautiously* to 10 ml. of water, stirring the mixture meanwhile, and then cool the diluted acid in ice-water. Place 16 ml. of the cold acid in a 500 ml. beaker, add 8 g. of the pure oxime, and warm the mixture cautiously until effervescence begins, and then at once remove the heat. A vigorous reaction occurs, and is soon complete. Repeat this operation with another 8 g. of the oxime in a second beaker: the reaction is too vigorous to be carried out with larger quantities.

Unite the two reaction-mixtures and cool in ice-salt: add 40 g. of crushed ice to the mixture, and stir it mechanically whilst *slowly* adding 25% aqueous potassium hydroxide solution (about 200 ml.) until the mixture is faintly alkaline to phenolphthalein: ensure that the temperature does not rise above 20° during this operation. A considerable amount of potassium sulphate crystallises from the mixture. Filter the latter at the pump, and wash the residual sulphate on the filter with 30 ml. of chloroform. Run the filtrate and washings into a separating-funnel, run off the chloroform, and extract the aqueous layer three times with chloroform, using 30 ml. on each occasion. Dry the united chloroform extracts with sodium sulphate, filter, and distil off the chloroform, finally distilling the residual caprolactam at water-pump pressure. It distils at 140–142°/15 mm., and solidifies in the receiver. Yield, 10 g. from 16 g. of oxime. The caprolactam, m.p. 68–70°, may be recrystallised from petroleum (b.p. 60–80°) and obtained as colourless plates, m.p. 69–70°.

Benzaldehyde Phenylhydrazone. $C_6H_5CH:N\cdot NHC_6H_5$. (Semi-micro Scale.)

Phenylhydrazine condenses readily with aldehydes and ketones to give *phenylhydrazones*, which, being usually crystalline compounds of sharp

$$C_6H_5CHO + H_2NNHC_6H_5 \rightarrow C_6H_5CH:NNHC_6H_5 + H_2O$$

Benzaldehyde   Phenylhydrazine   Benzaldehyde
Phenylhydrazone

melting-point, can therefore be used to identify the aldehydes and ketones from which they have been formed. For this purpose phenylhydrazones are frequently more suitable than oximes (p. 93) since their greater molecular weight causes a lower solubility in most solvents, and they can therefore often be more easily isolated and recrystallised. The phenylhydrazones of the lower aliphatic aldehydes and ketones, however, often have low melting-points, and are thus not suitable for identification purposes: to overcome this difficulty, substituted phenylhydrazines such as *p*-nitrophenylhydrazine, $(NO_2C_6H_4NHNH_2)$, 2,4-dinitrophenylhydrazine (pp. 263, 346), and *p*-bromophenylhydrazine are often used, since the corresponding substituted phenylhydrazones usually crystallise well, and are of low solubility and high melting-point.

Phenylhydrazine is usually dissolved in acetic acid for hydrazone formation: if a salt of phenylhydrazine with an inorganic acid is used, it must be mixed with an excess of sodium acetate (see preparation of osazones, p. 137).

Required: Acetic acid, 0·3 ml.; phenylhydrazine, 0·4 ml.; benzaldehyde, 0·2 ml.

Dissolve 0·3 ml. of glacial acetic acid in 2 ml. of water in a 25 ml. conical flask, and add 0·4 ml. (0·44 g.) of phenylhydrazine. Mix thoroughly to obtain a clear solution of phenylhydrazine acetate and then add 0·2 ml. (0·21 g.) of benzaldehyde. Cork the flask securely and shake the contents vigorously. A yellow crystalline mass of the hydrazone soon begins to separate. Allow to stand for 15 minutes, with occasional shaking, and then filter the solid product at the pump, wash first with very dilute acetic acid and then with water, and finally drain thoroughly. Recrystallise the material from rectified or methylated spirit, the benzaldehyde phenylhydrazone being thus obtained in fine colourless needles, m.p. 157°: yield, 0·4 g.

Hydrobenzamide. $(C_6H_5CH)_3N_2$.

Benzaldehyde reacts with ammonia to give hydrobenzamide, in accordance with the equation:

$$3C_6H_5CHO + 2NH_3 = (C_6H_5CH)_3N_2 + 3H_2O$$

This behaviour is in marked contrast to that of the aliphatic aldehydes, which usually give direct addition products with ammonia, although polymerisation

$$CH_3CHO + HNH_2 = CH_3CH(OH)NH_2 \longrightarrow (C_2H_7ON)_3$$

may follow. Formaldehyde is an exception among the aliphatic aldehydes, since it undergoes condensation with ammonia to give hexamethylene tetramine (or

$$6CH_2O + 4NH_3 = (CH_2)_6N_4 + 6H_2O$$

urotropine (p. 379), a reaction which resembles that given by benzaldehyde.

Required: Benzaldehyde, 5 ml.; concentrated ammonia, 50 ml.

Place 5 ml. of benzaldehyde in a wide-necked stout-walled bottle of about 100 ml. capacity (a conical flask is too fragile for this purpose) and add 50 ml. of concentrated (d, 0·880) ammonia solution. Cork the bottle securely, shake vigorously, and then allow to stand for 24 hours, by which time the layer of benzaldehyde at the bottom of the bottle will have been converted into a hard mass of hydrobenzamide. (If after 24 hours the crude hydrobenzamide is still syrupy, shake the mixture vigorously and allow to stand for another hour, when the conversion will be complete.) Break up the solid pellet with a strong spatula, filter at the pump, wash with water and drain thoroughly. Recrystallise from ethanol: methylated spirit should not be used, as it contains sufficient water to cause partial hydrolysis back to benzaldehyde and ammonia. Hydrobenzamide is obtained as colourless crystals, m.p. 101° (and not 110° as frequently quoted): yield, 4 g.

Hydrobenzamide is readily hydrolysed even by cold dilute acids.

Benzylidene-aniline. $C_6H_5CH{:}NC_6H_5$. (Semi-micro Scale.)

Aldehydes undergo condensation with primary amines with the elimination of water to give compounds known as Schiff's Bases, which can also be used to characterise aldehydes. Benzaldehyde for example condenses readily with

$$C_6H_5CHO + H_2NC_6H_5 \rightarrow C_6H_5CH{:}NC_6H_5 + H_2O$$

aniline to give benzylidene-aniline. In other cases in which the condensation is not so rapid, it may be hastened considerably by the addition of a trace of anhydrous zinc chloride.

Required: Benzaldehyde, 1 ml.; aniline, 1 ml.

Mix 1 ml. of benzaldehyde and 1 ml. of aniline in a small evaporating-basin, place the latter on a boiling water-bath and stir the mixture gently with a glass rod. Globules of water soon appear on the oily layer. After about 20 minutes place the basin in ice-water, and stir the contents well, whereupon solidification should rapidly occur. (If the material does not solidify, replace the basin on the boiling water-bath for a further 10 minutes.) Break up the solid material in the basin, transfer to a conical flask, and recrystallise from rectified spirit. The benzylidene-aniline is obtained as colourless crystals, m.p. 52°: yield, 0·8 g.

Dibenzal-acetone. $C_6H_5CH:CHCOCH:CHC_6H_5$ (Claisen Reaction). (Semi-micro Scale.)

When an ethanolic solution containing both acetone and two equivalents of benzaldehyde is made alkaline with sodium hydroxide, rapid condensation occurs with the formation of dibenzal-acetone, or dibenzylidene-acetone. This

$$2C_6H_5CHO + CH_3COCH_3 = C_6H_5CH:CHCOCH:CHC_6H_5 + 2H_2O$$
Dibenzal-acetone.

is a particular example of the Claisen Reaction,* for Claisen showed that aldehydes under the influence of sodium hydroxide will condense with (i) another aldehyde, or (ii) a ketone, with the elimination of water. Thus benzaldehyde will condense with (i) acetaldehyde to give cinnamic aldehyde, and with (ii) one equivalent of acetone to give (mono) benzal-acetone. In these

(i) $C_6H_5CHO + HCH_2CHO = C_6H_5CH:CH \cdot CHO + H_2O$
Cinnamic aldehyde.

(ii) $C_6H_5CHO + HCH_2COCH_3 = C_6H_5CH:CHCOCH_3 + H_2O$
Benzylidene-acetone.

reactions it is probable that an intermediate hydroxy-compound is formed ($C_6H_5CH(OH)CH_2CHO$ and $C_6H_5CH(OH)CH_2COCH_3$ respectively) and water is then lost from the unstable $-CH(OH)CH_2-$ group.

Required: Benzaldehyde, 1 ml.; acetone, 0·4 ml.; methylated spirit, 10 ml.

Dissolve 1 ml. of benzaldehyde and 0·4 ml. of pure acetone in 10 ml. of methylated spirit contained in a conical flask or wide-mouthed bottle of about 50 ml. capacity. Dilute 2 ml. of 10% aqueous sodium hydroxide solution with 8 ml. of water, and add this dilute alkali solution to the former solution. Shake the mixture vigorously in the securely corked flask for about 10 minutes (releasing the pressure from time to time if necessary) and then allow to stand for 30 minutes, with occasional shaking: finally cool in ice-water for a few minutes. During the shaking, the dibenzal-acetone separates at first as a fine emulsion which then rapidly forms pale yellow crystals. Filter at the pump, wash well with water to eliminate traces of alkali, and then drain thoroughly. Recrystallise from hot methylated or rectified spirit. The dibenzal-acetone is obtained as pale yellow crystals, m.p. 112°: yield, 0·6 g.

Benzyl Alcohol, $C_6H_5CH_2OH$, and Benzoic Acid, C_6H_5COOH. (Cannizzaro's Reaction).

When benzaldehyde is treated with a concentrated caustic alkali solution, polymerisation occurs with the formation of benzyl benzoate, which then

---

* This Reaction should be carefully distinguished from the *Claisen Condensation*, which is the condensation of an ester, under the influence of *sodium ethoxide*, with (i) another ester, (ii) a ketone, or (iii) a nitrile, with the elimination of alcohol. For details of this condensation, see Ethyl Acetoacetate, p. 264.

undergoes hydrolysis giving benzyl alcohol and the alkali salt of benzoic acid. The final result is equivalent to the reduction of one molecule of benzaldehyde

$$C_6H_5CHO + OHCC_6H_5 = C_6H_5COOCH_2C_6H_5$$
$$C_6H_5COOCH_2C_6H_5 + KOH = C_6H_5CH_2OH + C_6H_5COOK$$

to the corresponding alcohol, and oxidation of the second molecule to the corresponding acid. The two products can be readily separated by treatment with water, in which the potassium benzoate dissolves, whilst the benzyl alcohol separates as an insoluble oil which can be removed by extraction with ether: acidification of the residual aqueous solution by concentrated hydrochloric acid then precipitates the benzoic acid.

This reaction is given by most aromatic aldehydes having the aldehyde group directly joined to the benzene ring: it is also given by formaldehyde, with the formation of methanol and formic acid. Other aliphatic aldehydes do not give Cannizzaro's reaction under these conditions.

Required: Potassium hydroxide, 27 g.; benzaldehyde, 30 ml.

Dissolve 27 g. of potassium hydroxide* in 20 ml. of water contained in a small beaker or conical flask, keeping the latter partly immersed in ice-water to prevent the mixture from boiling as the potash dissolves, and finally to ensure that the complete solution is thoroughly cooled. Pour the cold solution into a stout-walled bottle of about 250 ml. capacity, and add 30 ml. (31·5 g.) of benzaldehyde; *cork* the bottle securely (a glass stopper must not be used because the alkaline solution on standing would cement it firmly in position) and then shake the mixture vigorously until it has been converted into a thick emulsion, which may finally coagulate into a heavy dough-like mass. Allow the product to stand for at least 4 hours (preferably overnight), and then add sufficient water (about 100 ml.) to dissolve all the solid matter present. Pour the liquid into a separating-funnel, rinse out the bottle with about 20 ml. of ether, and then add this ether to the solution in the funnel. Shake the solution in order to extract the benzyl alcohol with the ether, separate the lower aqueous solution, and then repeat the extraction twice more, using about 20 ml. of ether on each occasion. If the original reaction product has been allowed to stand overnight, the ethereal solution of the benzyl alcohol will be free from unchanged benzaldehyde: if it has been allowed to stand for only about 4 hours, shake the united ether extracts with a moderately concentrated solution of sodium bisulphite to remove traces of benzaldehyde, and then shake the

---

* The cost of this preparation (particularly for large classes) can be appreciably reduced by using a solution of 20 g. of sodium hydroxide in 25 ml. of water, in place of the potassium hydroxide solution. In this case, however, the product on standing overnight forms a very hard mass, which should be dissolved in *warm* water. The yields of alcohol and acid are unchanged.

ethereal solution in turn with dilute sodium hydroxide solution (to ensure complete removal of the bisulphite) and lastly with a small quantity of water. Finally, in either case, dry the ethereal solution by shaking with powdered anhydrous potassium carbonate, and then distil off the ether from the filtered solution, using the usual apparatus for this purpose (p. 163): then replace the water-condenser by an air-condenser and distil the benzyl alcohol over a gauze, collecting the fraction of b.p. 200–207°. Benzyl alcohol is a colourless liquid of b.p. 205° and d, 1·04: it is almost odourless, and is only slightly soluble in water. Yield, 14 g.

To obtain the benzoic acid, add an excess of concentrated hydrochloric acid carefully with stirring to the aqueous alkaline solution remaining from the original extraction. When no further precipitation of benzoic acid occurs, cool the solution (if perceptibly warm) in ice-water, and then filter at the pump. Wash the benzoic acid thoroughly with cold water, drain, and then recrystallise from a large volume of boiling water. Benzoic acid is obtained as colourless crystals, m.p. 121°: yield, 19–20 g.

For reactions of benzyl alcohol, see p. 336, and of benzoic acid, p. 347.

Benzoin. $C_6H_5CH(OH)COC_6H_5$.

Many aromatic aldehydes (having the – CHO group joined directly to the benzene ring) undergo polymerisation when heated with a solution of potassium cyanide in aqueous ethanol. Thus benzaldehyde gives benzoin, a compound of double function, since it contains both a secondary alcoholic and a ketonic

$$2C_6H_5CHO = C_6H_5CH(OH)COC_6H_5$$

grouping. The reaction is probably due to the potassium cyanide undergoing partial hydrolysis, generating hydrogen cyanide, which then adds on to the benzaldehyde giving benzaldehyde cyanhydrin: the latter then reacts with

$$C_6H_5CH(OH)CN + HCOC_6H_5 \rightarrow C_6H_5CH(OH)COC_6H_5 + HCN$$

unchanged benzaldehyde, giving benzoin and regenerating the hydrogen cyanide

Required: Potassium cyanide, 5 g.; ethanol, 50 ml.; benzaldehyde, 25 ml.

Add 5 g. of powdered potassium cyanide* to a mixture of 20 ml. of water and 50 ml. of ethanol contained in a 200 ml. conical flask, and then add 25 ml. (26 g.) of freshly distilled benzaldehyde. Fit the flask with a reflux water-condenser, and boil the mixture gently on a water-bath for 30 minutes, a clear solution being rapidly obtained. Then pour the solution into a beaker and cool; the benzoin separates as a crystalline mass

* See footnote, p 191.

Filter at the pump, and wash well with water. (Yield, about 20 g.) Recrystallise a portion from hot methylated spirit, reserving the remainder for the following preparation. Benzoin is a very pale yellow (almost colourless) crystalline substance, m.p. 137°.

Benzil. $C_6H_5CO \cdot COC_6H_5$.

The secondary alcohol group, $-CH(OH)-$, in benzoin is readily oxidised to a ketone group, and thus benzil, a diketone, is obtained.

$$C_6H_5CH(OH)COC_6H_5 + O = C_6H_5CO \cdot COC_6H_5 + H_2O$$

For this purpose, the usual oxidising agent is nitric acid, which in these circumstances (i.e., in the absence of sulphuric acid) does not nitrate the benzene ring. Owing to the nitrous fumes formed by the reduction of the nitric acid, the experiment should be performed in a fume-cupboard.

Required: Benzoin, 10 g.; nitric acid, 25 ml.

Place 10 g. of powdered benzoin and 25 ml. of concentrated nitric acid in a 150 ml. flask fitted with a reflux water-condenser, and heat the flask on a boiling water-bath. A flask having a ground-glass neck fitting directly to the condenser is best for this purpose. If this is not available, fit the flask to the condenser by means of a cork (*not* a rubber stopper) and clamp both flask and condenser securely in position during the heating on the water-bath: the nitrous fumes rot the cork during the heating, and if only one clamp is used, the flask may possibly slip away from the condenser, or alternatively the latter may fall sideways under its own weight. Continue the heating for $1\frac{1}{2}$ hours, when the crystalline benzoin will have been completely replaced by the oily benzil. Then pour the mixture into a beaker of cold water, when on vigorous stirring the oil will crystallise into a yellow solid. Filter off the latter at the pump, and wash *thoroughly* with water to ensure complete elimination of acid. Recrystallise from methylated or rectified spirit. Benzil separates as clear yellow crystals, m.p. 95°: yield, 9 g.

Benzil Osazone. $C_6H_5C(:N \cdot NHC_6H_5)C(:N \cdot NHC_6H_5)C_6H_5$. (Semi-micro Scale.)

The ready oxidation of the secondary alcohol group in benzoin to a ketone group is also shown by the action of phenylhydrazine, which when present in excess first gives benzoin phenylhydrazone, $C_6H_5CH(OH)C(:NNHC_6H_5)C_6H_5$, then oxidises the latter to the ketone, $C_6H_5COC(:NNHC_6H_5)C_6H_5$, and finally gives the diphenylhydrazone, i.e., the osazone of benzil, the complete action being similar to the formation of glucosazone (p. 135). Benzil osazone can therefore be prepared either (a) from benzoin or (b) directly from benzil, and its constitution thus placed beyond doubt.

Required: Benzoin, 1 g.; acetic acid, 15 ml.; phenylhydrazine, 2 ml.

(*a*) Dissolve 1 g. of powdered benzoin in 15 ml. of hot glacial acetic acid contained in a boiling-tube, and add 2 ml. of phenylhydrazine. Heat the tube in a boiling water-bath for 20 minutes. The osazone crystallises out either during the heating or when the tube is removed from the bath and the contents stirred. Cool the tube thoroughly in water, filter off the yellow crystals at the pump through a small Buchner funnel, drain, and then wash thoroughly first with glacial acetic acid and then with ethanol, in order to remove all traces of the original mother-liquor. The benzil osazone is thus obtained as fine yellow crystals, which when dry are pure. M.p. 225°. Yield, 1 g. The osazone can be recrystallised from acetic acid, or (better) from benzene, although the benzene solution may require seeding or scratching before crystallisation starts.

(*b*) Repeat the preparation, using 1 g. of benzil instead of 1 g. of benzoin. The benzil osazone crystallises out readily in yellow needles, usually after about 5 minutes' heating. Continue heating for 20 minutes, and then isolate as before. Yield, 1·4 g. Carry out a mixed melting-point determination to show that the two products are identical.

Benzilic Acid. $(C_6H_5)_2C(OH)\cdot COOH.$

When benzil is heated with potassium hydroxide solution, it undergoes a "molecular rearrangement" with the formation of the potassium salt of benzilic acid, or diphenyl-glycollic acid:

$$C_6H_5\cdot CO\cdot CO\cdot C_6H_5 + KOH \longrightarrow (C_6H_5)_2C(OH)\cdot COOK$$

This reaction applies to many 1,2-diketones, and is termed the *Benzilic Acid Rearrangement*. It provides a ready method for the preparation of disubstituted α-hydroxy-carboxylic acids. When applied to a cyclic 1,2-diketone, the ring system is necessarily reduced by one carbon atom: for example, cyclohexan-1,2-

dione gives the potassium salt of 1-hydroxycyclopentane-carboxylic acid.

Required: Benzil, 5 g.; potassium hydroxide, 5 g.

Dissolve 5 g. of benzil in 15 ml. of boiling ethanol in a conical flask fitted with a reflux water-condenser. Then add a solution of 5 g. of potassium hydroxide in 10 ml. of water, and heat the mixture (which rapidly develops a purple colour) on a boiling water-bath for about 15 minutes. Cool and stir the solution, from which the potassium benzilate separates in fine crystals.

Filter the product at the pump, using an alkali-resisting filter-paper, or a sintered glass filter-funnel. Wash the crystals on the filter with a small quantity of ethanol to remove the purple colour, and then drain thoroughly.

To obtain the free acid, dissolve the potassium salt in 50 ml. of cold water, filter the solution if a small undissolved residue remains, and then boil the clear solution *gently* whilst dilute sulphuric acid is added until the separation of the acid is complete. Cool the solution and filter off the pale orange-coloured crystals of the benzilic acid: wash the crystals on the filter with some hot distilled water, drain well, and then dry in a desiccator. Yield of crude acid, 4 g. Recrystallise from benzene (about 50 ml.) to which a small quantity of animal charcoal has been added, filtering the boiling solution through a preheated funnel fitted with a fluted filter-paper, as the benzilic acid readily crystallises as the solution cools; alternatively, recrystallise from much hot water. The benzilic acid is obtained as colourless crystals, m.p. 150°.

Cinnamic Acid. $C_6H_5CH{:}CH{\cdot}COOH$. (Perkin's Reaction.)

Cinnamic acid is usually prepared by Perkin's reaction, benzaldehyde being heated with sodium acetate in the presence of acetic anhydride. It is probable that the benzaldehyde and the acetic anhydride combine under the catalytic action of the sodium acetate, and the product then readily loses water to give mono-benzylidene acetic anhydride (A). The latter, when subsequently

$$C_6H_5CHO + HCH_2CO{\cdot}O{\cdot}OCCH_3 \rightarrow C_6H_5CH(OH)CH_2CO{\cdot}O{\cdot}OCCH_3$$
$$C_6H_5CH(OH)CH_2CO{\cdot}O{\cdot}OCCH_3 \rightarrow H_2O + C_6H_5CH{:}CHCO{\cdot}O{\cdot}OCCH_3 \ (A)$$

heated with sodium carbonate solution, undergoes hydrolysis to sodium cinnamate and acetate.

$$C_6H_5CH{:}CHCO{\cdot}O{\cdot}OCCH_3 + Na_2CO_3 \rightarrow C_6H_5CH{:}CHCOONa$$
$$+ CH_3COONa + CO_2$$

Although the *cis-trans* isomerism about the double bond is possible in cinnamic acid, Perkin's reaction gives rise only to the stable *trans* form, of m.p. 133°, the *cis* form (known as *allo*-cinnamic acid) being unstable and easily converted to the *trans* form. In substituted ethylene compounds, it is frequently found that if the two groups joined to either of the double-linked carbon atoms differ considerably in nature or in mass (*e.g.*, in cinnamic acid, the phenyl group and hydrogen atom on one carbon, or the hydrogen atom and the – COOH group on the other carbon), then one isomeride is formed to the almost complete exclusion of the other.

Required: Benzaldehyde, 20 ml.; acetic anhydride, 30 ml.; anhydrous sodium acetate, 10 g.

Place 20 ml. (21 g.) of benzaldehyde (freshly distilled to ensure absence of benzoic acid), 30 ml. of acetic anhydride, and 10 g. of finely powdered *anhydrous* sodium acetate* in a 100 ml. round-bottomed flask fitted with a water-condenser closed at the top by means of a calcium chloride tube bent downwards (*cf.* Fig. 61, p. 105). Now heat the flask in an oil-bath at 175–180° for 8 hours: the mixture boils vigorously under reflux and white particles separate in the liquid. Pour the mixture whilst still hot into 100 ml. of water contained in a round-bottomed flask (of about 1 litre capacity) which has previously been fitted for steam-distillation. Now add with vigorous shaking a saturated aqueous solution of sodium carbonate until a drop of the liquid withdrawn on a rod turns red litmus-paper a distinct blue. (Sodium hydroxide must not be used for this purpose, as it may generate benzoic acid by the Cannizzaro reaction from any unchanged benzaldehyde.) Now steam-distil the solution until unchanged benzaldehyde has been removed and the distillate is no longer turbid. Cool the residual solution until the small quantity of insoluble oily impurity has formed a semi-solid sticky mass, and then filter at the pump. Acidify the clear filtrate by adding concentrated hydrochloric acid *cautiously* with vigorous stirring until the evolution of carbon dioxide ceases and the precipitation of cinnamic acid is complete. Cool if necessary in ice-water, and then filter off the cinnamic acid, wash thoroughly with water, and drain. Recrystallise from a mixture of 3 volumes of water and 1 volume of rectified spirit: yield, 18 g. Cinnamic acid is thus obtained as colourless crystals, m.p. 133°: it has a faint and pleasant odour and is almost insoluble in cold water.

If in the above preparation 8 hours' continuous heating is impracticable, the heating may be stopped after about 4 hours, the mixture allowed to stand (*e.g.*, overnight) and the heating then continued to make up the total period: in these circumstances the yield usually drops to about 15 g.

For reactions of cinnamic acid, see p. 353.

Ethyl Cinnamate. $C_6H_5CH:CHCOOC_2H_5$. *Required:* Cinnamic acid, 20 g.; rectified spirit, 20 ml.

Cinnamic acid can be readily esterified by the Fischer-Speier method without any risk of the addition of hydrogen chloride at the double bond. Proceed precisely as for the preparation of ethyl benzoate (p. 104), using 20 g. of cinnamic acid and 20 ml. of rectified spirit. When the crude product is poured into water, a sharp separation of the ester is not readily obtained, and hence the addition of about 10 ml. of carbon tetrachloride is particularly desirable. Finally distil off the carbon

* Cf. p. 116 for preparation.

tetrachloride *slowly* from the dried product and then collect the ester as the fraction boiling at 269–272°. Yield, 17 g.

Ethyl cinnamate is a colourless liquid of b.p. 271° and d, 1·05; it possesses a pleasant and characteristic odour.

1,8-Diphenyloctatetrene.
$$C_6H_5 \cdot CH{:}CH \cdot (CH{:}CH)_2 \cdot CH{:}CH \cdot C_6H_5.$$

This reaction illustrates one of the methods by which R. Kuhn synthesised long polyene chains terminated at each end by phenyl groups.

When cinnamaldehyde, succinic acid and acetic anhydride are heated in the presence of litharge (PbO), the aldehyde and the succinic acid condense to give the dicarboxylic acid (I), which undergoes decarboxylation to give the pale yellow crystalline 1,8-diphenyloctatetrene (II). Kuhn has shown that as the

$$PhCH{:}CH{\cdot}CHO + H_2C\text{------}CH_2 + OCH{\cdot}CH{:}CHPh$$
$$\begin{array}{cc} | & | \\ COOH & COOH \end{array}$$
$$\downarrow$$
$$PhCH{:}CH{\cdot}CH{:}C\text{------}C{:}CH{\cdot}CH{:}CHPh$$
$$\begin{array}{cc} | & | \\ COOH & COOH \end{array} \qquad (I)$$
$$\downarrow$$
$$PhCH{:}CH{\cdot}CH{:}CH{\cdot}CH{:}CH{\cdot}CH{:}CHPh \qquad (II)$$

length of the polyene chain increases in such compounds, the colour steadily darkens, and becomes red when the chain contains 9 double bonds.

Although a compound such as (II) could theoretically exist in a number of geometrically-isomeric forms, only one form is produced in this synthesis: it is almost certainly the *trans* form throughout the chain.

Required: Cinnamaldehyde, 16·3 ml. (18 g.); succinic acid, 8 g.; acetic anhydride, 18·5 ml. (20 g.); powdered litharge, 15 g.

For this preparation, the cinnamaldehyde must first be purified by careful redistillation at the water-pump, and a fraction of steady b.p. (e.g., 126°/15 mm.) collected.

Prepare a mixture of the above compounds in the stated quantities in a flask fitted with a reflux water-condenser. Shake the mixture thoroughly, and then heat it in an oil-bath at 145–150° for 3 hours. After about 10 minutes' heating, the mixture gives a clear red solution which should be shaken occasionally during the subsequent heating.

Allow the reddish-yellow solution to cool to about 40° and then filter off at the pump the polyene which has separated: this filtration should be performed as rapidly as possible to avoid contamination with lead acetate, and a Buchner funnel of not less than 6 cm. diameter should therefore be used to avoid clogging the filter. Wash the crude production the filter with *ca.* 10 ml. of chloroform to remove sticky impurity. Weight of crude dark yellow product, 3 g. Recrystallise from xylene or from a much greater volume of chloroform. The 1,8-diphenyloctatetrene is obtained as bright yellow crystals, m.p. 228°. Yield, 2 g. If the preparation is carried out on a much larger scale, mechanical stirring of the heated mixture is advisable.

Since the octatetrene contains two ·CH:CH·CH:CH· units, it will readily combine with two molecules of maleic anhydride and other adducts by the Diels-Alder reaction (p. 292).

Benzoic Acid, C_6H_5COOH, from Benzyl Chloride, $C_6H_5CH_2Cl$.

When an aromatic compound having an aliphatic side chain is subjected to oxidation, fission of the side chain occurs between the first and second carbon atoms from the benzene ring, the first carbon atom thus becoming part of a carboxyl (–COOH) group. For example:

$$C_6H_5CH_3 \longrightarrow C_6H_5COOH \qquad\qquad C_6H_5CH_2CH_3 \longrightarrow C_6H_5COOH$$
$$C_6H_5COCH_3 \longrightarrow C_6H_5COOH \qquad C_6H_5CH:CH·COOH \longrightarrow C_6H_5COOH$$

Such oxidations are frequently important for determining the position of a side chain relative to other substituents in the benzene ring. The oxidation is usually carried out with a mixture of potassium permanganate and sodium carbonate in aqueous solution, or alternatively with dilute nitric acid (1:1 by volume). These oxidations are, however, often very slow, particularly if the side chain is a simple alkyl group: to overcome this difficulty, the alkyl group is frequently chlorinated in order to increase its susceptibility to oxidation. Thus the side chain in toluene, $C_6H_5CH_3$, is only very slowly oxidised by either of the above reagents, whereas that in benzyl chloride is rapidly oxidised: this rapid oxidation is due to the fact that with an aqueous oxidising agent, the benzyl chloride is first hydrolysed to benzyl alcohol, which then undergoes the normal oxidation of a primary alcohol to the corresponding carboxylic acid.

In the following preparation, the oxidation of benzyl chloride instead of toluene is therefore given in order to reduce the time required. It should be borne in mind, however, that the procedure is otherwise independent of the nature of the side chain.

Required: Anhydrous sodium carbonate, 5 g.; potassium permanganate, 10 g.; benzyl chloride, 5 ml.; sodium sulphite, *ca.* 20 g.

To 200 ml. of water contained in a 500 ml. bolt-head flask

add in turn 5 g. of anhydrous sodium carbonate, 10 g. of potassium permanganate, and finally 5 ml. (5·5 g.) of benzyl chloride. Fit the flask with a reflux water-condenser, and boil the mixture gently for 1–1½ hours, *i.e.*, until the reaction is complete and the liquid running down from the condenser contains no oily drops of unchanged benzyl chloride. During this boiling, the permanganate is slowly reduced, and manganese dioxide separates as a dark brown precipitate. Now cool the flask, and add concentrated hydrochloric acid (about 50 ml.) cautiously until the mixture is strongly acid, and all the benzoic acid has been precipitated. Then add a 20% aqueous solution of crystalline sodium sulphite (about 100 ml.) slowly with shaking until the manganese dioxide is completely dissolved* and only the white precipitate of benzoic acid remains. When the mixture is quite cold, filter off the benzoic acid at the pump, and wash well with water. Recrystallise from boiling water. The benzoic acid is obtained as colourless needles, m.p. 121°: yield, about 4·5 g.

Benzoyl Chloride. C_6H_5COCl.

One of the general methods for the preparation of acid chlorides is the action of phosphorus pentachloride on the corresponding carboxylic acid:

$$RCOOH + PCl_5 = RCOCl + POCl_3 + HCl$$

One disadvantage of this method is that it is sometimes difficult to separate the acid chloride sharply from the phosphorus oxychloride by fractional distillation, and unless the boiling-points of these two substances are fairly wide apart, traces of the oxychloride will occasionally pass over in the vapour of the acid chloride. If, however, thionyl chloride is used instead of phosphorus

$$RCOOH + SOCl_2 = RCOCl + SO_2 + HCl$$

pentachloride, this difficulty does not arise, as the acid chloride is now the only liquid product of this reaction.

Required: Benzoic acid, 20 g.; thionyl chloride, 15 ml.

For this preparation, which must be performed in the fume-cupboard, assemble the apparatus shown in Fig. 67(A). **C** is a 150 ml. distilling-flask, to the neck of which is fitted a reflux single-surface water-condenser **D**, closed at the top **E** by a calcium chloride tube. The side-arm of **C** carries a cork **F** which fits the end **E** of the condenser for subsequent distillation. The side-arm of **C** is meanwhile plugged by a small rubber cork, or by a short length of glass rod. (Alternatively, use the ground-glass flask and condenser (Fig. 22 (A) and (C), p. 43), and

* Sulphur dioxide reacts with manganese dioxide giving the soluble colourless manganese dithionate: $MnO_2 + 2SO_2 = MnS_2O_6$. Some manganese sulphate is also formed: $MnS_2O_6 + MnO_2 = 2MnSO_4$. In the presence of hydrochloric acid, some of the dioxide is also reduced to the monoxide, which then dissolves to give manganous chloride, $MnCl_2$.

for the later distillation use the adaptor and receiver (Fig. 23(A) and (B), p. 45) in place of **G** in Fig. 67(B).)

Place 20 g. of dry powdered benzoic acid in **C**, add 15 ml. (25 g., *i.e.*, a 30% excess) of thionyl chloride and some fragments of porcelain, and then clamp the apparatus on a boiling water-bath as shown so that no liquid can collect in the side-arm of **C**. Heat for one hour (with occasional gentle shaking), by which time the evolution of gas will be complete. Cool the flask **C**, detach the condenser and fit it to the side-arm for distillation, using a 360° thermo-meter for the neck of **C**. To the lower end of the condenser fit a small conical flask **G** (Fig. 67(B)) by a cork carrying also a cal-cium chloride tube. In place of the con-ical flask **G**, a small Buchner flask may be used with the calcium chloride tube fitted to the side-arm, but in either case a dupli-cate flask for the second fraction should be available.

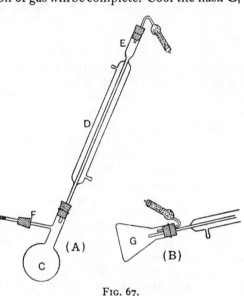

FIG. 67.

Now distil the contents of **C** by heating carefully over a gauze. A small initial fraction of unchanged thionyl chloride boiling at 78–80° comes over, and the temperature then rises rapidly to 194°. Directly this happens, stop the distillation, allow the condenser to drain thoroughly, and then replace **G** by the duplicate receiver. Run the water out of the condenser so that it acts as an air-condenser, and then continue the distillation. Collect the benzoyl chloride as the fraction boiling at 194–198°. Yield, 19 g.

In the distilling-flask remains a very small high-boiling fraction of benzoic anhydride (b.p. 366°), formed by the dehydrating action of the thionyl chloride on the benzoic acid:

$$2C_6H_5COOH + SOCl_2 = (C_6H_5CO)_2O + SO_2 + 2HCl.$$

Benzoyl chloride is a colourless highly refractive liquid, having b.p. 198° and d, 1·21. It has a very irritating odour, and its vapour causes copious watering of the eyes. Benzoyl chloride has similar properties to acetyl chloride, but is much less reactive, *e.g.*, it is only slowly hydrolysed by cold water to benzoic acid and hydrochloric acid. It is largely used as a reagent for identifying alcohols and primary and secondary amines (see below).

For reactions of benzoyl chloride, see p. 364.

3,5-Dinitrobenzoic Acid. $(NO_2)_2C_6H_3COOH$.

Required: Benzoic acid, 50 g.; conc. sulphuric acid, 230 ml.; fuming nitric acid, 73 ml.

Dissolve 50 g. of benzoic acid in 230 ml. of concentrated sulphuric acid in a litre flask fitted with a ground-glass reflux water-condenser. (Rubber or cork must not be used.) Now add a few ml. of the fuming nitric acid down the condenser, shake the flask well and keep it cool by immersion in ice-water. Continue the intermittent addition of nitric acid (about 10 ml. at a time) with continuous shaking and cooling: a great deal of heat is evolved on each addition and a clear yellow solution is obtained. When the addition is complete, add a few pieces of unglazed porcelain and transfer the flask to a cold water-bath. Raise the temperature of the latter gradually during 45 minutes to 100°. [At 70–80° the reaction sometimes tends to become vigorous, and should then be moderated by careful immersion in cold water.] Maintain the mixture at 100° for 15 minutes, with occasional shaking, and then transfer the flask to an oil-bath at 100°. Raise the temperature gradually to 130° during 30 minutes and then maintain it between 130° and 140° for 1 hour. Thus the total period of heating is $2\frac{1}{2}$ hours during which the temperature is gradually raised to 140°. Now cool the flask: crystals of 3,5-dinitrobenzoic acid begin to separate at about 90°. When cold pour the contents of the flask in 3–4 l. of ice-water. Filter off the crystals on a Buchner funnel and wash with water. After drying, the crystals have m.p. 204° (yield, 49 g.) and are sufficiently pure for the preparation of 3,5-dinitrobenzoyl chloride (see below).

If desired, the 3,5-dinitrobenzoic acid may be recrystallised from water as almost colourless rhombs, m.p. 204°.

3,5-Dinitrobenzoyl Chloride. $(NO_2)_2C_6H_3COCl$.

This preparation illustrates the use of phosphorus pentachloride for the preparation of acyl chlorides: in this case no difficulty is experienced in separating the 3,5-dinitrobenzoyl chloride from the phosphorus oxychloride formed simultaneously (*cf.* p. 240), because the former is readily isolated as a crystalline solid. This acyl chloride is used extensively for the preparation of crystalline derivatives of alcohols, phenols, amines and amino-acids (*cf.* pp. 335, 338 381)

Required: 3,5-Dinitrobenzoic acid, 15 g.; phosphorus pentachloride, 17 g.

Assemble in a fume-cupboard the apparatus shown in Fig. 67(A).* Place 15 g. of 3,5-dinitrobenzoic acid and 17 g. of phosphorus pentachloride in the flask **C**, and heat the mixture in an oil-bath for 1¼ hours. Then reverse the condenser as shown in Fig. 67(B), but replace the calcium chloride tube by a tube leading to a water-pump, the neck of the reaction-flask **C** being closed with a rubber stopper. Now distil off the phosphorus oxychloride under reduced pressure by heating the flask **C** in an oil-bath initially at 25–30°, increasing this temperature ultimately to 110°. Then cool the flask, when the crude 3,5-dinitrobenzoyl chloride will solidify to a brown crystalline mass. Yield, 16 g., *i.e.*, almost theoretical. Recrystallise from carbon tetrachloride. The chloride is obtained as colourless crystals, m.p. 66–68°. Yield, 13 g. Further recrystallisation of small quantities can be performed using petrol (b.p. 40–60°). The chloride is stable almost indefinitely if kept in a calcium chloride desiccator.

The Schotten-Baumann Reaction. I. Benzoylation.

Acetylation (*i.e.*, the introduction of the acetyl group, CH_3CO –) as a means of characterising and identifying hydroxy-compounds and primary and secondary amines has already been described (p. 107). It is, however, frequently preferable to introduce an aromatic acyl group (such as the *benzoyl* group, C_6H_5CO –) for this purpose rather than the acetyl group. Benzoylation has two important advantages over acetylation: (*a*) acetyl chloride and acetic anhydride are so readily hydrolysed that acetylation has usually to be performed in absence of water; benzoyl chloride, C_6H_5COCl, is so slowly hydrolysed by water that benzoylation can be carried out freely in an aqueous medium; (*b*) benzoyl derivatives usually have higher melting-points than the corresponding acetyl compounds, and are usually much less soluble in most solvents: they can therefore be more readily crystallised. Moreover, benzoyl compounds are all insoluble in water and can thus be readily isolated from the crude reaction product, whereas acetyl compounds (particularly of the aliphatic amines) are frequently soluble in water and therefore difficult to isolate.

In the *Schotten-Baumann* method of benzoylation, the hydroxyl- or amino-compound (or a salt of the latter) is dissolved or suspended in an excess of 10% aqueous sodium hydroxide solution, a small excess (about 10% more than the theoretical amount) of benzoyl chloride is then added and the mixture vigorously shaken. Benzoylation proceeds smoothly under these conditions, and the solid benzoyl compound, being insoluble in water, separates out. The sodium hydroxide then hydrolyses the excess of benzoyl chloride, giving sodium

$$C_6H_5COCl + 2NaOH = NaCl + C_6H_5COONa + H_2O$$

chloride and benzoate, which remain in solution.

* P. 241.

Thus phenol when subjected to the Schotten-Baumann reaction first dissolves in the sodium hydroxide to give sodium phenoxide, which then undergoes

$$C_6H_5COCl + NaOC_6H_5 \rightarrow C_6H_5COOC_6H_5 + NaCl$$

benzoylation to give phenyl benzoate. An aqueous suspension of aniline similarly gives benzoyl-aniline, or phenyl-benzamide (frequently called benz-

$$C_6H_5NHH + ClCOC_6H_5 \rightarrow C_6H_5NHCOC_6H_5 + HCl$$

anilide); whilst monomethylaniline gives benzoyl-monomethylaniline or

$$C_6H_5N(CH_3)H + ClCOC_6H_3 \rightarrow C_6H_5N(CH_3)COC_6H_5 + HCl$$

N-methylphenylbenzamide. Tertiary amines clearly cannot react in this way.

When these benzoyl compounds separate in the course of the Schotten-Baumann reaction, they frequently occlude traces of unchanged benzoyl chloride, which thus escapes hydrolysis by the alkali: it is advantageous therefore to recrystallise the benzoyl compounds whenever possible from ethanol or methylated spirit, since these solvents will esterify the unchanged chloride and so remove the latter from the recrystallised material.

Occasionally benzoyl chloride gives a product which does not crystallise well: in such cases the difficulty may frequently be overcome by using p-nitrobenzoyl chloride, $NO_2C_6H_4COCl$, or 3,5-dinitrobenzoyl chloride, $(NO_2)_2C_6H_3COCl$ (p. 240), which usually give highly crystalline derivatives.

Phenyl Benzoate. $C_6H_5COOC_6H_5$. (Semi-micro Scale.)

Required: Phenol, 1 g.; benzoyl chloride, 2 ml.

Dissolve 1 g. of phenol in 15 ml. of 10% sodium hydroxide solution contained in a strong wide-mouthed bottle of about 50 ml. capacity. Then add 2 ml. of benzoyl chloride, cork the bottle securely and shake the mixture vigorously for 15 minutes. At the end of this time the reaction should be complete, and a solid product obtained, although a faint smell of unchanged benzoyl chloride may possibly still persist, owing to slight occlusion by the solid product, absorption by the cork, *etc.* Filter off the solid ester at the pump, breaking up any lumps on the filter with a spatula, and then wash thoroughly with water and drain. Recrystallise the crude ester from methylated spirit: for this purpose use a quantity of the hot solvent approximately twice the minimum required for complete solution, in order to ensure that the phenyl benzoate does not separate until the temperature of the solution has fallen below the melting-point of the ester: filter the hot solution if necessary through a funnel preheated by the filtration of some boiling solvent. Phenyl benzoate is thus obtained as colourless crystals, m.p. 69°: yield, 1.2–1.5 g.

Hydrolysis of Phenyl Benzoate. The hydrolysis of phenyl benzoate (and of phenol esters generally) is of particular interest, because both products of hydrolysis are acidic in type: if the hydrolysis is carried out with sodium

$$C_6H_5COOC_6H_5 + H_2O = C_6H_5COOH + C_6H_5OH$$

hydroxide, both compounds remain in solution as their sodium derivatives. They may, however, be separated by acidifying the solution (in order to liberate both acid and phenol) and then adding an excess of sodium carbonate. The benzoic acid readily displaces carbonic acid giving sodium benzoate, whereas the phenol is too weakly acidic to give a similar reaction and so remains free in solution (*cf.* p. 347).

Boil a mixture of 1 g. of phenyl benzoate and 15 ml. of 10% aqueous sodium hydroxide* in a 50 ml. conical flask under reflux until the molten ester has completely disappeared (about 1 hour). During the boiling, a small quantity of unchanged ester may have volatil-ised in the steam and crystallised again in the condenser: therefore pour about 3 ml. of 10% sodium hydroxide solution down the condenser to dislodge this ester, and continue the boiling for a further 10 minutes until the solution is clear. Cool the solution in ice-water, and then add dilute sulphuric acid with stirring until a faint but *permanent* precipitate of benzoic acid is produced (test with litmus-paper to ensure that solu-tion is acidic). Now add dilute sodium carbonate solution with *vigorous* stirring until the precipitate is just redissolved and the solution is definitely alkaline to litmus-paper. Extract the solution twice with ether, dry the united ethereal extracts with potassium carbonate, and after filtering, distil off the greater part of the ether. Pour the remainder whilst hot into an evaporating-basin; the phenol will crystallise when the residual ether has evaporated. Confirm the identity of the phenol by the tests given on p. 337. Meanwhile, add hydrochloric acid to the aqueous solution from the ether extraction: the sodium car-bonate is first neutralised and the benzoic acid then precipitated. Filter off the benzoic acid at the pump, wash with water, and then recrystallise from boiling water. Benzoic acid is obtained as colourless crystals, m.p. 121°.

Benzanilide (Benzoyl-aniline). $C_6H_5NHCOC_6H_5$. (Semi-micro Scale.)

Required: Aniline, 1 ml.; benzoyl chloride, 1·5 ml.

Add 1 ml. (1·04 g.) of aniline to 15 ml. of 10% aqueous sodium hydroxide solution contained in a wide-necked bottle as before, and then add 1·5 ml. (1·7 g.) of benzoyl chloride, and shake vigorously for 15–20 minutes. The mixture becomes warm, and the crude benzoyl derivative separates as a white

* If about 10 ml. of ethanol are added to the mixture, the time required for complete hydrolysis is reduced to about 20 minutes, and any volatilised ester which tends to collect in the condenser is redissolved and returned to the flask. When hydrolysing an unknown ester (p. 353) for identification purposes, however, it is often best to omit the ethanol to avoid confusion.

powder, or, if the shaking has not been sufficiently vigorous, as small pellets: when the reaction is complete, filter off the product at the pump, break up any pellets with a spatula on the filter, and then thoroughly wash with water and drain. Recrystallise the benzanilide from hot methylated spirit: for this purpose use rather more of the hot solvent than the minimum required for complete solution, and filter the latter through a funnel pre-heated by the filtration of some of the boiling solvent, as the benzanilide may crystallise rapidly as the solution cools: it is only slightly soluble in cold methylated spirit. Benzanilide is thus obtained as colourless crystals, m.p. 163°: yield, 1·6 g.

For reactions of benzanilide, see p. 379.

Hydrolysis of Benzanilide. For this hydrolysis, it is necessary to use 70% sulphuric acid (see Hydrolysis of Acetanilide, p. 108). Add 1 g. of benzanilide to 10 ml. of 70% sulphuric acid, and boil the mixture gently in a small flask under a reflux water-condenser for 30 minutes. Hydrolysis will now be complete, but much of the benzoic acid will have vaporised in the steam and then solidified in the conden-

$$C_6H_5NHCOC_6H_5 + H_2O + H_2SO_4 = C_6H_5NH_2,H_2SO_4 + C_6H_5COOH$$

ser. Therefore remove the flask, run the water out the condenser jacket, and then pour about 10 ml. of hot water down the inner tube, which is held vertically over a beaker. The benzoic acid is thus dislodged and largely dissolved. Then add the hot solution from the flask, and cool in ice-water. Benzoic acid rapidly crystallises, but at this dilution the aniline sulphate, although sparingly soluble, does not separate. Filter off the benzoic acid, wash with water, drain, and apply the tests given on p. 347. Note the m.p. (121°). With the filtrate, perform the tests for aniline (pp. 372–373).

Benzyl p-Nitrobenzoate. $NO_2C_6H_4COOCH_2C_6H_5$. (Semi-micro Scale.)

A crystalline derivative of benzyl alcohol cannot be obtained by using benzoyl chloride, because the benzyl benzoate, $C_6H_5COOCH_2C_6H_5$, so obtained has m.p. 18°, and is thus usually liquid: the present preparation illustrates therefore the use of a substituted benzoyl chloride (p-nitrobenzoyl chloride, m.p. 75°) in order to obtain a crystalline derivative of suitably high m.p.

Required: Benzyl alcohol, 1 ml.; p-nitrobenzoyl chloride, 1·9 g.

Place 1 ml. of benzyl alcohol in a boiling-tube and add 6 ml. of 10% sodium hydroxide solution: add also 6 ml. of water to moderate the subsequent reaction, otherwise the rise in temperature may cause hydrolysis of some of the ester produced. Now add 1·9 g. of finely powdered p-nitrobenzoyl chloride, and shake the well-corked tube vigorously. The mixture becomes warm, and the solid ester rapidly separates, the reaction being complete after about 5 minutes' shaking. Filter the ester at the pump, wash with dilute sodium hydroxide solution, then thoroughly with water, and drain. Recrystallise from methylated spirit, allowing the hot solution to cool slowly at first: finally cool in ice-water. The benzyl p-nitrobenzoate separates in colourless crystals, m.p. 84°. Yield, 1·6 g.

Methyl 3,5-Dinitrobenzoate. $(NO_2)_2C_6H_3COOCH_3$. (Semi-micro Scale.)

The reaction between 3,5-dinitrobenzoyl chloride and compounds containing the OH, NH_2, or NH groups is very rapid, and therefore is particularly suitable for identification purposes (cf. pp. 335, 338, 381). It is usual to have sodium hydroxide present during the reaction with phenols and amino-acids, but this is not necessary with alcohols if they are dry.

Required: 3,5-Dinitrobenzoyl chloride, 1 g.; methanol, 2·5 ml.

Place 1 g. of powdered 3,5-dinitrobenzoyl chloride in a small conical flask, add 2·5 ml. of dry methanol, and warm on a water-bath until the solid has dissolved. Cool and filter off the 3,5-dinitrobenzoate which has separated. Recrystallise from ethanol* or petroleum (b.p. 60–80°). The ester separates in colourless crystals, m.p. 108°. Yield, 0·6 g.

The Schotten-Baumann Reaction. II. Sulphonylation.

The Schotten-Baumann reaction may also be carried out, using, for example, benzene sulphonyl chloride, $C_6H_5SO_2Cl$ (*i.e.*, the acid chloride of benzene sulphonic acid, $C_6H_5SO_2OH$) in place of benzoyl chloride, and similar derivatives are obtained. Thus when phenol is dissolved in an excess of 10% sodium hydroxide solution, and then shaken with a small excess of benzene sulphonyl

$$C_6H_5SO_2Cl + NaOC_6H_5 \rightarrow C_6H_5SO_2OC_6H_5 + NaCl$$

chloride, phenyl benzenesulphonate, a crystalline ester, is readily formed, and the excess of the sulphonyl chloride then undergoes hydrolysis by the alkali, giving the soluble sodium benzenesulphonate. A suspension of aniline in sodium hydroxide when similarly treated with benzenesulphonyl chloride gives benzenesulphonyl-aniline, whilst monomethylaniline gives benzenesulphonyl-methylaniline: alternatively, these two compounds may be regarded as being

$$C_6H_5NHH + ClSO_2C_6H_5 \rightarrow C_6H_5NHSO_2C_6H_5 + HCl$$

$$C_6H_5N(CH_3)H + ClSO_2C_6H_5 \rightarrow C_6H_5N(CH_3)SO_2C_6H_5 + HCl$$

mono-and di-substituted derivatives of benzenesulphonamide, $C_6H_5SO_2NH_2$ and thus termed benzenesulphonphenylamide, and benzenesulphon-methylphenylamide respectively. Sulphonylation, like benzoylation, can there-

* Esters of one alcohol should not normally be recrystallised from another alcohol. In the above case, however, no interchange of alkyl groups occurs on rapid recrystallisation.

fore be used to obtain crystalline derivatives of hydroxyl compounds, and also of primary and secondary amines: tertiary amines cannot undergo sulphonylation.

There is, however, one important difference between the benzoyl and the sulphonyl derivatives of amines. It has been shown that primary and secondary amines, when treated with benzoyl chloride, give mono- and di-substituted derivatives of benzamide, and when treated with benzenesulphonyl chloride, give similar derivatives of benzene sulphonamide. A carboxylic acid amide, such as benzamide, possesses only very weak amphoteric properties (p. 120), and is therefore practically neutral, and its derivatives are consequently insoluble in dilute aqueous solutions of alkalis or acids. A sulphonic acid amide, such as benzenesulphonamide, is devoid of basic properties, but has its acidic properties correspondingly increased, and therefore each of the hydrogen atoms in the $-NH_2$ group can in turn show marked acidic properties. It follows that sulphonamides and their mono-substitution derivatives are definitely acidic and will therefore dissolve freely in sodium hydroxide solution, although they are insoluble in acids: their di-substitution derivatives, having no acidic hydrogen atoms, are neutral and therefore insoluble in both alkalis and acids.

The acidic properties of sulphonamides and their mono-substitution derivatives are particularly well illustrated in the alkyl-substitution compounds, which by reason of these properties can be prepared by two distinct methods. Thus mono- and di-ethylamine, when subjected to the Schotten-Baumann reaction using benzenesulphonyl chloride, give benzenesulphonethylamide, and benzenesulphondiethylamide respectively. These compounds can also

$$C_6H_5SO_2Cl + HNHC_2H_5 = C_6H_5SO_2NHC_2H_5 + HCl$$
$$C_6H_5SO_2Cl + HN(C_2H_5)_2 = C_6H_5SO_2N(C_2H_5)_2 + HCl$$

be prepared from benzenesulphonamide by direct substitution. If an ethanolic solution of the sulphonamide is treated with sodium ethoxide, the sulphon-sodio-amide is formed and may crystallise out: if this compound is then heated with ethyl bromide or iodide, the sulphonethylamide (A) is formed. The latter still retains an acidic hydrogen atom and therefore, when

$$C_6H_5SO_2NH_2 \xrightarrow{NaOC_2H_5} C_6H_5SO_2NHNa \xrightarrow{C_2H_5I} C_6H_5SO_2NHC_2H_5 \quad (A)$$

treated in ethanolic solution with sodium ethoxide, gives the sulphon-sodio-

$$C_6H_5SO_2NHC_2H_5 \xrightarrow{NaOC_2H_5} C_6H_5SO_2NNaC_2H_5 \xrightarrow{C_2H_5I} C_6H_5SO_2N(C_2H_5)_2 \quad (B)$$

ethylamide, which when heated in turn with ethyl iodide, gives the neutral sulphon-diethylamide (B).

Hinsberg has based a method of separating primary, secondary and tertiary amines upon the solubility of mono-substituted sulphonamides in sodium hydroxide solution If, for example, a mixture of aniline, monomethylaniline and dimethylaniline is shaken with benzenesulphonyl chloride in the presence of an excess of sodium hydroxide solution, the aniline gives benzenesulphonyl-aniline, $C_6H_5NHSO_2C_6H_5$, which, being acidic, remains dissolved in the alkaline solution. The monomethylaniline gives benzenesulphonyl-methylaniline, $C_6H_5N(CH_3)SO_2C_6H_5$, which, being neutral, is insoluble and therefore separates out. The dimethylaniline is unaffected. When the sulphonylation is complete, the unchanged dimethylaniline can therefore be recovered by steam-distillation. The reaction product is then cooled and the insoluble sulphonyl-methylaniline filtered off. The filtrate is then acidified, and the sulphonyl-aniline thus precipitated. Hydrolysis of these two sulphonyl compounds then regenerates the secondary and primary amines respectively.

Although benzenesulphonyl chloride has for simplicity been used in the above discussion, toluene-p-sulphonyl chloride, $CH_3C_6H_4SO_2Cl$, is more frequently used in the laboratory, owing to its much lower cost, the latter being due in turn to the fact that toluene-p-sulphonyl chloride is a by-product in the commercial preparation of saccharin. Toluene-p-sulphonyl chloride is a crystalline substance, of m.p. 68°: the finely powdered chloride will, however, usually react readily with amines in the Schotten-Baumann reaction; it does not react so readily with alcohols, but the reaction may be promoted considerably by first dissolving the chloride in some inert water-soluble solvent such as acetone.

Phenyl Toluene-p-sulphonate. $CH_3C_6H_4SO_2OC_6H_5$. (Semi-micro Scale.)

Required: Phenol, 0·4 g.; 10% sodium hydroxide, 2·5 ml.; toluene-p-sulphonyl chloride, 0·9 g.; acetone, 4 ml.

Dissolve 0·4 g. of phenol in 2·5 ml. of 10% aqueous sodium hydroxide solution contained in a 25 ml. conical flask, and then add a solution of 0·9 g. of toluene-p-sulphonyl chloride in 4 ml. of cold acetone: cork the flask *securely* and shake it vigorously for 15–20 minutes. When the mixed solutions are first shaken, a fine emulsion forms and the mixture becomes warm: on continued shaking (which prevents the emulsion from separating into two well-defined layers) the fine oily drops crystallise as the temperature falls, and when the shaking is complete, a crop of small heavy crystals will have separated from the clear supernatant liquid. Now cool the flask in water, and then pour the contents into about 25 ml. of water, finally washing out the flask to remove any crystals adhering to the sides. Filter the well-stirred aqueous mixture at the pump, wash the crystals thoroughly with water, and drain. Recrystallise the product from methylated spirit, of which about 12 ml. will be required. Phenyl toluene-p-sulphonate is thus obtained as colourless crystals, m.p. 95°: yield, 0·7 g.

Separation of a Mixture of Aniline, Monomethylaniline,* and Dimethylaniline.† Hinsberg's Method.

The principle of this method has been explained above. The reaction is best carried out in a wide-necked 250 ml. conical flask for which a cork having the usual two delivery-tubes for steam-distillation is available: when the

* Strictly termed N-methylaniline.
† Strictly termed N,N-dimethylaniline.

sulphonylation is complete, the reaction product can then be steam-distilled without transference to another vessel.

Required: Aniline, 4 ml.; monomethylaniline, 4 ml.; dimethylaniline, 4 ml.; toluene-*p*-sulphonyl chloride, 16 g.

Prepare a mixture containing 4 ml. of each of the above three amines. Place the mixture in the conical flask, add 60 ml. of 10% sodium hydroxide solution, and also 60 ml. of water to moderate the subsequent reaction. Add 16 g. of finely powdered toluene-*p*-sulphonyl chloride, cork the flask securely and shake the contents vigorously for 20–30 minutes: the mixture becomes warm, and a fine emulsion of the unchanged dimethylaniline and the molten sulphonyl-methylaniline forms in the alkaline solution. Finally the temperature falls towards the end of the above period of shaking. Now replace the cork by the steam-distillation fitting, and steam-distil the reaction mixture until fine drops of dimethylaniline can no longer be detected in the distillate leaving the condenser. Then stop the distillation, and cool the reaction mixture by shaking the flask in a stream of cold water under the tap, in order to ensure that the sulphonyl-methylaniline solidifies in small particles and not in one large hard lump.

Extract the dimethylaniline by shaking the distillate in a separating-funnel with a few ml. of ether, and then dry the ethereal solution over potassium carbonate: distil the filtered ethereal solution from a small distilling-flask (*e.g.*, Fig. 36, p. 63) with the usual precautions, and finally the dimethylaniline, b.p. 193°. Yield, almost theoretical.

Meanwhile, filter the original cold reaction product at the pump, and wash the sulphonyl-methylaniline on the filter first with 10% sodium hydroxide solution (to ensure complete removal of the sulphonyl-aniline) and then with water: drain thoroughly. Recrystallise from ethanol: toluene-*p*-sulphonyl-methylaniline, $C_6H_5N(CH_3)SO_2C_6H_4CH_3$, is thus obtained as colourless crystals, m.p. 95°: yield, 7·5 g.

Finally, add an excess of concentrated hydrochloric acid slowly with stirring to the alkaline filtrate remaining from the original reaction product. As the solution becomes acid, the sulphonyl-aniline separates as a thick sticky syrup which, when stirred, rapidly crystallises. Cool the mixture in ice-water if necessary, and then filter off the solid product at the pump, wash well with water, and drain. Recrystallise from a mixture of 2 volumes of ethanol and 1 volume of water: to prevent the sulphonyl-aniline from separating as an emulsion, allow the hot solution to cool spontaneously (with occasional stirring) until crystallisation starts, and then cool in ice-water to complete the process. The toluene-p-sulphonyl-aniline, $C_6H_5NHSO_2C_6H_4CH_3$, when filtered and drained is obtained as colourless crystals, m.p. 102°: yield, 6 g.

The aniline and the monomethylaniline can be obtained from their respective sulphonyl derivatives by hydrolysis with 70% sulphuric acid (preparation, p. 109), the mixture of the sulphonyl compound and the acid being gently boiled under reflux: to illustrate the *separation* of the three amines, however, this is not necessary.

The chief disadvantage of Hinsberg's method is that partial hydrolysis of the two sulphonyl amines by the sodium hydroxide may occur during the steam-distillation: if, however, only a small excess of the hydroxide is used in the sulphonylation, this hydrolysis becomes negligible, particularly as the sulphonyl amides are far less readily hydrolysed by alkalis than by acids. This point does not arise in the separation of a similar mixture of *aliphatic* amines, since all the lower members are soluble in water. Therefore if a mixture of mono-, di- and tri-ethylamine were treated as above with toluene-p-sulphonyl chloride, the sulphonyl mono-ethylamine, $C_2H_5NHSO_2C_6H_4CH_3$, and the unchanged triethylamine would remain dissolved in the sodium hydroxide solution, whilst the neutral sulphonyl diethylamine $(C_2H_5)_2NSO_2C_6H_4CH_3$, would separate, and could then be filtered off. Acidification of the filtrate would then precipitate the sulphonyl monoethylamine, whilst the triethylamine remained in solution as a salt of the acid. After filtering off the sulphonyl monoethylamine, the filtrate could be made alkaline again, and the liberated triethylamine steam-distilled off from the crude residual solution.

Toluene-p-sulphonamide. $CH_3C_6H_4SO_2NH_2$.

Toluene-p-sulphonyl chloride reacts with aqueous ammonia to give the

$$CH_3C_6H_4SO_2Cl + HNH_2 \rightarrow CH_3C_6H_4SO_2NH_2 + HCl$$

sulphonamide, but the reaction is slow. A more rapid reaction may be obtained by heating the sulphonyl chloride with ammonium carbonate, which dissociates readily into carbon dioxide and ammonia, and converts the chloride almost quantitatively into the amide.

Required: Toluene-p-sulphonyl chloride, 5 g.; ammonium carbonate, 10 g.

Thoroughly mix 5 g. of toluene-p-sulphonyl chloride and 10 g. of ammonium carbonate by grinding together in a mortar until a fine uniform powder is obtained. Then heat the mixture in an evaporating-basin on a boiling water-bath for 15–20 minutes, stirring the mixture *continuously* with a glass rod meanwhile. Conversion of the chloride to the amide is now complete and only a small quantity of unchanged ammonium carbonate remains. Recrystallise the powder from about 120 ml. of boiling water. Toluene-*p*-sulphonamide is thus obtained in colourless crystals, m.p. 137°. Yield 4·2–4·4 g.

Toluene-*p*-sulphonamide is almost insoluble in cold water, but dissolves readily in sodium hydroxide solution (as the sodium derivative) and is immediately reprecipitated on the addition of strong acids. To show the formation of the sodium derivative, dissolve about 0·2 g. of metallic sodium in about 10 ml. of ethanol, cool the solution, and then add it to a solution of 1 g. of the sulphonamide in 20 ml. of cold ethanol. On shaking the mixture, fine white crystals of the sodium derivative, $CH_3C_6H_5SO_2NHNa$, rapidly separate, and may be obtained pure by filtering at the pump, and washing first with a few ml. of ethanol, and then with ether.

Toluene-*p*-sulphonchloro-sodio-amide ("Chloramine-T"), $CH_3C_6H_4SO_2NNaCl,3H_2O$, and Toluene-*p*-sulphon-dichloro-amide (" Dichloramine-T "), $CH_3C_6H_4SO_2NCl_2$.

When toluene-*p*-sulphonamide is dissolved in an excess of sodium hypochlorite solution, toluene-*p*-sulphon-chloro-sodio-amide is formed, and, being soluble in water, does not crystallise unless concentrated solutions are used:

$$CH_3C_6H_4SO_2NH_2 + NaClO = CH_3C_6H_4SO_2NNaCl + H_2O$$

This compound is similar in type to the sodium acet-bromoamide, $CH_3CONNaBr$, which is an intermediate compound in Hofmann's amine synthesis (p. 127). If a weak acid (such as acetic acid) is now added to the solution of the chloro-sodio-amide, the latter compound reacts with the hypo-chlorous acid giving the sulphon-dichloro-amide, which being insoluble in water, rapidly separates:

$CH_3C_6H_4SO_2NNaCl + HOCl + CH_3COOH$
$$= CH_3C_6H_4SO_2NCl_2 + CH_3COONa + H_2O$$

When the sulphon-dichloro-amide is gently boiled with sodium hydroxide solution, the reverse change occurs, and the chloro-sodio-amide crystallises out at a suitable concentration:

$$CH_3C_6H_4SO_2NCl_2 + 2NaOH = CH_3C_6H_4SO_2NNaCl + NaOCl + H_2O$$

The chloro-sodio-amide can thus be made either directly from toluene-*p*-sul-phonamide or from the intermediate dichloro-amide. The chloro-sodio-amide and the dichloro-amide are known commercially as Chloramine-T and Dichlor-amine-T respectively.

DICHLORAMINE-T. Dilute 80 ml. of *freshly prepared* 2*N* sodium hypochlorite solution (preparation, p. 525) with 80 ml. of water, and then add with stirring 5 g. of finely powdered toluene-*p*-sulphonamide, a clear solution being rapidly obtained. Cool in ice-water, and then add about 50 ml. of a mixture of equal volumes of glacial acetic acid and water *slowly* with stirring until precipitation is complete: the dichloro-amide separates at first as a fine emulsion, which rapidly forms brittle colourless crystals. Filter off the latter at the pump, wash well with water, drain thoroughly, and dry without delay either with drying-paper or (better) in a desiccator. Yield, 6·8–7·0 g. (theoretical). The dichloramine-T is thus obtained in a high state of purity: it may, however, be crystallised with very little loss from 60–80° petrol, and obtained as needles, m.p. 83°.

CHLORAMINE-T. (a) *From Dichloramine-T.* For this purpose use dichloramine-T which has been prepared as above, and thoroughly drained but not necessarily dried. Heat 40 ml. of 10% sodium hydroxide solution in a beaker over a gauze until the solution is almost boiling, and then add the dichloramine-T in small quantities, stirring the mixture gently after each addition until a clear solution is obtained. When the addition is complete, cool the solution in ice-water, whereupon the chloramine-T will rapidly separate in colourless crystals. Filter at the pump, and drain thoroughly. Yield, 8 g. (almost theoretical). The chloramine-T, which is now practically pure, may if desired be recrystallised from a small quantity of hot water: dry the final product with drying-paper or in a calcium chloride desiccator, as water of crystallisation is readily lost over sulphuric acid or in a vacuum. Chloramine-T has no definite m.p., for on heating it first loses water of crystallisation and then decomposes vigorously at 175–180°.

(b) *Direct from toluene-p-sulphonamide.* Mix 45 ml. of the freshly prepared $2M$ sodium hypochlorite solution and 40 ml. of 10% sodium hydroxide solution in a 200 ml. conical flask, and then add 5 g. of finely powdered toluene-p-sulphonamide. Shake the corked flask vigorously for 3–5 minutes, whereupon the sulphonamide will dissolve and be largely replaced by white crystalline chloramine-T. Now warm the mixture in the open flask until a clear solution is obtained (in order to ensure removal of any dichloramine-T) and then cool. The chloramine-T separates on slow cooling in needles, and on quick cooling in characteristic leaflets. Filter, drain, and dry. Yield 7·5 g.

Both chloramine-T and dichloramine-T have marked antiseptic properties, chloramine-T being most frequently used because of its solubility in water. Aqueous solutions of chloramine-T can be used either for external application, or for internal application to the mouth, throat, *etc.*, as chloramine-T in moderate quantities is non-toxic: its aqueous solution can also be effectively used when the skin has come in contact with many of the vesicant liquid "poison-gases," as the latter are frequently organic sulphur or arsenic derivatives which combine with or are oxidised by chloramine-T and are thus rendered harmless.

Both chloramine-T and dichloramine-T can be readily estimated, because they liberate iodine from potassium iodide quantitatively in the presence of

$$CH_3C_6H_4SO_2NNaCl + 2KI + 2CH_3COOH$$
$$= CH_3C_6H_4SO_2NH_2 + NaCl + I_2 + 2CH_3COOK$$
$$CH_3C_6H_4SO_2NCl_2 + 4KI + 4CH_3COOH$$
$$= CH_3C_6H_4SO_2NH_2 + 2HCl + 2I_2 + 4CH_3COOK$$

acetic acid. For this purpose, a solution of a known quantity of chloramine-T in water containing acetic acid, or dichloramine-T in acetic acid itself, is diluted with an excess of potassium iodide solution, and the iodine is then estimated by direct titration with standard sodium thiosulphate solution.

Aromatic Ketones.

Aromatic ketones may be divided into two classes:

(1) The true ketones, in which the >CO group is in the side chain, the most common examples being acetophenone or methyl phenyl ketone, $C_6H_5COCH_3$, and benzophenone or diphenyl ketone, $C_6H_5COC_6H_5$. These ketones are usually prepared by a modification of the Friedel-Crafts' reaction, an aromatic hydrocarbon being treated with an acyl chloride (either aliphatic or aromatic) in the presence of aluminium chloride. Thus benzene reacts with acetyl chloride

$$C_6H_5H + ClCOCH_3 \rightarrow C_6H_5COCH_3 + HCl$$

readily in these circumstances to give acetophenone.

A probable mechanism of the reaction is as follows:

$$CH_3COCl + AlCl_3 \rightarrow \overset{+}{C}H_3CO + \overset{-}{AlCl_4}$$
$$(I)$$

The benzene nucleus is then attacked by the carbonium ion (I) (*cf.* attack by $\overset{+}{N}O_2$ ion, p. 157):

$$C_6H_5H + \overset{+}{C}H_3CO \rightarrow C_6H_5COCH_3 + \overset{+}{H}$$

followed by:

$$\overset{+}{H} + \overset{-}{AlCl_4} \rightarrow HCl + AlCl_3.$$

(2) The quinones, in which the carbon of the >CO group is part of the ring; for this reason, the properties of the >CO group are sufficiently modified to make the quinones quite distinct from the true ketones of class (1). Quinones may often be prepared by direct oxidation of the corresponding hydrocarbon: thus anthracene (A) on oxidation gives anthraquinone (B) whilst phenanthrene (C) gives phenanthraquinone (D), these quinones being

(A)   (B)   (C)   (D)

examples of *para* and *ortho* quinones respectively. The specific term quinone is usually applied to *p*-benzoquinone (F) which cannot easily be prepared by the direct oxidation of benzene on a laboratory scale. It can, however, be readily prepared by the addition of a mild oxidising agent, such as ferric chloride, to an aqueous solution of hydroquinone (E), a reaction which is readily reversible by reducing agents such as sulphur dioxide: it is also technically prepared by the more complicated oxidation of compounds such as aniline.

The preparation of a member of each of the above classes of ketones is given below.

Acetophenone. $C_6H_5COCH_3$.

Required: Aluminium chloride, 30 g.; benzene, 75 ml.; acetyl chloride, 20 ml.

Place 30 g. of anhydrous *finely powdered* aluminium chloride* in a 300 ml. *dry* round-bottomed bolt-head flask, and add 75 ml. of dry benzene (free from toluene). Fit a water-condenser to the flask, and then in turn fit a small dropping-funnel securely in the top of the condenser by means of a cork having a shallow V-shaped groove cut vertically in the side to give open access to the air. (Alternatively use the apparatus shown in Fig. 23(A), p. 45, the outlet-tube **A** being closed with a calcium chloride tube.) Cool the contents of the flask in a basin of cold water (ice-water must not be used, in case the benzene crystallises): now place 20 ml. (22 g.) of acetyl chloride in the dropping-funnel, and allow it to run *slowly* down the condenser into the flask, the latter being shaken from time to time to ensure thorough mixing of the contents. When all the acetyl chloride has been added, heat the flask *in* a water-bath at 50° for 1 hour in order to complete the reaction, a vigorous evolution of hydrogen chloride occurring meanwhile. The heating should therefore be carried out in the fume-cupboard, the dropping-funnel being replaced by a calcium chloride tube, bent downwards as in Fig. 61, p. 105. Alternatively, the heating may be carried out in the open laboratory, in which case a delivery-tube should be securely fitted at one end to the top of the condenser (or to the outlet-tube **A** in Fig. 23(A)), and at the other end to the stem of an inverted glass filter-funnel, the latter being placed in a beaker of water so that the rim dips *just* below the surface: the hydrogen chloride is thus absorbed without

---

* Aluminium chloride is usually supplied by dealers either in stoppered bottles or in sealed glass flasks. Great care should be taken in opening the sealed flasks, as they frequently contain hydrogen chloride under considerable pressure. The flask or tube should first be chilled in ice-water or ice-salt, and then enveloped in a thick duster so that only the tip of the neck protrudes. A scratch is made across the neck with a sharp file and the scratch then touched with the hot end of a fine glass rod: the end of the neck may fly off with great violence and should therefore be pointing in a safe direction.

risk of water "sucking back" through the tube into the reaction mixture (*cf.* Fig. 62, p. 128).

When the heating is complete, cool the reaction mixture and then pour it into 200 ml. of water contained in a flask of about 750 ml. capacity. Then cork the flask and vigorously shake it, cooling in water if necessary: aluminium chloride and hydrogen chloride are thus extracted by the water, whilst the acetophenone remains dissolved in the benzene. Pour the mixture into a separating-funnel and run off the lower aqueous layer: shake the benzene solution with a dilute aqueous sodium hydroxide solution to ensure complete removal of hydrogen chloride, and again separate the benzene and then dry it over calcium chloride for about 15 minutes. Filter the dry solution and remove the benzene by distillation. For this purpose fit a 100 ml. distilling-flask containing some fragments of unglazed porcelain with a dropping-funnel and a water-condenser: run a portion of the benzene solution into the flask, which is then heated on a sand-bath, the remainder of the solution being added as the benzene distils over. (Alternatively, the flask may be heated *in* a boiling water-bath, since benzene will not readily distil from a flask heated on a water-bath.) When almost all the benzene has been removed, replace the dropping-funnel by a 360° thermometer, and the water-condenser by a short air-condenser similar to that used in the preparation of acetamide (p. 117). Then continue the distillation by careful heating over a gauze, and finally collect the acetophenone as the fraction of b.p. 195–202°. Yield, 20 g. This fraction should be collected directly into a weighed specimen-tube, and should crystallise readily when the tube is cooled in ice-water. If it does not crystallise, it should be redistilled.

Acetophenone is a colourless compound, having m.p. 20° and b.p. 201°; except in cold weather it is therefore usually a liquid, of d, 1·03. It has only a faint odour. Acetophenone was at one time used medicinally under the name of *hypnone* as a soporific, but for this purpose it has now been largely superseded by other and more suitable drugs.

Acetophenone. (Semi-micro Scale.)

Required: Aluminium chloride, 3 g.; benzene, 7·5 ml.; acetyl chloride, 2 ml.

The student should first read the directions for the macro-scale preparation above.

Place in a 25 or 50 ml. round-bottomed flask, 3 g. of finely powdered anhydrous aluminium chloride and 7·5 ml. of dry benzene. Fit the flask with a reflux water-condenser. Place the flask in a cold water-bath in a fume-cupboard and add slowly down the condenser, from a calibrated dropping-tube, 2 ml. of acetyl chloride. Shake the flask after each addition (about 0·5 ml. at a time). When all the acetyl chloride has been added, fit the top of the condenser with a calcium chloride tube bent downwards (*cf.* Fig. 61, p. 105), and heat the flask *in* the water-bath at 50° for about 30 minutes. This usually suffices to remove all the hydrogen chloride. When no more hydrogen chloride is evolved pour the mixture into a 100 ml. flask containing 20 ml. of water. Shake the flask vigorously: aluminium chloride and hydrogen chloride are thus extracted by the water. Now pour the mixture into a small separating-funnel and run off the lower aqueous layer. Wash the benzene layer with dil. NaOH solution and again run off the lower layer. Transfer the benzene layer to a small dry flask and dry with anhydrous calcium chloride for 15 minutes. Transfer the dry benzene solution (or a portion of it at a time) to a 10 ml. pear-shaped flask (Fig. 37, p. 63). Distil off the benzene using preferably a vigorously boiling water-bath. The benzene may, in this instance, be collected directly in the boiling-tube C. When all the benzene has been distilled off, remove the boiling-tube C and the water-condenser D from the side-arm of the flask. Now heat the flask A directly with a small semi-micro Bunsen flame. Discard everything that comes over below 195°. Collect the fraction boiling between 195° and 202° in a small weighed specimen tube. Yield of acetophenone, 2 g. Immerse the tube in ice-water and note that crystallisation takes place.

For reactions of acetophenone, see p. 345.

The student should note that ketones in class (1), *i.e.*, those having the >CO group in the side chain, will form additive compounds with sodium bisulphite *only* if this >CO group is not directly joined to the benzene ring: acetophenone therefore will not form such compounds, whereas benzyl methyl ketone, $C_6H_5CH_2COCH_3$, will do so. Many quinones, particularly *ortho* quinones such as phenanthraquinone, form additive compounds with sodium bisulphite.

Acetophenone Phenylhydrazone. $CH_3(C_6H_5)C:N·NHC_6H_5$. (Semi-micro Scale.)

Required: Acetophenone, 1 ml.; phenylhydrazine, 1·25 ml.; acetic acid, 5 ml.

Dissolve 1 ml. (1 g.) of acetophenone in 5 ml. of glacial acetic acid contained in a boiling-tube for which a well-fitting cork is available. Dissolve 1·25 ml. of phenylhydrazine in a mixture of 2·5 ml. of glacial acetic acid and 2·5 ml. of water, and add this solution to that of the acetophenone, at once corking and vigorously shaking the boiling-tube. The mixture becomes slightly warm, and the phenylhydrazone rapidly separates as colourless crystals. After 5 minutes' shaking, cool the tube in cold water, and then filter the contents at the pump: wash the crystals on the filter with *dilute* acetic acid and then with water. Recrystallise the phenylhydrazone from ethanol (*not* from methylated spirit, which causes decomposition) and dry thoroughly: m.p. 105°. Yield,

1·4 g. The phenylhydrazone, after standing for a few days, develops a brown colour and ultimately decomposes.

Acetophenone similarly gives an oxime, $CH_3(C_6H_5)C:NOH$, of m.p. 59°: owing to its lower m.p. and its greater solubility in most liquids, it is not as suitable as the phenylhydrazone for characterising the ketone. Its chief use is for the preparation of 1-phenyl-ethylamine, $CH_3(C_6H_5)CHNH_2$, which can be readily obtained by the reduction of the oxime or by the Leuckart reaction (p. 223), and which can then be resolved by d-tartaric acid and l-malic acid into optically active forms. The optically active amine is frequently used in turn for the resolution of racemic acids.

Acetophenone Semicarbazone. $CH_3(C_6H_5)C:N\cdot NHCONH_2$. (Semi-micro Scale.)

Aldehydes and ketones may frequently be identified by their *semicarbazones*, obtained by direct condensation with semicarbazide (or amino-urea), $NH_2NHCONH_2$, a compound which is a monacidic base and usually available as its monohydrochloride, $NH_2CONHNH_2,HCl$. Semicarbazones are particularly useful for identification of compounds (such as acetophenone) of which the oxime is too soluble to be readily isolated and the phenylhydrazone is unstable: moreover, the high nitrogen content of semicarbazones enables very small quantities to be accurately analysed and so identified. The general conditions for the formation of semicarbazones are very similar to those for oximes and phenylhydrazones (pp. 93, 229): the free base must of course be liberated from its salts by the addition of sodium acetate.

Required: Semicarbazide hydrochloride, 1 g.; anhydrous sodium acetate, 0·9 g.; acetophenone, 1 ml.

Add first 1 g. of powdered semicarbazide hydrochloride and then 0·9 g. of anhydrous sodium acetate (or 1·25 g. of the crystalline acetate) to 5 ml. of water, and warm gently until a clear solution is obtained. Then add a solution of 1 ml. (1 g.) of acetophenone in 5 ml. of rectified spirit, and warm the mixed solutions gently on a water-bath for

$$CH_3(C_6H_5)CO + H_2N\cdot NHCONH_2 \rightarrow$$
$$CH_3(C_6H_5)C:N\cdot NHCONH_2 + H_2O$$

15 minutes. The semicarbazone rapidly crystallises whilst the solution is still being heated. Finally cool, filter off the acetophenone semicarbazone, wash thoroughly with water, and drain. Yield, 1·4 g. (theoretical). The semicarbazone when dry has m.p. 197-198° and is practically pure. It may be recrystallised from ethanol and obtained as colourless crystals, m.p. 201°.

2,4-Dihydroxy-acetophenone. (Resacetophenone.) (The Hoesch Reaction.)

The Hoesch Reaction is employed for the introduction of the $-COR$ group into the aromatic ring of phenol or a phenolic ether, and usually proceeds particularly readily with polyhydric phenols. If an ethereal solution of resorcinol (I) containing acetonitrile and zinc chloride is saturated with hydrogen chloride, the acetonitrile forms the unstable but reactive imine, $CH_3 \cdot C(Cl):NH$, which

under the influence of the zinc chloride reacts with the resorcinol to give the keto-imine (II). Keto-imines are basic and form salts, which are readily hydrolysed by aqueous acids to the corresponding ketone. The keto-imine (II) will therefore separate initially as the chlorozincate, which on hydrolysis gives 2,4-dihydroxy-acetophenone.

Required: Resorcinol, 5 g.; acetonitrile, 3·5 ml.; zinc chloride, 2 g.; anhydrous ether, 25 ml.

The Hoesch Reaction requires anhydrous conditions: therefore the ether and the acetonitrile should each be dried and distilled before use, and the resorcinol should be dried in a desiccator. Fit a 50 ml. conical flask with a rubber stopper carrying a long inlet and a short outlet tube, the latter being joined to a calcium chloride guard-tube. Add in turn 25 ml. of ether, 5 g. of resorcinol and 2·8 g. (3·5 ml.) of acetonitrile. Then rapidly pulverise 2 g. of zinc chloride in a mortar (which preferably has been preheated in an oven), transfer it to the mixture, and replace the stopper. Clamp the flask securely in a basin of ice-water, and pass a stream of dry hydrogen chloride (*cf.* p. 104) into the mixture, swirling the latter occasionally. When the mixture is saturated, close the inlet tube with a clip, and set the flask aside overnight. Then filter off the chlorozincate of the imine (II) which has separated, and wash it on the filter with a small quantity of ether. For hydrolysis, add the chlorozincate to 50 ml. of dilute hydrochloric acid, and boil the mixture under reflux for 30 minutes. Cool the clear solution, filter off the 2,4-dihydroxy-acetophenone which separates, and (after drying) recrystallise it from toluene; drain thoroughly and dry in a desiccator over paraffin shavings (p. 20): cream-coloured crystals, m.p. 145–146°. Yield, 3·5–4·0 g.

Anthraquinone. $C_6H_4 \Big\langle \begin{matrix} CO \\ CO \end{matrix} \Big\rangle C_6H_4$.

Anthracene is oxidised by chromium trioxide, CrO_3, to anthraquinone. As the reaction is carried out in solution, a solvent is required which will dissolve both the anthracene and the chromium trioxide, and at the same time be unaffected by the vigorous oxidising action of the latter compound: acetic acid fulfils these conditions admirably.

Required: Anthracene, 10 g.; acetic acid, 150 ml.; chromium trioxide, 20 g.

Assemble an apparatus precisely similar to that used for the preparation of acetophenone (p. 255), *viz.*, a 500 ml. bolt-head flask having a reflux water-condenser, into the top of which is fitted a 100 ml. dropping-funnel by means of a cork having a V-shaped groove cut vertically in the side to allow escape of air. (Alternatively, use the apparatus shown in Fig. 23(A), p. 45.) Place 10 g. of finely powdered anthracene and 100 ml. of glacial acetic acid in the flask, mix thoroughly by shaking and then heat the flask over a gauze so that the acetic acid boils gently under reflux, and the greater part of the anthracene goes into solution. Then dissolve 20 g. of chromium trioxide in 15 ml. of water, add 50 ml. of glacial acetic acid, and pour the well-stirred mixture into the dropping-funnel. Now allow the chromium oxide solution to run drop by drop down the condenser at such a rate that the total addition takes about 40 minutes. As the oxidation proceeds, the anthracene dissolves up completely in the boiling acetic acid. When the addition of the chromium oxide solution is complete, continue the boiling for a further 20 minutes, and then allow the solution to cool somewhat before pouring it into a large excess (about 500 ml.) of cold water. The crude anthraquinone separates as a greenish-grey powder. Stir the mixture vigorously in order to wash out as much acetic acid and chromium derivatives as possible from the anthraquinone, and then filter off the latter under *gentle* suction of the pump, wash it thoroughly on the filter with hot water, then with a hot *dilute* solution of sodium hydroxide, and finally with much cold water, before draining it well. Dry the anthraquinone as completely as possible by pressing it between several thick sheets of drying-paper. Yield, 10–11 g. (almost theoretical).

Anthraquinone sublimes readily on being heated, and may easily be obtained in a high state of purity by this method. Assemble the apparatus shown in Fig. 10, p. 23. Place about half of the crude product in the small evaporating-basin, and first warm the latter gently over a gauze (using a *very* small flame) in order to dry the product completely: when the evolution of steam is no longer perceptible, place over the basin a filter-paper through which a number of small holes (about 2 mm. in diameter) have been pierced upwards. Then place in turn a cold dry filter-funnel (of slightly smaller diameter than the basin) over the filter-paper, and heat the basin rather more strongly than before, at the same time protecting the apparatus from draughts. After a few minutes, the vapour of the anthraquinone passes through the holes, and condenses on the upper surface of the filter-paper and on the walls of the funnel in beautiful long yellow needles: these are pure and have m.p. 277°. During the process of sublimation, adjust the rate of heating so that the anthraquinone is slowly yet steadily volatilised, but the funnel does not become more than slightly warm.

Recrystallise the remaining half of the crude anthraquinone from boiling acetic acid, using animal charcoal: filter the hot solution through a Buchner funnel which has been preheated by the filtration of some of the boiling solvent, as the anthraquinone crystallises rapidly as the solution cools. Cool the filtrate in cold water and then filter at the pump, drain, wash with methylated spirit and dry. Yield, 4–5 g.

Anthraquinone. (Semi-micro Scale.)

Required. Anthracene, 1 g.; chromium trioxide, 2 g.; glacial acetic acid, 15 ml.

Dissolve 1 g. of anthracene in 10 ml. of glacial acetic acid and place in 50 ml. bolt-head flask fitted with a reflux water-condenser. Dissolve 2 g. of chromium trioxide in 2 ml. of water and add 5 ml. of glacial acetic acid. Pour this solution down the condenser, shake the contents of the flask and boil gently for 10 minutes. Cool and pour the contents of the flask into about 20 ml. of cold water. Filter off the crude anthraquinone at the pump, wash with water, drain well and dry. Yield, 1 g. Purify by recrystallisation from glacial acetic acid or by sublimation using the semi-micro sublimation apparatus (Fig. 35, p. 62, or Fig. 50, p. 70).

For reactions of anthraquinone, see pp. 370.

Anthraquinone is of great technical importance, as many of its derivatives form valuable dyes: notable among these are the hydroxy-derivatives (alizarin, *etc.*), the amino-derivatives (indanthrene, *etc.*) and the sulphonic acids.

ω-Dimethylaminopropiophenone Hydrochloride.
$C_6H_5COCH_2CH_2N(CH_3)_2$. (The Mannich Reaction.)

The *Mannich Reaction* involves the condensation of formaldehyde with ammonia or a primary or secondary amine and with a third compound containing a reactive methylene group: these compounds are most frequently those in which the methylene group is activated by a neighbouring keto group. Thus when acetophenone is boiled in ethanolic solution with paraformaldehyde and dimethylamine hydrochloride, condensation occurs readily with the formation of

$$C_6H_5COCH_3 + H_2CO + (CH_3)_2NH,HCl \rightarrow C_6H_5COCH_2CH_2N(CH_3)_2,HCl$$

ω-idimethylaminopropiophenone hydrochloride. The reaction therefore affords a ready synthesis of certain keto-amines.

It will be clear that the above reaction, if carried out with ammonia would give first a primary amine, and if performed with a primary amine would give a secondary amine. Furthermore, if the above reaction were carried out with monomethyl-

$$\text{(A)} \quad C_6H_5COCH_2CH_2NH(CH_3). \qquad (C_6H_5COCH_2CH_2)_2NCH_3 \quad \text{(B)}$$

amine hydrochloride, the initial product would be the hydrochloride of ω-methylaminopropiophenone (A), but this compound could react again to give the compound (B). In the reaction described below, such secondary reactions do not occur.

Required: Acetophenone, 5 g.; paraformaldehyde, 1·25 g.; dimethylamine hydrochloride, 3·5 g.

NOTE. Dimethylamine hydrochloride is a deliquescent substance: the sample if damp *must* be dried in a vacuum desiccator and then *rapidly* weighed before use.

Add 5 ml. (5 g.) of acetophenone, 1·25 g. of finely powdered paraformaldehyde, and 3·5 g. of dry dimethylamine hydrochloride to 8 ml. of absolute ethanol, and then boil the mixture under reflux for 1·5 hours. Filter the solution (which is now almost entirely clear) through a preheated filter-funnel, and cool the filtrate in ice-water with stirring. The ω-dimethylamino-propiophenone hydrochloride rapidly separates as white crystals; filter off the crystals at the pump and recrystallise from a small quantity of ethanol: m.p. 155–156°. Yield, 2·5 g.

2,4-Dinitrophenylhydrazine. $(NO_2)_2C_6H_3 \cdot NH \cdot NH_2$.

2,4-Dinitrophenylhydrazine is a very important reagent for the identification of aldehydes and ketones (pp. 342, 346). It is readily prepared from chloro-2,4-dinitrobenzene (I). In the latter compound the chlorine is very reactive in

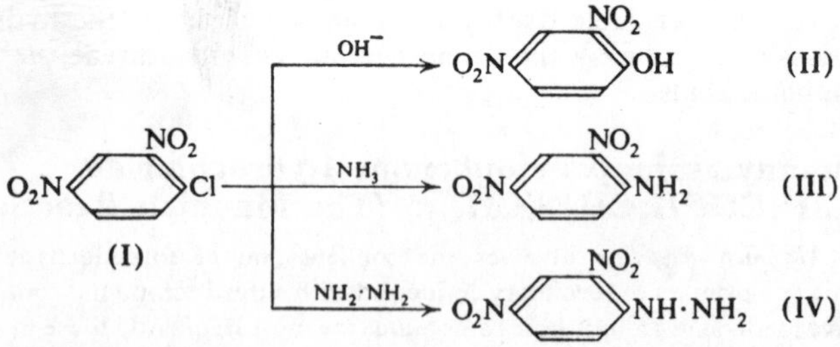

marked contrast to the extremely unreactive chlorine atom in chlorobenzene (p. 391). This high reactivity of the chlorine atom is caused by the presence of the two (ortho and para) nitro groups in the ring. Chloro-2,4-dinitrobenzene is readily converted by dilute alkali into 2,4-dinitrophenol (II) and by ammonia into 2,4-dinitroaniline (III). Similarly it reacts with one molecular equivalent of hydrazine to give 2,4-dinitrophenylhydrazine (IV).

Required: Chloro- 2,4-dinitrobenzene, 10 g.; hydrazine hydrate, 8 ml. (64% w/w); dioxan,* 50 ml.

Dissolve 10 g. of chloro- 2,4-dinitrobenzene† in 50 ml. of dioxan in a 250 ml. conical flask. Dilute 8 ml. of hydrazine hydrate with an equal volume of water and add this slowly with shaking to the dioxan solution, keeping the temperature between 20° and 25°. Heat under reflux for 10 minutes to complete the reaction and then add 5 ml. of ethanol and heat again for 5 minutes. Cool and filter off the orange 2,4-dinitrophenylhydrazine. Recrystallise the dry product from ethyl acetate: m.p. 200° (decomp.). Yield, 7 g.

Preparation of 2,4-Dinitrophenylhydrazones. 2,4-Dinitrophenylhydrazine is much more reactive than phenylhydrazine towards aldehydes and ketones: consequently a compound having a carbonyl group of low reactivity may often readily give a 2,4-dinitrophenylhydrazone, although the unsubstituted phenylhydrazone is difficult to prepare. Furthermore, 2,4-dinitrophenylhydrazones usually have lower solubilities and higher melting-points than the corresponding unsubstituted phenylhydrazones, and therefore separate from solution and crystallise far more readily.

On the other hand, the two nitro groups make 2,4-dinitrophenylhydrazine a very weak base, and it has therefore to be used in reasonably concentrated acid solution.

Two solutions are recommended for use:

Reagent A. Dissolve 0·5 g. of the powdered dinitrophenylhydrazine in a mixture of 80 ml. of concentrated hydrochloric acid and 100 ml. of distilled water by gently heating the mixture on a water-bath. Cool the solution and add 120 ml. of water. If necessary, filter the pale yellow solution.

Reagent B. Suspend 1 g. of the powdered dinitrophenylhydrazine in 30 ml. of stirred methanol and cautiously add 2 ml. of concentrated sulphuric acid. If necessary, filter the solution whilst it is still warm and cool the filtrate.

Both reagents should be stored in a cool place and preferably in the dark. They should be stable for several weeks, but ultimately give a brown deposit.

Reagent A is particularly useful for the treatment of the lower aliphatic aldehydes and ketones which are soluble in water (*cf.* acetaldehyde, p. 342; acetone, p. 346). The Reagent is a very dilute solution of the dinitrophenylhydrazine, and therefore is used more to detect the presence of a carbonyl group in a compound than to isolate sufficient of the hydrazone for effective recrystallisation and melting-point determination.

* Dioxan should be manipulated with care, for the vapour is toxic.
† Care must be taken when dealing with this substance as it can cause dermatitis and also irritate the respiratory system.

Reagent B is valuable for use with aldehydes or ketones which are insoluble in water, and therefore unsuitable for treatment with Reagent A (*cf.* benzaldehyde, p. 342; benzophenone, p. 346). It is much more concentrated than A, and consequently can be more readily used for the isolation and purification of the required hydrazone.

Use. If the substance under investigation is soluble in water, dissolve about 0·1 g. in 1–2 ml. of water, and add 5–10 ml. of Reagent A. On shaking for a few minutes, with scratching if necessary, the yellowish-orange hydrazone will usually separate: if this does not occur, warm the solution *gently* in a hot water-bath for 5–10 minutes.

If the substance under investigation is insoluble in water, dissolve about 0·1 g. in a *minimum* of methanol or ethanol, with heating if necessary, and then add 0·5–1 ml. of Reagent B: then proceed as above.

Precautions. (1) The above tests must be carried out with discretion. If the substance is only moderately soluble in the solvent selected, and a comparatively large volume of the latter is required, the consequent dilution of the acid in the reagent may cause the separation of the free 2,4-dinitrophenylhydrazine (although this is more likely to happen with Reagent B than with A). Furthermore, if the compound under investigation should have basic properties, the neutralisation of part of the acid in the reagent may have the same result.

(2) 2,4-Dinitrophenylhydrazones usually separate in well-formed crystals. These can be filtered at the pump, washed with a diluted sample of the acid in the reagent used, then with water, and then (when the solubility allows) with a *small* quantity of ethanol: the dried specimen is then usually pure. It should, however, be recrystallised from a suitable solvent, a process which can usually be carried out with the dinitrophenylhydrazones of the simpler aldehydes and ketones. Many other hydrazones have a very low solubility in most solvents, and a "recrystallisation" which involves prolonged boiling with a large volume of solvent may be accompanied by partial decomposition, and with the ultimate deposition of a sample less pure than the above washed, dried and unrecrystallised sample.

Ethyl Acetoacetate. $CH_3COCH_2COOC_2H_5$. (Claisen Condensation.)

Ethyl acetoacetate is a tautomeric substance which at room temperature exists as an equilibrium mixture of the *keto* and *enol* forms, the latter form being present to the extent of about 7%.

$$CH_3COCH_2COOC_2H_5 \rightleftharpoons CH_3C(OH){:}CHCOOC_2H_5$$
$$\textit{keto} \qquad\qquad\qquad \textit{enol}$$

It is readily prepared by the action of metallic sodium on dry ethyl acetate. The reaction, which occurs only in the presence of a trace of ethanol, is complex, but may be considered (in effect) as a condensation of two molecules of ethyl acetate under the influence of sodium ethoxide, the sodium derivative of the *enol* form being thus obtained. Clearly, only a trace of ethanol is thus initially

$$CH_3COOEt + HCH_2COOC_2H_5 + C_2H_5ONa \rightarrow$$

$$CH_3C(ONa){:}CHCOOC_2H_5 + C_2H_5OH$$

required. Treatment of the crude sodium derivative with a weak acid, *e.g.*, dilute acetic acid, then gives the normal equilibrium mixture of the *keto* and *enol* forms.

This preparation was discovered independently by Geuther (1863) and by Frankland and Duppa (1865). The reaction was subsequently investigated in detail and so widely extended by Claisen that it has become solely a specific example of the more general process known as the Claisen Condensation.* Claisen showed that an ester under the influence of sodium ethoxide would not only condense with itself (as in the preparation of ethyl acetoacetate), but also with (i) another ester, (ii) a ketone, if of formula RCH_2COR, (iii) a nitrile, if of formula RCH_2CN, in each case with the elimination of alcohol. Examples of these modifications are:

(i) $C_6H_5COOC_2H_5 + HCH_2COOC_2H_5 \rightarrow C_6H_5COCH_2COOC_2H_5 + C_2H_5OH$

   Ethyl benzoate   Ethyl acetate   Ethyl benzoylacetate.

(ii) $CH_3COOC_2H_5 + HCH_2COCH_3 \rightarrow CH_3COCH_2COCH_3 + C_2H_5OH$

   Ethyl acetate   Acetone   Acetyl-acetone.

(iii) $C_2H_5OOC \cdot COOC_2H_5 + HCH_2CN \rightarrow C_2H_5OOC \cdot COCH_2CN + C_2H_5OH$

   Ethyl oxalate   Acetonitrile Ethyl β-cyanopyruvate.

Many other examples of the Claisen Condensation will be found in textbooks of theoretical organic chemistry.

The mechanism of the Claisen Ester condensation has been suggested along the following lines:

$$CH_3 \cdot CO_2 \cdot Et + {}^-OEt \rightarrow \overline{C}H_2 \cdot CO_2 \cdot Et + EtOH$$

$$CH_3 \cdot C \underset{OEt}{\overset{O}{\big/\!\big/}} CH_2 \cdot CO_2 \cdot Et \rightarrow CH_3 \cdot C \underset{OEt}{\overset{O^-}{\diagup}} - CH_2 \cdot CO_2 \cdot Et$$

$$CH_3 \cdot C \underset{OEt}{\overset{O^-}{\diagdown}} CH_2 \cdot CO_2 \cdot Et \rightarrow CH_3 \cdot \overset{O}{\overset{\|}{C}} - CH_2 \cdot CO_2 \cdot Et$$

$$\overset{O}{\overset{\|}{CH_3 \cdot C}} - CH_2 \cdot CO_2 \cdot Et + EtO^- \rightarrow \overset{O}{\overset{\|}{CH_3 \cdot C}} \overline{} \overline{C}H \cdot CO_2 \cdot Et + EtOH$$

$$\downarrow$$

$$CH_3 \cdot \overset{O^-}{\overset{|}{C}} = CH \cdot CO_2 \cdot Et$$

Thus the sodio derivative (I) of the enol form of ethyl acetoacetate is obtained. This mechanism can clearly apply also to the condensation of an ester with a suitable ketone or nitrile, as in the above reactions (ii) and (iii) respectively.

* This Condensation should not be confused with the *Claisen Reaction*, which is the condensation of an aldehyde with (i) another aldehyde, or (ii) a ketone, under the influence of *sodium hydroxide*, and with the elimination of *water*. For details, see Dibenzal-acetone, p. 231.

Required: Ethyl acetate, 200 ml.; sodium, 15 g.; saturated brine, 200 ml.

The ethyl acetate used in the preparation must first be dried. For this purpose place about 200 ml. of ethyl acetate over granular calcium chloride, shake thoroughly and allow to stand, preferably overnight: then filter through a fluted filter-paper directly into a distilling-flask fitted with a water-condenser and distil carefully over a gauze. Use rubber stoppers or ground-glass joints for the distillation apparatus, as bark corks contain appreciable quantities of water.

Fit a 750 ml. bolt-head flask (also by a rubber stopper) to a reflux water-condenser closed at the top by a calcium chloride tube: ensure that flask and condenser are quite dry. Place 150 ml. of the dried ethyl acetate in the flask and add 15 g. of sodium. The sodium for this purpose should preferably be added in the form of wire directly from a sodium press (Fig. 55, p. 82): alternatively the sodium may be added as thin slices, but in this case each slice should be quickly pressed between drying-paper before being added to the acetate to remove the wet film which may have formed during the weighing and cutting of the metal.

Now heat the mixture on the water-bath, or (preferably) at 100° in an oil-bath or an electric heater. Very little reaction occurs whilst the acetate is still cold, but on warming a vigorous reaction ensues and hydrogen is evolved. Continue heating until a clear pale brown liquid entirely free from metallic sodium is obtained—this usually requires 2–2½ hours' heating, depending largely on the initial condition of the sodium. Then cool thoroughly and add dilute acetic acid (1:1 by volume) cautiously with shaking until the liquid is just definitely acid to litmus-paper; the addition of the acid first causes the formation of a semi-solid white mass which redissolves to a clear solution as the mixture becomes acid. Pour the solution into about 200 ml. of cold almost saturated brine contained in a separating-funnel and shake the mixture vigorously. The ethyl acetoacetate separates sharply above the brine solution. Run off the lower layer of brine and then transfer the ester to a conical flask; add some powdered anhydrous sodium sulphate, and allow to stand for about 30 minutes with occasional shaking.

Meanwhile fit up a Claisen flask (of about 175 ml. capacity) with a fine capillary and thermometer (see Fig. 12(A), p. 29), taking care that the range of temperature of 70°–100° is not obscured by the cork. Then filter the crude ester at the pump using a Buchner funnel and flask, quickly drain the residue of sodium sulphate in the funnel, and then rinse out the conical flask with a few ml. of the original dried ethyl acetate, filtering the latter through the sodium sulphate residue into the ester below. Pour the latter into the Claisen flask, add some unglazed porcelain and, temporarily discarding the capillary and thermometer, cork the necks of the flask, connect it to a water-condenser and then place it *in* a boiling water-bath. The greater part of the unchanged ethyl acetate now distils over. When distillation ceases, remove the flask, replace the capillary and thermometer, and fit an apparatus for vacuum-distillation to the Claisen flask: for this purpose the Perkin triangle apparatus (Fig. 14, p. 31), or that shown with a "pig" (Fig. 23(F), p. 46), is preferable, but the more simple apparatus shown in Fig. 12(A), p. 29, gives good results. When a steady low pressure is attained in the apparatus, heat the Claisen flask in an oil-bath, increasing the temperature of the bath cautiously so that the distillation proceeds slowly. The boiling-point of the distillate rises slowly as the low-boiling impurities come over first, and finally becomes almost constant as the ethyl acetoacetate distils. Therefore ensure by slow distillation that the low-boiling impurities pass over as completely as possible before the ethyl acetoacetate starts to distil; if the apparatus shown in Fig. 12(A) is used, the receiver must of course be changed at this stage. The distillation of the acetoacetate can readily be recognised from the following boiling-points, $73°/15$ mm., $82°/20$ mm., $87°/30$ mm., $92°/40$ mm., and a fraction boiling over a range of $3-5°$ should be collected. Yield, 40–45 g. A brown residue remains in the flask.

Refractionation of the low-boiling impurities gives a further quantity of the acetoacetate, but if the initial distillation has been carefully conducted, the amount recovered is less than 1 g., and the refractionation is not worth while. If possible, complete the preparation in one day. If this is not possible, it is best to allow the cold crude sodium derivative (before acidification) to stand overnight, the flask being closed by a cork carrying a calcium chloride tube; the yield will now fall to about 38 g. Alternatively, the crude ester may be allowed to remain overnight in contact with the sodium sulphate, but in this case the yield will fall to about 30 g.

The ethyl acetoacetate obtained as above is sufficiently pure for most purposes: it should, however, be refractionated under reduced pressure if a sample of specially high purity is required.

If a vacuum-distillation apparatus is not available for the above preparation, the crude product may be distilled at atmospheric pressure and the acetoacetate collected as the fraction boiling at 175–185°. A pure preparation cannot be obtained in this way, however, because the ester decomposes slightly when distilled at atmospheric pressure.

Ethyl acetoacetate is a colourless liquid, d, 1·03, slightly soluble in water, but almost insoluble in brine. It has a faint but pleasant odour. It is widely used in chemical syntheses.

Demonstrate both the presence and the interconversion of the *keto* and *enol* forms in the ester thus:

(1) Dissolve about 1 ml. of the ester in about 3 ml. of ethanol and then add 2–3 drops of aqueous ferric chloride solution. A deep violet-red coloration at once appears. This is strong evidence for the presence of the *enol* form, since similar colorations with ferric chloride are given by most phenols (p. 338) and many higher aliphatic hydroxy-compounds. Now pour the solution into about 100 ml. of distilled water in a beaker and add bromine water *drop* by *drop* with vigorous stirring until the solution *just* becomes colourless. On standing, the violet-red ferric chloride coloration soon reappears with increasing intensity. The bromine has thus added on at the double bond of the *enol* form, giving the unstable dibromo derivative (A), which readily loses hydrogen

$$CH_3C(OH){:}CHCOOC_2H_5 \xrightarrow{Br_2} CH_3C(OH)Br{\cdot}CHBrCOOC_2H_5 \xrightarrow{-HBr}$$
$$(A)$$
$$CH_3CO{\cdot}CHBrCOOC_2H_5$$
$$(B)$$

bromide to give the monobrom-*keto* ester (B). Since the violet-red ferric chloride coloration is given only by the *enol* form, the temporary removal of the latter by the bromine causes the solution to become momentarily colourless. Some of the unchanged *keto* form then changes over to the *enol* in order to re-establish the original equilibrium, and the ferric chloride coloration therefore reappears. The process can be repeated several times by the subsequent addition of bromine. If a *slight* excess of bromine water is originally added after the solution becomes colourless, the slow fading of the yellow bromine solution can be observed as it reacts with the *enol* form, then the solution becomes momentarily colourless, and finally the violet-red coloration reappears as before.

(2) To 2 ml. of the ester in a test-tube add slightly more than the same volume of a cold *saturated* aqueous copper acetate solution. The blue colour of the latter turns immediately to a pale green. Now shake the tube vigorously in order to produce an emulsion of the ester in the aqueous layer. Scratch the sides of the tube with a rod, and shake vigorously as before. Crystallisation may be delayed for about 5 minutes, but, when once started, rapidly gives a copious precipitate

of the pale green cupric derivative (C) of the *enol* form. If the contents of the tube are now shaken with chloroform, the crystals of the cupric compound readily dissolve in the lower chloroform layer, showing clearly that it is not a normal ionised salt.

$$CH_3C:CH \cdot C \cdot OC_2H_5$$

$$CH_3COCH_2COOC_2H_5 + NaHSO_3$$
$$\downarrow$$
$$CH_3C(OH).CH_2COOC_2H_5$$
$$|$$
$$SO_3Na \ (D)$$

$$CH_3C:CH \cdot C \cdot OC_2H_5 \ (C)$$

(3) To 2 ml. of the ester, add 2–3 drops of a saturated *freshly prepared* solution of sodium bisulphite. On shaking, a gelatinous precipitate of the bisulphite addition product (D) of the *keto* form separates, and on standing for 5–10 minutes usually crystallises out. This is a normal reaction of a ketone (see p. 344): hydrogen cyanide adds on similarly to give a cyanhydrin.

Note. To obtain satisfactory results with tests (2) and (3), pure redistilled ethyl acetoacetate should be used.

For further experimental evidence for the presence of the *enol* form, see Tests 1, 2 (*a*) and 2 (*b*), p. 274.

SYNTHETIC USE OF ETHYL ACETOACETATE. In view of the great importance of the ester in synthetic work, the following practical points concerning its use should be borne in mind.

Mono- and Di-substitution Derivatives. The enolic sodium derivative of ethyl acetoacetate (E) is prepared by mixing ethanolic solutions of the ester and of sodium ethoxide. It should not be prepared by the direct action of metallic sodium on the ester, as the reaction is slow and the nascent hydrogen evolved reduces some of the ester to ethyl β-hydroxy-butyrate, $CH_3CH(OH)CH_2COOEt$.

When the sodium derivative, which is used in ethanolic solution without intermediate isolation, is boiled with an alkyl halide, *e.g.*, methyl iodide,

$$CH_3COCH_2COOEt \xrightarrow{\text{NaOEt}} CH_3CO\bar{C}HCOOEt \xrightarrow{\text{MeI}} CH_3COCH(Me)COOEt$$
$$(E) \qquad\qquad (F)$$

$$CH_3COCH(Me)COOEt \xrightarrow{\text{NaOEt}} CH_3C(ONa):C(Me)COOEt \xrightarrow{\text{EtI}} -$$
$$(F) \qquad\qquad (G) \qquad CH_3COC(Me)COOEt$$
$$(H)$$

the methyl derivative (F) of the ketonic form is produced. The latter can then be treated again with sodium ethoxide (both in ethanolic solution as before) and the enolic sodium derivative (G) of the methyl compound thus formed. The latter can then be boiled in solution as before with an alkyl halide such as ethyl iodide, and the methyl-ethyl compound (H) obtained. It follows therefore that (1) even with a large excess of sodium ethoxide, a di-sodium derivative cannot be obtained and therefore a di-substituted derivative (H) must be prepared through the intermediate formation of the mono-substituted derivative (F); (2) the substituent groups* must be alkyl groups or substituted alkyl groups such as benzyl, $C_6H_5CH_2-$, and that aryl groups cannot be introduced, because, *e.g.*, iodo-benzene would not react with sodium derivatives such as (E) or (G). Therefore the synthesis of aryl compounds has usually to be accomplished by entirely different means, such as by the Grignard reagent.

Hydrolysis. Ethyl acetoacetate when treated with cold dilute sodium hydroxide solution gives the sodium salt of acetoacetic acid. This acid is unstable, and readily breaks down into acetone and carbon dioxide: it is of considerable

$$CH_3COCH_2COOH = CH_3COCH_3 + CO_2$$

physiological importance, as it occurs with acetone in diabetic urine, both compounds being initially formed from β-hydroxy-butyric acid.

The important methods of hydrolysis of acetoacetic ester derivatives are however:

(1) *Ketonic Hydrolysis.* Hot dilute caustic alkalis or hydrochloric acid first hydrolyse off the ethyl group, and then remove carbon dioxide, a mono- or di-substituted acetone being thus obtained:

$$CH_3COCH(Me)CO_2Et \qquad CH_3COC(Me)(Et)CO_2Et$$
$$\downarrow H_2O \qquad\qquad \downarrow H_2O$$
$$CH_3COCHMe + CO_2 + EtOH \qquad CH_3COCHMeEt + CO_2 + EtOH$$

(2) *Acidic Hydrolysis.* Hot concentrated caustic alkalis first hydrolyse off the ethyl group, and then split the molecule to give one equivalent of acetic acid and one equivalent of the mono- or di-substituted acetic acid (as their alkali salts).

$$CH_3CO|CH(Me)COO|Et \qquad\qquad CH_3CO|C(Me)(Et)COO|Et$$
$$OH|H \quad \downarrow \quad H|OH \qquad\qquad OH|H \quad \downarrow \quad H|OH$$
$$CH_3COOH + MeCH_2COOH + EtOH \qquad CH_3COOH + MeEtCHCOOH + EtOH$$

In brief, suitable hydrolysis of ethyl acetoacetate derivatives will give mono- or di-*alkyl* substituted acetones or acetic acids. Tri-substituted acetones or acetic acids cannot be obtained: moreover, the di-substituted acetones must

---

* Acyl halides, both aliphatic and aromatic, react with the sodium derivative, but the product depends largely on the solvent used. Thus acetyl chloride reacts with the sodium derivative (E) suspended in ether to give mainly the C-derivative (1) and in pyridine solution to give chiefly the O-derivative (2). These isomeric compounds can be readily distinguished, because the C-derivative (1) can still by enolisation act as a weak acid and is therefore

$$(1) \quad CH_3COCHCOOEt \qquad\qquad (2) \quad CH_3C:CHCOOEt$$
$$\qquad\qquad | \qquad\qquad\qquad\qquad\qquad\qquad\qquad |$$
$$\qquad\qquad COCH_3 \qquad\qquad\qquad\qquad\qquad\qquad OCOCH_3$$

soluble in alkalis, while the O-derivative (2) is neutral and insoluble in alkalis.

have the two substituents joined to the same carbon atom, symmetrically substituted ketones not being obtainable from the ester by the above methods.

For other examples of the synthetic application of ethyl acetoacetate, see below and pp. 293 295.

Methyl-phenyl-pyrazolone.

The preparation of methyl-phenyl-pyrazolone illustrates one of the synthetic uses of ethyl acetoacetate, as distinct from those involving the hydrolysis of substitution derivatives.

If ethyl acetoacetate is warmed with an equivalent quantity of phenyl-hydrazine, the corresponding phenylhydrazone (A) is readily formed. On

$$CH_3CO + H_2NNHC_6H_5 \qquad CH_3C{:}NNHC_6H_5$$
$$| \qquad \qquad \rightarrow H_2O + \qquad |$$
$$CH_2COOC_2H_5 \qquad \qquad CH_2COOC_2H_5 \ (A)$$

further heating, ring formation occurs with the loss of ethanol and the pro-

$$CH_3C{:}N{\cdot}N{\cdot}HC_6H_5 \qquad CH_3C{:}N{\cdot}NC_6H_5$$
$$| \qquad \qquad \rightarrow C_2H_5OH + \quad | \quad |$$
$$CH_2COOC_2H_5 \qquad \qquad CH_2{-}CO \qquad (B)$$

duction of methyl-phenyl-pyrazolone (B). To indicate the position of the substituents in the pyrazolone ring, the atoms in this ring are numbered as shown, and the compound is thus 3-methyl-1-phenyl-5-pyrazolone.

$$CH_3C{:}N{\cdot}NC_6H_5$$
$$\begin{vmatrix} 3 & 2 & 1 \\ & & \\ 4 & 5 \end{vmatrix}$$
$$CH_2{-}CO$$

Required: Ethyl acetoacetate, 6·2 ml.; phenylhydrazine, 5 ml.

Mix 6·2 ml. (6·4 g.) of pure ethyl acetoacetate and 5 ml. of pure phenylhydrazine* in an evaporating-basin of about 75 ml. capacity, add 0·5 ml. of acetic acid and then heat the mixture on a briskly boiling water-bath (preferably in a fume-cupboard) for 1 hour, occasionally stirring the mixture with a short glass rod. Then allow the heavy yellow syrup to cool somewhat, add 30–40 ml. of ether, and stir the mixture vigorously; the syrup may now dissolve and the solution shortly afterwards deposit the crystalline pyrazolone, or at lower temperatures the syrup may solidify directly. (*Note.* If the laboratory has been "inoculated" by previous preparations, the syrup may solidify whilst still on the water-bath: in this case the solid product when cold must be chipped out of the basin, and ground in a mortar with the ether.) Now filter the product at the pump, and wash the solid material thoroughly with ether. Recrystallise the product from a small quantity of a mixture of equal volumes of water and ethanol. The methyl-phenyl-pyrazolone is obtained

* The use of impure reactants may give a deep red syrup and delay considerably the final solidification: they should, therefore, be redistilled in a vacuum before use.

as colourless crystals, m.p. 127°. Yield of recrystallised material, 6.0–6.5 g.

The tautomerism shown by the pyrazolones is of considerable interest. Thus the above methyl-phenyl-pyrazolone when fused or in solution can exist in the tautomeric forms (C), (D), and (E).

$$CH_3C : N \cdot NC_6H_5 \qquad CH_3C \cdot NH \cdot NC_6H_5 \qquad CH_3C : N \cdot NC_6H_5$$
$$\mid \quad \mid \quad \rightleftharpoons \quad \parallel \quad \mid \quad \rightleftharpoons \quad \mid \quad \mid$$
$$CH_2{-}CO \ (C) \qquad\quad CH{-}CO \ (D) \qquad\quad CH{=}C(OH) \ (E)$$

When the methyl-phenyl-pyrazolone is heated with methyl iodide in methanolic solution, it acts in the form (D), the —NH— group undergoing methylation, with the formation of the hydriodide of 2,3-dimethyl-1-phenyl-5-pyrazolone, or *antipyrine* (F), a drug used (either as the free base or as the

$$CH_3C \cdot N(CH_3) \cdot NC_6H_5 \qquad\qquad CH_3C \cdot N(CH_3) \cdot NC_6H_5$$
$$\parallel \quad\quad \mid \qquad\qquad\qquad \parallel \quad\quad \mid$$
$$CH{-}\!\!-\!\!-\!\!-CO \ (F) \qquad (CH_3)_2N \cdot C \ -\!\!-\!\!-\!\!- \ CO \ (G)$$

salicylate) to remove pain and also to reduce the body temperature. Antipyrine in turn can be converted to 2,3-dimethyl-4-(dimethylamino)-1-phenyl-5-pyrazolone, or *pyramidon* (G), a drug which has physiological properties similar to those of antipyrine, but which is effective in smaller doses and is more free from harmful after-effects.

Ethyl Malonate. $CH_2(COOC_2H_5)_2$.

A concentrated solution of monochloroacetic acid is neutralised with sodium bicarbonate, and then heated with potassium cyanide, whereby sodium cyanoacetate is obtained:

$$CH_2ClCOONa + KCN = CH_2(CN)COONa + KCl$$

The crude product is evaporated to dryness and then heated with a mixture of ethanol and sulphuric acid: the cyano group is thus hydrolysed giving malonic acid, which then undergoes esterification to give diethyl malonate.

$$CH_2\!\!\diagup^{COONa}_{\diagdown CN} \ \xrightarrow{\text{Hydrolysis}} \ CH_2\!\!\diagup^{COOH}_{\diagdown COOH} \ \xrightarrow{\text{Esterification}} \ CH_2\!\!\diagup^{COOC_2H_5}_{\diagdown COOC_2H_5}$$

Required: Monochloroacetic acid, 30 g.; sodium bicarbonate, 30 g.; potassium cyanide, 24 g.; sulphuric acid, 50 ml.; rectified spirit, 70 ml.

The first part of this preparation (as far as the solidification of the sodium cyanoacetate) *must be carried out in the fume-cupboard.* Add 30 g. of monochloroacetic acid to 60 ml. of water contained in a wide evaporating-basin (about 12–15 cm. in diameter) and warm the mixture gently on a sand-bath until the temperature reaches about 55°, using a 260° thermometer as a stirrer for this purpose. Now add powdered sodium bicarbonate* (about 30 g.) in small quantities at a time with stirring until the evolution of carbon dioxide is complete, and the solution is just alkaline to litmus-paper: during this operation keep the temperature of the mixture between 55° and 60°. Now remove the basin from the sand-bath and cautiously add 24 g. of powdered potassium cyanide,† continuing the stirring both during and after the addition. The temperature of the mixture rises spontaneously after the addition is complete and the cyanide rapidly dissolves. When the temperature of the well-stirred mixture reaches 90–95°, a vigorous effervescence usually occurs for a few seconds and then rapidly subsides. When this reaction is over, replace the basin on the sand-bath and heat gently, meanwhile stirring the brown solution with the thermometer until the temperature reaches 135° (about 30 minutes' heating is usually required). Maintain the temperature at 135° for a further 5 minutes, and then remove the basin from the sand-bath and continue stirring until the product solidifies.

Without undue delay, chip out the brown solid mass (which is deliquescent when cold) and place the coarsely broken mass in a 400 ml. round-bottomed flask fitted with a reflux water-condenser: add 20 ml. of rectified spirit and shake well around until the product is uniformly wet. Now add 50 ml. (92 g.) of concentrated sulphuric acid *carefully* with shaking to 50 ml. (40 g.) of rectified spirit in a 200 ml. conical flask, keeping the mixture well cooled in ice-water during the addition. Pour this solution in small portions down the reflux condenser, shaking well after each addition. When the addition is complete, heat the flask on a boiling water-bath for 1 hour, with occasional shaking. Then allow it to cool somewhat (the contents will become almost solid if allowed to become quite cold), add 70 ml. of water down the condenser, and shake vigorously. Filter any insoluble material at the pump, and wash the residue on the filter several times with a few ml. of ether. Transfer the filtrate (with the ether washings) to a separating-funnel and extract several times with ether. Discard the aqueous layer, return the united ethereal extracts to the funnel, and shake them *cautiously* with sodium carbonate solution several times until no further evolution of carbon dioxide occurs: traces of sulphuric acid and of ethanol are thus removed. Finally separate the ethereal layer and dry it over granular calcium chloride in a small conical flask for at least 30 minutes.

* Strictly named by IUPAC nomenclature as sodium hydrogen carbonate.
† See footnote, p. 191.

Meanwhile fit up an apparatus for ether distillation precisely similar to that shown in Fig. 64 (p. 163), except that a 100 ml. Claisen flask is used instead of the simple distillation-flask shown in the figure, *i.e.*, as in Fig. 23(E), p. 45. The dropping-funnel is fitted to the main neck of the Claisen flask, the side-neck being corked. Filter the dry ethereal solution through a fluted filter-paper directly into the dropping-funnel, finally washing the conical flask and the calcium chloride with a few ml. of fresh ether. Then distil off the ether in the usual way, allowing the solution to fall from the dropping-funnel into the flask as fast as the ether itself distils over—*observe all the usual precautions for ether distillations*. When the distillation of the ether is complete and only the crude ester remains in the Claisen flask, fit up the latter for vacuum-distillation, using the simple apparatus shown in Fig. 12(A), (p. 29) or a Perkin triangle with condenser (Fig. 14, p. 31) or the condenser and "pig" shown in Fig. 23(F), p. 46, and heating the flask in an oil-bath. The ethyl malonate usually distils as a sharp fraction boiling over a range of about 2–3°: it may be recognised from the following b.p.s: 93°/16 mm., 105°/26 mm. Yield, about 35 g. If necessary the ethyl malonate may be distilled at atmospheric pressure, at which it has b.p. 198°: slight decomposition occurs in these circumstances, however, and the distillate, although colourless, has a slightly acrid odour.

Diethyl malonate is a colourless liquid, *d*, 1·07; it has a faint pleasant odour, and is only slightly soluble in water.

Ethyl malonate, like ethyl acetoacetate, exists as a tautomeric mixture of *keto* and *enol* forms, although in the case of ethyl malonate

$$C_2H_5OOC\cdot CH_2\cdot COOC_2H_5 \rightleftharpoons C_2H_5OOC\cdot CH:C(OH)OC_2H_5$$
$$keto \qquad\qquad\qquad enol$$

the proportion of *enol* form present at room temperature is exceedingly small. Experimental evidence for the presence of the *enol* form is, however, given by the following tests:

(1) To 2 ml. of a freshly prepared dilute aqueous solution of sodium nitroprusside, add 2 drops of ethyl malonate and shake: then add 2–3 drops of 10% aqueous sodium hydroxide solution and shake again. A red coloration at once appears, but fades in a few minutes to pale brown.

(2) (a) Dissolve about 0·1 g. of *pure m*-dinitrobenzene in 2–3 ml. of ethanol, and then add an equal volume of 10% aqueous sodium hydroxide solution. (Ignore traces of the dinitrobenzene that may be reprecipitated by the soda.) Now add 2 drops of ethyl malonate and shake. A deep reddish-violet coloration is produced, but rapidly changes to a deep red.

(b) Dissolve 0·2 g. of 3,5-dinitrobenzoic acid in 2–3 ml. of 10%

aqueous sodium hydroxide solution, and then add 2 drops of ethyl malonate and shake. A violet coloration is produced, rapidly fading to red and eventually to pale yellow. Excess of the malonate discharges the red colour rapidly, giving the yellow solution.

Precisely similar results are obtained with ethyl acetoacetate, except that in tests 2 (a) and 2 (b) the deep red coloration is produced without a preliminary violet coloration.

These coloration changes are given by most compounds which possess the $-CH_2 \cdot CO-$ group: for further examples, see Tests 4 (a) and (b) for Ketones, p. 344.

SUBSTITUTION DERIVATIVES OF ETHYL MALONATE. Ethyl malonate resembles ethyl acetoacetate in that it gives rise to mono- and di-substituted derivatives in precisely similar circumstances. Thus when ethanolic solutions of ethyl malonate and of sodium ethoxide are mixed, the sodium derivative (A) of the *enol* form is produced in solution. On boiling this solution with an *alkyl* halide, *e.g.*, methyl iodide, the methyl derivative (B) of the *keto* form is obtained. When this is treated again in ethanolic solution with sodium ethoxide, the

$$
\begin{array}{ccc}
- & \text{MeI} & \text{NaOEt} \\
\text{EtOOCCHCOOEt} & \longrightarrow \text{EtOOC} \cdot \text{CH(Me)COOEt} & \longrightarrow \\
\text{(A)} & \text{(B)} & \\
- & \text{EtI} & \\
\text{EtOOCC(Me)COOEt} & \longrightarrow \text{EtOOC} \cdot \text{C(Me)(Et)COOEt} \\
\text{(C)} & \text{(D)}
\end{array}
$$

corresponding sodium derivative (C) is formed: this in turn when boiled in ethanolic solution with any alkyl halide, *e.g.*, ethyl iodide, gives the ethyl-methyl derivative (D), *i.e.*, the diethyl ester of ethylmethylmalonic acid. In this way, any mono-substituted (B) or di-substituted (D) alkyl derivative may be obtained.

Hydrolysis. Ethyl malonate and its derivatives are usually readily hydrolysed on boiling with aqueous alkalis, the salts of the corresponding dicarboxylic acids being thus obtained: the course of this hydrolysis is unaffected by the concentration of the alkali used. The free acids, having two $-COOH$ groups joined to one carbon atom, are unstable when heated, and immediately above their melting-points (or sometimes in boiling aqueous solution) lose carbon dioxide, a monobasic acid being obtained. Thus the mono-substituted ester (B) on hydrolysis gives mono-methyl-malonic acid (E) which on being heated to its m.p. gives methyl-acetic or propionic acid (F). The di-substituted ester (D) similarly gives first ethylmethylmalonic acid (G) and then ethylmethyl-acetic acid (H).

$$
\begin{array}{cccc}
\text{EtOOC} \cdot \text{CH(Me)COOEt} & \longrightarrow & \text{HOOCCH(Me)COOH} & \longrightarrow \\
\text{(B)} & & \text{(E)} & \text{CH}_2\text{(Me)COOH} + \text{CO}_2 \\
& & & \text{(F)} \\
\text{EtOOC} \cdot \text{C(Me)(Et)COOEt} & \longrightarrow & \text{HOOCC(Me)(Et)COOH} & \longrightarrow \\
\text{(D)} & & \text{(G)} & \text{CH(Me)(Et)COOH} + \text{CO}_2 \\
& & & \text{(H)}
\end{array}
$$

It follows therefore that ethyl malonate can be used (just as ethyl aceto-acetate) to prepare any mono- or di-substituted acetic acid: the limitations are identical, namely the substituents must necessarily be alkyl groups (or aryl-alkyl groups such as $C_6H_5CH_2$), and tri-substituted acetic acids cannot be prepared. Ethyl malonate undergoes no reaction equivalent to the ketonic hydrolysis of ethyl acetoacetate, and the concentration of the alkali used for the hydrolysis is therefore not important.

Ethane Tetracarboxylic Ethyl Ester.
$(C_2H_5OOC)_2CH \cdot CH(COOC_2H_5)_2$.

When an ethanolic solution of the sodium derivative of ethyl malonate is shaken with a solution of iodine, the latter withdraws the sodium, and the ethyl malonate residues link together in pairs to give the tetra-ethyl ester of

$$I_2 + \begin{array}{l} NaCH(COOC_2H_5)_2 \\ \\ NaCH(COOC_2H_5)_2 \end{array} \longrightarrow \begin{array}{l} CH(COOC_2H_5)_2 \\ | \\ CH(COOC_2H_5)_2 \end{array} + 2NaI$$

sym-ethane tetracarboxylic acid.

Required: Ethanol, 30 ml.; sodium, 1·4 g.; iodine, 7·7 g.; ethyl malonate, 9 ml.; sodium thiosulphate solution.

Place 30 ml. of ethanol in a 200 ml. conical flask fitted to a reflux water-condenser, and then add 1·4 g. of sodium cut into small pieces. The sodium rapidly dissolves to give a solution of sodium ethoxide, the ethanol boiling under the heat of the reaction. When the sodium has completely dissolved, detach the flask and cool it in ice-water.

While the sodium ethoxide solution is cooling, prepare a solution of 7·7 g. of finely powdered iodine in 60 ml. of ether. *When this solution is ready*, add 9 ml. (9·6 g.) of ethyl malonate to the ethanolic sodium ethoxide solution, mix well and then allow to stand for 30–60 seconds (*not longer*): then cautiously add the ethereal solution of the iodine, mixing *thoroughly* during the addition in order to avoid local overheating by the heat of the re-action. (If, after the ethyl malonate has been added to the sodium ethoxide, a considerable delay occurs before the iodine is added, the yield of the final product is markedly decreased.)

Now cork the flask securely, and shake it vigorously for about 5 minutes: the solution should now have only a faint brown colour due to unchanged iodine. Cool the mixture in ice-water, pour it into a separating-funnel, and extract it twice with water to remove sodium iodide and most of the ethanol. Then shake the residual ethereal solution with a dilute aqueous solution of sodium thiosulphate: the excess of iodine is thus removed and the ethereal solution becomes colourless. Separate the ether, dry it over calcium chloride for about 20 minutes, and then filter it through a fluted filter-paper directly into a 100 ml. conical flask. Fit the latter with a delivery knee-tube and water-condenser, and then, observing all the usual precautions (p. 163), distil off the ether on a water-bath until about 10–15 ml. remain. Pour this solution whilst still hot into a small evaporating basin and swirl it gently around: the hot ether rapidly evaporates and the ethane tetracarboxylic ester crystallises out. Allow it to stand exposed to the air for about 10–15 minutes, and then well press the crystals between several layers of thick drying-paper to remove any liquid residue. Recrystallise from a small quantity of rectified spirit or of light petroleum (b.p. 60–80°). The ester is obtained as colourless crystals, m.p. 76°: yield, 6·0–6·5 g.

This tetra-ethyl ester is difficult to hydrolyse: the corresponding tetra-methyl ester can, however, be hydrolysed to give ethane tetracarboxylic acid, $(HOOC)_2CH \cdot CH(COOH)_2$. The latter readily loses 2 molecules of carbon dioxide (on being heated or even on boiling with water) to give succinic acid, $HOOC \cdot CH_2 \cdot CH_2 COOH$.

Ethane tetracarboxylic ethyl ester can be regarded as composed of two malonic ester residues, each acting as a mono-alkyl substituent to the other. The two remaining hydrogen atoms therefore still retain acidic properties, and consequently the ester gives with sodium ethoxide a di-sodium derivative,

$$
\begin{array}{ccc}
NaC(COOEt)_2 & & C(COOEt)_2 \\
| & + I_2 = & \| & + 2NaI \\
NaC(COOEt)_2 & & C(COOEt)_2
\end{array}
$$

which when treated with iodine gives in turn ethylene tetracarboxylic ethyl ester, m.p. 57°.

5,5-Dimethyl-cyclohexan-1,3-dione. (Dimedone.) (The Michael Reaction.)

The Michael Addition Reaction consists in the addition of the sodio-derivative of ethyl acetoacetate, ethyl malonate or ethyl cyanoacetate to an olefine group

$$
\begin{array}{l}
\underset{(I)\ \overset{+}{Na}\ \ \overset{-}{C}H(COOEt)_2}{MeC = CH - \overset{O}{\overset{\|}{C}} \cdot CH_3} +
\underset{(II)\ CH(COOEt)_2\ \ \overset{+}{Na}}{Me_2C - CH = \overset{O^-}{\overset{|}{C}} \cdot CH_3} \longrightarrow
\underset{(III)\ CH(COOEt)_2}{Me_2C \cdot CH_2 \cdot CO \cdot CH_3}
\end{array}
$$

$$
\longrightarrow Me_2C \overset{CH_2 \cdot CO}{\underset{CH \cdot CO}{\big<\quad\big>}} CH_2 \longrightarrow Me_2C \overset{CH_2 \cdot CO}{\underset{CH_2 \cdot CO}{\big<\quad\big>}} CH_2
$$

$$
\text{(IV)}\ COOEt \qquad\qquad \text{(V)}
$$

which is activated by (in particular) a keto, nitrile or ester (·COOR) group. Thus the addition of diethyl sodio-malonate to mesityl oxide (I) may be regarded essentially as an ionic addition to give the anion (II), which on acidification gives the ester (III) with the keto group regenerated. The Michael Reaction has clearly a wide scope in synthetic work.

The compound (III) can however lose ethanol by an internal Claisen ester condensation (p. 264) to give the cyclohexane derivative (IV), which, being the ester of a β-keto acid, in turn readily undergoes hydrolysis and decarboxylation to give 5,5-dimethyl-cyclohexan-1,3-dione (V) or "Dimedone," a valuable reagent for the detection and estimation of formaldehyde.

Required: Ethanol, 40 ml.; sodium, 2·3 g.; ethyl malonate, 17 g.; mesityl oxide, 10·2 g.; sodium hydroxide, 10 g.

The mesityl oxide (b.p. 130°) *and the ethyl malonate* (b.p. 199°, 95°/18 mm.) *should be redistilled before use.*

Assemble a 250 ml. three-necked flask, fitted with a stirrer, a reflux condenser and a dropping-funnel, as in Fig. 22(A) and (J), p. 43, or Fig. 23(G), p. 46 (or a two-necked flask, with the funnel fitted by a grooved cork (p. 255) to the top of the condenser). Place 40 ml. of ethanol in the flask, and then add 2·3 g. of sodium cut into small pieces. When all the sodium has dissolved, heat the stirred solution on the water-bath,* and run in from the funnel 17 g. (17 ml.) of ethyl malonate and then (more slowly) 10·2 g. (12 ml.) of mesityl oxide, the reaction-mixture meanwhile forming a thick slurry. Boil the stirred mixture under reflux for 1 hour, and then add a solution of 10 g. of sodium hydroxide in 50 ml. of water, and continue boiling the pale honey-coloured solution for 1½ hours more.

Whilst the solution is still hot, add dilute hydrochloric acid until the stirred solution is just acid to litmus, and then distil off as much ethanol as possible, using the water-bath. Now add more dilute hydrochloric acid to the residual hot solution until it is just acid to methyl-orange. The 5,5-dimethyl-cyclohexan-1,3-dione separates as an oil which solidifies on cooling. Filter the product at the pump, wash it with ice-cold water, and dry it in a desiccator. Yield of the pale cream-coloured crystals, 12 g.; m.p. 136–145° (preliminary softening).

Recrystallisation from a mixture of equal volumes of petroleum (b.p. 60–80°) and acetone gives colourless crystals, m.p. 146–148°.

Reactions. The methylene group in the 2 position in 5,5-dimethyl-cyclohexan-1,3-dione (V) is strongly activated by the

---

* The whole apparatus can conveniently be assembled on the water-bath, which is heated as the last pieces of sodium are reacting.

two adjacent carbonyl groups. The reactivity is shown by the following reactions:

(1) If a warm aqueous solution is treated with aqueous sodium hypoiodite solution, a reaction analogous to the iodoform reaction occurs, with the formation of $\beta\beta$-dimethylglutaric acid

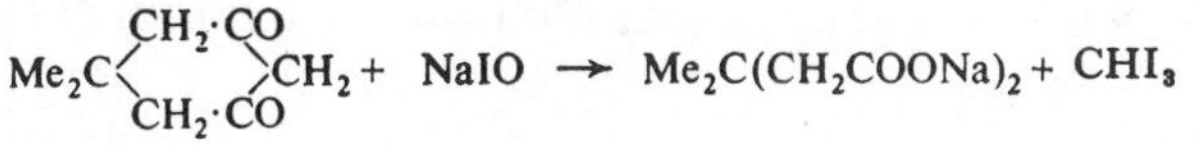

$$Me_2C\underset{CH_2\cdot CO}{\overset{CH_2\cdot CO}{\big<}}CH_2 + NaIO \rightarrow Me_2C(CH_2COONa)_2 + CHI_3$$

and iodoform.

(2) The "Dimedone" (V) in ethanolic solution reacts rapidly with formaldehyde to give "methylene-dimedone" (VI) which,

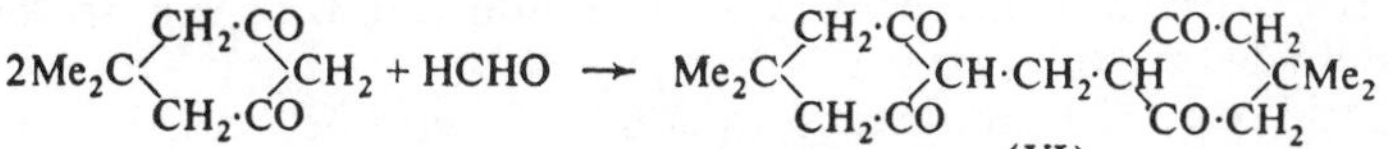

$$2Me_2C\underset{CH_2\cdot CO}{\overset{CH_2\cdot CO}{\big<}}CH_2 + HCHO \rightarrow Me_2C\underset{CH_2\cdot CO}{\overset{CH_2\cdot CO}{\big<}}CH\cdot CH_2\cdot CH\underset{CO\cdot CH_2}{\overset{CO\cdot CH_2}{\big>}}CMe_2$$
$$\text{(VI)}$$

having a low solubility, readily crystallises out, and has a sharp m.p. (cf. p. 146). Many aldehydes can be identified by their analogous "alkylidene-dimedone" derivatives, which also serve to distinguish aldehydes from ketones.

Sorbic Acid. $CH_3\cdot(CH{:}CH\cdot)_2COOH$. (The Knoevenagel Condensation.)

The term Knoevenagel Condensation was originally applied to the base-catalysed condensation of the carbonyl (:CO) group of aldehydes and ketones with the reactive methylene group of malonic acid, with loss of water:

$$RCHO + H_2C(COOH)_2 \rightarrow R\cdot CH{:}CH\cdot COOH + H_2O + CO_2$$

It is now applied more widely to include malonic acid derivatives, such as diethyl monoethyl-malonate, ethyl cyanacetate, etc. Various amines may be used as catalysts, and usually the most effective is piperidine (hexahydro-pyridine): a mixture of piperidine and pyridine, or pyridine alone, is also often used.

The role of the base is apparently primarily that of a proton remover from the reactive methylene group: thus if B represents the base, reaction (i) gives the carbanion, which then combines with the positive carbon of the carbonyl group (reaction ii): the product regains a proton from the piperidinium ion, and then by loss of water followed by mono-decarboxylation of the malonic acid residue gives the final acid.

(i) $CH_2(COOH)_2 + 3B \rightarrow \bar{C}H(COOH,B)_2 + \overset{+}{B}H$

(ii) $R \cdot \overset{+}{C} \overset{\frown}{=} \overset{-}{O} + \cdot \bar{C}H(COOH,B)_2 \rightarrow R \cdot \overset{\overset{\bar{O} \ H}{|}}{\underset{|}{C}} \overset{H}{\underset{}{}} \overset{}{C}(COOH,B)_2$

$\overset{+}{\underset{BH}{\longrightarrow}} R \cdot \overset{\overset{H}{|}}{\underset{\overset{|}{H}}{\underset{O \ H}{C}}} \overset{}{C}(COOH,B)_2 \rightarrow R \cdot CH:C(COOH)_2 \rightarrow R \cdot CH:CH \cdot COOH$

The reaction is readily illustrated by the formation of crystalline sorbic acid by the condensation of crotonaldehyde and malonic acid in hot pyridine solution:

$$CH_3 \cdot CH:CH \cdot CHO + H_2C(COOH)_2 \rightarrow CH_3 \cdot CH:CH \cdot CH:CH \cdot COOH$$
$$+ H_2O + CO_2$$

Required: Malonic acid, 4 g.; pyridine, 4 ml. (4 g.); crotonaldehyde, 3·1 ml. (2·7 g.).

Add 4 g. of malonic acid to 4 ml. of pyridine, and then add 3·1 ml. of crotonaldehyde. Boil the mixture gently under reflux over an asbestos-covered gauze, using a small Bunsen flame, for 40 minutes and then cool it in ice-water. Meanwhile add 2 ml. of concentrated sulphuric acid carefully with shaking to 4 ml. of water, cool the diluted acid, and add it with shaking to the chilled reaction-mixture. Sorbic acid readily crystallises from the solution. Filter the sorbic acid at the pump, wash it with a small quantity of cold water and then recrystallise it from water (*ca.* 25 ml.). The colourless crystals, m.p. 132–133°, weigh 1·0–1·2 g.

Sorbic acid could theoretically, by virtue of the two olefine linkages, exist in four geometrically-isomeric forms. The above synthesis gives only one form, which is undoubtedly the *trans-trans* form, analogous to the $\alpha\omega$-diphenylpolyenes (p. 238) which are also normally produced solely in one form.

The Grignard Reagent.

Grignard reagents are prepared by the interaction of alkyl or aryl halides (of general formula RX) with magnesium in the presence of ether, or (much more rarely) certain other solvents. Although the ether certainly takes part both in the formation and the composition of the Grignard reagent, the formation of the latter can, for the purpose of interpreting its reactions, be represented as a simple addition:

$$RX + Mg = RMgX.$$

For the preparation of the Grignard reagent, the following factors should be noted:

(1) Alkyl and aryl iodides *usually* react with magnesium more rapidly than the corresponding bromides, and the bromides very much more rapidly than the chlorides. Aryl (as distinct from alkyl) chlorides have usually only a slow reaction with magnesium and are therefore very rarely used. With alkyl and aryl iodides in particular, however, a side reaction often occurs with the formation of a hydrocarbon and magnesium iodide:

$$2RI + Mg = R-R + MgI_2$$

Hence as a general rule the bromides are used.

(2) The formation of the Grignard reagent is inhibited by traces of water, which also decompose the reagent when it is formed. Therefore the apparatus used must be thoroughly dry, and the ether anhydrous (p. 82). Specially prepared magnesium turnings* should preferably be used: if magnesium ribbon is employed, it should first be drawn through two layers of fine emery paper to remove the superficial film of oxide, *etc.*

(3) In spite of these precautions, it is sometimes found difficult to start the formation of the reagent, although when once the formation has started, it proceeds with increasing speed. In such cases it is advisable to add a small crystal of iodine, which is allowed to fall through the ethereal solution of the organic halide on to the surface of the magnesium below. If the mixture is undisturbed, a local concentration of iodine in solution is thus obtained in immediate contact with the magnesium: the latter then usually becomes reactive, and the formation of the Grignard reagent, starting in the immediate neighbourhood of the iodine, rapidly spreads throughout the magnesium turnings. Alternatively, a trace of methyl iodide can be added to the ether to stimulate the reaction with the magnesium, although the resulting Grignard solution will then contain minute quantities of methyl magnesium iodide.

No attempt is made to isolate the Grignard reagent from its ethereal solution before use. The reagent (usually also in ethereal solution) is added to the solution of the Grignard reagent, and when the reaction is complete the product is hydrolysed.

The method of hydrolysis depends on the nature of the product. It is usually sufficient to add dilute sulphuric acid to the ethereal solution and to shake thoroughly, when the magnesium enters the aqueous solution, whilst the organic compound remains in the ether. Alternatively, however, the ethereal solution may be poured on to ice and water, and then treated with dilute sulphuric acid. Should the product be affected by this acid, the hydrolysis can be carried out with an aqueous solution of ammonium chloride. In the following examples the hydrolysis is usually shown as a simple double decomposition

* Supplied for this purpose by chemical dealers.

with water, giving magnesium hydroxy-iodide: it will be understood that the latter dissolves in the dilute acid to give a mixture of magnesium iodide and sulphate.

SYNTHETIC USE OF GRIGNARD REAGENTS. Grignard reagents can be used to synthesise a wide variety of organic compounds, and are consequently of very great value in organic chemistry: the *chief* reactions are summarised in the following table, in which magnesium methyl iodide (denoted as MeMgI, in order to differentiate the methyl group introduced by the reagent from any methyl groups already present in the organic compound) is used as a typical Grignard reagent.

(1) Water, alcohols and hydroxy compounds generally, and also primary and secondary amines, give the *hydrocarbon* corresponding to the Grignard reagent,

$$\text{MeMgI} + \text{HOH} \quad \rightarrow \text{MeH} + \text{Mg (OH)I}$$

$$\text{MeMgI} + \text{EtOH} \quad \rightarrow \text{MeH} + \text{Mg(OEt)I}$$

$$\text{MeMgI} + \text{EtNHH} \rightarrow \text{MeH} + \text{Mg(NHEt)I}$$

(2) Oxygen is directly absorbed, and the product on hydrolysis gives the corresponding *alcohol*.

$$\text{MeMgI} \xrightarrow{\text{O}} \text{MeOMgI} \qquad \text{MeOMgI} + \text{HOH} \rightarrow \text{MeOH} + \text{Mg(OH)I}$$

(3) Carbon dioxide is similarly absorbed, and gives the corresponding *carboxylic acid*.

$$\text{MeMgI} \xrightarrow{\text{CO}_2} \text{MeCOOMgI}$$
$$\text{MeCOOMgI} + \text{HOH} \rightarrow \text{MeCOOH} + \text{Mg(OH)I}$$

(4) Aldehydes form addition products at the double bond of the carbonyl ($>$C:O) group, and hydrolysis gives *secondary alcohols*. Thus acetaldehyde gives isopropyl alcohol:

$$\text{CH}_3\text{C:O} + \text{MeMgI} = \text{CH}_3\overset{\displaystyle H}{\underset{\displaystyle Me}{\text{C}}}\!\!-\!\text{OMgI}$$

$$\text{CH}_3\text{C}\!-\!\text{O MgI} + \text{HOH} \rightarrow \text{CH}_3\overset{\displaystyle H}{\underset{\displaystyle Me}{\text{C}}}\!\!-\!\text{OH} + \text{Mg(OH)I}$$

Note. Formaldehyde is a special case. It reacts similarly, but a *primary alcohol* is necessarily produced. This alcohol, however, will always contain one carbon atom more than that obtained in Reaction (2).

$$\text{HC:O} + \text{MeMgI} = \text{HC}\overset{\displaystyle H}{\underset{\displaystyle Me}{}}\!\!-\!\text{OMgI}$$

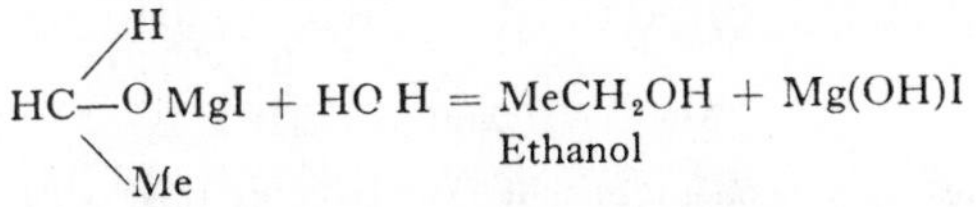

$$\text{HC}\underset{\text{Me}}{\overset{\text{H}}{\diagup}}\text{O MgI} + \text{HO H} = \text{MeCH}_2\text{OH} + \text{Mg(OH)I}$$

Ethanol

This reaction is of great value for ascending the homologous series of alcohols:

$$\text{ROH} \rightarrow \text{RBr} \rightarrow \text{RMgBr} \rightarrow \text{RCH}_2\text{OH}$$

Note that ethylene oxide reacts with the Grignard reagent to give a 2-substituted ethanol: e.g. with methyl magnesium iodide:

$$\text{Me·CH}_2\text{CH}_2\text{OMgI} \rightarrow \text{Me·CH}_2\text{CH}_2\text{OH}$$

(5) Ketones similarly give *tertiary alcohols*.

$$\underset{\text{CH}_3}{\overset{\text{CH}_3}{\diagdown}}\text{C:O} + \text{MeMgI} = \underset{\text{CH}_3}{\overset{\text{CH}_3}{\diagdown}}\text{C}\underset{\text{Me}}{\overset{\text{OMgI}}{\diagup}}$$

Acetone

$$\underset{\text{CH}_3}{\overset{\text{CH}_3}{\diagdown}}\text{C}\underset{\text{Me}}{\overset{\text{OMgI}}{\diagup}} + \text{HOH} \rightarrow \underset{\text{CH}_3}{\overset{\text{CH}_3}{\diagdown}}\text{C}\underset{\text{Me}}{\overset{\text{OH}}{\diagup}} + \text{Mg(OH)I.}$$

Tertiary butanol

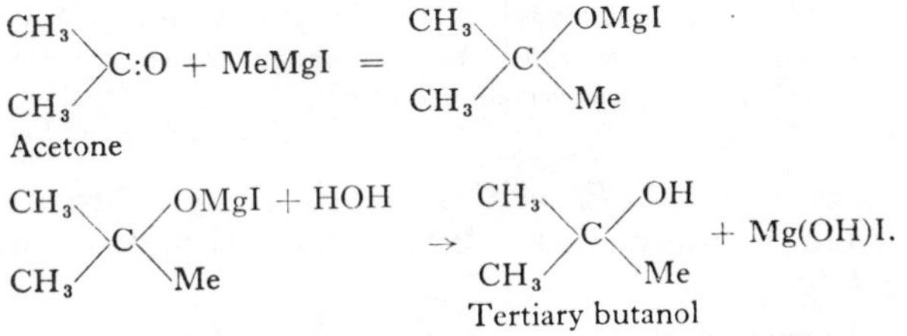

Note.—Grignard reagents readily act as dehydrating agents by virtue of Reaction (1). Since aliphatic tertiary alcohols usually readily lose water, an excess of the Grignard reagent may take the above reaction one stage further to give an unsaturated hydrocarbon.

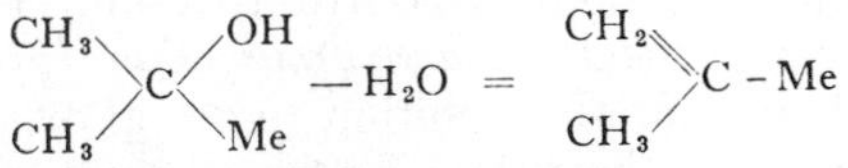

$$\underset{\text{CH}_3}{\overset{\text{CH}_3}{\diagdown}}\text{C}\underset{\text{Me}}{\overset{\text{OH}}{\diagup}} - \text{H}_2\text{O} = \underset{\text{CH}_3}{\overset{\text{CH}_2}{\diagdown}}\text{C} - \text{Me}$$

(6) Esters (*a*) and acid chlorides (*b*) readily react with Grignard reagents to give ketones, which immediately react with a second equivalent of the reagent as in (5) to give *tertiary* alcohols as before.

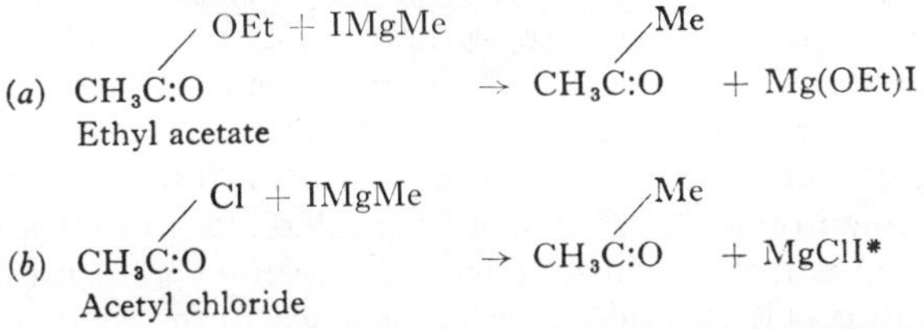

(*a*) $\text{CH}_3\text{C:O}\overset{\diagup \text{OEt}}{} + \text{IMgMe} \rightarrow \text{CH}_3\text{C:O}\overset{\diagup \text{Me}}{} + \text{Mg(OEt)I}$

Ethyl acetate

(*b*) $\text{CH}_3\text{C:O}\overset{\diagup \text{Cl}}{} + \text{IMgMe} \rightarrow \text{CH}_3\text{C:O}\overset{\diagup \text{Me}}{} + \text{MgClI*}$

Acetyl chloride

(7) Nitriles also react with Grignard reagents to give ketones, which arise from the hydrolysing action of the dilute sulphuric acid on the intermediate addition product. Acid amides behave similarly.

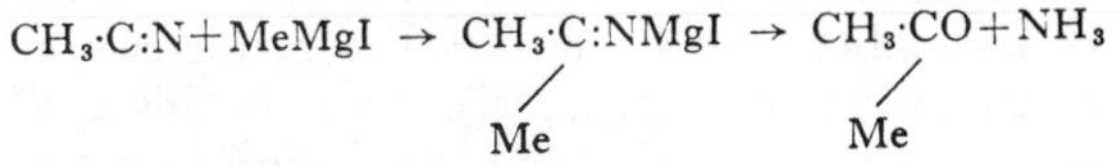

$$\text{CH}_3\text{·C:N} + \text{MeMgI} \rightarrow \text{CH}_3\text{·C:NMgI} \rightarrow \text{CH}_3\text{·CO} + \text{NH}_3$$

$$\overset{\diagup}{\text{Me}} \qquad\qquad \overset{\diagup}{\text{Me}}$$

* *i.e.*, equimolecular quantities of magnesium chloride and iodide.

$$CH_3 \cdot CO \cdot NH_2 + 2MeMgI \rightarrow CH_3 \cdot C \cdot OMgI \rightarrow CH_3 \cdot CO + NH_3$$

$$\overset{\diagup \quad \diagdown}{Me \quad NH \cdot MgI} \qquad \overset{|}{Me}$$

(8) Non-metallic halides and covalent metallic halides give their *organic derivatives*.

$$AsCl_3 + 3IMgMe \rightarrow AsMe_3 + 3MgClI$$

$$SnCl_4 + 4IMgMe \rightarrow SnMe_4 + 4MgClI$$

$$HgCl_2 + 2IMgMe \rightarrow HgMe_2 + 2MgClI$$

Since Grignard reagents can easily be obtained from aryl halides, they are of special value in the synthesis of many aromatic compounds, particularly as, for reasons already stated (pp. 270, 276), aromatic compounds cannot generally be prepared by means of ethyl acetoacetate and ethyl malonate.

Triphenyl-carbinol, $(C_6H_5)_3COH$, from Ethyl Benzoate and Phenyl Magnesium Bromide. (Grignard Reaction 6 (*a*).)

Required: Bromobenzene, 10·5 ml.; dry ether, 75 ml.; granulated magnesium, 2·5 g.; dry ethyl benzoate, 5 ml. (5·29 g.).

Fit a 250 ml. round-bottomed flask to a reflux water-condenser (each being *thoroughly* dry) and close the top of the condenser with a calcium chloride tube. Dissolve 10·5 ml. (15·7 g.) of dry bromobenzene in 50 ml. of *anhydrous* ether (preparation, p. 82), and add about half this solution to 2·5 g. of granulated magnesium contained in the round-bottomed flask, meanwhile keeping the rest of the ethereal solution in a small, well-corked conical flask. Now, since the formation of phenyl magnesium bromide seldom begins spontaneously, add a crystal of iodine carefully to the magnesium mixture so that it rests on top of the metal and there slowly dissolves. If the mixture is allowed to stand quietly, the formation of the Grignard reagent will probably start in the neighbourhood of the iodine within a few minutes (being accompanied by a cloudiness and complete disappearance of the iodine), and will then continue with increasing vigour until the ether is boiling. (If this does not happen, warm the mixture acrefully (without shaking) on the water-bath and then, when the cation begins, turn out the gas.) When the boiling of the ether begins to cease, pour about 10 ml. of the remainder of the ethereal solution of the bromobenzene down the reflux condenser, at once replacing the calcium chloride tube. Continue in this way until all the bromobenzene has been added, the solution in the flask boiling steadily meanwhile. If the bromobenzene solution is added too rapidly, check excessive boiling of the ether by immersing the flask in cold water for a few minutes, taking care, however, not to stop the reaction entirely.

When the addition of the bromobenzene is complete and the ether is boiling gently, reheat the flask on the water-bath for a further 15 minutes to ensure completion of the reaction: the solution will now be slightly dark in colour, and only a trace of metallic magnesium should remain.

Now remove the flask from the water-bath, and *slowly* add a solution of 5 ml. (5·2 g.) of dry ethyl benzoate in 15 ml. of anhydrous ether down the condenser in small quantities at a time, mixing the contents of the flask thoroughly between each addition. When the boiling of the ether again subsides, return the flask to the water-bath and reheat for a further 15 minutes. Then cool the mixture in ice-water, and carefully pour off the ethereal solution into a mixture of about 60 ml. of dilute sulphuric acid and 100 g. of crushed ice contained in a flask of about 500 ml. capacity fitted for steam-distillation, taking care to leave behind any unchanged magnesium.

Fit securely to the lower end of the condenser (as a receiver) a Buchner flask, the side-tube carrying a piece of rubber tubing which falls well below the level of the bench. Steam-distil the ethereal mixture for about 30 minutes: discard the distillate, which contains the ether, possibly a trace of unchanged ethyl benzoate, and also any biphenyl, $C_6H_5{\cdot}C_6H_5$, which has been formed. The residue in the flask contains the triphenyl- carbinol, which solidifies when the liquid is cooled. Filter this residual product at the pump, wash the triphenyl-carbinol *thoroughly* with water, drain, and then dry by pressing between several layers of thick drying-paper. Yield of crude dry product, 8 g. The triphenyl-carbinol can be recrystallised from methylated spirit (yield, 6 g.), or, if quite dry, from benzene, and so obtained as colourless crystals, m.p. 162°.

Triphenyl-carbinol (Semi-micro Scale).

Required: Bromobenzene, 1·05 ml.; dry ether, 7·5 ml.; granulated magnesium, 0·25 g.; ethyl benzoate, 0·5 ml.

First read the details of the macro-scale preparation above.

Fit a 50 ml. round-bottomed flask to a reflux water-condenser fitted with a calcium chloride tube. Dissolve 1·05 ml. of dry bromobenzene in 5 ml. of dry ether and add this solution to 0·25 g. of magnesium contained in the round-bottomed flask. Now add a crystal of iodine so that it rests on the magnesium. Warm if necessary to start the reaction: if the latter becomes too vigorous immerse the flask in cold water, but do not stop the reaction. Now gently boil the mixture on a water-bath for 15 minutes to complete the reaction, then remove the flask from the water-bath and add slowly a solution of 0·5 ml. of dry ethyl benzoate in 1·5 ml. of dry ether down the condenser. When the boiling of the ether subsides, continue heating on the water-bath for 15 minutes.

Cool the flask in ice-water and pour the ethereal solution into a mixture of about 6 ml. of dil. H_2SO_4 and 10 g. of crushed ice contained in a 50 ml. flask fitted for steam-distillation, taking care to leave behind any unchanged magnesium. Fit to the lower end of the condenser a small Buchner flask or boiling-tube with side-arm (45°) carrying a piece of rubber tubing which falls well below the level of the bench.

Steam-distil the ethereal solution and discard the distillate. The residue in the flask is triphenyl-carbinol and solidifies on cooling. Filter at the pump, wash with water, drain and dry. Yield of crude product 0·6 g. Recrystallise when dry from benzene to obtain colourless crystals: m.p. 162°.

Ethyl β-Phenyl-β-hydroxy-propionate.
$C_6H_5CH(OH)CH_2COOEt$. (Reformatsky Reaction.)

The *Reformatsky Reaction* consists of the interaction of an ester of an α-halogeno-acid with an aldehyde, a ketone or another ester in the presence of zinc. For example, if a mixture of ethyl bromoacetate and benzaldehyde is heated with zinc, the latter undoubtedly first combines with the ethyl bromo-acetate to form a Grignard-like reagent (reaction A), which then adds on to the benzaldehyde just as a Grignard reagent would do (reaction B). The complex so formed, on acidification gives ethyl β-phenyl-β-hydroxy-propionate (reaction C). Note that reaction A could not satisfactorily be carried out using

$$BrCH_2COOC_2H_5 + Zn \longrightarrow BrZnCH_2COOC_2H_5 \ (A)$$

$$C_6H_5CHO + BrZnCH_2COOC_2H_5 \longrightarrow C_6H_5\overset{H}{\underset{CH_2COOC_2H_5}{C-OZnBr}} \quad (B)$$

$$C_6H_5\overset{H}{\underset{CH_2COOC_2H_5}{C-OZnBr}} \xrightarrow{\text{dilute acid}} C_6H_5CH(OH)CH_2COOC_2H_5 \ (C)$$

magnesium instead of zinc, because the magnesium Grignard reagent as fast as it was formed would react with the ester grouping (p. 283). The Reformatsky reaction is therefore of great value for the preparation of β-hydroxy acids, and also for the preparation of αβ-unsaturated acids, to which the β-hydroxy acids can often be readily converted by dehydration.

Note also that if another ester, of general formula $R \cdot COOC_2H_5$, were used in place of benzaldehyde in the above reaction, a similar complex would be formed, and on acidification would give an unstable β-hydroxy-β-ethoxy ester, which would very readily lose ethanol with the formation of a β-keto-ester.

$$R \cdot \overset{O}{\overset{\|}{C}} - OC_2H_5 \longrightarrow R \cdot \overset{OZnBr}{\overset{/}{\underset{\backslash}{C}}} - CH_2COOC_2H_5 \longrightarrow R \cdot \overset{OH}{\overset{/}{\underset{\backslash}{C}}} - CH_2COOC_2H_5$$
$$\longrightarrow R \cdot CO \cdot CH_2COOC_2H_5$$

Required: Zinc powder, 20 g.; ethyl bromoacetate,* 28 ml.; benzaldehyde, 32 ml.

PREPARATION OF REAGENTS.† It is essential for this preparation that the zinc powder should be in an active condition. For this purpose, it is usually sufficient if a sample of ordinary technical zinc powder is vigorously shaken in a flask with pure ether, and then filtered off at the pump, washed once with ether, quickly drained and without delay transferred to a vacuum desiccator. If, however, an impure sample of zinc dust fails to respond to this treatment, it should be vigorously stirred in a beaker with 5% aqueous sodium hydroxide solution until an effervescence of hydrogen occurs, and then filtered at the pump, washed *thoroughly* with distilled water, and then rapidly with ethanol and ether, and dried as before in a vacuum desiccator. The ethyl bromoacetate (b.p. 159°) and the benzaldehyde (b.p. 179°) should be dried and distilled before use.

A 1500 ml. flask is fitted (preferably by means of a three-necked adaptor) with a rubber-sleeved or mercury-sealed stirrer (Fig. 20, p. 39), a reflux water-condenser, and a dropping-funnel (*cf.* Fig. 23(C), p. 45, in which only a two-necked adaptor is shown: or Fig. 23(G)). The dried zinc powder (20 g.) is placed in the flask, and a solution of 28 ml. of ethyl bromoacetate and 32 ml. of benzaldehyde in 40 ml. of dry benzene containing 5 ml. of dry ether is placed in the dropping-funnel. Approximately 10 ml. of this solution is run on to the zinc powder, and the mixture allowed to remain unstirred until (usually within a few minutes) a vigorous reaction occurs. (If no reaction occurs, warm the mixture on the water-bath until the reaction starts.) The stirrer is now started, and the rest of the solution allowed to run in drop-wise over a period of about 30 minutes so that the initial reaction is steadily maintained. The flask is then heated on a water-bath for 30 minutes with continuous stirring, and is then cooled in an ice-water bath. The well-stirred product is then hydrolysed by the addition of 120 ml. of 10% sulphuric acid. The mixture is transferred to a separating-funnel, the lower aqueous layer discarded, and the upper benzene layer then

* Ethyl bromoacetate is lachrymatory, and the preparation should therefore be carried out in a fume-cupboard.

†The reactive dry zinc "wool" can be used without the described treatment.

extracted twice with 20 ml. of 10% sulphuric acid, then with 20 ml. of 10% sodium carbonate solution, twice again with the dilute sulphuric acid, and finally twice with 20 ml. of distilled water. The benzene solution is then separated and dried over anhydrous magnesium sulphate or (more slowly) over sodium sulphate.

A 75 ml. Claisen flask is fitted with a small dropping-funnel in the main neck, and the filtered benzene solution then run into the flask from the funnel at approximately the rate at which the benzene is being distilled off by heating the flask in an oil-bath. When the solvent has thus been removed, the residue is allowed to cool whilst the funnel is replaced by the usual capillary tube, and the distillation is then continued at low pressure obtained by an efficient water-pump. The ester is obtained as a colourless liquid, b.p. 145–155°/15 mm.: yield, 27–30 g. A second distillation gives a product of sharper boiling-point. If during the distillation the ester tends to decompose with foaming, it indicates that the above washing has not been sufficiently thorough: the application of a lower pressure (*e.g.*, *ca.* 5 mm. by means of an oil-pump) will usually give smooth distillation without decomposition. The ester has b.p. 128–130°/5 mm.

Ethyl-benzene. $C_6H_5 \cdot C_2H_5$. (The Fittig Reaction.)

Two methods may conveniently be used to ascend the homologous series of aromatic hydrocarbons:

(1) *The Friedel-Crafts Reaction*, in which an aromatic hydrocarbon reacts with an alkyl halide under the influence of aluminium chloride:

$$C_6H_5H + BrC_2H_5 \rightarrow C_6H_5 \cdot C_2H_5 + H \cdot Br$$

The preparation of acetophenone (p. 255) is a modification of this method, the alkyl halide being replaced by an acid chloride, with the consequent formation of a ketone.

(2) *The Fittig Reaction*, in which sodium reacts with a mixture of an aryl and an alkyl halide, forming the sodium halide and the corresponding hydrocarbon:

$$C_6H_5Br + 2Na + BrC_2H_5 \rightarrow C_6H_5 \cdot C_2H_5 + 2NaBr$$

This reaction is precisely parallel to the Wurtz Reaction in the aliphatic series, by which, for instance, *n*-butane can be obtained by the action of sodium on ethyl bromide.

$$2C_2H_5Br + 2Na = C_2H_5 \cdot C_2H_5 + 2NaBr$$

The Fittig Reaction is employed in the following preparation of ethylbenzene.

[NOTE. Hydrocarbons such as ethyl-benzene can also be prepared by the *Clemmensen* reduction of the corresponding ketone. This is exemplified by the reduction of *p*-methylacetophenone (p. 290)].

Required: Sodium, 22·5 g.; dry ether, 100 ml.; bromobenzene, 34 ml.; ethyl bromide, 31 ml.

Using the sodium press described on p. 82, press 22·5 g. of sodium into wire, and allow the latter to fall directly into 100 ml. of *anhydrous* ether (preparation, p. 82) contained in a 750 ml. round-bottomed flask. Fit the latter with an efficient (preferably double-surface) reflux water-condenser, and stand the flask on a cork ring. Now pour down the condenser a mixture of 34 ml. (50 g.) of dry bromobenzene and 31 ml. (45·5 g., *i.e.*, a 30% excess) of ethyl bromide. Close the top of the condenser with a calcium chloride tube and shake the mixture thoroughly. After 10–15 minutes, the reaction will cause the ether to boil steadily. Shake the mixture occasionally during the next two hours in order to prevent the wire from becoming coated with sodium bromide, but do not cool the flask unless the boiling of the ether becomes very vigorous: ultimately a bluish-grey sludge forms in the mixture, in addition to unchanged wire. Allow the mixture to stand in this way for a total period of at least 3 hours, and preferably overnight—in the latter case ensure that the condenser-water is turned off during the night.

Now assemble the apparatus for ether distillation shown in Fig. 64, p. 163, except that, in place of the small distilling-flask **A**, use a wide-necked 100 ml. bolt-head flask, closed by a cork carrying the dropping-funnel **B** and also a bent delivery-tube (or "knee-tube") for connection to the condenser **C**. (Alternatively, use the apparatus shown in Fig. 23(E), p. 45.) Carefully decant the ethereal solution of the ethyl-benzene into the dropping-funnel **B** (Fig. 64), leaving as much solid material behind in the 750 ml. flask as possible: wash this solid residue with a further quantity of ether, decanting the latter in turn into the dropping-funnel. (The residue in the flask may still contain some unchanged sodium: therefore place some methylated spirit in the flask, and then, *when all effervescence has subsided*, dilute carefully with water, and finally pour into the sink.) Now distil the ether, running the ethereal solution into the bolt-head flask as fast as the ether itself distils over, and observing all the usual precautions for ether-distillations (p. 163). When no more ether distils over, detach the bolt-head flask, and fit to it a short fractionating column, similar to that shown in Fig. 11(B), p. 26, a water-condenser being then connected in turn to the column. Carefully fractionate the crude ethyl-benzene, collecting the fraction of b.p. 130–135°. Yield, 16 g.

Ethyl-benzene is a colourless liquid of b.p. 134°, and d, 0·876: it has only a faint odour.

p-Ethyltoluene. $C_2H_5 \cdot C_6H_4 \cdot CH_3$. (Clemmensen Reduction.)

Many aldehydes and ketones can be reduced directly by *Clemmensen's* method, in which the aldehyde or ketone is boiled with dilute hydrochloric acid and amalgamated zinc. p-Methylacetophenone (or methyl p-tolyl ketone) is reduced under these conditions to p-ethyltoluene. An excess of the reducing agent is employed in order to prevent the formation of unsaturated hydrocarbons.

The p-methylacetophenone is readily prepared by the Friedel-Crafts' reaction (*cf*. p. 254), toluene being treated with acetyl chloride in the presence of aluminium chloride. The toluene is employed in considerable excess so that it

$$CH_3 \langle\!\!\!\bigcirc\!\!\!\rangle + ClCOCH_3 \longrightarrow CH_3 \langle\!\!\!\bigcirc\!\!\!\rangle COCH_3 + HCl$$

may act both as a reagent and a solvent. Note that in this reaction *ortho*-substitution is negligible, and the pure p-methylacetophenone is obtained.

p-METHYLACETOPHENONE. *Required:* Toluene, 250 ml.; acetyl chloride, 35 ml.; aluminium chloride, 40 g.

This preparation should be carried out in a fume-cupboard.

Fit a 500 ml. flask (preferably by means of a three-necked adaptor) with a stirrer having a rubber-sleeved or mercury seal, a dropping-funnel and, by means of the third outlet, with a calcium chloride tube. Place 250 ml. of *dry* toluene and 40 g. of aluminium chloride in the flask, and cool the latter in an ice-water bath inside a fume-cupboard. (Ensure that the aluminium chloride is a fresh sample, *i.e.*, that it has not been long stored in a previously opened bottle, and pulverise it if necessary immediately before use.) When the mixture has been thoroughly cooled, place 35 ml. of acetyl chloride in the dropping-funnel, and allow it to run drop-wise into the flask over a period of 30 minutes, maintaining the stirring and cooling throughout. Hydrogen chloride is steadily evolved. When the addition of the acetyl chloride is complete, replace the ice-bath by a water-bath, and maintain the temperature of the latter at 20–25° for 2 hours with constant stirring. During this period hydrogen chloride continues to be liberally evolved, and the product darkens considerably in colour. Now pour the product cautiously into 500 ml. of dilute hydrochloric acid and 100 g. of chipped ice in a separating-funnel, and shake the mixture thoroughly: this operation removes the dark colour, and the toluene solution becomes yellow. Run off the lower acid layer, and extract the toluene three times with water. Finally dry the toluene solution over calcium chloride.

Fit a 75–100 ml. Claisen flask with a small dropping-funnel in the main neck, and a water-condenser to the side-arm, and then run the

filtered toluene solution slowly into the flask at such a rate that
the volume of solution entering is approximately the same as that of the
toluene (b.p. 111°) distilling over. When the unchanged toluene has
thus been removed, replace the funnel by a capillary tube, and continue the distillation under reduced pressure by means of a water-
pump. The *p*-methylacetophenone is obtained as a colourless liquid,
b.p. 110–112°/15 mm., leaving a dark residue in the flask. Yield
20–25 g. The ketone may require redistillation to obtain a sharply-
boiling fraction. It can be distilled at atmospheric pressure, and has
b.p. 220–224°/760 mm.

p-ETHYLTOLUENE. *Required:* *p*-Methylacetophenone,
15 g.; granulated zinc, 40 g.; mercuric chloride, 5 g.

To prepare the amalgamated zinc, place 40 g. of granulated
zinc in a 750 ml. flask, and clean the surface by first shaking
the zinc with a small quantity of acetone, then decanting off the
acetone and repeating the process with distilled water. Dissolve
5 g. of mercuric chloride in 100 ml. of distilled water containing 5 ml. of concentrated hydrochloric acid, add the solution
to the zinc, and shake the mixture gently for about 5 minutes.
Decant the solution from the amalgamated zinc, and then pour
on to the latter 200 ml. of water and 200 ml. of concentrated
hydrochloric acid. Add 15 g. of *p*-methylacetophenone, fit
the flask to a reflux water-condenser, and boil the mixture for 6
hours: during the latter half of this period add 30 ml. of concentrated hydrochloric acid, *ca.* 5 ml. at a time, down the condenser.

Cool the mixture and pour the liquid reaction product into a
separating-funnel. Rinse out the flask (which may contain some
unchanged zinc) with ether, pour the latter into the funnel, and
extract the aqueous solution with the ether. Repeat the extraction with a second quantity of ether, unite the ether extracts,
wash them by extracting once with water, and then dry the
ethereal extract over sodium sulphate.

Filter the dried extract, and then distil off the ether from a
small flask, using the customary precautions: if the volume of
ether is large, fit a dropping-funnel to the flask so that the
ethereal extract can be run into the flask as the ether distils off
(*cf.* Fig. 23(E), p. 45). When the ether has been removed,
replace the water-condenser by an air-condenser, and continue
the distillation. The *p*-ethyltoluene distils at 161–162° as a
colourless liquid. Yield, 10 g.

9,10-Dihydroanthracene-9,10-*endo*-αβ-succinic Anhydride. (The Diels-Alder Reaction.)

The *Diels-Alder Reaction* consists in the direct combination of a compound containing a conjugated diene system with a reagent which possesses a double or triple bond activated by suitable adjacent groups. Examples of such reagents are maleic anhydride, *p*-benzoquinone, acraldehyde and acetylene dicarboxylic esters. Combination always occurs at the 1,4 positions of the diene system:

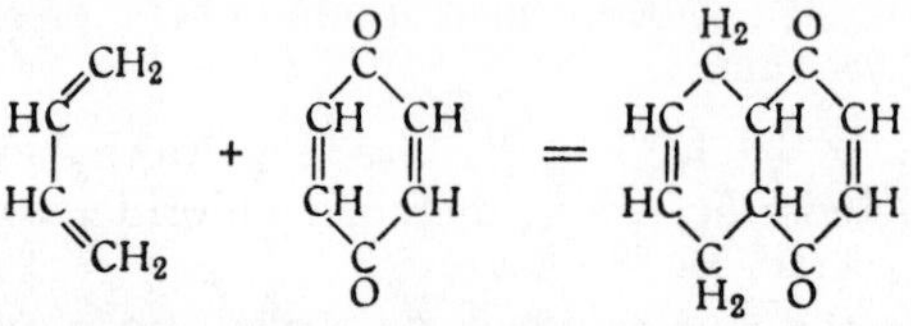

thus butadiene combines with *p*-benzoquinone as shown above; in this case a second molecule of butadiene can similarly add on to the opposite side of the *p*-benzoquinone ring.

The Diels-Alder Reaction usually occurs readily: it is of great value (*a*) for diagnosing the presence of a conjugated diene grouping, (*b*) for synthetic purposes in the preparation of cyclic systems.

In the following preparation, this reaction is exemplified by the union of anthracene with maleic anhydride, to form 9,10-dihydroanthracene-9,10-*endo*-αβ-succinic anhydride: note that as a result of this reaction both the outer rings of the anthracene system become truly aromatic in character.

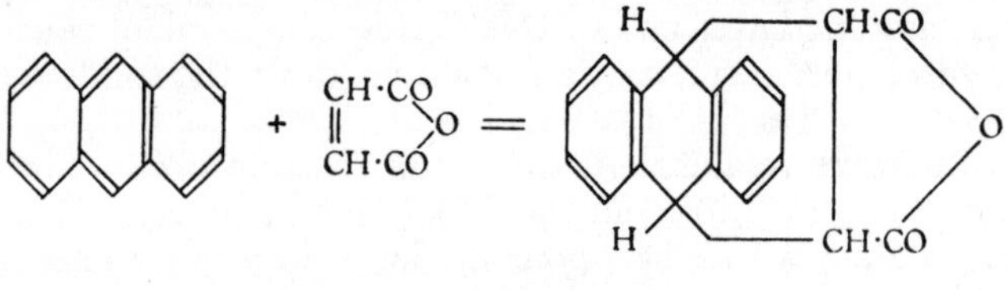

Required: Anthracene, 2 g.; maleic anhydride, 1 g.

Add 2 g. of anthracene and 1 g. maleic anhydride to 25 ml. of dry xylene, and boil the mixture under reflux: during the early stages of the heating, keep the mixture gently shaken until a clear solution is obtained, otherwise a portion of the reagents may adhere to the base of the flask and darken because of local over-heating. After boiling for 20 minutes, cool the solution, when the addition product will rapidly crystallise. Filter at the pump, and drain well. (Yield of crude material, which is almost pure, *ca.* 2·7 g.) Recrystallise from about 50 ml. of xylene with the addition if necessary of a small quantity of animal charcoal: filter the solution through a small preheated funnel, as the solute rapidly crystallises as the solution begins to cool. Place the recrystallised material in a vacuum desiccator, preferably over fresh paraffin-wax shavings to absorb traces of xylene. The addition product is obtained as colourless crystals, m.p. 256–258°. Yield *ca.* 2 g.

2,4-Dimethylpyrrole-3,5-dicarboxylic Acid Diethyl Ester.

This synthesis of the pyrrole ring system, due to Knorr, consists in the condensation of an α-aminoketone with a 1,3-diketone or the ester of a β-keto-acid.

α-Aminoketones are unstable in the free state, readily undergoing self-condensation: consequently they must be prepared, by the reduction of an α-nitroso (or oximino) ketone, in the presence of the 1,3-diketone or β-ketoester, to ensure rapid interaction.

In the present preparation, ethyl acetoacetate is treated with sufficient nitrous acid to convert half into the α-nitroso (or α-oximino) ester, which is reduced by zinc and acetic acid to the α-amino ester (I). The latter then condenses with

$$CH_3COCH(\cdot NO)\cdot COOC_2H_5 \rightleftharpoons CH_3COC(:NOH)\cdot COOC_2H_5$$

$$\downarrow$$

$$CH_3COCH(\cdot NH_2)\cdot COOC_2H_5(I)$$

$$\begin{array}{ccc}
CH_3\cdot C\cdot OH & HC\cdot COOC_2H_5 & CH_3\cdot C\text{———}C\cdot COOC_2H_5 \\
\| & + \quad \| & \rightarrow \qquad \| \qquad \| \\
C_2H_5OOC\cdot C\cdot NH_2 & HO\cdot C\cdot CH_3 & C_2H_5OOC\cdot C \qquad C\cdot CH_3 \\
(I) & (II) & (III) \quad \diagdown \quad \diagup \\
& & N \\
& & H
\end{array}$$

unchanged ethyl acetoacetate (II), both reagents being shown above in their *enol* forms, to give the diethyl ester of 2,4-dimethylpyrrole-3,5-dicarboxylic acid (III).

The synthesis will therefore normally produce a 2,4-substituted pyrrole, with in addition an ester group or an acyl group at the 3-position, if a keto-ester or a diketone respectively has been employed, and an ester group or an alkyl (aryl) group at the 5-position, according to the nature of the amino-ketone.

Required: Ethyl acetoacetate, 20 g.; sodium nitrite, 5·4 g.; zinc dust, 11 g.; glacial acetic acid, 60 ml.

Fit a three-necked 250 ml. flask with a central rubber-sleeved or mercury-sealed stirrer, *cf.* Fig. 23(c), p. 45, where only two necks are shown, and with a thermometer the bulb of which reaches as near the bottom of the flask as the stirrer allows: the third neck will carry at first a dropping-funnel and later a reflux condenser. Place 20 g. (19·5 ml.) of ethyl acetoacetate and 45 ml. of glacial acetic acid in the flask and by ice-water cooling adjust the temperature of the stirred mixture to 5–7°: maintain this temperature whilst adding a solution of 5·4 g. of sodium nitrite in 8 ml. of water slowly from the dropping-funnel during 15 minutes. Continue the stirring for 20–30 minutes, and then remove the external cooling so that the mixture slowly attains room temperature. After 3 hours, replace the separating-funnel by a reflux condenser, and the thermometer by a stopper. Add 11 g. of zinc dust in small portions by rapid removal of the stopper at such a rate that the liquid is first brought to the boil (usually about 2 portions of 2 g. each) and is then maintained gently boiling. *Avoid too rapid addition of the zinc*, otherwise the reaction will become too vigorous, and rapid immersion of the flask in ice-water will be necessary to control the effervescence. When the reaction is complete, heat the stirred mixture carefully under reflux over a Bunsen burner and asbestos gauze for 1 hour: if the mixture becomes too thick for efficient stirring, add up to 15 ml. of acetic acid. Now decant the hot mixture into 500 ml. of vigorously-stirred ice-cold water: wash the residual zinc thoroughly with glacial acetic acid (2 portions each of 1–2 ml.), decanting the acid also into the stirred water.

The diethyl ester which is precipitated rapidly solidifies on stirring. Filter it at the pump, wash with water (2 portions each of about 20 ml.), and recrystallise from methylated spirit or from 95% ethanol. Yield of pale yellow crystals, 8–9 g.; m.p. 135–137°.

1,2,3,4-Tetrahydro-carbazole.   (The Fischer Indolisation Reaction.)

The *Fischer Indolisation Reaction* occurs when the phenylhydrazone of a suitable aldehyde or ketone undergoes cyclisation with loss of ammonia, under the influence of various reagents, such as zinc chloride, ethanolic hydrogen chloride, or acetic acid. For example, the phenylhydrazone of acetophenone (p. 257) when heated with zinc chloride gives 2-phenylindole:

$$C_6H_5NHNH_2 + CH_3COC_6H_5 \longrightarrow C_6H_5NHN:\overset{CH_3}{C}\cdot C_6H_5$$

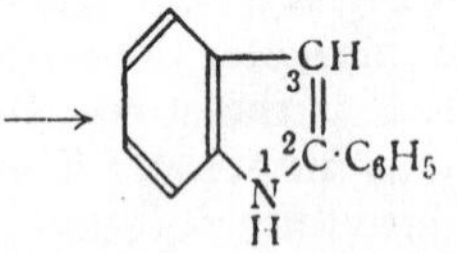

(For the mechanism of this reaction, see Robinson and Robinson, *J.C.S.*, 1918, **113**, 639; 1924, **145**, 827.) The reaction is of wide application: for example, the use of methyl-phenyl-hydrazine, $C_6H_5(CH_3)N\cdot NH_2$, in the above reaction gives 1-methyl-2-phenylindole, whereas pyruvic acid, $CH_3\cdot CO\cdot COOH$, when converted to its phenylhydrazone and then indolised, gives indole-2-carboxylic acid. The ease of cyclisation of various hydrazones varies greatly. Indole itself cannot be prepared from acetaldehyde phenylhydrazone: on the other hand, the phenylhydrazones of some saturated cyclic ketones undergo cyclisation very readily even when boiled with acetic acid. This is illustrated in the following preparation, in which cyclohexanone is converted into its phenylhydrazone, and the latter, without isolation, is converted into 1,2,3,4-tetrahydrocarbazole by boiling with acetic acid:

Required: Cyclohexanone, 9 ml.; phenylhydrazine, 8 ml. Dissolve 8·8 g. (9·0 ml.) of cyclohexanone in 50 ml. of glacial acetic acid, add 8 ml. of phenylhydrazine, and boil the solution under reflux for 5 minutes. Cool the solution, when the tetrahydrocarbazole will crystallise out. Filter at the pump, drain well, and recrystallise either from aqueous ethanol or (better) from aqueous acetic acid. The recrystallisation should be performed rapidly, for the tetrahydrocarbazole undergoes atmospheric oxidation in hot solutions: after recrystallisation, the compound should be dried in a vacuum desiccator and not in an oven. Repeated recrystallisation should be avoided. The tetrahydrocarbazole, after thorough drying, is obtained as colourless crystals, m.p. 118°: yield of recrystallised material, 11 g.

If cold *saturated* ethanolic solutions of the recrystallised tetrahydrocarbazole and of picric acid are mixed and stirred, the chocolate-brown picrate of the carbazole slowly crystallises. After it has been filtered off at the pump, washed with a small quantity of ethanol, and dried, it has m.p. 145–146°.

Diethyl Collidine-3,5-dicarboxylate.
(The Hantzsch Reaction.)

This reaction consists of the condensation of two molecular equivalents of a 1,3-diketone (or a β-keto-ester) with one equivalent of an aldehyde and one of ammonia. Thus the interaction of ethyl acetoacetate and acetaldehyde and ammonia affords the 1,4-dihydro-pyridine derivative (I), which when boiled with dilute nitric acid readily undergoes dehydrogenation and "aromatisation" to give the diethyl ester of collidine (or 2,4,6-trimethyl-pyridine-3,5-dicarboxylic acid (II)). For the initial condensation the solid aldehyde-ammonia can conveniently be used in place of the separate reagents.

To obtain the free acid, the ester is hydrolysed by ethanolic potash to the dipotassium salt, which is converted into the insoluble silver salt. A hot aqueous

$$
\begin{array}{ccc}
& \overset{\displaystyle CH_3}{\underset{\displaystyle}{CH}} & \\
EtOOC \cdot CH_2 \quad \overset{\displaystyle}{O} \quad H_2C \cdot COOEt & & \\
\mid \qquad\qquad\qquad \mid & \longrightarrow & \\
CH_3 \cdot CO \qquad\quad OC \cdot CH_3 & & \\
NH_3 & &
\end{array}
$$

(I) H

(II)

suspension of this salt when treated with hydrogen sulphide gives the dicarboxylic acid.

Required: Ethyl acetoacetate, 32 g. (32 ml.); acetaldehyde-ammonia, 10 g. (*Note.* The aldehyde-ammonia should preferably be fresh material: the quantity should be increased to 15 g. if an old sample, which has formed brown sticky lumps, is employed.)

Gently warm a mixture of 32 g. (32 ml.) of ethyl acetoacetate and 10 g. of aldehyde-ammonia in a 400 ml. beaker by direct heating on a gauze, stirring the mixture carefully with a thermometer. As soon as the reaction starts, remove the heating, and replace it when the reaction slackens, but do not allow the temperature of the mixture to exceed 100–110°: the reaction is rapidly completed. Add to the mixture about twice its volume of 2N-hydrochloric acid, and stir the mass until the deposit either becomes solid or forms a thick paste, according to the quality of the aldehyde-ammonia employed. Decant the aqueous acid layer, repeat the extraction of the deposit with more acid, and again decant the acid, or filter off the deposit if it is solid. Transfer the deposit to a conical flask and recrystallise it twice from ethanol (or methylated spirit) diluted with an equal volume of water. The 1,4-dihydro-collidine-3,5-dicarboxylic diethyl ester (I) is obtained as colourless crystals, m.p. 130–131°. Yield: 12·5 g.

For dehydrogenation, add this ester to dilute nitric acid (20 ml. of the concentrated acid diluted with 40 ml. of water) and boil the mixture under reflux for about 5 minutes, during which the ester gently effervesces and finally gives a clear solution. Cool this solution in ice-water, make alkaline with aqueous sodium carbonate solution and extract twice with ether (50 ml. for each extraction). Dry the extract with sodium sulphate, filter, and then distil using a small distilling-flask

(Fig. 41(A) and (B), p. 65) into which the ethereal extract is allowed to run from a dropping-funnel at approximately the rate at which the solvent is distilling. When the ether has been removed, fit a capillary tube and thermometer, and continue the distillation at water-pump pressure. The diethyl ester of collidine-3,5-dicarboxylic acid (II) distils as a pale golden oil, b.p. 176–178°/14 mm. Yield, 5 g. from 6 g. of the ester (I).

Collidine-3,5-dicarboxylic acid. Boil a mixture of 5 g. of the ester (II) and 50 ml. of 15% ethanolic potash under reflux for 30 minutes. The dipotassium salt crystallises during the boiling and during the subsequent cooling. Filter off the potassium salt at the pump and wash it with a *small* quantity of ethanol. Dilute the filtrate with about an equal volume of ether to precipitate a further small crop of the salt. Yield of combined crops: 4·5 g. from 5 g. of the ester (I).

To obtain the free acid, add a solution of 2 g. of the potassium salt in 15 ml. of hot water slowly with stirring to 50 ml. of boiling 6% aqueous silver nitrate solution, and then gently boil the complete mixture for a few minutes to coagulate the precipitated silver salt. Filter the hot mixture at the pump, wash the silver salt with water and drain well. Transfer the silver salt to a large boiling-tube, add 30 ml. of water, and stir the mixture to give a uniform suspension. Heat to boiling and pass a stream of hydrogen sulphide through the mixture until all the silver has formed the heavy sulphide, leaving a clear solution above. Heat again almost to boiling, and filter the supernatant solution through a pre-heated funnel: boil the residual silver sulphide with 10–15 ml. of water, filter and evaporate the united filtrates to about 25 ml. The solution, when cooled and stirred, slowly deposits the colourless crystalline dicarboxylic acid, which can be recrystallised from ethanol containing 20% of water. Yield, 1 g.

The use of lead nitrate in place of silver nitrate is to be avoided, for the precipitated lead sulphide occludes most of the free acid.

Quinoline. C_9H_7N. (Skraup's Synthesis.)

When a mixture of aniline, nitrobenzene, glycerol and concentrated sulphuric acid is heated, a vigorous reaction occurs with the formation of quinoline. It is probable that the sulphuric acid first dehydrates the glycerol giving acrolein or acraldehyde (A), which then condenses at its double bond with the amino group of the aniline to give acrolein-aniline (B). The latter in its *enol*

$$CH_2(OH)\cdot CH(OH)\cdot CH_2(OH) - 2H_2O = CH_2:CH\cdot CHO \text{ (A)}$$
$$C_6H_5NH_2 + CH_2:CH\cdot CHO = C_6H_5NHCH_2CH_2CHO \text{ (B)}$$

form (C) then undergoes ring-closure to give the unstable intermediate compound (D), which is at once oxidised by the nitrobenzene to quinoline (E).

The nitrobenzene is thus itself reduced to aniline, which can then react as before.

When the crude reaction product is made alkaline and steam-distilled, a mixture of quinoline and some unchanged aniline passes over. Pure quinoline can be isolated from this mixture by one of the following methods:

(1) The mixed bases are dissolved in dilute hydrochloric acid and sodium nitrite solution added. The aniline is thus diazotised and, if the mixture is subsequently boiled, converted into phenol. The solution is then made alkaline and steam-distilled, the quinoline passing over, while the phenol remains behind in the alkaline solution.

(2) The mixed bases are boiled with an acetic acid-acetic anhydride mixture to convert the aniline into acetanilide. The product is poured into water, when the acetanilide crystallises out while the quinoline remains in solution as quinoline acetate. The acetanilide is filtered off, and the filtrate made alkaline and steam-distilled.

(3) The mixed amines are dissolved in hydrochloric acid and zinc chloride solution added. The quinoline chlorozincate,* $(C_9H_7N)_2,H_2ZnCl_4$, crystallises out, being almost insoluble in water, while the aniline chlorozincate remains in solution. The quinoline chlorozincate is then filtered off and decomposed by alkalis, and the liberated quinoline extracted with ether or steam-distilled.

Of the above methods for separating the amines, number (3) is the best.

Required: Aniline, 24 ml.; nitrobenzene, 13 ml.; anhydrous glycerol, 62 ml.; sulphuric acid, 36 ml.; zinc chloride, 23 g.

The reaction is carried out in a 2-litre *long-necked* round-bottomed flask, to which is fitted an efficient reflux water-condenser, capable of condensing a sudden rush of vapour without choking. For this purpose, a long bulb-condenser, similar to that shown in Fig. 3(A) (p. 9) is best, but the inner tube must be of wide bore (at least 12 mm.). Alternatively, an air-condenser of wide bore may be used, and a short double-surface water-condenser fitted to its top. A steam-distillation fitting for the flask should also be prepared in advance, so that the crude product can subsequently be steam-distilled directly from the flask. The glycerol used in the preparation must be anhydrous, and should therefore be dehydrated by the method described on p. 113.

Place 24 ml. (24·5 g.) of aniline, 13 ml. (15·5 g.) of nitrobenzene,† and 62 ml. (75 g.) of the anhydrous glycerol in the flask and mix thoroughly. (If the glycerol is still warm from the dehydration, cool the mixture in water.) Now add slowly 36 ml. (66 g.) of concentrated sulphuric acid, shaking the mixture thoroughly during the addition. The mixture at first

* These chlorozincates must not be confused with the non-ionic compounds which quinoline and aniline bases give with neutral zinc chloride: the latter have the formulae $[(C_9H_7N)_2ZnCl_2]$ and $[(C_6H_7N)_2ZnCl_2]$ respectively, and both are only slightly soluble in water.

† The initial reaction proceeds more smoothly if 37 g. of *dry* arsenic acid are used in place of the nitrobenzene for oxidation purposes. The yields when arsenic acid is used are, however, uncertain and often low.

becomes semi-solid owing to the separation of aniline sulphate, but later becomes mobile as the temperature rises during the further addition of the acid. Now add some fragments of un-glazed porcelain, fit the reflux condenser to the flask, and support the latter on a gauze-covered tripod, preferably in a fume-cupboard; clamp the condenser so that it is inclined at about 60° to the horizontal, as "choking" is less likely in this position than in a vertical position. Now heat the flask cautiously with a Bunsen flame: *immediately* the reaction starts and bubbles of vapour form in the liquid, turn out the gas. (It is advisable to have a duster soaked in cold water at hand: if, when the reaction starts, the duster is wrapped around the upper part of the body of the flask, the risk of the condenser choking becomes negligible.)

When the vigorous reaction subsides, replace the gauze by a sand-bath and boil the mixture gently for 3 hours. By this time the reaction is complete, and no unchanged nitrobenzene should remain. Then add about an equal volume of water, cool, and add concentrated sodium hydroxide solution until the mixture is definitely alkaline to litmus-paper. Steam-distil the product until the crude quinoline has been driven completely over and the distillate leaving the condenser is no longer turbid (usually about 700 ml.). Extract the quinoline with ether and then either distil off the ether taking the usual precautions (p. 163), or, if the amount of ether used is small, evaporate the ether in an open basin on a water-bath, the gas being turned out immediately before the basin is placed in position. (Chloroform may be used instead of ether, but its complete removal from the quinoline requires distillation.). Dissolve the crude residual quinoline in 200 ml. of dilute hydrochloric acid (1 vol. concentrated acid to 4 vols. water), warm the solution to about 60°, and add a solution of 23 g. of zinc chloride in 40 ml. of dilute hydrochloric acid. The quinoline chlorozincate soon starts to crystallise. Cool the well-stirred mixture thoroughly in ice-water and when crystallisation is complete, filter at the pump, wash well with dilute hydrochloric acid, and drain.

Transfer the quinoline chlorozincate to a beaker, add a small quantity of water, and then add 10% sodium hydroxide solution until the initial precipitate of zinc hydroxide completely redis-solves, and the free quinoline separates. Transfer the mixture to a separating-funnel, wash out the beaker with ether, adding the washings also to the solution in the funnel, and then extract the quinoline twice with ether. Dry the united ethereal extracts by adding an ample quantity of powdered potassium hydroxide and allowing the mixture to stand overnight. Then filter the ethereal solution, wash the residual potash with more ether and then distil off the ether from a small (75 ml.) flask with the usual precautions (Fig. 64, p. 163). Then replace the water-condenser by an air-condenser and distil the quinoline. Collect the fraction of b.p. 234–237°. Yield, 18 g.

Quinoline is a colourless liquid, having b.p. 236° and d, 1·095. It has an odour similar to, but fainter than, that of pyridine: unlike pyridine, it is almost insoluble in water.

Quinaldine. $C_{10}H_9N$. (The Doebner-Miller Synthesis.)

Quinaldine (or 2-methylquinoline) can be prepared by the Doebner-Miller Synthesis, which in some respects is closely similar to the Skraup Synthesis (p. 297) but has some significant differences.

When a mixture of aniline, hydrochloric acid and acetaldehyde is heated (in the absence of an oxidising agent), a vigorous reaction occurs with the production of quinaldine. In these circumstances, the main reactions are undoubtedly, (i) the acetaldehyde undergoes the aldol condensation, and the

$$2CH_3 \cdot CHO \rightarrow CH_3 \cdot CH(OH) \cdot CH_2 \cdot CHO \rightarrow CH_3 \cdot CH{:}CH \cdot CHO \qquad (I)$$

product then loses water to give crotonaldehyde (I); (ii) the aniline then undergoes a 1,4-addition to the crotonaldehyde to give the intermediate compound

(II), which by cyclic dehydration forms 1,2-dihydro-1-methylquinoline (III). These stages are closely similar to those of the Skraup Synthesis which produce the compound (D) (p. 297). The dihydro derivative (III) readily loses hydrogen to give quinaldine (IV).

Since no oxidising agent is present in the reaction-mixture, this dehydrogenation must involve the reduction of other components of the mixture. The reduced products are mainly N-ethylaniline, $C_6H_5NH \cdot C_2H_5$, and N-n-butylaniline, $C_6H_5NH \cdot (CH_2)_3 \cdot CH_3$, together with a small quantity of 6-ethylquinaldine. It is reasonably certain that a small proportion of the aniline must combine with the acetaldehyde and with the crotonaldehyde to give the corresponding Schiff's bases (V) and (VI) respectively: these compounds are then

$$C_6H_5 \cdot N{:}CH \cdot CH_3 \quad (V) \qquad C_6H_5 \cdot N{:}CH \cdot CH{:}CH \cdot CH_3 \quad (VI)$$

reduced by the dihydro derivative (III), which by losing its 1,2-hydrogen atoms attains the increased stability of the aromatic system (IV).

The small quantity of 6-ethylquinaldine probably arises by the acetaldehyde attacking the p-position of the aniline to give the p-CH$_3$CH(OH)·C$_6$H$_4$·NH· group, either in the aniline itself or in one of the intermediates, followed by both cyclisation and reduction.

The secondary amines present in the crude quinaldine are most effectively removed by acetylation.

It is convenient to replace the volatile free acetaldehyde by paraldehyde, which by dissociation in the reaction-mixture generates acetaldehyde *in situ*.

Required: Aniline, 30 ml. (30·5 g.); paraldehyde, 45 ml. (45 g.); concentrated hydrochloric acid, 60 ml.

The reaction is best carried out in the apparatus used in the preparation of quinoline, a 1500 ml. flask being fitted with a wide-bore air-condenser carrying in turn a water-condenser: a still-head to fit the flask for subsequent steam-distillation should be assembled in advance.

Add 60 ml. of concentrated hydrochloric acid with shaking to 30 ml. of aniline in the flask, cool the mixture to about 50°, and then add 45 ml. of paraldehyde and some fragments of un-glazed porcelain; assemble the apparatus without delay in a fume-cupboard with the condenser inclined at an angle of about 60°.

It is best now to proceed as in the Skraup Synthesis (p. 297) and warm the mixture over an asbestos-covered gauze with a Bunsen flame until the reaction starts, and have at hand a duster soaked in cold water so that when the reaction starts, the heating can be at once removed and the duster wrapped round the shoulders of the flask to aid condensation.

When the reaction has subsided, boil the reaction-mixture under reflux for 2 hours: then make it alkaline with sodium hydroxide solution, and distil it in steam until oily drops no longer come over in the aqueous distillate (1½–2 litres). Extract the distillate thoroughly with ether (*ca.* 150 ml.), and dry the ethereal extract over powdered sodium hydroxide. Filter the dry extract through a fluted filter-paper moistened with ether into a 200 ml. flask. Fit the flask with a distillation-head, or a "knee-tube", and distil off the ether. Now replace the distillation-head by a reflux water-condenser, add 10 ml. of acetic anhydride, and boil the mixture under reflux for 10–15 minutes.

The pure quinaldine can now be isolated by either of the following methods. (*a*) Transfer the acetylated mixture to a Claisen flask (preferably having a short fractionating column below the side-arm) and distil the mixture *slowly* at water-pump pressure by heating the flask in an oil or silicone bath. The first fraction, of b.p. *ca.* 50°/15 mm., contains acetic acid and anhydride. The next fraction is a golden liquid, b.p. 120–130°/15 mm., of almost pure quinaldine, weighing 18 g. If this fraction has been distilled *slowly*, the distillation will stop when this fraction is complete. Stronger heating then causes a rapid rise of the boiling-point as the by-products begin to distil, and should be avoided. The quinaldine should be redistilled from a clean flask, and obtained as a colourless hygroscopic liquid, 120–123°/15 mm., weighing 15–16 g. (*b*) The second method requires far more time. Cool the acetylated liquid, make it alkaline with saturated aqueous sodium carbonate, replace the condenser by a steam-distillation head, and again steam-distil until all the quinaldine has passed over. Extract the distillate with ether, dry the extract as before, and distil the filtered extract, taking off the ether at atmospheric pressure and the quinaldine at water-pump pressure. Collect the quinaldine, of b.p. 120–122°/15 mm. Yield, 15 g.

Quinaldine Methiodide. Boil a mixture of 3 ml. of quinaldine, 2 ml. of methanol and 3 ml. of methyl iodide gently under reflux for $1\frac{1}{2}$ hours, during which the methiodide will start to crystallise. Cool the mixture thoroughly in ice-water, filter off the methiodide and recrystallise it from ethanol: pale yellow crystals, m.p. 194°.

Dissolve a small quantity of the methiodide in cold water and add it with shaking to an excess of cold saturated aqueous sodium picrate solution. A yellow double salt* of quinaldine methopicrate and sodium picrate,

$$[C_{11}H_{12}N]C_6H_2N_3O_7,NaC_6H_2N_3O_7,$$

m.p. 218–220°, is rapidly precipitated, but when filtered off and recrystallised from water gives the simple quinaldine methopicrate, $[C_{11}H_{12}N]C_6H_2N_3O_7$, m.p. 141°.

p-Dimethylaminostyryl-quinoline. The methyl group in 2-methylquinoline (quinaldine) and in 4-methylquinoline (lepidine) has comparatively high reactivity, whereas that in 3-methylquinoline has low reactivity. The reactivity of the methyl group in quinaldine is shown by its ready condensation with aldehydes: in general, this condensation with the quinaldine base occurs most readily in an acid medium, whereas that with quinaldine methiodide (and other quaternary salts) best in a basic medium, *e.g.*, in the presence of a small quantity of piperidine.

Mix 1 g. of quinaldine and 1 g. of powdered *p*-dimethylaminobenzaldehyde, add 2–3 drops of 10% ethanolic zinc chloride solution, and heat under reflux in an oil-bath at 150° for 1 hour. Cool the product in ice-water, and recrystallise it from ethanol. *p*-Dimethylaminostyryl-quinoline (I) separates as bright yellow crystals, m.p. 177–178°.

---

* For examples of other similar methopicrates uniting with picric acid or sodium picrate to give "double picrates" of various stabilities, see F. G. Mann and F. C. Baker, *J. Chem. Soc.*, 1961, 3845.

Dissolve *ca.* 0·2 g. of product (I) in cold ethanol, and add with shaking 1–2 drops of *dilute* sulphuric acid. A deep purple coloration appears at once. This shows that salt formation has occurred on the quinoline nitrogen atom to form the cation (IIA), which will form a resonance hybrid with the quinonoid form (IIB). [Note that the forms (IIA) and (IIB) differ only in electron position, and they are not therefore tautomeric.] If, however, salt formation had occurred on the dimethylamino group to give the cation (III), this charge separation could not occur, and the deep colour would be absent.

Now add more dilute sulphuric acid drop by drop: the colour almost completely fades, as salt formation occurs on both nitrogen atoms with suppression of the resonance hybrid formation.

A wide variety of compounds similar in general type to (IIA–B) but prepared from quinaldine methiodide or ethiodide for greater stability are used as photographic sensitisers. The *p*-dimethylaminophenyl group can be replaced by various heterocyclic nitrogen systems, but in all these compounds the two nitrogen atoms must necessarily be linked through a conjugated system containing an odd number of carbon atoms to satisfy the above conditions. These compounds are known as cyanine dyes: when added in trace quantities to a silver bromide-silver iodide emulsion on a photographic plate or film, the sensitivity, which otherwise would be limited to the ultraviolet and visible violet and blue regions, may be extended well into the red region.

Acridone. $C_{13}H_9NO$.

Acridone (I) can be readily prepared by the cyclisation of *N*-phenylanthranilic acid (p. 217); using sulphuric acid. Many substituted acridones may be

similarly prepared. Acridone is a highly stable, bright yellow compound, only slightly soluble in most organic solvents. The colour and the chemical stability, *i.e.*, the absence of many normal properties of a ketone and of a secondary amine, indicate a marked contribution by the polar form (II), which is confirmed by the infrared spectrum of acridone.

Required: N-Phenylanthranilic acid, 4 g.; sulphuric acid, 10 ml.

Prepare a mixture of 4 g. of N-phenylanthranilic acid and 10 ml. of concentrated sulphuric acid in a conical flask, and heat it for $1\frac{1}{2}$ hours on a steam-bath. Then pour the hot dark green solution *slowly and cautiously* into 200 ml. of boiling water in a 500 ml. beaker, allowing the acid to run down the side of the beaker to prevent "spattering". Then boil the mixture for 5 minutes, and filter it whilst hot through a Buchner funnel, and wash the acridone on the filter with hot water. For purification, transfer the acridone to a solution of 4 g. of hydrated sodium carbonate in 50 ml. of water, boil the mixture for 5 minutes, and then filter it whilst hot: wash the acridone with boiling water and dry thoroughly. Yield, almost theoretical (3·7 g.). The acridone, m.p. 345–346°, thus prepared has usually a rather dull yellow colour. Recrystallisation from acetic acid using charcoal, or (better) sublimation as described on p. 23, gives the bright yellow product: the sublimed material has m.p. 351 –352°.

Quinoxalines.   (Semi-micro Scale.)

o-Phenylenediamine condenses readily with 1,2-diketones to give the corresponding 2,3-disubstituted quinoxalines. Thus benzil (preparation, p. 234) gives 2,3-diphenylquinoxaline: phenanthraquinone (II) (see p. 370) gives the corresponding derivative (III).

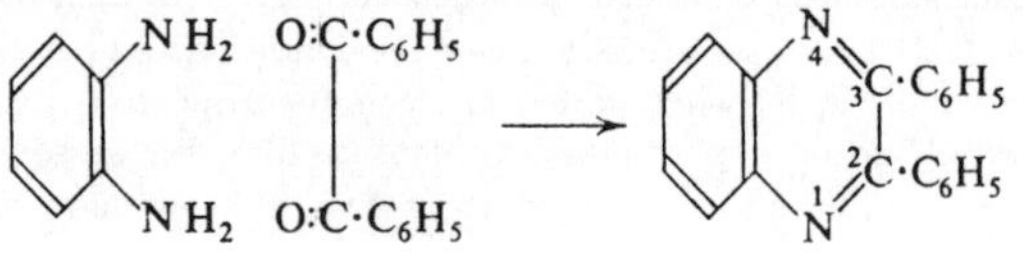

(I)

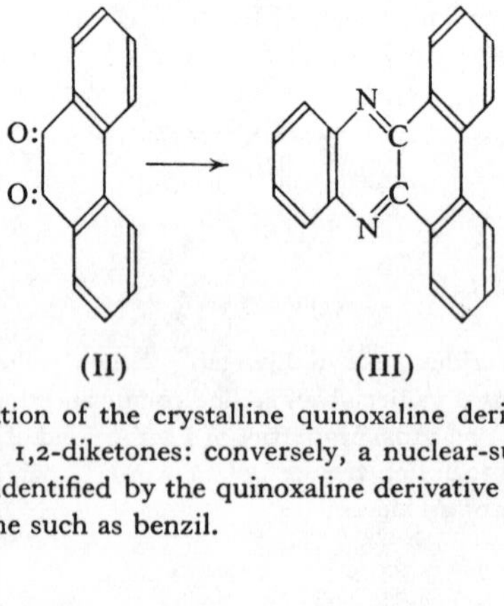

(II)   (III)

This rapid formation of the crystalline quinoxaline derivative can therefore be used to identify 1,2-diketones: conversely, a nuclear-substituted o-phenylenediamine can be identified by the quinoxaline derivative which it forms with a known 1,2-diketone such as benzil.

(A) 2,3-DIPHENYLQUINOXALINE

Required: N-Phenylanthranilic acid, 4 g.; sulphuric acid, 10 ml.

Prepare a mixture of 4 g. of N-phenylanthranilic acid and 5 ml. of ethanol, and boil the solution under reflux for 20 minutes. Cool the mixture, when the 2,3-diphenylquinoxaline will rapidly crystallise. Filter off the quinoxaline at the pump, and recrystallise it from ethanol. It forms colourless crystals, m.p. 125°. Yield, 1·0 g.

(B) THE QUINOXALINE (III)

Required: o-Phenylenediamine, 0·5 g.; phenanthraquinone, 1 g.

Proceed as in (A), using 50 ml. of ethanol, with boiling for 20 minutes. The quinoxaline (III) crystallises readily during the boiling. Cool the mixture, filter off the quinoxaline, and wash it with ethanol. The dry product, of m.p. 220–225°, weighs 1·3 g. Recrystallise the quinoxaline from chloroform or acetic acid; pale yellow crystals, m.p. 226°. Yield, 0·9–1·0 g.

Both the above condensations can alternatively be carried out in acetic acid (p. 372).

2-Amino-4-methylthiazole. C_4H_6NS (Hantzsch).

This preparation illustrates the ready formation of the thiazole ring by the condensation of an α-halogeno-ketone and a thioamide. Thus chloroacetone, which may conveniently be represented in the *enol* form (I), condenses with thiourea (II) to give 2-amino-4-methylthiazole (III).

$$
\begin{array}{ccc}
\text{HCCl} & \text{HS·C·NH}_2 & \\
\parallel \quad + & \parallel & \rightarrow \\
\text{CH}_3\text{·C·OH} & \text{HN} & \\
(I) & (II) &
\end{array}
$$

Required: Thiourea, 15 g.; chloroacetone, 18·5 g. (16 ml.); powdered (or "flake") sodium hydroxide, 40 g.

Note. The chloroacetone, which should be freshly distilled (b.p. 119°), is lachrymatory, and therefore the distillation and the preparation should be performed in a fume-cupboard.

Fit a 250 ml. three-necked flask with a stirrer, a reflux condenser and a dropping-funnel. (Alternatively, use a two-necked flask, with the dropping-funnel fitted by a grooved cork into the condenser.) Place 15 g. of powdered thiourea and 40 ml. of water in the flask and stir the mixture whilst 18·5 g. (16 ml.) of chloroacetone are added dropwise over a period of 20 minutes: the thiourea will dissolve and the temperature of the mixture rise. Then boil the mixture under reflux for 2 hours, and cool it in ice-water. Now add 40 g. of powdered (or "flake") sodium hydroxide slowly to the chilled mixture, shaking the latter gently around. Avoid vigorous shaking, which may produce an emulsion. If a solid material separates, redissolve it by the addition of a minimum of *cold* water. Transfer the mixture to a separating-funnel, separate the upper oily layer, and then extract the aqueous layer three times with ether (40 ml. for each extraction). Dry the united oily layer and ethereal extracts with sodium hydroxide, filter, and distil from a small Claisen distilling-flask (e.g. Fig. 41(A) and (B), p. 65), the ethereal solution being run in slowly from a dropping-funnel as fast as the ether distils over. Then fit a capillary tube to the flask and distil the residue at water-pump pressure. 2-Amino-4-methylthiazole distils at 124–125°/14 mm. as a colourless liquid which solidifies on cooling, and has m.p. 42–44°. Yield, 15·5–16 g.

2-Amino-4-methylthiazole slowly decomposes on storage to a red viscous mass. It can be stored as the nitrate, which is readily deposited as pink crystals when dilute nitric acid is added to a cold ethanolic solution of the thiazole. The nitrate can be recrystallised from ethanol, although a faint pink colour persists. Alternatively, water can be added dropwise to a boiling suspension of the nitrate in acetone until the solution is just clear; charcoal is now added and the solution, when boiled for a short time, filtered and cooled, deposits the colourless crystalline nitrate, m.p. 192–194° (immersed at 185°). The thiazole can be regenerated by decomposing the nitrate with aqueous sodium hydroxide, and extracting the free base with ether as before.

Thiobarbituric Acid.

Barbituric acid and 2-thiobarbituric acid are readily prepared by the condensation of diethylmalonate with urea and thiourea respectively, in the presence of sodium ethoxide. The use of substituted derivatives of urea and thiourea and of diethyl malonate will clearly lead to a wide range of barbituric and thiobarbituric acids having substituents in the 1, 3, or 5 positions.

$$
\begin{array}{ccc}
NH_2 & C_2H_5OOC & HN_1\!\!-\!\!_6CO \\
| & | & | \quad\quad | \\
S\!:\!C \quad + & CH_2 \quad\rightarrow & S\!:\!C_2 \quad _5CH_2 \\
| & | & | \quad\quad | \\
NH_2 & C_2H_5OOC & HN^3\!\!-\!\!^4CO
\end{array}
$$

The acidic nature of thiobarbituric acid is due partly to the hydrogen atoms in the 5-position, and partly to those in the 1 and 3 positions. The acid may be regarded systematically, in its fully "enolised" form, as 2-thiol-4,5-dihydroxy-pyrimidine.

Required: Sodium, 1·3 g.; ethyl malonate, 10 g.; thiourea, 5·3 g.; absolute ethanol, 120 ml.

Dissolve 1·3 g. of sodium in 30 ml. of absolute ethanol in a 250 ml. flask carrying a reflux condenser, then add 10 g. (9·5 ml.) of redistilled ethyl malonate, and place the flask on a boiling water-bath. *Without delay*, add a solution of 5·3 g. of thiourea in a minimum of boiling absolute ethanol (about 100 ml.). The sodium salt of thiobarbituric acid rapidly begins to separate. Fit the water-condenser with a calcium chloride guard-tube (Fig. 61, p. 105), and boil the mixture on the water-bath for 1 hour. Cool the mixture, filter off the sodium salt at the pump and wash it with a small quantity of cold acetone. Dissolve the salt in warm water and liberate the acid by the addition of 30 ml. of concentrated hydrochloric acid diluted with 30 ml. of water. Cool the mixture, filter off the thiobarbituric acid, and recrystallise it from hot water. Colourless crystals, m.p. 245° with decomposition (immersed at 230°). Yield, 3·5–4·0 g.

7-Hydroxy-4-methyl-coumarin.

Coumarin is usually prepared by heating salicylaldehyde with acetic anhydride and sodium acetate (*i.e.*, the Perkin cinnamic acid synthesis, p. 236), whereby the o-hydroxy-cinnamic acid (I) undergoes cyclisation to coumarin. Coumarins having substituents in the benzene ring can often be similarly prepared.

(I)   (II)   (III)

For the preparation of 4-substituted coumarins, a phenol may be condensed with ethyl acetoacetate under the influence of sulphuric acid. Thus resorcinol (II) readily undergoes this condensation (which is represented diagrammatically above) to give 7-hydroxy-4-methyl-coumarin (III). Note that the coumarins, like all 2-pyrones, are systematically lactones.

Required: Resorcinol, 3·7 g.; ethyl acetoacetate, 4·5 g.

Stir 15 ml. of concentrated sulphuric acid mechanically in a wide-necked 50 ml. flask with external ice-water cooling until the temperature of the acid is about 5°.

Meanwhile add 3·7 g. of powdered resorcinol to 4·5 g. (4·4 ml.)

of ethyl acetoacetate, stirring the mixture until a complete solution is obtained. Now add this solution slowly to the sulphuric acid, so that the temperature of the mixture does not rise above 10°; then continue the stirring for 30 minutes. Pour the mixture on to crushed ice (about 100 g.), when the solid 7-hydroxy-4-methyl-coumarin separates. Filter off the coumarin at the pump. For purification, first dissolve the coumarin in cold 10% aqueous sodium hydroxide solution and reprecipitate it by the addition of dilute hydrochloric acid, and then recrystallise it from ethanol or methylated spirit, using charcoal if necessary. Yield of the colourless crystals, 3·5–4·0 g.; m.p. 188–190°.

Alkyl Phosphites. The Interaction of Phosphorus Trichloride and Alcohols.

Phosphorus trichloride reacts readily with three equivalents of an alcohol e.g., ethanol, in the presence of a tertiary amine such as pyridine, dimethylaniline, or diethylaniline, to form triethyl phosphite and hydrogen chloride, the latter being immediately neutralised by the tertiary amine.

$$PCl_3 + 3HOC_2H_5 + 3C_5H_5N \rightarrow P(OC_2H_5)_3 + 3C_5H_5N,HCl$$

In the absence of a tertiary amine, the initial reaction is again the formation of a trialkyl phosphite and hydrogen chloride. The latter now reacts rapidly with the trialkyl phosphite to give the alkyl chloride and the dialkyl hydrogen

$$PCl_3 + 3HOC_2H_5 \rightarrow P(OC_2H_5)_3 + 3HCl$$

$$
\begin{array}{c}
OC_2H_5 \\
/ \\
P-OC_2H_5 + HCl \\
\backslash \\
OC_2H_5
\end{array}
\rightarrow
C_2H_5Cl +
\begin{array}{c}
OC_2H_5 \\
/ \\
P-OC_2H_5 \\
\backslash \\
OH
\end{array}
\rightleftharpoons
\begin{array}{c}
OC_2H_5 \\
/ \\
HP \\
\| \backslash \\
O \quad OC_2H_5
\end{array}
$$

(I)   (II)

phosphite (I). The dialkyl hydrogen phosphites (I), however, behave in almost all their reactions as the tautomeric form (II).

The following preparation of triethyl phosphite illustrates the interaction of phosphorus trichloride and ethanol in the presence of dimethylaniline: the preparation of di-isopropyl hydrogen phosphite illustrates that of phosphorus trichloride and isopropanol in the absence of a tertiary amine.

Triethyl Phosphite. $P(OC_2H_5)_3$.

Required: Phosphorus trichloride, 30 g. (17·6 ml.); dimethylaniline, 59·2 g. (62 ml.); absolute ethanol, 30·2 g. (38 ml.); dry ether, 75 ml.

It is essential to use dry apparatus and reagents: lower yields are frequently obtained, particularly on humid days, unless due care is taken.

NOTE: The preparations on pp. 308–312 form an introduction to some organo-phosphorus products; those on pp. 312–315 similarly to some organo-arsenic products.

Fit a 500 ml. conical flask with a two-holed cork, through which are passed a dropping-funnel and an outlet-tube furnished with a calcium chloride guard-tube. Place a solution of 17·6 ml. of phosphorus trichloride in 35 ml. of dry ether in the dropping-funnel, and fit the latter also with a calcium chloride guard-tube. Place 38 ml. of absolute ethanol, 62 ml. of dimethylaniline and 40 ml. of dry ether in the conical flask, shake the mixture until a clear solution is obtained, and then close the flask with the dropping-funnel and outlet-tube. Place the flask in ice-water, and then add the ethereal solution of phosphorus trichloride *slowly* from the funnel, keeping the contents of the flask well shaken throughout the addition. Towards the end of the reaction the separation of dimethylaniline hydrochloride causes the mixture to set to an almost solid mass. Finally set the mixture aside for 2 hours at room temperature.

Filter off the dimethylaniline hydrochloride through a Buchner funnel, and wash the hydrochloride on the filter with about 15 ml. of dry ether. Dry the united extract and washings with anhydrous sodium sulphate. Meanwhile set up the ether distillation apparatus shown in Fig. 23(E), p. 45), using however a 60 ml. Claisen flask having an efficient fractionating column in the distillation neck. Now filter the dried ethereal solution through a fluted filter-paper directly into the dropping-funnel: control the rate of distillation so that the solution runs into the distilling-flask approximately as fast as the ether is distilling over. When all the ether has been removed, replace the dropping-funnel by a capillary tube, and the adaptor and receiver by a "pig" (Fig. 23(F)), and fractionally distil the residue under water-pump pressure. Discard any low-boiling distillate, and collect the fraction boiling steadily at 48°/13 mm. Yield of triethyl phosphite, 24 g., 70%.

Triethyl phosphite is a colourless mobile liquid, insoluble in water. Trialkyl phosphites are valuable intermediates in the preparation of many organophosphorus compounds: they readily form dialkyl esters of alkylphosphonic acids by the Arbusov reaction (p. 311).

Di-isopropyl Hydrogen Phosphite. $O{:}PH[{\cdot}OCH(CH_3)_2]_2$.

Two modifications (A) and (B) of this preparation are given: (B) is the simpler but gives a smaller yield of the phosphite.

(A) *Required:* Phosphorus trichloride, 23 g. (13·5 ml.); dry isopropanol, 30 g. (38 ml.); dry ether, 45 ml.; ammonia from a cylinder.

Assemble an apparatus similar to that used in the previous experiment, *i.e.*, a 500 ml. conical flask fitted at the neck with a freshly-charged calcium chloride tube, a dropping-funnel, and in addition an outlet-tube joined to the water-pump so that dry air can be drawn through the calcium chloride tube and thence through the conical flask. The purpose of the air-stream is to remove as much as possible of the excess of hydrogen chloride. Pour a solution of 38 ml. of dry isopropanol in 30 ml. of dry ether into the flask, and a solution of 13·5 ml. of phosphorus chloride in 15 ml. of dry ether into the dropping-funnel. Now turn on the pump to draw a stream of dry air through the flask, and cool the latter in ice-water. Add the phosphorus trichloride solution *slowly* to the solution in the flask, shaking the reaction-mixture throughout the addition. When the addition of the trichloride is complete, continue the air-stream for a further 30 minutes. Then turn off the pump, and replace the calcium chloride tube by an inlet-tube passing down into the flask *just* below the surface of the liquid. Through this tube pass in a stream of dry ammonia in order to precipitate any remaining hydrogen chloride as ammonium chloride. Filter off the ammonium chloride at the pump.

Meanwhile set up the ether distillation apparatus as used in the preparation of triethyl phosphite (p. 308). Distil off the ether and then fractionally distil the residue at water-pump pressure. The di-isopropyl hydrogen phosphite distils at 79°/14 mm.: other b.ps. are 80°/15 mm., 82·5°/17 mm. Yield, 25 g., 89%.

Di-isopropyl hydrogen phosphite is a colourless mobile liquid, which, unlike triethyl and tri-isopropyl phosphite, is completely miscible with water, due undoubtedly to the polar $P=O$ group.

Isopropanol has been used in the above experiment because it gives a greater yield of the phosphite than ethanol gives of diethyl hydrogen phosphite. The latter, b.p. 74°/14 mm., can be prepared by replacing the isopropanol in the above experiment by 29 ml. (23 g.) of ethanol.

(B) The following simpler preparation of di-isopropyl hydrogen phosphite using the same quantities of reactants requires no solvent or ammonia, but gives a lower yield.

Place 38 ml. of isopropanol in a two-necked 500 ml. round-bottomed flask fitted with (*a*) a reflux water-condenser having a calcium chloride tube at the top, and (*b*) a dropping-funnel. Cool the flask in ice-water and then run 13·5 ml. of phosphorus trichloride in from the dropping-funnel during 15 minutes. Then allow the reaction-mixture to attain room temperature. Now replace the condenser and the dropping-funnel by an inlet-tube (which carries a calcium chloride tube and which dips just below the surface of the reaction-mixture) and an outlet-tube. Draw dry air through the mixture for 45 minutes to remove as much hydrogen chloride as possible. Distil under reduced pressure and collect the fraction of b.p. 81°/15 mm. Yield, about 15 g.

The unsubstituted hydrogen atom of the dialkyl hydrogen phosphites can be readily replaced by chlorine, and thence by many other substituents including fluorine.

Diethyl Ethylphosphonate. $C_2H_5PO(OC_2H_5)_2$.

When an alkyl halide is heated with a trialkyl phosphite, an ester of a phosphonic acid is produced. This is known as the Arbusov Reaction:

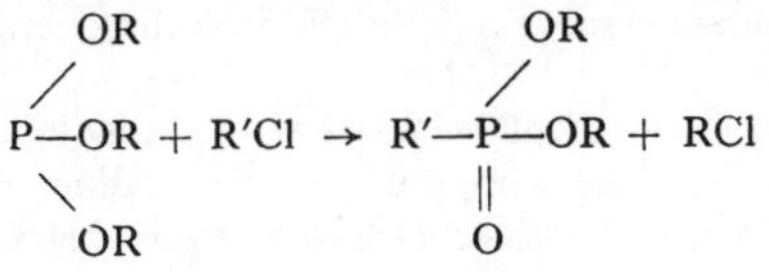

$$
\begin{array}{ccc}
& OR & OR \\
& / & / \\
P{-}OR + R'Cl & \rightarrow & R'{-}P{-}OR + RCl \\
\backslash & & \| \\
OR & & O \\
& & (I)
\end{array}
$$

If $R = R'$, the reaction appears to be catalytic as a small quantity of $R'Cl$ will suffice to convert a considerable quantity of the trialkyl phosphite into the dialkyl alkylphosphonate (I). As little as 0·1 mol. of the alkyl iodide will suffice to isomerise the trialkyl phosphite.

The Arbusov Reaction probably takes the following course.

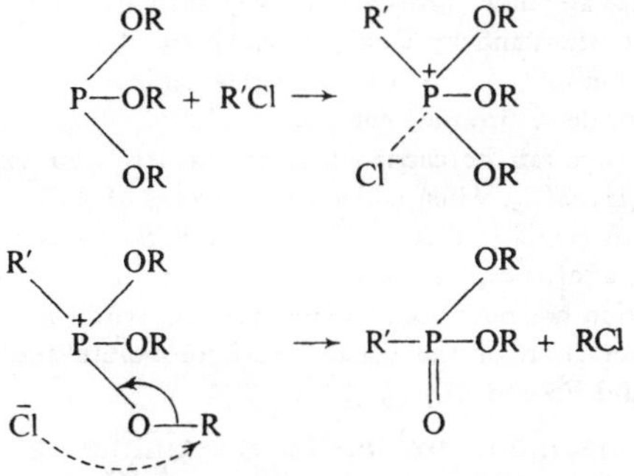

$$
\begin{array}{cc}
OR & R' \quad OR \\
/ & \backslash_{+}/ \\
P{-}OR + R'Cl \longrightarrow & P{-}OR \\
\backslash & / \backslash \\
OR & Cl^- \quad OR
\end{array}
$$

$$
\begin{array}{cc}
R' \quad OR & OR \\
\backslash_{+}/ & / \\
P{-}OR & \longrightarrow R'{-}P{-}OR + RCl \\
\backslash & \| \\
\bar{Cl} \quad O{-}R & O
\end{array}
$$

In the reaction described below triethyl phosphite (p. 308) is heated with ethyl iodide to give diethyl ethylphosphonate. Although theoretically a very small amount of ethyl iodide would suffice, it is advantageous to use more than the minimum amount so as to reduce the temperature of the boiling reaction-mixture.

Required: Triethyl phosphite, 16·9 g.; ethyl iodide, 10 g.
Heat together under a good reflux water-condenser fitted with

a calcium chloride guard-tube 16·9 g. of triethyl phosphite and 10 g. of ethyl iodide for 2 hours. Cool the mixture, distil off the ethyl iodide (b.p. 72°) and distil the residue under reduced pressure using a Claisen flask fitted with a good fractionating column. Collect the fraction of b.p. 86·5–88°/16 mm. Yield of the ethylphosphonate, 10·6 g.

Phenylarsonic Acid. $C_6H_5AsO(OH)_2$. (The Bart Reaction.)

Arylarsonic acids are most readily prepared by the Bart Reaction, in which a diazonium salt in aqueous solution is run into a solution of sodium arsenite in an excess of sodium carbonate. The addition of copper sulphate to the

$$C_6H_5\overset{+}{N_2}\overset{-}{Cl} + (NaO)_3As \rightarrow C_6H_5AsO(ONa)_2 + N_2 + NaCl$$

arsenite often induces a more regular effervescence of nitrogen and markedly increases the yield.

Arylarsonic acids have usually a very low solubility in cold water. They are however amphoteric, since with, for example, sodium hydroxide they form sodium salts as above and with acids such as hydrochloric acid they form salts of the type $[C_6H_5As(OH)_3]Cl$. Both types of salt are usually soluble in water, and to isolate the free acid the aqueous solution has to be brought to the correct pH: for most arsonic acids this can be achieved by making the solution only just acid to Congo Red, when the free acid will usually rapidly separate.

The success of the Bart reaction when applied to nuclear-substituted anilines is often much affected by the pH of the reaction-mixture. Furthermore, the yields obtained from some m-substituted anilines, which under the normal conditions are usually low, are considerably increased by the modifications introduced by Scheller, and by Doak, in which the diazotisation is carried out in ethanolic solution followed by reaction with arsenic trichloride in the presence of a cuprous chloride or bromide catalyst.

The Bart reaction can be carried a stage further. For example, dichlorophenylarsine, $C_6H_5AsCl_2$, when added to an excess of sodium carbonate solution, gives $C_6H_5As(ONa)_2$: this solution, if similarly treated with benzenediazonium chloride, affords diphenylarsinic acid, $(C_6H_5)_2As(:O)OH$.

The Bart reaction has now been extended to the synthesis of arylphosphonic acids by the interaction of the diazonium fluoroborate and phosphorus trichloride (Doak and Freedman, 1951).

Required: Arsenious oxide, 27 g.; aniline, 20 ml. (20 g.); anhydrous sodium carbonate, 55 g.; crystalline copper sulphate, 1 g.; sodium nitrite, 15·6 g.

Add in turn 55 g. of anhydrous sodium carbonate, 27 g. of powdered arsenious oxide and 1 g. of hydrated copper sulphate to 175 ml. of water in a 2 litre beaker, and heat the stirred mixture until an almost clear solution is obtained: then immerse the stirred solution in ice-water, and cool it to 5°.

Meanwhile add 20 g. (20 ml.) of aniline to a mixture of

45 ml. of concentrated hydrochloric acid and 225 ml. of water, cool this solution also to 5°, and diazotise it in the usual way by the dropwise addition of a solution of 15·6 g. of sodium nitrite in 50 ml. of water. Allow the temperature of the solution finally to rise to 10–12° for 10 minutes to ensure complete diazotisation.

Now add the diazonium solution slowly from a dropping-funnel to the vigorously-stirred arsenite solution, keeping the temperature of the latter at 5–7°. The frothing caused by the evolution of nitrogen will probably be dispersed by the stirrer: if not, the addition of 1–2 ml. of ether, preferably in a fine jet from a wash-bottle, will cause it to subside.

When the addition of the diazonium solution is complete, **remove** the external cooling and continue the stirring for 30–40 minutes. Then filter the solution and evaporate it (by direct boiling) to about 150 ml. Then add concentrated hydrochloric acid (about 35 ml.) carefully to the hot solution until effervescence ceases and the separation of gummy material is complete. Filter the warm solution, and chill the filtrate in ice-water. Then add concentrated hydrochloric acid (*ca.* 10 ml.) *slowly* with stirring until the solution is *just* acid to Congo Red: for this purpose, use Congo Red paper with external spotting with a glass rod.

The phenylarsonic acid should separate from the cold stirred solution within 10–20 minutes. If separation does not occur (due to the addition of too much acid), add a few drops of dilute aqueous sodium hydroxide and again bring the solution very carefully to the desired pH.

Filter off the precipitated phenylarsonic acid at the pump, and purify it by either of the following methods. (*a*) Dissolve the crude acid in a minimum of cold 10% aqueous sodium carbonate solution, a second small crop of the gummy impurity remaining undissolved. Add 1–2 g. of animal charcoal, stir for a few minutes and filter at the pump. Add concentrated hydrochloric acid as before until the filtrate is just acid to Congo Red. Chill the precipitated acid, filter it at the pump, wash with a few ml. of cold water, drain and finally dry it in a vacuum desiccator. Yield, 24–25 g. [The cream-coloured acid, when heated from room temperature, shrinks at *ca.* 100° and melts at 148–152°, with subsequent resolidification as water is lost and the compound $C_6H_5AsO_2$ is formed.] (*b*) Recrystallise the crude acid from a minimum of boiling water, adding charcoal to the boiling solution. Filter through a preheated Buchner funnel, and chill the filtrate. Filter off the acid and wash, drain and dry it as in (*a*).

Yield, 22–23 g. This product has m.p. 152–155° when heated from room temperature, and 155–156° when immersed in a heating-bath at 140°.

Arsonic acids, like carboxylic and sulphonic acids (pp. 349, 353), usually give crystalline benzylthiouronium salts. Add just sufficient dilute aqueous sodium hydroxide dropwise with shaking to a suspension of 0·5 g. of phenylarsonic acid in 10 ml. of water to give a clear solution. Then add 0·5 g. of benzylthiouronium chloride dissolved in 10 ml. of water. Filter off the precipitated benzylthiouronium salt, wash with water and dry: m.p. 114–117°: it tends to dissociate on attempted recrystallisation.

Benzylphenylarsinic Acid. $C_6H_5 \cdot CH_2(C_6H_5) \cdot As:O(OH)$. (The Meyer Reaction.)

The Meyer Reaction in arsenic chemistry bears some analogy to the Arbusov Reaction in phosphorus chemistry.

If, for example, methyl iodide is added to a solution of arsenic trioxide in an excess of aqueous sodium hydroxide, *i.e.*, an alkaline solution of sodium arsenite, combination similar in general type to quaternisation appears to occur, the

$$As(ONa)_3 + CH_3I \rightarrow [CH_3\overset{+}{A}s(ONa)_3\bar{I}] \rightarrow CH_3AsO(ONa)_2 \rightarrow CH_3AsO(OH)_2$$

unstable product losing sodium iodide to form disodium methylarsonate, which on acidification liberates methylarsonic acid. Note that this synthesis is limited to alkylarsonic acids, whereas the Bart synthesis (p. 312) is limited to arylarsonic acids.

The process may now be continued. Methylarsonic acid, when reduced by sulphur dioxide in concentrated hydrochloric acid, gives dichloromethylarsine, CH_3AsCl_2. If this arsine is added to aqueous sodium hydroxide, it is hydrolysed to the weakly acidic methylarsenous acid, $CH_3As(OH)_2$, which in the alkali

$$CH_3 \cdot As(ONa)_2 + CH_3I \rightarrow (CH_3)_2AsO(ONa) \rightarrow (CH_3)_2AsO(OH)$$

reacts again with methyl iodide to form sodium dimethylarsinite. The dimethylarsinic acid so obtained can again be put through the cycle of reduction to chlorodimethylarsine† and treatment with alkali and methyl iodide to obtain trimethylarsine oxide, and thence by the sulphur dioxide reduction to trimethylarsine. Note that different alkyl groups may thus be inserted at the consecutive stages for "mixed arsine" synthesis.

In the example given below, phenylarsonic acid is reduced to dichlorophenylarsine, $C_6H_5AsCl_2$.* This compound when added to aqueous sodium hydroxide and treated with benzyl chloride gives benzylphenylarsinic acid, which is readily isolated from solution.

Required: Phenylarsonic acid, 15 g.; concentrated hydrochloric acid, 30 ml.; sulphur dioxide from a cylinder.

(A) *Dichlorophenylarsine.** Add 15 g. of phenylarsonic acid to 30 ml. of concentrated hydrochloric acid in a 150 ml. round-

---

* Now usually named unambiguously as phenylarsonous dichloride.
† Similarly named dimethylarsinous chloride.

bottomed flask. Add 0·1–0·2 g. of potassium iodide to facilitate the reduction. Heat the mixture on a boiling water-bath *in a fume-cupboard*, and pass a vigorous stream of sulphur dioxide from a cylinder down a delivery tube to the bottom of the solution. The solution rapidly becomes milky in appearance as fine drops of the insoluble dichloroarsine separate. Continue the sulphur dioxide for 1 hour, when the heavy dichloroarsine will have sunk to the bottom. Then cool the mixture in ice-water, transfer it to a separating-funnel, and run off the lower layer of dichloroarsine. Dry the arsine over anhydrous sodium sulphate. Filter the arsine through a small filter-funnel at the pump: wash the residual sodium sulphate in the drying-flask with a small quantity of dry petroleum (b.p. 60–80°) and filter the petroleum through the funnel to wash the sulphate which is on the filter. Distil the united arsine and washings in a fume-cupboard, taking off the petroleum at atmospheric pressure and then the arsine at water-pump pressure. The dichlorophenylarsine is collected as a colourless liquid, b.p. 125°/15 mm. Yield, 12–13 g.

Great care should be taken to keep dichlorophenylarsine, alone or in solution, from the hands: if this precaution is observed, the cold liquid is easily and safely handled. The vapour from the hot liquid, or a fine spray of liquid itself, is poisonous if inhaled: these conditions should not however arise in the above experiment.

(B) *Benzylphenylarsinic acid.* Place 35 ml. of 40% aqueous sodium hydroxide in a 100 ml. round-bottomed flask: cool the flask in ice-water, and add with gentle shaking first 5·1 ml. (7 g.) of dichlorophenylarsine and then 4·2 ml. (4·6 g.) of benzyl chloride. Attach a reflux water-condenser and heat the mixture on a boiling water-bath for 1 hour with occasional shaking. (If the preparation is carried out on a larger scale, mechanical stirring is advisable during the mixing and heating stages.)

Cool the reaction-solution, and pour it into a 250 ml. beaker, washing out the flask with *ca.* 50 ml. of water into the beaker. Chill the solution in ice-water and add dilute hydrochloric acid with stirring until the solution is just acid when "spotted" externally on to Congo Red paper. The arsinic acid rapidly separates. Filter at the pump, wash well with water and drain. (Yield of crude dry product, 7·5–8·0 g.; m.p. 200–203°.)

The arsinic acid thus obtained is of high quality: after draining, however, it can be directly recrystallised from ethanol or from a large volume of hot water: m.p. of recrystallised acid, 205–206°.

PART III

REACTIONS AND IDENTIFICATION OF ORGANIC COMPOUNDS

THE following pages contain an account of the chief reactions of the commoner organic compounds, arranged in a series of short sections with a view to the identification of an unknown organic compound. The first nine sections contain various preliminary tests which should be applied to an unknown compound in order to obtain *general* information with regard to its identity. Each of the remaining seventeen sections is devoted to one class of organic compound, and a description is given of the general reactions of members of this class and then of any important special reactions which individual members may show. Only the commoner members of each class are described, because it is considered desirable that students should get a thorough grasp of the reactions of these members before they proceed to wider and more ambitious schemes for the identification of organic compounds.

The following is a list of the sections, together with a complete catalogue of the compounds included:

SECTION:

1. Heating on a crucible lid.
2. Identification of elements present.
3. Heating with soda-lime.
4. Treatment with sodium hydroxide solution.
5. Treatment with sodium carbonate solution.
6. Treatment with concentrated sulphuric acid.
7. Reactions and colorations with ferric chloride solution.
8. Reaction with 2,4-dinitrophenylhydrazine.
9. Reactions with hydroxylamine.
10. Alcohols. *Methanol, ethanol, n-propanol, propan-2-ol, n-butanol, glycol, glycerol, benzyl alcohol, cyclohexanol.*
11. Phenols. *Phenol, o-, m- and p-cresol, catechol, resorcinol, hydroquinone (and other nuclear substituted phenols), 1- and 2-naphthol.*
12. Aldehydes. *Formaldehyde, metaformaldehyde, acetaldehyde, paraldehyde, chloral hydrate, benzaldehyde, salicylaldehyde (and other substituted benzaldehydes).*
13. Ketones. *Acetone, ethyl methyl ketone, diethyl ketone, acetophenone,*

benzophenone (and their nuclear substituted derivatives), *cyclohexanone.*

14. Acids.   (A) Carboxylic Acids. *Formic, acetic* (and higher aliphatic acids); *oxalic, succinic, lactic, tartaric, citric, benzoic, salicylic* (and their nuclear substituted derivatives), *phthalic, cinnamic* (and nuclear substituted derivatives).

(B) Sulphonic Acids. *Simple aromatic sulphonic acids.*

15. Esters.   *Methyl, ethyl,* n-*propyl,* n-*butyl, benzyl, cyclohexyl esters* of all acids in Section 14 (except lactic acid); *phenyl esters* of *acetic, benzoic* and *salicylic acids.*

16. Ammonium salts, amides, imides and nitriles.

(A) *Ammonium salts of acids* given in Section 14 (except lactic acid).

(B) *Formamide, acetamide, oxamide, urea, benzamide, salicylamide; thiourea.*

(C) *Succinimide, phthalimide.*

(D) *Acetonitrile, benzonitrile* (and nuclear substituted derivatives).

17. Acid chlorides and anhydrides.

(A) *Acetyl chloride, benzoyl chloride* (and substituted derivatives).

(B) *Acetic, succinic anhydride; phthalic anhydride* (and substituted derivatives).

18. Carbohydrates.
Glucose, fructose, sucrose, maltose, starch.

19. Quinones.   *Benzoquinone, p-toluquinone, 1,2-naphthoquinone, 1,4-naphthoquinone, anthraquinone, phenanthraquinone; alizarin.*

20. Amines.   (A) Primary aromatic amines. *Aniline,* o-, m- and p-*toluidine* (and other nuclear substituted anilines); 1- *and* 2-*naphthylamines.*

(B) Secondary amines. (i) *Aromatic amines. Monomethyl* and *monoethylaniline, diphenylamine.* (ii) *Aliphatic and other amines. Diethylamine, di-n-propylamine, di-isopropylamine. Also piperidine; piperazine (diethylene-diamine).*

(C) Tertiary amines. (i) *Aliphatic amines. Triethylamine,* tri-n-*propylamine,* and *tri-isopropylamine.* (ii) *Dialkylarylamines. Dimethylaniline, diethylaniline.* (iii) *Triarylamines. Triphenylamine.* (iv) *Heterocyclic amines. Pyridine, the picolines, quinoline, quinaldine, lepidine.* (v) *Special compounds. Hexamethylenetetramine.*

21. Anilides.   *Acetanilide, benzanilide* (and their nuclear- and N-substituted derivatives).

22. Amino-acids.
>   (A) Amino-aliphatic carboxylic acids. *Glycine, tyrosine,* cystine**.
>   (B) Amino-aromatic carboxylic acids. *Anthranilic acid.*
>   (C) Amino-aromatic sulphonic acids. *Sulphanilic acid.*

23. Nitro-compounds.
>   (A) Nitro-hydrocarbons. *Nitrobenzene, p-nitrotoluene, m-dinitrobenzene.*
>   (B) Nitro-phenols. *o- and p-Nitrophenols.*
>   (C) Nitro-anilines. *o-, m- and p-Nitro-anilines.*

24. Purines. *Uric acid.*

25. Halogeno-hydrocarbons.
>   *Methyl iodide, ethyl bromide and iodide, higher alpihatic halides; chloroform, iodoform, carbon tetrachloride; chlorobenzene, bromobenzene, iodobenzene; benzyl chloride.*

26. Hydrocarbons.
>   *Benzene, toluene, anthracene, phenanthrene, biphenyl.*
>   Aromatic hydrocarbons with unsaturated side-chains. *Styrene, stilbene.*

27. Ethers. *Diethyl ether, di-n-propyl ether, di-isopropyl ether, anisole, phenetole, guiacol, methyl 2-naphthyl ether.*

In each of the Sections 10–27, the chief physical properties of the compounds concerned are first briefly indicated: a list of the general reactions† is then given, followed by practical directions for the application or illustration of these general reactions. The types of crystalline derivatives which can be most readily and reliably prepared are then given, with practical examples. Finally, any important special reactions of individual members are described.

It is suggested that students should work systematically through these sections, undertaking one or more sections at each practical class, according to the time available. It is strongly recommended, however, that after the first or second practical class, students should always be given two or three unknown compounds at each class, and should then obtain as much information with regard to the chemical character of the compounds as their previous work allows, a complete identification not in general being expected until the end of the sections is reached.

---

* Tyrosine and cystine have been included primarily for students of biochemistry, physiology and medicine; these two amino-acids might, however, be omitted by other students.

† The success of the test-tube reactions described in Sections 10–27 depends largely on the use of the reagents in the correct proportions. The quantities specified are given as a guide for this purpose, but need not in general be rigidly observed.

In this way the student's knowledge of the organic reactions is consolidated as he proceeds through the sections, his experience of the general method of identification steadily increases, and the investigation of the unknown compounds forms a welcome break from the systematic pursuit of the sectional work.

NOTE. It is not expected that a student will attempt to memorise all the colour tests given in Part III. He might for example be expected to know the Phthalein Reaction for phenol itself (p. 339). Details of the divergence from the "standard" result are recorded primarily for reference, so that a student will not be diverted from his line of investigation if he observes that a "suspected" phenol does not respond exactly to the standard colour changes.

Section 1. Heating on a Crucible Lid.

Heat a small portion of the following substances on an inverted porcelain or stainless steel crucible lid. At first, heat one side of the lid *gently*, so that the heat travels along the lid to the organic substance: later heat the lid more strongly. Note carefully in particular (*a*) the change in appearance, (*b*) whether readily inflammable, (*c*) any odour produced, (*d*) whether a non-volatile residue is left.

It must be emphasised that the following substances are merely representative of widely different classes of compounds, and that the test when applied to an unknown compound often provides only a *general* indication of the probable class to which the compound belongs. Moreover, the behaviour of a compound when heated is often determined more by the nature of its substituent groups than by its general character.

Alcohols.—Burns rapidly with a clear flame. Typical of many aliphatic substances.

Aniline.—Burns with a very smoky flame, clouds of soot being produced. Typical of many aromatic substances.

1,2–Dibromoethane.—Does not burn until vapour becomes hot and then burns with a slightly smoky flame. Typical of substances rich in halogens such as chloroform, chloral hydrate, and carbon tetrachloride. (Note, however, that iodoform evolves copious fumes of iodine when heated in this way.)

Sodium benzoate.—Burns with great difficulty, and after prolonged heating leaves a white infusible residue of Na_2CO_3. Scrape this residue into a test-tube, and test for carbonate in the usual way. Typical of alkali salts of carboxylic acids.

In similar circumstances, silver salts leave a residue of metallic silver; lead and copper salts usually leave a residue of the corresponding oxide; calcium and barium salts leave a residue of the carbonate or oxide. Identify the metal in all such cases by the usual tests of qualitative inorganic analysis. Metals other than the above are seldom encountered in elementary qualitative analysis.

Sodium sulphanilate.—Burns with difficulty, leaving a residue of (chiefly) sodium sulphide. Add dil. HCl, and confirm without delay the evolution of H_2S by means of a filter-paper moistened with lead acetate solution. Typical of salts of the sulphonic acids.

Acetone sodium bisulphite.—Almost non-inflammable, leaving a colourless residue of sodium sulphite and sulphate. Transfer residue to a test-tube, add dil. HCl, warm, and confirm the SO_2 evolved.

Cane sugar.—Melts, darkens, then chars, and finally burns, with a marked odour of burnt sugar. Typical of the changes given by mono- and di-saccharides.

Tartaric acid and tartrates also swell up, blacken and give an odour resembling burnt sugar. Citrates and lactates also char, and give off odours resembling burnt sugar.

A large variety of organic compounds char without melting, *e.g.*, starch, oxamide, sulphonic acids, uric acid, *etc.*

NOTE. (1) Care should be taken to distinguish between a residue of carbon which may be very difficult to burn off completely, and a really non-volatile residue due to the presence of a metallic derivative. Thus for instance starch leaves a hard black residue of carbon which can best be burned away by moistening with a saturated solution of ammonium nitrate and then reheating.

(2) Aqueous solutions do not usually ignite even though the solute is highly inflammable, *e.g.*, an aqueous solution of ethanol containing less than 50% of the latter. When aqueous solutions of solid substances are heated on a crucible lid, they usually "spit" vigorously immediately before solidification.

Section 2. Identification of Elements present in an Organic Compound.

1. Carbon and Hydrogen. The presence of these elements is usually assumed. If a direct test is required, a mixture of about 0·1 g. of the powdered substance and 2–3 g. of finely powdered copper oxide is heated in the tube **A** (Fig. 68) and the

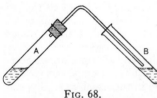

FIG. 68.

gases issuing from the delivery-tube are then collected above the lime-water in the tube **B**. When the delivery-tube is withdrawn and the tube **B** closed and shaken, a white precipitate indicates carbon dioxide, and hence the presence of carbon. (Alternatively, the delivery-tube may dip into the lime-water during the heating, but in this case the lime-water is apt to "suck back" into **A** if the heating is irregular.) If the compound contains sulphur, the issuing gases must first be passed through a solution of potassium dichromate in dilute sulphuric acid to remove the sulphur dioxide (which is oxidised to sulphuric acid) before passing into lime-water.

A mist of condensed water on the upper portion of the tube **A** indicates the presence of hydrogen. To detect the presence of hydrogen in this way, however, the copper oxide must first be strongly heated in a crucible and then allowed to cool in a good desiccator: otherwise the water normally absorbed by the very hygroscopic copper oxide will always give a mist on the tube **A**.

2. Nitrogen. The Lassaigne Sodium Test.*

This test is general for organic nitrogen compounds. The organic compound is heated with molten sodium, the nitrogen present thus forming sodium cyanide. The latter is extracted with water and then identified by first adding ferrous sulphate and then boiling the alkaline mixture in order to convert the cyanide to ferrocyanide:

$$6NaCN + Fe(OH)_2 = Na_4[Fe(CN)_6] + 2NaOH$$

Ferric chloride solution is then added to convert the sodium ferrocyanide to the deep blue ferric ferrocyanide (or Prussian Blue), dilute sulphuric acid being also added to dissolve any ferrous and ferric hydroxides present in the other-

$$3Na_4[Fe(CN)_6] + 4FeCl_3 = Fe_4[Fe(CN)_6]_3 + 12NaCl$$

wise alkaline solution The blue coloration is thus a definite test for nitrogen in the original organic compound.

Place about 50 mg. of the organic compound† in a short hard-glass test-tube, and add two small pellets of metallic sodium (roughly 3 mm. in diameter). Grasping the tube firmly with a test-tube holder, heat the mixture in a Bunsen flame, at first *gently* and then, after any initial reaction‡ has subsided, more vigorously until fumes have ceased to be evolved and a well-roasted product has been obtained. While holding the tube in *a vertical position*, plunge it firmly and without delay into about 10 ml. of *distilled* water contained in a small clean mortar. A vigorous action occurs as the tube fractures and the excess of sodium oxide reacts with the water: hence the need to hold the tube vertically in the water until all reaction has ceased, in case a portion of the contents should be blown out. Plunging the

---

* For Middleton's sodium carbonate-zinc method for the detection of elements, see p. 326.

† Note that, in addition to the recognised unstable compounds (such as polynitro derivatives), *chloroform* and *carbon tetrachloride* should never be submitted to Lassaigne's sodium test, as violent explosions may result.

‡ If a vigorous initial reaction occurs, remove the tube from the flame until the reaction subsides, and then continue heating.

end of the tube into water should *always* be performed immediately after heating: if the tube is allowed to cool somewhat
beforehand, the reaction may then be far more violent.

The sodium fusion and extraction, if performed strictly in accordance with the above directions, should be safe operations. In crowded
laboratories, however, additional safety may be obtained by employing
the following modification. Suspend the hard-glass test-tube by the
rim through a hole in a piece of stout copper sheet (Fig. 69). Place
1–2 pellets of sodium in the tube, and heat gently until the sodium melts.
Then drop the organic compound, in *small quantities* at a time, down

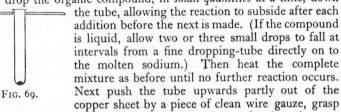

the tube, allowing the reaction to subside after each
addition before the next is made. (If the compound
is liquid, allow two or three small drops to fall at
intervals from a fine dropping-tube directly on to
the molten sodium.) Then heat the complete
mixture as before until no further reaction occurs.
Next push the tube upwards partly out of the
copper sheet by a piece of clean wire gauze, grasp

FIG. 69.

the neck firmly with a test-tube holder, and transfer the tube to a
fume-cupboard. There reheat the tube, and then without delay plunge
it as before into about 10 ml. of distilled water contained in a mortar
placed immediately behind a small sheet of plate-glass clamped vertically
to act as a screen.

The first method should be used, however, by experienced students,
as it has the advantage that the initial reaction of the compound with the
sodium as the cold mixture is warmed can be observed, and frequently
gives an indication of the general nature of the compound: thus a
vigorous reaction in the cold, or immediately on gentle warming, may
indicate an acidic substance, whereas a vigorous reaction after the
mixture has been gently heated may indicate a compound rich in
oxygen; evolution of violet vapour of iodine indicates a substance
rich in iodine, *etc.*

Now grind up the mixture of solution and glass in the mortar
to ensure extraction of the sodium salts, and then filter. Divide
the filtrate into three portions, reserving two portions for testing
for halogens and sulphur.

Add about 0·2 g. of ferrous sulphate crystals to the first portion of the filtrate contained in a boiling-tube. An immediate
dark greenish-grey* precipitate of ferrous hydroxide should
occur: if the mixture remains clear, add a few ml. of sodium
hydroxide solution. Now boil the mixture gently for a few
minutes to ensure formation of the ferrocyanide, cool under the
tap, add *one drop* of ferric chloride solution, and then acidify

* If the original compound contains sulphur, a black precipitate may be
produced at this stage.

with dilute sulphuric acid. A greenish-blue coloration, sometimes followed slowly by an actual precipitation of Prussian blue,
indicates nitrogen. If only a green coloration is obtained, it often
indicates insufficient reaction with the sodium: if, however, such
a solution is filtered, "specks" of deep blue material can frequently be seen collected on the filter-paper and are a clear
indication of the presence of nitrogen.

(1) Some nitrogenous organic compounds react very slowly with
sodium even under the above conditions of fusion, and give in consequence only a feeble indication for nitrogen. If, in spite of this feeble
indication, the general properties of the substance point to the presence
of nitrogen, repeat the fusion using the apparatus shown in Fig. 69, but
heat the sodium until it boils gently in the vertical tube. Then drop the
substance, in *very small portions* at a time, down the tube, so that it falls
through the column of sodium vapour into the boiling metal. Nitrogen
is often yielded up under these conditions when the former less drastic
method fails.

(2) Lassaigne's test is obviously a test also for carbon in the presence
of nitrogen. It can be used therefore to detect nitrogen in carbon-free
inorganic compounds, *e.g.*, complex nitrites, amino-sulphonic acid
derivatives, *etc.*, but such compounds must before fusion with sodium
be mixed with some non-volatile nitrogen-free organic compound such
as starch

The Soda-lime Test. Certain classes of nitrogenous organic
compounds (*e.g.*, amides, *etc.*) evolve ammonia when heated with
soda-lime. In view of the limited application of this test, however, it may well be reserved for Section 3, where it is included
with other compounds reacting with soda-lime.

Halogen. (1) THE BEILSTEIN TEST. For this very
rapid test, which should precede Lassaigne's sodium test for
halogen, secure a fragment of copper oxide **C** (Fig. 70(A)) by a
platinum wire **D** held in turn by a glass rod: the latter may conveniently be thrust through a cork which fits a short test-tube so
that the wire may be safely carried in the pocket. An alternative
and cheaper apparatus for large classes consists
of a piece of fine copper gauze **E** about 2 cm.
square (Fig. 70(B)) securely rolled around one
end of a stout copper wire carrying a cork for
use as a holder. Heat the copper oxide **C** (or the
copper gauze **E**) in a Bunsen flame until any
initial green coloration caused by impurities on
the copper has disappeared. Withdraw the
wire, and dip the hot oxide (or the oxidised

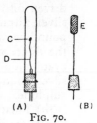

FIG. 70.

gauze) into a small quantity of the *powdered* organic compound, *e.g.*, chloral hydrate. Now insert the wire into the vertical edge of the flame about one inch from the top of the burner. A bright green coloration, often lasting only a few seconds, indicates halogen in the organic compound.

This test depends on the hot copper oxide decomposing a small quantity of the organic compound with the formation of the corresponding copper halide, which, being volatile at high temperatures, gives the usual green copper coloration. A few halogen-free amides, such as urea, thio-urea, and some pyridine compounds, give volatile cuprous cyanide under these conditions, however, and therefore also give the green coloration. It can be said therefore that a *negative* result for halogen is decisive, whereas a *positive* result means that halogen is *probably* present. The great value of this test for halogen is that, unlike the Lassaigne test, it is usually unaffected by the presence of nitrogen, and thus gives a *rapid* indication of the definite absence or probable presence of halogen.

(2) THE LASSAIGNE SODIUM TEST. (*a*) *Nitrogen being absent.* In this case the halogen has been converted during the sodium fusion into the corresponding sodium halide. Therefore acidify the second portion of the filtrate with dilute nitric acid, and add silver nitrate solution. A white or yellow precipitate indicates halogen.

(*b*) *Nitrogen being present.* In this case, if silver nitrate is added to the acidified solution, a white precipitate of silver cyanide will be obtained and will be mixed with silver halide if halogen is present: it is necessary therefore either (i) to remove cyanide before testing for halogen, or (ii) to test for silver halide in a possible mixture of silver cyanide and halide.

(i) Take a portion of the clear filtrate from the sodium fusion, make it *just* acid with dilute nitric acid, and then evaporate it to about half-bulk by gentle boiling in an evaporating-basin. The very volatile hydrogen cyanide is thus driven off. Now cool and test for halogen by addition of silver nitrate. Note furthermore that if the organic compound contains sulphur, the hydrogen sulphide liberated by the dilute nitric acid will be driven off with the hydrogen cyanide during the evaporation, and the final precipitate of silver halide will therefore be entirely free also from silver sulphide.

(ii) Treat the clear filtrate with dilute nitric acid and silver nitrate (as in (*a*) above), and add mercurous nitrate drop by drop. Note that the white precipitate of silver salts turns black (showing the presence of silver cyanide). Now add an *excess* of mercurous nitrate: the black precipitate redissolves, but the silver halide remains undissolved.

To determine which halogen is present, take 1–2 ml. of the filtrate from the sodium fusion, and add dilute sulphuric acid until *just* acid to litmus. Add about 1 ml. of benzene and then about 1 ml. of chlorine water and shake. A yellowish-brown colour in the benzene indicates bromine, and a violet colour iodine. If neither colour appears, the halogen is chlorine. The result may be confirmed by testing the solubility of the silver halide (free from cyanide) in *dilute* ammonia solution: silver chloride is readily soluble, whereas the bromide dissolves with difficulty, and the iodide not at all.

Sulphur. THE LASSAIGNE SODIUM TEST. The sodium fusion will have converted any sulphur present in the original compounds to sodium sulphide. Dissolve a few crystals of sodium nitroprusside, $Na_2[Fe(CN)_5NO],2H_2O$, in water, and add the solution to the third portion of the filtrate obtained from the sodium fusion. A brilliant purple coloration (resembling permanganate) indicates sulphur; the coloration slowly fades on standing. *Note.* (i) Sodium nitroprusside is unstable in aqueous solution and therefore the solution should be freshly prepared on each occasion. (ii) This is a *very* delicate test for sulphides, and it is essential therefore that all apparatus, particularly test-tubes, should be quite clean.

Sodium Fusion on Semi-micro Scale. The Lassaigne test can be readily carried out with as little as 0·01 g. of material, using sodium pellets about 2 mm. in diameter in a tube about $3'' \times \frac{3}{8}''$. After fusion, the red-hot tube is plunged into distilled water in a small porcelain crucible or in a boiling-tube. The mixture is then heated, filtered and tested as already described.

The following compounds are suggested for practising the identification of these elements:

(*a*) *Nitrogen.* Benzamide, ammonium benzoate, *p*-toluidine, glucosazone, acetanilide and benzanilide (require care to obtain definite blue coloration).

(*b*) *Halogen.* Chloral hydrate, sodium chloroacetate, chlorobenzene, *p*-chlorophenol, dichlorhydrin, bromobenzene, iodobenzene.

(*c*) *Nitrogen and Halogen.* Aniline hydrochloride, ammonium chloroacetate, *p*-chloroacetanilide, suitable mixtures of (*a*) and (*b*).

(*d*) *Sulphur.* Potassium ethyl sulphate, acetone sodium bisulphite, benzaldehyde sodium bisulphite, toluene-*p*-sulphonic acid and salts.

(*e*) *Nitrogen and Sulphur.* Sulphanilic acid, toluene-*p*-sulphonamide, thiocarbanilide, aniline sulphate.

(*f*) *Nitrogen, Halogen and Sulphur.* Chloramine-T, suitable mixtures of (*c*) and(*d*), and (*c*) and (*e*).

It is essential that students practise these tests until they can be reasonably certain of accurate results with unidentified compounds. The following scheme for the identification of organic compounds is based largely on an initial classification of the compounds according to the elements they contain: hence an error in the identification of these elements may lead a student completely astray throughout the subsequent investigation.

The Sodium Carbonate-Zinc Method for Detecting Nitrogen, Halogens and Sulphur in Organic Compounds.

This method, due to Middleton (*Analyst*, 1935, **60**, 154), has the advantage over Lassaigne's method (pp. 321–326) that the use of metallic sodium is avoided: it has the disadvantage, however, that the reagents are not so readily obtained pure, and the method requires rather more time.

The organic compound is heated with a mixture of sodium carbonate and zinc dust, when nitrogen and halogens are split off as sodium cyanide and halides respectively, and sulphur as zinc sulphide. The sodium cyanide and halides are extracted with water and detected as in Lassaigne's method: the zinc sulphide in the residue is decomposed with acid and the hydrogen sulphide then detected with lead acetate paper. In these circumstances compounds which contain both nitrogen and sulphur do not give thiocyanates, a further minor advantage over Lassaigne's method.

Preparation of the Reagent. Grind thoroughly together in a dry mortar 25 g. of pure anhydrous ("Analar") sodium carbonate and 50 g. of the purest obtainable zinc dust. Preserve the reagent in a wide-necked stoppered bottle until required.

Zinc dust of good quality usually contains only negligible quantities of halogen and sulphur, and is nitrogen-free. A blank for these elements should, however, be made with every fresh batch of reagent prepared: if perceptible traces of halogen or sulphur are present, a blank or control test must be performed side by side with that on the organic compound, and the results compared.

The Fusion. (i) *Solid Compounds.* Place about 0·2 g. of the powdered compound in a small dry hard-glass test-tube, add sufficient of the reagent to give a column about 1 cm. high and then shake the closed tube until the contents are thoroughly mixed. Now add more reagent (without mixing with the material already in the tube) until a total height of about 3–4 cm. is obtained.

(ii) *Liquid Compounds.* Fill the hard-glass tube to a height of about 1 cm. with the reagent. Add 2–3 drops of the liquid to be tested, and allow it to soak well into the reagent. Now add more reagent (without mixing) until a total height of about 4 cm. is obtained.

Proceed as follows for both solid and liquid compounds. By means of a test-tube holder, hold the tube in a horizontal position, and by means of a small flame *gently* heat the mixture at the open end. Increase the size of the flame gradually until the mixture is red-hot at this end. Now slowly and cautiously extend the heating towards the closed end until the whole of the mixture is red-hot. (If during the extension of the heating, the mixture tends to be pushed out of the tube by the evolution of gas, stop the heating momentarily, and rotate the tube whilst still in a horizontal position in order to redistribute the contents: then continue the heating cautiously.) Finally heat the tube strongly in a vertical position for a short time. While the end of the tube is still red-hot, plunge the tube vertically into about 20 ml. of cold distilled water in an evaporating-basin. Boil the contents of the dish gently, allow to cool slightly and then decant the supernatant liquid through a filter. Retain the residue in the basin for the sulphur test. Divide the clear filtrate into two portions.

NITROGEN. To one portion of the filtrate, add 2–3 ml. of 10% aqueous sodium hydroxide solution, then add about 0·2 g. of ferrous sulphate and proceed as in the Lassaigne nitrogen test (p. 322). Note, however, that the final acidification with dilute suphuric acid must be made with care, owing to the vigorous evolution of carbon dioxide from the carbonate present.

HALOGENS. Test the second portion of the filtrate for halogens in the usual way, as described under the Lassaigne halogen test (p. 324). Note that cyanides if present must first be eliminated as usual.

SULPHUR. Moisten the centre of a filter-paper with lead acetate solution. Then add about 10 ml. of dilute hydrochloric acid to the residue in the evaporating-basin, and at once cover the latter with the paper. If zinc sulphide is present in the residue, the hydrogen sulphide evolved will give a *definite* dark brown coloration with the lead acetate paper. The presence of hydrogen sulphide can often be confirmed by its odour.

Section 3. Heating with Soda-lime.

Mix about 0·2 g. of each of the following powdered substances with about 1 g. of powdered soda-lime, preferably by grinding in a small clean mortar. The odour of ammonia in the cold usually indicates an ammonium salt, that of chloroform indicates chloral hydrate. Place the intimate mixture in a hard-glass test-tube (which thus should be not more than half-full), close the tube by a cork and delivery-tube, and then incline the tube as shown in Fig. 71, so that any liquid which subsequently condenses cannot run back into the hot part of the tube. Now heat the tube very gently at first and then more strongly. A non-condensible product such as hydrogen or methane is best detected by collecting a sample of the gas in a test-tube as shown in Fig. 71(A). A condensible product

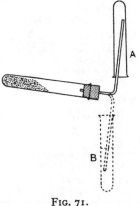

FIG. 71.

such as benzene or phenol should be collected by twisting the delivery-tube downwards and collecting the liquid in a few ml. of water in a test-tube as shown in Fig. 71(B).

Substance	Class	Result
Ammonium acetate CH_3COONH_4	Ammonium salts	Ammonia evolved in the cold (turns moist red litmus-paper blue). Methane may be evolved by stronger and more prolonged heating.
Acetamide CH_3CONH_2 Urea H_2NCONH_2 }	Acid amides	Ammonia evolved.
Glycine H_2NCH_2COOH	Amino-carboxylic acids	Methylamine evolved (fishy odour, alkaline reaction).
Sodium acetate CH_3COONa	Carboxylic acids and salts	Methane evolved.
Sodium succinate $(CH_2COONa)_2$	,,	Ethane evolved.
Sodium benzoate C_6H_5COONa	,,	Yields benzene (odour).
Sodium formate HCOONa Sodium oxalate $(COONa)_2$ }	,,	Hydrogen evolved.
Sodium salicylate HOC_6H_4COONa	,,	Yields phenol (odour, and also violet coloration when $FeCl_3$ is added to aqueous solution).
Cane sugar $C_{12}H_{22}O_{11}$	Carbohydrates	Odour of burnt sugar.
Tartaric acid $[\cdot CH(OH)COOH]_2$ Citric acid $C_3H_4(OH)(COOH)_3$ }	Some aliphatic hydroxy-acids and their salts	Odour resembling burnt sugar.
Chloral hydrate $CCl_3CH(OH)_2$		Chloroform (characteristic odour, heavier than water).
Sulphanilic acid $H_2NC_6H_4SO_3H$	Amino-aromatic sulphonic acids	Yields aniline (violet and then brown coloration with bleaching powder solution).
Anthranilic acid $H_2NC_6H_4COOH$	Amino-aromatic carboxylic acids	Yields aniline.
Cinnamic acid $C_6H_5CH:CHCOOH$	Unsaturated aromatic acid	Yields benzene and usually some styrene ($C_6H_5CH:CH_2$, colourless oily liquid, insoluble in water, pleasant characteristic odour).
Uric acid $C_5H_4N_4O_3$	Purine	Ammonia evolved.

NOTE. (1) Heating with soda-lime can sometimes be carried out satisfactorily on a semi-micro scale thus: Place about 0·1 g. of the substance in a dry hard-glass test-tube and add about 0·5 g. of dry powdered soda-lime and shake to obtain a uniform mixture. Draw into the lower end of the glass bulb **B** (Fig. 51(A), p. 70) one drop of a suitable reagent. Now place the bulb carefully on the rim of the test-tube and heat the mixture, gently at first and then more strongly. Note any changes in the nature or colour of the reagent (*e.g.*, bleaching-powder solution turned purple by aniline).

(2) There is no satisfactory chemical way of distinguishing between ethane and methane, both of which burn with an almost non-luminous flame: this fact however is quite unimportant at this stage of the investigation. Hydrogen also burns with a non-luminous flame and when the open end of a test-tube full of the gas is placed in a Bunsen flame, a mild explosion with a very characteristic report takes place.

(3) It frequently happens that more than one volatile product is evolved, a fact which may be of considerable value. For example, benzamide, $C_6H_5CONH_2$, will give off first ammonia, and then benzonitrile and benzene on stronger heating: salicylamide, $HOC_6H_4CONH_2$, will give off ammonia and then phenol. Sulphanilamide, $NH_2C_6H_4SO_2NH_2$ (p. 181), gives off ammonia and aniline.

It must be emphasised that the above reactions are solely of an exploratory nature, and serve merely to indicate the *probable* class to which the compound belongs.

Section 4. Treatment with 10% NaOH solution.

Place about 0·1 g. of the following substances in a boiling-tube and add about 5 ml. of 10% aqueous NaOH solution. Note any reaction in the cold. Then add a small piece of un-glazed porcelain (to prevent "bumping"), and boil *gently* for a few minutes. Note any further reaction.

Substance	Class	Result
Ammonium acetate CH_3COONH_4	Ammonium salt of any acid	Ammonia evolved in the cold.
Acetamide CH_3CONH_2	Acid amides	⎫
Acetonitrile CH_3CN	Acid nitriles	⎬ Ammonia evolved on heating.
Phthalimide $C_6H_4(CO)_2NH$	Imides of dibasic acids	⎭
Acetanilide $C_6H_5NHCOCH_3$	Acid anilides*	Hydrolysis takes place *very slowly*, and after heating for some time aniline is liberated.

* These compounds require a more concentrated NaOH solution (*e.g.*, 30%) for a quick reaction on a test-tube scale.

Substance	Class	Result
Aniline hydrochloride $C_6H_5NH_2,HCl$	Salts of aromatic amines	Aniline is liberated in the cold and floats on the surface.
Ethyl benzoate $C_6H_5COOC_2H_5$	Esters of aromatic acids*	Hydrolyses to ethanol and acid on being heated for a few minutes. Cool, add a few ml. of water and then conc. HCl, and cool again. Crystals of benzoic acid separate out. Complete hydrolysis cannot be carried out effectively on a test-tube scale. (see p. 355).
Acetaldehyde CH_3CHO (aqueous solution)	Aliphatic aldehydes (not given by formaldehyde)	On heating gives a yellow resin having a characteristic colour.
Benzaldehyde C_6H_5CHO	Aromatic aldehydes*	Undergoes Cannizzaro's reaction, giving benzyl alcohol and benzoic acid (p. 229). Warm gently for several minutes, cool, add a few ml. of water and then conc. HCl, and cool again. Crystals of benzoic acid separate out on scratching the sides of the tube with a glass rod. The Cannizzaro reaction cannot be carried out very satisfactory on a test-tube scale.
Chloral hydrate $CCl_3CH(OH)_2$		On gentle warming gives chloroform, which separates out as oily liquid, characteristic odour.
Glucose $C_6H_{12}O_6$	Certain carbohydrates	Turns brown on heating.

Section 5. Treatment with Sodium Carbonate solution.

Place about 5 ml. of Na_2CO_3 solution in (p. 318) a test-tube, add a few fragments of unglazed porcelain, and boil gently to ensure complete absence of bicarbonate and of free carbon dioxide. Cool the solution, add about 0·1 g. of the substance to be tested, and

* See footnote p. 329.

at once fit a bent delivery-tube as shown in Fig. 68, p. 320. Now insert the delivery-tube into another test-tube containing lime-water, so that the end of the delivery-tube just does not touch the surface of the lime-water (if it dips below the surface of the lime-water, intermittent "sucking-back" is liable to occur later). Boil the sodium carbonate *gently* for 2–3 minutes, and then remove the delivery-tube, close the lime-water tube with the thumb and shake vigorously. A white precipitate indicates that carbon dioxide has been evolved.

The following classes of compound yield carbon dioxide when treated in this way.

(*a*) Carboxylic acids, *e.g.*, tartaric acid, benzoic acid (but not most phenols, hence this reaction can be used to distinguish between carboxylic acids and phenols, see p. 347),

(*b*) Sulphonic acids, *e.g.*, sulphanilic acid.

(*c*) Salts of weak bases, *e.g.*, aniline hydrochloride, which hydrolyses in aqueous solution to aniline and free hydrochloric acid.

(*d*) Nitrophenols, *e.g.*, *o*-nitrophenol. In these compounds the nitro group enhances the acidic properties of the phenolic grouping, which is thus able to liberate CO_2 from Na_2CO_3 solution.

NOTE. Methyl oxalate, unlike most other esters, hydrolyses very rapidly in aqueous solution: hence it will evolve CO_2 in the above test, owing to the formation of methanol and free oxalic acid.

Section 6. Action of concentrated Sulphuric Acid.

Place a *small* quantity (*i.e.*, about 0·1 g.) of the following substances (finely powdered) in a clean dry test-tube and add about 1 ml. of conc. H_2SO_4. Note any reaction in the cold, and then warm gently. Note any effervescence and any pronounced blackening (as distinct from mere darkening in colour).

Substance	Class	Result
Cane sugar $C_{12}H_{22}O_{11}$ Starch $(C_6H_{10}O_5)_n$ } Carbohydrates		Blackening with effervescence. CO and (or) CO_2 and SO_2 being evolved.
Tartaric acid [·CH(OH)COOH]$_2$ Lactic acid $CH_3CH(OH)COOH$ } Certain hydroxy-aliphatic acids and their salts		,,
Citric acid $C_3H_4(OH)(COOH)_3$	Certain hydroxy-aliphatic acids and their salts	CO and CO_2 evolved, mixture turns yellow, no charring.
Resorcinol $C_6H_4(OH)_2$	Polyhydric phenols	Blackening without effervescence.

Substance	*Class*	*Result*
Sodium formate HCOONa	Formates	CO evolved, no blackening.
Oxalic acid $(COOH)_2, 2H_2O$	Oxalates	CO and CO_2 evolved, no blackening.
Uric acid $C_5H_4N_4O_3$	Purines	Dissolves on gentle warming and is reprecipitated unchanged on dilution. The solution in conc. H_2SO_4 darkens on heating.

Section 7. Reactions and colorations with aqueous Ferric Chloride solution.

This test is frequently of great value for identification purposes, but it is essential that the conditions given below are rigidly observed, because the careless application of the reagent may give erroneous results.

Ferric chloride solution sometimes contains a large excess of HCl which would interfere with the following reactions. If it is *very* markedly acidic add *dil.* NaOH solution, drop by drop, to the ferric chloride solution until a small but permanent precipitate of ferric hydroxide is obtained. Filter this off through a small fluted filter-paper, and use the clear filtrate. The latter is still not quite neutral owing to hydrolysis, but this feeble acidity does not interfere with the tests given below.

Colorations or coloured precipitates are frequently given by the reaction of ferric chloride solution with (i) solutions of neutral salts of acids, (ii) phenols and many of their derivatives, (iii) a few amines. If a free acid is under investigation it must first be neutralised as follows: Place about 0·1 g. of the acid in a boiling-tube and add a slight excess of ammonia solution, *i.e.*, until the solution is just alkaline to litmus-paper. Add a piece of unglazed porcelain and boil until the odour of ammonia is *completely* removed, and then cool. To the solution so obtained add a few drops of the "neutralised" ferric chloride solution. Perform this test with the following acids and note the result:

Note. For a very weak acid, the ammonium salt of which may dissociate rapidly on heating, conversion into the sodium salt is recommended. Place 0·1 g. of the acid in a boiling-tube and add NaOH solution until the mixture is just alkaline to litmus-paper. Add *dil.* HNO_3 until just acid and then a slight excess of ammonia until again just alkaline. Add a piece of unglazed porcelain, and boil until the odour of ammonia is removed, and then cool.

Substance	*Class*	*Result**
(*a*) Formic acid ⎱ Acetic acid ⎰	Lower aliphatic acids	Deep red coloration. Boil for one minute and note the formation of a brown ppt. of basic ferric salt. Add dil. HCl: the ppt. dissolves, giving a clear solution.
(*b*) Oxalic acid		Very faint yellow.
(*c*) Succinic acid		Buff-coloured ppt. in the cold. Add dil. H_2SO_4: the ppt. dissolves giving clear solution.
(*d*) Benzoic acid	Aromatic acids (except phenolic carboxylic acids)	Buff-coloured ppt. in the cold. Add dil. H_2SO_4: the ppt. dissolves, but simultaneously a white ppt. of benzoic acid is produced.
(*e*) Salicylic acid	Phenolic acid	Violet coloration. (Note however that a dilute solution of salicylic acid will give this coloration without any preliminary neutralisation.)

(*f*) Take two test-tubes **A** and **B**: in **A** place about 5 ml. of neutralised tartaric acid solution and in **B** place 5 ml. of distilled water. To each solution add 3–4 drops of ferric chloride solution. Place a piece of white paper under the tubes, look down their length and note that **A** is definitely yellow compared with the control tube **B**. This yellow colour is given by α-hydroxy-carboxylic-acids, *e.g.*, lactic acid, tartaric acid, citric acid.

(*g*) Dissolve a few crystals of phenol in water and add ferric chloride solution: a violet coloration is produced. Repeat, using 1–2 drops of *m*-cresol shaken up with about 1 ml. of water: a violet coloration is again produced. Catechol (in dilute solution) gives a green coloration.

(*h*) Dissolve 2–3 drops of *o*-toluidine in a few drops of dil. HCl and add 2–3 drops of ferric chloride solution: a green coloration is produced and is slowly replaced by a bluish-green or blue precipitate.

---

* Unless *all* the excess of ammonia has been driven off in the preparation of the neutral salt, the result obtained on adding ferric chloride will be misleading owing to the precipitation of ferric hydroxide. If this is suspected, the tests should be repeated using an aqueous solution of the *pure* sodium salts of these acids for comparison.

Section 8. Reaction with 2,4-Dinitrophenylhydrazine.

This is a test for the $>C=O$ group. Most aldehydes and ketones readily condense with this reagent* giving yellow- or orange-coloured precipitates.

To a few drops of formalin solution add a few drops of dinitrophenylhydrazine reagent A (p. 263): a yellow precipitate is produced in the cold. Acetaldehyde and acetone give orange-coloured precipitates. Dissolve water-insoluble compounds (*e.g.*, benzaldehyde, salicylaldehyde, acetophenone and benzophenone) in a small volume of methanol before adding reagent B. With benzophenone the precipitate forms slowly.

Section 9. Reaction of Esters with Hydroxylamine.

As esters are usually difficult to detect, this test is of considerable value. In general esters react when heated with hydroxylamine to give a hydroxamic acid (I). The latter gives a coloured complex (II) with ferric salts in acid solution.

$$R \cdot COOR' + H \cdot NHOH = R'OH + R \cdot CO \cdot NH \cdot OH \quad (I)$$

$$R \cdot CO \cdot NH \cdot OH + Fe^{+++} = R \cdot C \underset{O \ldots \ldots Fe/3}{\overset{NH - O}{<}} \quad (II)$$

Hydroxamic acid formation resembles amide formation (pp. 117–119) and therefore certain other classes of substances will respond to the test, *e.g.*, acid chlorides and acid anhydrides, but these substances are readily distinguished by other reactions.

$$\begin{matrix} R \cdot CO \\ \end{matrix} \! \! > \! O + H \cdot NHOH = R \cdot CO \cdot NH \cdot OH + R \cdot COOH$$

Amides themselves (*e.g.*, acetamide) also often respond to the reaction:

$$R \cdot C \overset{O}{\underset{NH_2}{<}} + H \cdot NHOH \rightarrow R \cdot \overset{NH \cdot OH}{\underset{NH_2}{C} - OH} \rightarrow R \cdot CO \cdot NH \cdot OH + NH_3$$

Some anilides may give the reaction.

To a few drops of the ester, add 0·2 g. of hydroxylamine hydrochloride and about 5 ml. of 10% NaOH solution and *gently* boil the mixture for 1–2 minutes. Cool and acidify with HCl, cool again and then add a few drops of $FeCl_3$ solution. A violet or deep red-brown colour develops immediately.

* Details of the preparation of the reagent are given on p. 263.

Section 10. Alcohols. —OH. (*cf.* Tables IV, V. 536–537)

Methanol, ethanol, n-propanol (propan-1-ol), isopropanol (propan-2-ol), n-butanol, glycol, glycerol, benzyl alcohol, cyclohexanol.

Physical Properties. All colourless liquids, completely miscible with water, except benzyl alcohol and cyclohexanol, which are slightly soluble. Pure glycol and glycerol have high viscosity, which falls as the hygroscopic liquids absorb water from the air.

Glycol and glycerol are odourless: the other alcohols have faint odours, that of benzyl alcohol being characteristic.

GENERAL REACTIONS.

1. Give crystalline esters with 3,5-dinitrobenzoyl chloride.

2. Give crystalline urethanes with phenylisocyanate.

3. Primary alcohols (·CH$_2$OH) are oxidised to aldehydes and then to acids. Secondary alcohols (>CHOH) are oxidised to ketones.

4. Alcohols containing the CH$_3$CH(OH)· group give the iodoform reaction.

1. *3,5-Dinitrobenzoylation.* To 0·5 g. of powdered 3,5-dinitrobenzoyl chloride (preparation, p. 240) in a dry test-tube, add 2 ml. of dry methanol and warm the mixture until a clear solution is obtained. Cool and filter off the solid ester which separates. Recrystallise from petroleum (b.p. 60–80°), and take the m.p.   (M.ps., pp. 536, 537.)

2. *Urethanes.* The reaction with phenylisocyanate should be used for crystalline derivative formation (see below), and not as a general reaction for alcohols.

3. *Oxidation.* (i) Dissolve 5 g. of potassium dichromate in 20 ml. of dil. H$_2$SO$_4$ in a 100 ml. bolt-head flask. Cool and add 1 ml. of methanol. Fit the flask with a reflux water-condenser and warm gently: a vigorous reaction soon occurs and the solution turns green. The characteristic pungent odour of formaldehyde is usually detected at this stage. Continue to heat for 3 minutes and then fit the flask with a knee-tube (Fig .59, p. 100) and distil off a few ml. Test the distillate with blue litmus-paper to show that it is definitely acid. Then apply Test 3 p. 350) for formic acid. (The reflux-distillation apparatus (Fig. 38, p. 63) can conveniently be used for this test.)

By a similar reaction ethanol gives acetaldehyde (tests, p. 341) and isopropanol gives acetone (tests, p. 345). *n*-Butanol gives butyraldehyde (pleasant characteristic odour and precipitate with 2,4-dinitrophenylhydrazine, m.p. 122°).

Glycol gives the non-volatile oxalic acid. After heating the mixture under reflux for 10 minutes, transfer 2 ml. of the cold product to a test-tube and add 4 ml. of conc. H$_2$SO$_4$. Note the production of carbon monoxide and carbon dioxide on heating (p. 350).

Cyclohexanol gives the non-volatile adipic acid, HOOC·(CH$_2$)$_4$COOH. After heating the mixture under reflux for 10 minutes, cool the flask, transfer a few ml. of the product to a test-tube, and note the separation of white crystals of adipic acid on scratching (m.p. 153°).

(ii) *Oxidation of benzyl alcohol to benzoic acid.* Boil a mixture of 0·5 ml. of benzyl alcohol, 25 ml. of saturated potassium permanganate solution and 0·5 g. of Na_2CO_3 under reflux for 15 minutes. Cool somewhat, acidify carefully with conc. HCl, and then add 25% sodium sulphite solution until the brown precipitate of manganese dioxide has dissolved. On cooling, benzoic acid crystallises out. Filter through a small Buchner funnel, wash with water and identify (see p. 347). The benzoic acid after recrystallisation from water has m.p. 121°.

3. *Iodoform Reaction.* To 0·5 ml. of ethanol add 3 ml. of 10% KI solution and 10 ml. of NaOCl solution. Warm *gently*: fine yellow crystals of CHI_3 separate. Isopropanol gives CHI_3 in the cold. *Pure* methanol and the other alcohols in this section go not give the reaction.

CRYSTALLINE DERIVATIVES FOR IDENTIFICATION.

(A) 3,5-*Dinitrobenzoates*. Preparation, see above. (M.ps., pp. 536–537.) *p*-Nitrobenzoates can often be prepared as for phenols (p. 337), but the *p*-nitrobenzoates of many of the simpler alcohols have m.ps. too low to be of practical value. (M.ps., p. 535–537).

(B) *Phenylurethanes*. Primary and secondary alcohols usually combine readily with phenylisocyanate to give crystalline urethanes:

$$R\cdot OH + C_6H_5\cdot NCO = C_6H_5NH\cdot CO\cdot OR.$$

Three factors must be considered: (*a*) the phenylurethanes of the simpler alcohols have low melting-points: 1-naphthylisocyanate, $C_{10}H_7\cdot NCO$, gives better products with these alcohols. (*b*) The alcohol should be dried if necessary, for water will react with phenylisocyanate to give ultimately diphenylurea, $(C_6H_5NH)_2CO$, m.p. 239°. If a mixed product is thus obtained, recrystallisation from petroleum (b.p. 100–120°), in which the urea is almost insoluble, will usually give the pure urethane. (*c*) The evidence for the allocation of the compound to the class of alcohols (or phenols, p. 337) must be sound, for primary and secondary amines give crystalline ureas with this reagent (pp. 375, 377).

Some alcohols react readily with phenylisocyanate at room temperature, and others require heating, preferably in petroleum. Phenylisocyanate *is poisonous*, and should not be heated outside a fume-cupboard except under a condenser.

Example. Add a solution of 0·5 ml. of benzyl alcohol in 5 ml. of petroleum (b.p. 100–120°) to a similar solution of 0·5 ml. of phenylisocyanate, and boil the mixture gently *under reflux* for 20 minutes. Filter hot if necessary from any insoluble diphenylurea, and cool. Filter off the crystalline urethane, and recrystallise from the petroleum: colourless crystals, m.p. 76°.

Some alcohols require longer heating to complete this reaction, and others give urethanes much less soluble in the boiling petroleum. The student must exercise his judgement to determine the minimum effective time of boiling, and the volume of petroleum which may have to be added to the boiling solution to ensure that the urethane has entirely

dissolved, and the residue is solely diphenylurea. (M.ps. of phenyl-
and 1-naphthyl-urethanes, p.536–537.)

(C) *Carboxylic acids* For aryl-substituted alcohols, such as benzyl
alcohol, oxidation readily gives the corresponding acid (*cf.* p. 336).

SPECIAL REACTIONS.

Methanol (methyl alcohol). CH_3OH.

1. *Methyl salicylate test.* Heat 1 ml. of methanol with 0·5 g. of
sodium salicylate (or free salicylic acid) and a few drops of conc.
H_2SO_4 *gently* for 1 minute. Cool, pour into a few ml. of cold water
in a boiling-tube, and shake. Note the odour of methyl salicylate
(oil of wintergreen).

Ethyl salicylate (prepared by the same method) has an odour similar to that
of methyl salicylate but less intense: it is therefore usually impracticable to
attempt to distinguish methanol and ethanol by this test alone.

Ethanol (ethyl alcohol). C_2H_5OH.

1. *Ethyl acetate test.* Heat 1 ml. of ethanol with 0·5 g. of sodium
acetate and a few drops of conc. H_2SO_4 *gently* for about 1 minute.
Cool and pour into a few ml. of water in a boiling-tube. Note fruity
odour of the ethyl acetate.

Here again the odour of methyl acetate is similar, and the student must
decide for himself what reliance he can place on the difference.

Glycerol. $CH_2OH \cdot CHOH \cdot CH_2OH$.

1. *Acrolein test.* Heat 0·5 ml. with about 1 g. of finely powdered
$KHSO_4$. Acrolein, $CH_2{:}CH \cdot CHO$, produced by dehydration of the
glycerol, is readily detected by its characteristic and irritating odour
(*smell cautiously*).

Benzyl alcohol. $C_6H_5CH_2OH$.

1. *Action of sulphuric acid.* To 0·5 ml. of the alcohol, add 0·5 ml.
of conc. H_2SO_4 and shake the mixture. Heat is evolved and a white
gelatinous polymer gradually separates. The reaction is hastened by
warming and the product darkens.

Section 11. Phenols. −OH. (*cf.* Table VI, p. 538)

Phenol, o-, m- and p-cresol, catechol, resorcinol, hydroquinone
(and other nuclear-substituted phenols); *1- and 2-naphthol.*

Physical properties. All solid except *m*-cresol, $CH_3C_6H_4OH$, which
is a liquid. All colourless when pure, but frequently slightly coloured
due to atmospheric oxidation. All have in varying degrees a characteristic odour of "carbolic acid." Phenol, the cresols and resorcinol
have a *caustic action on the skin.*

Phenol, C_6H_5OH, catechol, $o\text{-}C_6H_4(OH)_2$, resorcinol, $m\text{-}C_6H_4(OH)_2$, and hydroquinone, p-$C_6H_4(OH)_2$, are soluble in water; the remainder are sparingly soluble or insoluble in water. All phenols are soluble in sodium hydroxide solution, in some cases (*e.g.*, catechol, resorcinol, hydroquinone) with rapid darkening in colour.

GENERAL REACTIONS.*

1. Do not liberate CO_2 from Na_2CO_3 solutions (distinction from carboxylic acids, p. 347).
2. Give characteristic colorations with ferric chloride.
3. Give toluene-p-sulphonyl derivatives.
4. Give benzoyl, p-nitrobenzoyl and 3,5-dinitrobenzoyl derivatives.
5. Give urethanes with phenylisocyanate.
6. Couple in alkaline solution with diazotised amines to give orange or red azo-dyes.
7. Form phthaleins.
8. Certain phenols give white bromo-derivatives with bromine water.
9. Certain phenols give the Liebermann Nitroso Reaction.

1. *Sodium carbonate solution* (*cf.* Section 5, p. 330). Note that phenols (except those containing acidic groups, *e.g.*, nitrophenols) give no reaction with sodium carbonate solution.

2. *Ferric chloride coloration.* To a very dilute aqueous solution of the phenol or to a minute crystal of the solid add 1 drop of ferric chloride solution. Phenol, resorcinol, o-, m-, and p-cresol give violet or blue colorations. Catechol gives a green coloration which rapidly darkens. Hydroquinone undergoes oxidation: it gives a deep green solution (crystals may separate), and on further addition of ferric chloride, a yellow solution of p-benzoquinone is obtained. 1- and 2-Naphthol do not give characteristic colorations.

3. *Toluene-p-sulphonyl derivatives.* See directions, p. 249. Perform on this scale. (M.ps., p. 538.)

4. (*a*) *Benzoylation* (*cf.* p. 244). Dissolve 1 g. of the phenol in about 15 ml. of 10% NaOH solution contained in a strong boiling-tube. Add 2 ml. of benzoyl chloride, cork the tube securely and shake vigorously for 10 minutes. Filter, wash well, and recrystallise from methylated spirit. Take the m.p. (M.ps., p. 410.)

(*b*) 3,5-*Dinitrobenzoylation.* Dissolve 0·5 g. of phenol in 10 ml. of N-NaOH solution in a small mortar. Grind into the mortar 1·2 g. of powdered 3,5-dinitrobenzoyl chloride (preparation, p. 342). After 1 minute filter off the solid residue, wash with dil. NaOH solution and recrystallise from ethanol. Phenyl 3,5-dinitrobenzoate has m.p. 146°. (M.ps., p. 538.)

---

* Many of the reactions of phenols are frequently given also by their derivatives, *e.g.*, salicylic acid (p. 352) behaves like phenol towards a number of reagents.

p-*Nitrobenzoyl* derivatives can be prepared as in (*a*) or (*b*) above. If direct shaking, as in (*a*), is employed, the *p*-nitrobenzoyl chloride should first be finely powdered. Alternatively, dissolve the phenol in dry pyridine, add the *p*-nitrobenzoyl chloride and boil gently under reflux for 20 minutes. Cool and pour into dil. HCl. Collect the precipitate and stir it thoroughly with dil. Na_2CO_3 solution to ensure removal of *p*-nitrobenzoic acid: filter off the residue, wash it with water and recrystallise. (This method can sometimes be profitably used for 3,5-dinitrobenzoylation.)   (M.ps., p. 538.)

5. *Urethane formation.* See (C) below. This reaction should be used for crystalline derivative formation, and not as a general reaction for phenols.

6. *Azo-dye formation.* Dissolve 2–3 drops of aniline in 1 ml. of conc. HCl and add 3 ml. of water. Shake to dissolve any hydrochloride which may have separated and cool in ice. Add a few drops of 20% sodium nitrite solution. Add this cold diazonium solution to a cold solution of the phenol in an *excess* of aqueous NaOH solution. Solutions or precipitates of azo-dyes ranging in colour from orange through scarlet to dark red, according to the phenol used, are obtained. Note in particular that 1-naphthol gives a brownish-red, 2-naphthol a scarlet precipitate. Catechol decomposes.

7. *Phthalein reaction.* Place in a dry test-tube about 0·2 g. of the phenol and an equal quantity of phthalic anhydride (or acid), moisten with 2 drops (not more) of conc. H_2SO_4 and gently fuse together for about 1 minute. Allow to cool somewhat, and then add 10% NaOH solution in excess.

Characteristic colorations, recorded for reference, are produced as follows: phenol, red (phenolphthalein); *o*-cresol, red; *m*-cresol, bluish-purple; *p*-cresol, nil; catechol, usually blue (alizarin) although this requires longer, but not stronger, heating; resorcinol, green fluorescent solution (fluorescein); hydroquinone, deep purple; 1-naphthol, green; 2-naphthol, very faint green with slight fluorescence.

8. *Action of bromine water.* To a concentrated aqueous solution of the phenol or to the phenol itself, add bromine water gradually. At first the bromine is decolorised and then on adding an *excess* a white or yellowish-white precipitate of a polybromo-derivative is produced with all except catechol, hydroquinone, 1- and 2-naphthol.

On adding 1 drop of bromine water to catechol, a deep red coloration is produced immediately. On gradually adding bromine water to a solution of hydroquinone, a deep red coloration is produced, followed by the separation of deep green crystals which then dissolve giving a yellow solution. 1- and 2-Naphthol will decolorise bromine water, but usually no precipitate of the bromo compound can be obtained.

The test is not very satisfactory with those phenols which are insoluble in water, owing to the difficulty of distinguishing the bromo compound from the original phenol.

9. *Liebermann Reaction.** To 1 *minute* crystal of sodium nitrite in a clean dry test-tube add 0·5 g. of phenol and heat very gently for about 20 seconds; allow to cool and add twice the volume of conc. H_2SO_4. On rotating the tube slowly in order to mix the contents, a deep green or deep blue coloration develops (sometimes only after 1–2 minutes). Dilute cautiously with water; the solution turns red. Now add an excess of NaOH solution; the green or blue coloration reappears.

Although phenol gives these marked colour changes, the test is unsatisfactory with many other phenols, the precise tint obtained varying with the purity of the phenol, amount of reagents used, and temperature and time of heating.

CRYSTALLINE DERIVATIVES FOR IDENTIFICATION.

(A) *Toluene*-p-*sulphonates.* For directions, using an acetone solution of toluene-*p*-sulphonyl chloride, see p. 249: use 0·3–0·5 g. of the phenol. Note that the chloride should be dissolved in a minimum of acetone, otherwise separation of the ester may be slow and incomplete.

For some phenols whose esters are readily hydrolysed, it is advantageous to add the powdered chloride to a pyridine solution of the phenol, warm the mixture on the water-bath for *ca.* 15 minutes, cool and pour into water, when the sulphonate will separate.

(M.ps., p. 538.)

(B) p-*Nitro-* and 3,5-*Dinitro-benzoates.* For directions, see 4 above. For reliable identification, these derivatives are preferable to the unsubstituted benzoates, some of which are liquid at room temperature, and others have low m.ps. (M.ps., p. 538.)

(C) *Phenylurethanes.* These derivatives, of formula $C_6H_5NH\cdot CO\cdot OR$, where R is the aryl portion of the phenol, can be prepared in the same way as the corresponding derivatives of alcohols (p. 336). The phenol should be dry. (M.ps., p. 538.)

---

* The colorations produced in this reaction arise from the action of nitrous acid on the phenol, giving *p*-nitrosophenol (I) which then reacts with excess of phenol to form an indophenol (II) which is an acid-base indicator:

$$C_6H_5OH \xrightarrow{HNO_2} ON\cdot C_6H_4\cdot OH \rightleftharpoons O{:}C_6H_4{:}NOH \qquad (I)$$

$$O{:}C_6H_4{:}NOH + C_6H_4OH \xrightarrow{H_2SO_4} O{:}C_6H_4{:}N\cdot C_6H_4OH \quad (II)$$

$$[HO\cdot C_6H_4\cdot N{:}C_6H_4{:}OH]\,\overset{-}{HSO_4} \qquad\qquad [O{:}C_6H_4{:}N\cdot C_6H_4\cdot O]\,\overset{-\;+}{Na}$$

$\xleftarrow{H_2SO_4 \downarrow\; \overset{+}{}\quad\overset{-}{}}$ (green) $\qquad\qquad \xrightarrow{\downarrow NaOH}$ (blue)

The Reaction has the following limitations: (1) a compound that can liberate nitrous acid in acid solution is required (*e.g.*, a metallic nitrite or a nitrosoamine, p. 204). (2) Nitrophenols and *p*-substituted phenols do not give the test. (3) Among the dihydroxyphenols, only resorcinol gives a satisfactory positive test.

Section 12. Aldehydes. —CHO. (*cf.* Tables, pp. 539, 540)

Formaldehyde, metaformaldehyde, acetaldehyde, paraldehyde, chloral hydrate, benzaldehyde, salicylaldehyde (and other substituted benzaldehydes).

Physical properties. All colourless. Formaldehyde, HCHO, is a gas, and only its aqueous solution, which has a characteristic pungent odour, is considered:* metaformaldehyde or "trioxymethylene", $(CH_2O)_3$, is a solid polymer, insoluble in water and ethanol.

Acetaldehyde, CH_3CHO, b.p. 21°, is generally used in aqueous solution, which has also a characteristic odour; paraldehyde, $(CH_3CHO)_3$, is a liquid polymer, b.p. 124°, slightly soluble in water, odour similar to that of acetaldehyde, but less intense. Chloral, CCl_3CHO, a liquid, is almost invariably encountered as the stable solid "hydrate", $CCl_3CH(OH)_2$, m.p. 57°. Both have a characteristic odour: the hydrate is readily soluble in water.

Benzaldehyde, C_6H_5CHO, and salicylaldehyde, HOC_6H_4CHO, are liquids insoluble in water. Benzaldehyde has a characteristic odour of bitter almonds: salicylaldehyde has a faint but also characteristic odour, resembling that of phenol. Salicylaldehyde stains the skin yellow.

GENERAL REACTIONS.

1. Aliphatic aldehydes usually restore the pink colour rapidly to Schiff's reagent.
2. Form phenylhydrazones, 2,4-dinitrophenylhydrazones and semicarbazones. (Many oximes are too soluble for ready isolation.)
3. Conc. NaOH solution reacts with:
    (*a*) aliphatic aldehydes (except formaldehyde) giving resins;
    (*b*) most aromatic aldehydes giving Cannizzaro's reaction.
4. Give silver mirror with ammoniacal silver nitrate.
5. Usually reduce Fehling's solution.
6. Oxidised by alkaline $KMnO_4$ to the corresponding acid.
7. Usually form bisulphite addition compounds, $R \cdot CH(OH)SO_3Na$.

1. *Schiff's reagent.*† Add about 1 ml. of Schiff's reagent to 1 ml. of (*a*) formaldehyde, (*b*) acetaldehyde. A magenta colour rapidly develops in the cold. Benzaldehyde restores the colour very slowly.

2. (*a*) *Phenylhydrazones* of benzaldehyde and salicylaldehyde. To 5 ml. of water add about 0·5 ml. of glacial acetic acid and of phenylhydrazine: then add 3 drops of the aldehyde and shake the mixture.

---

* A 40% solution of formaldehyde in water containing about 15% of methanol is known as "formalin".

† Schiff's reagent should never be warmed or treated with alkaline substances, otherwise the pink colour will be restored even in the absence of aldehydes or ketones. The coloration of Schiff's reagent by an aldehyde or ketone is probably due to the formation of a compound (distinct from magenta) resulting from the combined action of SO_2 and the aldehyde or ketone upon magenta. Excess of mineral acid reduces the sensitivity of the reagent.

After 1–2 minutes, a flocculent precipitate of the phenylhydrazone, RCH:NNHC₆H₅, is produced. Filter and recrystallise from ethanol and take the m.p. (M.ps., p. 539–540.)

The phenylhydrazones of formaldehyde and acetaldehyde are difficult to isolate and are seldom prepared.

(b) *2,4-Dinitrophenylhydrazones.* To a few drops of formalin, add a few drops of 2,4-dinitrophenylhydrazine reagent A (p. 261): a yellow precipitate is produced in the cold. Acetaldehyde gives an orange-coloured precipitate. Dissolve a few drops of benzaldehyde or salicylaldehyde in 2 ml. of methanol and then add a few drops of the reagent B: an orange-coloured precipitate is obtained. In each case filter and recrystallise from ethanol. Take the m.p. (M.ps., p. 539–540.)

(c) *Semicarbazones* (*cf.* p. 258). Add 0·5 g. of semicarbazide hydrochloride to 5 ml. of water, add 0·5 g. of anhydrous sodium acetate and warm *gently* until a clear solution is obtained. Then add a solution of 0·5 ml. of benzaldehyde in 2–3 ml. of ethanol, and warm on a waterbath. The semicarbazone readily crystallises. Cool, filter off the semicarbazone, wash with water, and recrystallise from ethanol; dry and take the m.p. (214°).

Many semicarbazones separate when the cold reaction-mixture is set aside for a short time. (M.ps., p. 539–540.)

3. *Action of sodium hydroxide.* (a) Warm 1 ml. of acetaldehyde with a few ml. of conc. (*e.g.*, 30%) NaOH solution. A yellow resin, having a characteristic odour of bad apples, is formed. Paraldehyde slowly gives a yellow resin.

(b) *Cannizzaro's reaction* (*cf.* p. 231). Place 0·5 ml. of benzaldehyde and 2 ml. of 30% aqueous sodium hydroxide in a test-tube, warm very gently and stir the mixture *well* with a glass rod for 5 minutes. Then add sufficient water to dissolve the sodium benzoate which has been formed. Decant the solution from any unchanged benzaldehyde, and add concentrated hydrochloric acid: a white precipitate of benzoic acid is obtained on cooling.

Salicylaldehyde gives a yellow coloration and forms salicylic acid very slowly. Cannizzaro's reaction is also given by formaldehyde but, owing to the difficulty in isolating the products, is not used as a test.

4. *Reduction of ammoniacal silver nitrate.* Place about 5 ml. of AgNO₃ solution in a *thoroughly* clean test-tube, and add 2–3 drops of dil. NaOH solution. Add dil. ammonia solution, drop by drop, until the precipitated silver oxide is *almost* redissolved, then add 2–3 drops of formaldehyde or acetaldehyde. A silver mirror is formed.

With paraldehyde and the aromatic aldehydes (being insoluble in water), it is advisable to warm the mixture gently on a water-bath, shaking the tube vigorously from time to time to break up the oily globules of the aldehyde.

5. *Fehling's solution.* Aqueous solutions of aliphatic aldehydes are almost invariably acidic owing to atmospheric oxidation, and therefore

frequently fail to reduce Fehling's solution, since the alkali of the latter is neutralised by the acid present. On the other hand, an excess of Fehling's solution is not recommended, as the blue colour may then mask the ensuing reduction. Therefore proceed thus: To 1 ml. of the aldehyde or aldehyde solution, add about 1 ml. of 10% Na_2CO_3 solution and then a few drops of Fehling's solution, and boil the mixture *gently* for 1 minute: the solution usually turns green and on standing a fine yellow or red precipitate* of cuprous oxide slowly separates. A control experiment using Fehling's solution alone should always be carried out to ensure that no reduction takes place on boiling.

Aliphatic aldehydes reduce Fehling's solution rapidly, benzaldehyde very slowly and indecisively, salicylaldehyde does not reduce it.

6. *Oxidation to acids.* Warm together in a small conical flask on a water-bath for 10 minutes a mixture of 0·5 ml. of benzaldehyde or salicylaldehyde, 15 ml. of saturated $KMnO_4$ solution, and 0·5 g. of Na_2CO_3. Then acidify with conc. HCl, and add 25% sodium sulphite solution until the precipitated manganese dioxide has redissolved. On cooling, benzoic or salicylic acid crystallises out.

7. *Bisulphite addition compound.* Shake 1 ml. of benzaldehyde with about 0·5 ml. of saturated $NaHSO_3$ solution. The mixture becomes warm, and the white addition product separates (rapidly on cooling).

Note. (*a*) Aqueous solutions of formaldehyde and acetaldehyde give these addition products, which are so soluble that they rarely separate: this reaction is therefore an unsatisfactory test for these aldehydes. (*b*) These addition products are also formed by ketones (p. 345).

CRYSTALLINE DERIVATIVES FOR IDENTIFICATION.

(A) *Phenylhydrazones and 2,4-Dinitrophenylhydrazones* (see 2 above). The latter are often to be preferred to phenylhydrazones because (*a*) the phenylhydrazones may separate as syrups, and also may decompose in hot solvents (*cf.* p. 257), (*b*) the 2,4-dinitrophenylhydrazones are often formed in the cold or with only brief warming, are much less soluble, and have higher m.ps. (p. 263).

Note. The 2,4-dinitrophenylhydrazones of many higher aldehydes and ketones may be insoluble in most solvents. In this case, filter them off, wash with ethanol, dry and take the m.p.: attempted recrystallisation may cause partial decomposition.   (M.ps., pp. 539–540.)

(B) *Semicarbazones.* These often form readily in the cold (see above): if not, employ a reasonably short period of heating, otherwise carbazide, $(\cdot NH \cdot CO \cdot NH_2)_2$, m.p. 244°, may be formed and may separate.
(M.ps., pp. 539–540.)

(C) *Acids.* Employ oxidation to acids (see 6 above) only if C_6H_5CHO or a substituted derivative is suspected. Aliphatic acids may be too soluble for ready isolation.

---

* The colour of the precipitate depends upon the size of the cuprous oxide particles, and this in turn upon the rate of reduction, concentration of the solution, *etc.*

SPECIAL REACTIONS.

Metaformaldehyde.

If boiled with water an aqueous solution is obtained which, owing to depolymerisation, gives the reactions for formaldehyde.

Acetaldehyde.

1. *Iodoform reaction.* To 1 ml. of the aldehyde solution, add 3 ml. of 10% KI solution and 10 ml. of freshly prepared sodium hypochlorite solution. Yellow crystals of iodoform, CHI_3, soon separate.

2. *Nitroprusside reaction.* Add 1 ml. of a freshly prepared solution of sodium nitroprusside to the aldehyde or its solution. Add dil. NaOH solution in excess: a red coloration is produced.

Paraldehyde.

Gives some of the tests for acetaldehyde, but more feebly: *e.g.*, it restores the colour to Schiff's reagent, gives a yellow resin with NaOH, and responds to the nitroprusside test. With ammoniacal $AgNO_3$, it gives a silver mirror only after 2–3 minutes' warming. It does not give the iodoform reaction.

To 1 ml. of paraldehyde in a test-tube add 5 ml. of dil. H_2SO_4 and distil gently into cold water contained in another test-tube (Fig. 68, p. 320). An aqueous solution of acetaldehyde is thus obtained.

Chloral Hydrate.

1. Does not restore the pink colour to Schiff's reagent.

2. *Action of sodium hydroxide.* Add a few ml. of NaOH solution

$$CCl_3CHO + NaOH = CHCl_3 + HCOONa$$

to about 0·5 g. of the hydrate and heat gently. Oily drops of chloroform are formed, recognised by characteristic odour.

3. Gives a silver mirror with ammoniacal silver nitrate.

4. *Fehling's solution.* Reduces Fehling's solution on warming: an excess of the latter should be used. The odour of chloroform is also noticeable, due to the action of the alkali in Fehling's solution.

5. *Bisulphite addition compound.* To 0·2 g. of *powdered* chloral hydrate add 2 ml. of *saturated* $NaHSO_3$ solution and stir. The hydrate dissolves and the white addition product separates. Stale or slightly diluted solutions of $NaHSO_3$ do not give this product.

6. *Action of sulphuric acid.* To 0·5 g. of powdered chloral hydrate add 2 ml. of conc. H_2SO_4, shake well and allow to stand. Liquid chloral gradually separates out as an oil on the surface of the acid.

7. *Isocyanide reaction.* Since chloral hydrate is readily converted into chloroform by alkali, it will give the isocyanide reaction. To a few crystals of the solid add about 5 ml. of alcoholic NaOH solution and a few drops of aniline, and heat: the disagreeable odour of phenyl isocyanide, C_6H_5NC, is rapidly detected.

Salicylaldehyde.

1. *Ferric chloride coloration.* Add a few drops of $FeCl_3$ solution to a few drops of the aldehyde: an intense violet coloration is produced.

2. Does not restore the colour to Schiff's reagent.

3. *Action of sodium hydroxide.* Does not undergo the Cannizzaro reaction. It dissolves in dil. NaOH solution, giving a yellow solution from which the aldehyde is precipitated unchanged on acidification. If heated with conc. NaOH solution, salicylaldehyde slowly undergoes atmospheric oxidation to salicylic acid.

4. Does not reduce ammoniacal $AgNO_3$ (except on long standing).

5. It does not reduce Fehling's solution, but turns it a pale green colour. (Note that salicylaldehyde turns ordinary copper sulphate solution a pale green.)

6. *Bisulphite addition compound.* The formation of the bisulphite compound is delayed and appears only after 2–3 minutes' shaking.

7. *Action of ammonia.* To 1 ml. of aldehyde add 1 ml. of aqueous ammonia: a precipitate of hydrosalicylamide, $(HOC_6H_4CH)_3N_2$, is rapidly produced.

Section 13. Ketones. C:O. (*cf.* Tables IX, X, 541–542)

Acetone, ethyl methyl ketone, diethyl ketone; acetophenone, benzophenone (and their nuclear-substituted derivatives). *Cyclohexanone.*

Physical properties. Above members all colourless. Acetone, CH_3COCH_3, b.p. 56°, soluble in water, characteristic odour. Ethyl methyl ketone, b.p. 80°, and diethyl ketone, b.p. 102°, are moderately and sparingly soluble in water respectively. Acetophenone, $C_6H_5COCH_3$, m.p. 20°, sparingly soluble, and benzophenone, $C_6H_5COC_6H_5$, m.p. 48°, insoluble in water.

GENERAL REACTIONS.

1. Aliphatic ketones containing the CH_3CO- group restore the colour very slowly to Schiff's reagent: other ketones have no reaction.

2. Form phenylhydrazones, 2,4-dinitrophenylhydrazones and semicarbazides. (Many oximes are too soluble for ready isolation.)

3. Ketones containing the CH_3CO- group give the iodoform reaction. (For other compounds which give this test, see p. 91.)

4. Ketones containing the CH_3CO- group give:
    (*a*) a red coloration with alkaline sodium nitroprusside;
    (*b*) a violet coloration with *m*-dinitrobenzene and sodium hydroxide.

5. Certain ketones give bisulphite addition compounds.

6. Do not reduce ammoniacal $AgNO_3$ or Fehling's solution (distinction from aldehydes).

1. *Schiff's reagent.* Add about 1 ml. of Schiff's reagent to about 1 ml. of acetone and note the very slow formation of a magenta colour. Neither acetophenone nor benzophenone reacts in this way.

2. (*a*) *Phenylhydrazones.* The phenylhydrazone of acetone has a low m.p. and is difficult to isolate. The phenylhydrazones of acetophenone and benzophenone are readily obtained: To 0·5 ml. of water add about 1 ml. of glacial acetic acid and 1 ml. of phenylhydrazine.

Then add 3 drops of acetophenone (or about 0·3 g. of powdered benzophenone dissolved in 1 ml. of acetic acid) and shake the mixture. A precipitate of the phenylhydrazone is produced on scratching.

(b) 2,4-*Dinitrophenylhydrazones*. To a few drops of acetone, add a few drops of dinitrophenylhydrazine reagent A (p. 263): an orange-coloured precipitate is produced in the cold. Dissolve 0·5 g. of acetophenone or benzophenone in 1 ml. of methanol before adding the reagent B: orange-coloured precipitates are again produced, although that from benzophenone appears slowly. Filter and recrystallise the acetone derivative from ethanol, and the acetophenone and benzophenone derivatives from benzene. (M.ps., pp. 541–542.)

(c) *Semicarbazones*. Using acetophenone, proceed as described on p. 340 for the preparation of benzaldehyde semicarbazone.

Note that many semicarbazones separate when the cold reaction-mixture is set aside for some time. (M.ps., pp. 541–542.)

3. *Iodoform reaction*. To 0·5 ml. of acetone add 3 ml. of 10% KI solution and 10 ml. of freshly prepared sodium hypochlorite solution and mix well. A pale yellow precipitate of iodoform is rapidly formed without heating. Acetophenone similarly gives iodoform, but the mixture must be shaken vigorously on account of the limited solubility of acetophenone in water. Benzophenone does not give iodoform.

4. (a) *Nitroprusside reaction*.* Add 1 ml. of a freshly prepared solution of sodium nitroprusside to 0·5 ml. of acetone or acetophenone. Add dil. NaOH solution in excess: a red coloration is produced. This is not given by benzophenone.

(b) m-*Dinitrobenzene test*.† To 1 ml. of acetone or acetophenone add about 0·1 g. of finely powdered m-dinitrobenzene and then an excess of dil. NaOH solution and shake. A violet coloration is produced, but slowly fades. Not given by benzophenone.

5. *Bisulphite addition compound*. Shake 1 ml. of acetone with 0·5 ml. of a saturated solution of $NaHSO_3$. A white precipitate is formed, the mixture becoming warm and then, on cooling, almost solid. Acetophenone and benzophenone, having the >CO group directly joined to the benzene ring, do not respond to the test (p. 257).

CRYSTALLINE DERIVATIVES FOR IDENTIFICATION.

(A) *Phenylhydrazones, 2,4-Dinitrophenylhydrazones and Semicarbazones*. These are prepared as described in 2 above, and as described for aldehydes (p. 341). (M.ps., pp. 541–542.)

* The coloration is caused by the conversion of acetone by alkali to the $CH_3COCH_2^-$ ion, which then reacts with the nitroprusside ion $[Fe(CN)_5NO]^{--}$ giving the highly coloured ion $[Fe(CN)_5NO \cdot CH_2COCH_3]^{--}$.

† This test is far more delicate if 3,5-dinitrobenzoic acid (preparation, p. 242) is used (owing to its solubility in aqueous sodium hydroxide), instead of the cheaper and more accessible m-dinitrobenzene.

The constitution of the coloured compound formed between a m-dinitro-compound and acetone is of the type $CH_3 \cdot CO \cdot CH_2$ See Saunders and Stark, *Tetrahedron*, 1958, 4, 1971.

SPECIAL REACTIONS.

Cyclohexanone. This is readily oxidised by a $K_2Cr_2O_7 - H_2SO_4$ mixture to the crystalline adipic acid, m.p. 152°, precisely as for cyclohexanol (p. 335).

Benzophenone. To 0·5 g. of benzophenone add 1 g. of naphthalene (as a solvent) and heat until completely molten. Add a small piece of sodium and heat again. The surface of the sodium becomes green, and the colour [which is that of the free radical, $(C_6H_5)_2\overset{\bullet}{C}\cdot ONa$] spreads throughout the molten mass on strong heating.

Section 14.

(A) CarboxylicAcids. — COOH. (*cf.* Tables, pp. 543–545)
(B) Sulphonic Acids. −SO₂OH. (*cf.* Table XIV, p. 548)

(A) CARBOXYLIC ACIDS. *Formic, acetic, oxalic, succinic, lactic, tartaric, citric; benzoic, salicylic* (and other substituted benzoic acids); *phthalic and cinnamic acids.*

Physical properties. All are colourless crystalline solids except formic acid, acetic acid (m.p. 18° when glacial) and lactic acid (m.p. 18°, usually a syrup). Formic acid (b.p. 100°) and acetic acid (b.p. 118°) are the only members which are readily volatile: lactic acid can be distilled only under reduced pressure. Formic and acetic acids have characteristic pungent odours: cinnamic acid has a faint, pleasant and characteristic odour.

The aliphatic acids are all soluble in cold water. The aromatic acids are very sparingly soluble in cold water, but readily soluble in boiling water. Phthalic acid, having two carboxyl groups, is more soluble than the other aromatic acids in cold water.

GENERAL REACTIONS.

1. Soluble in NaOH solution.
2. Soluble in Na_2CO_3 solution with the evolution of CO_2.
3. Heating the acids or their salts with soda-lime eliminates the carboxyl group, volatile products being often detectable.
4. With alcohols and sulphuric acid give esters which frequently have characteristic odours.
5. The neutral salts of many acids treated with ferric chloride give colorations or precipitates.

1. *Solubility in sodium hydroxide solution.* See Section 4, p. 329. Note also that phenols dissolve in NaOH solution to give phenoxides.

2. *Solubility in sodium carbonate solution.* Note that phenols, when soluble in water, will also dissolve in Na_2CO_3 solution, but usually *without* evolution of CO_2, *i.e.*, without the formation of a sodium derivative. This reaction can therefore be used *to distinguish between carboxylic acids and most phenols.* See Section 5, p. 330.

NOTE. Some substituted phenols, particularly nitrophenols, are sufficiently acidic to liberate CO_2 from Na_2CO_3. Nitrophenols, however, all give yellow or red solutions with Na_2CO_3.

3. *Heating with soda-lime.* See Section 3, p. 327. Note that this test is particularly useful for providing evidence of:

(a) Benzoic Acid. Gives benzene, detected by odour and by burning with a very smoky flame.

(b) Salicylic Acid. Gives phenol, detected by odour and by violet coloration with ferric chloride solution (p. 338).

(c) Phthalic Acid. Also gives benzene, but requires longer heating than benzoic acid.

(d) Cinnamic Acid. Gives styrene, $C_6H_5CH:CH_2$ (characteristic odour) and usually benzene.

4. *Ester formation.* Heat gently 1 ml. of ethanol with 0·5 g. of the acid or one of its salts and a few drops of conc. H_2SO_4 for about 1 minute. Cool and pour into a few ml. of water in a test-tube and note the odour. The test is particularly useful for identifying:

(a) Acetic Acid. Ester has strong odour of apples.

(b) Salicylic Acid. Ester has strong odour of oil of wintergreen.

The methyl ester formed by substituting methanol for ethanol in the above reaction has an even stronger odour and should be prepared if salicylic acid is suspected.

For detection of other esters, see Section 15, p. 354.

5. *Ferric chloride reaction.* For the success of this reaction it is important that the solution should be neutral. Excess of acid usually inhibits the production of colour or precipitate, and excess of alkali gives a reddish-brown precipitate of ferric hydroxide. A neutral solution may be made as follows:

Place about 0·5 g. of the acid in a boiling-tube and add a slight excess of ammonia solution until just alkaline to litmus-paper. Add a piece of unglazed porcelain and boil until the odour of ammonia is completely removed. (See also p. 332.) To the cold neutral solution add a few drops of *neutral** $FeCl_3$ solution.

(a) Formate and acetate give a deep red coloration which changes on boiling to a reddish-brown precipitate of the basic ferric salt.

(b) Succinate, benzoate, phthalate and cinnamate give buff or brownish coloured precipitates of the basic ferric salts in the cold. Add dil. H_2SO_4. The basic ferric succinate dissolves giving a clear solution: the other basic ferric salts also dissolve, but simultaneously a white precipitate of the free acid is also formed.

(c) A violet coloration denotes salicylate. Note however that a dilute solution of salicylic acid will give this coloration without preliminary neutralisation. No colour is formed in the presence of mineral acid.

(d) If (a), (b) and (c) give negative results, take two test-tubes **A** and **B**: in **A** place about 5 ml. of the neutral salt solution and in **B** place 5 ml. of water. To each add 3–4 drops of $FeCl_3$

* See p. 332.

solution. If **A** gives a marked yellow coloration compared with the control **B** (particularly when viewed down the length of the tube), then **A** contains the salt of an α-hydroxyacid (lactic, tartaric or citric): oxalates, however, give a very faint yellow coloration.

Isolation of the acid from its salt.

(i) If the salt is soluble in water, add conc. HCl to the solution. A precipitate indicates an aromatic acid: filter, wash with cold water, and drain. If no precipitate is obtained, the acid must be aliphatic.

(ii) If the salt is insoluble in water, boil with an excess of 10% aqueous Na_2CO_3 solution for several minutes and then filter. The residue contains the original metal as carbonate and should be examined in the usual way. The filtrate contains the sodium salt of the acid and an excess of Na_2CO_3. Add dil. HCl until distinctly acid to litmus-paper and note any precipitate as in (i).

The isolation of an aliphatic acid from its aqueous solution, particularly in the presence of metallic salts, is a tedious operation (*cf.* p. 56), although a few such acids, *e.g.*, succinic acid, can be extracted with ether. Since, however, a solution of an acid or one of its salts is admirably suited for most of the tests in this series, the isolation of the free acid is rarely necessary except as a means of distinguishing (as in (i)) between aliphatic and aromatic members.

CRYSTALLINE DERIVATIVES FOR IDENTIFICATION.

Aliphatic and aromatic acids, simple and substituted, vary considerably in their properties, and no one reaction for the preparation of crystalline derivatives is general. The following are recommended as most promising.

(A) *Benzylthiouronium salts.* The sodium salt of an acid in aqueous solution will react with benzylthiouronium chloride:

$$[C_6H_5CH_2 \cdot SC(:NH_2) \cdot NH_2]Cl$$

(preparation, p. 126), to give the benzylthiouronium salt, which usually has a sharp m.p. Certain types of acid, such as amino-acids and some polybasic acids, do not give satisfactory salts.

Example. Dissolve 0·3 g. of benzoic acid in a minimum of hot water (about 70 ml.) and add 5% aqueous sodium hydroxide until the solution is *just* alkaline to methyl-orange, then add 1 drop of *dilute* hydrochloric acid. Pour this solution of the sodium salt into a solution of 0·5 g. of benzylthiouronium chloride in 5 ml. of water, and cool the stirred mixture in ice-water. Filter off the benzylthiouronium salt which has separated, and recrystallise from ethanol containing 10% of water: cream-coloured crystals, m.p. 166°. (M.ps., pp. 543–545.)

(B) *Phenacyl and* p-*Bromophenacyl esters.* The sodium salt of an acid in aqueous-ethanolic solution will react with phenacyl bromide,* $C_6H_5COCH_2Br$, and with *p*-bromophenacyl bromide, $BrC_6H_4COCH_2Br$

---

* Both bromides have skin-irritant and lachrymatory properties: therefore keep the crystals or their solutions from the skin and avoid inhaling the vapour of hot solutions, or of mixtures in hot water.

to give the corresponding esters, which can usually be readily recrystallised. The p-bromophenacyl esters usually have higher m.ps. and
lower solubilities than the phenacyl esters.

Example. Dissolve 0·3 g. of p-chlorobenzoic acid in a small quantity of warm
ethanol (about 10 ml.), and *carefully* add 5% aqueous sodium hydroxide dropwise until the solution is *just* pink to phenolphthalein. Evaporate to dryness on
a water-bath. Dissolve the sodium p-chlorobenzoate in a minimum of water,
add a solution of 0·5 g. of phenacyl bromide in ethanol (about 5 ml.), and boil
the mixture under reflux for 1 hour, and then cool. The phenacyl ester usually
crystallises on cooling: if it does not, add water *dropwise* with stirring to the
chilled solution until separation of the ester just begins. Filter the ester, wash
on the filter with water, drain and recrystallise from ethanol: m.p. 90°. The
p-bromophenacyl ester is similarly prepared, and after recrystallisation from
aqueous ethanol has m.p. 128°. (M.ps., pp. 543–545.)

(C) p-*Nitrobenzyl esters.* The use of p-nitrobenzyl bromide in place
of phenacyl bromide in (B) above gives the p-nitrobenzyl ester of the
acid. These esters are particularly effective for aromatic acids. The
lower aliphatic acids and some polybasic acids do not give satisfactory
results. (M.ps., pp. 543–545.)

(D) *Benzylamides.* Many acids when heated directly with benzylamine in the presence of ammonium chloride as a catalyst give the

$$R·COOH + NH_2·CH_2C_6H_5 \rightarrow R·CO·NH·CH_2C_6H_5$$

corresponding N-benzylamide. This is particularly suitable for acids
such as citric acid that do not readily give derivatives by other methods.

Example. Heat together under reflux 0·5 g. of citric acid, 3 ml. of benzylamine
and 0·15 g. of ammonium chloride for 1 hour. Cool, shake with about
10 ml. of water and filter off the solid. Recrystallise from ethanol: small white
crystals: m.p. 170°. (M.ps., pp. 543–545.)

SPECIAL REACTIONS.

Formic acid. HCOOH.

1. *Carbon monoxide test.* Warm together carefully 0·5 ml. of formic
acid (or 0·5 g. of a formate) and 1 ml. of conc. H_2SO_4. Identify the
carbon monoxide by igniting the gas evolved and observing the pale
blue flame travel down the test-tube. Note that dilute solutions of
formic acid will not give this test. $HCOOH - H_2O = CO$.

2. *Mercuric chloride test.* Add mercuric chloride* solution to formic
acid or a solution of formate and warm. A white precipitate of mercurous chloride, insoluble in dil. HCl, is produced. Sometimes the reduction proceeds as far as metallic mercury, which appears as a grey
precipitate.

3. (a) *Reduction of acid permanganate.* Add a few ml. of dil. H_2SO_4 to a solution

---

* Salts of many organic acids give precipitates with mercuric chloride solution.
but these are usually soluble in dil. HCl.

of formic acid or of a formate: add a dilute solution of potassium permanganate drop by drop and note the decolorisation, which is hastened by warming.

(b) *Reduction of alkaline permanganate.* Dissolve about 0·1 g. of a formate (or 2–3 drops of a formic acid solution) in 5 ml. of a 10% Na_2CO_3 solution, add 1% aqueous $KMnO_4$ drop by drop: immediate decolorisation takes place in the cold with the simultaneous precipitation of manganese dioxide.

4. *Reduction of ammoniacal silver nitrate.* Add a few drops of a neutral solution of a formate to ammoniacal $AgNO_3$ (see Test 4, p. 342). A silver mirror or *more usually* a grey precipitate of metallic silver is produced on boiling.

Acetic acid. CH_3COOH.

1. Does not reduce $KMnO_4$, $HgCl_2$ or ammoniacal $AgNO_3$.
2. The odours of methyl and ethyl acetate are characteristic.

Oxalic acid. $(·COOH)_2$.

1. *Sulphuric acid test.* To 0·5 g. of oxalic acid or of an oxalate, add 1 ml. of conc. H_2SO_4 and warm: CO and CO_2 are evolved (*cf.* formic acid). The CO burns with a blue flame. Detect the CO_2 by passing the mixed gases evolved into lime-water. It is essential to test for the CO_2 in a *separate* reaction, or (if the same test-tube is used) before testing for CO.

2. *Reduction of acid permanganate.* Add a few ml. of dil. H_2SO_4 to 1 ml. of a solution of oxalic acid or of an oxalate. Warm gently and add a dilute solution of $KMnO_4$ drop by drop and note the decolorisation.

(*Note.* Oxalates do not reduce alkaline $KMnO_4$ in the cold (*cf.* Test 3 (b) for formic acid), and only extremely slowly on heating.)

3. *Calcium chloride test.** Add $CaCl_2$ solution to a neutral solution of an oxalate: a white precipitate of calcium oxalate is formed, insoluble in acetic acid, but soluble in dil. HCl.

Succinic acid. $(·CH_2COOH)_2$.

1. *Fluorescein test.* Fuse together carefully in a dry test-tube for about 1 minute a few crystals of resorcinol and an equal quantity of succinic acid or a succinate, moistened with 2 drops of conc. H_2SO_4. Cool, dissolve in water and add NaOH solution in excess. A red solution is produced which exhibits an *intense* green fluorescence.†

Lactic acid. $CH_3CH(OH)COOH$.

1. *Sulphuric acid test.* To 0·5 ml. of lactic acid or 0·5 g. of a

---

* It should be emphasised that the calcium chloride solution used in testing for acids is of Reagent concentration (p. 524) throughout.

† A similar *intense* green fluorescence is given by phthalic acid (p. 353). Very feeble fluorescences are sometimes given by other dibasic acids, but in general they are ill defined and not reliable in tests. A slight fluorescence is often given when resorcinol and conc. H_2SO_4 are heated together without an organic acid.

Certain salts of divalent metals (*e.g.*, lead and copper formate, calcium acetate) are exceptional in giving bright green fluorescences. In each case confirmatory tests must always be employed.

lactate add 1 ml. of conc. H_2SO_4 and warm gently. A brisk effervescence takes place, CO being evolved together with varying amounts of CO_2 and SO_2. The mixture blackens considerably, but there is no marked charring.

2. *Iodoform reaction.* To 0·5 ml. of lactic acid add 10% NaOH solution until alkaline to litmus. Then add 5 ml. of 10% KI solution and 10 ml. of freshly prepared sodium hypochlorite solution and mix well. A yellow precipitate of iodoform separates out almost immediately in the cold.

Tartaric acid. $[\cdot CH(OH)COOH]_2$.

1. *Sulphuric acid test.* Warm 0·5 g. of tartaric acid or a tartrate with 1 ml. of conc. H_2SO_4. Heavy charring takes place, CO and SO_2 being evolved.

2. *Reduction of ammoniacal silver nitrate.* Add 1 drop of dil. NaOH solution to about 5 ml. of $AgNO_3$ solution, and add dil. NH_3 solution drop by drop until the silver oxide is almost redissolved. Add $AgNO_3$ solution until a *faint* but permanent precipitate is obtained (see p.525). Then add 0·5 ml. of a neutral tartrate solution. Place the tube in warm water: a silver mirror is formed in a few minutes.

3. *Fenton's reagent.* To a solution of tartaric acid or a tartrate add 1 drop of freshly prepared ferrous sulphate solution, 1 drop of hydrogen peroxide solution and then excess of NaOH solution: an intense violet coloration is produced, due to the ferric salt of dihydroxyfumaric acid, HOOC·C(OH):C(OH)COOH.

Citric acid. $HOOC\cdot CH_2\cdot C(OH)(COOH)\cdot CH_2COOH$.

1. *Sulphuric acid test.* Heat 0·5 g. of citric acid or a citrate with 1 ml. of H_2SO_4: CO and CO_2 are evolved and the mixture turns yellow, but does *not* char. Acetone dicarboxylic acid, $OC(CH_2COOH)_2$, is also formed, and is tested for after heating the mixture for 1 minute: cool, add a few ml. of water and make alkaline with NaOH solution. Add a few ml. of a freshly prepared solution of sodium nitroprusside and note the intense red coloration (see Test 4 (*a*) for ketones, p. 346).

2. Does not reduce ammoniacal $AgNO_3$ solution (*cf.* tartaric acid)

3. No coloration with Fenton's reagent (*cf.* tartaric acid).

Benzoic acid. C_6H_5COOH.

1. Does not give Unsaturation Test with alkaline potassium permanganate (distinction from cinnamic acid, see below).

2. Does not form a phthalein or fluorescein (distinction from phthalic acid).

Salicylic acid. HOC_6H_4COOH.

1. The odour of methyl or ethyl salicylate is characteristic.

2. *Acetylation.* Boil 1 g. of salicylic acid with 4 ml. of an acetic anhydride-acetic acid mixture (equal volumes) under reflux for 10 minutes. Pour into water. Filter off the aspirin (p. 111), wash with water and recrystallise from aqueous acetic acid (1:1): m.p. 136°.

3. Phthalein formation. * Fuse together carefully in a dry test-tube a few crystals of salicylic acid or of a salicylate with an equal quantity of phthalic anhydride moistened with 2 drops of conc. H_2SO_4. Cool, dissolve in water and add NaOH solution in excess: a bright red coloration is developed.

Phthalic acid. $C_6H_4(COOH)_2$.

1. *Phthalein reaction.* Fuse together carefully in a dry test-tube a few crystals of phthalic acid or of a phthalate and an equal quantity of phenol moistened with 2 drops of conc. H_2SO_4. Cool, dissolve in water and add NaOH solution in excess: the bright red colour of phenolphthalein in alkaline solution is produced.

2. *Fluorescein reaction.*† Repeat Test 1, using however resorcinol instead of phenol. A reddish solution having an intense green fluorescence is produced.

Cinnamic acid. $C_6H_5CH:CHCOOH$.

1. *Oxidation.* (a) *Unsaturation test.* Dissolve about 0·1 g. of cinnamic acid or of a soluble cinnamate in about 5 ml. of 10% Na_2CO_3 solution. To the *cold* solution add 1% aqueous $KMnO_4$ drop by drop. *Immediate* decolorisation denotes unsaturation. (Note. Many easily oxidisable substances, *e.g.*, formic acid, acetaldehyde, *etc.*, also rapidly decolorise alkaline permanganate. Cinnamates, however, do not reduce Fehling's solution.)

(b) *Formation of benzaldehyde.* Place 0·2 g. of cinnamic acid (or a cinnamate) in a boiling-tube, add 5 ml. of $KMnO_4$ solution and 5 ml. of Na_2CO_3 solution, and boil: note the odour of benzaldehyde.

2. *Formation of bromostyrene.* Dissolve 0·2 g. of cinnamic acid (or a cinnamate) in about 5 ml. of Na_2CO_3 solution. Add bromine-water *drop by drop*, and note the rapid separation of bromostyrene, $C_6H_5CH:CHBr$, as a colourless oil, having a pleasant characteristic odour.

(B) SULPHONIC ACIDS. Aliphatic sulphonic acids are rarely encountered, for they are very soluble in water, and many are deliquescent. The aromatic sulphonic acids, although less uncommon, are encountered most frequently as their derivatives (*e.g.*, the sulphonamides, pp. 247, 251), or as nuclear-substituted acids (*e.g.*, sulphanilic acid, p. 384).

Aromatic sulphonic acids are usually soluble in water, forming a strongly acidic solution.

CRYSTALLINE DERIVATIVES FOR IDENTIFICATION.

(A) *Benzylthiouronium salts.* The sulphonic acid in aqueous solution, if neutralised and treated with benzylthiouronium

---

* It is important to note that in these reactions salicylic acid is functioning as a phenol.

† See footnote, p. 351.

chloride, precisely as described for carboxylic acids (p. 349), gives the benzylthiouronium salt, usually of sharp m.p. Many of these salts can be recrystallised readily from water, and are the most rapidly prepared derivatives. (M.ps., p. 548.)

(B) *Sulphonamides.* Mix 0·5 g. of the sulphonic acid or its alkali salt with 1·5 g. of phosphorus pentachloride, and heat under reflux in a silicone- or oil-bath at 150° for 30 minutes; then allow it to cool.

(i) To prepare the sulphonamide, add 10 ml. of concentrated (*d*, 0·880) ammonia *cautiously* down the condenser, shaking the mixture meanwhile. Then detach and *securely* cork the flask, and shake it vigorously for several minutes. If a large lump of material forms, break it up carefully with a thick glass rod, and shake the mixture again. Filter off the solid product at the pump, wash it with water, and drain well. Then recrystallise preferably from boiling water, or if necessary from aqueous ethanol, filtering the hot solution. Filter off the crystalline sulphonamide and determine the m.p.

(ii) To prepare the *N*-benzenesulphonamide (or sulphonanilide), add the above molten reaction-mixture whilst still warm, in small portions at a time, to a chilled suspension of 0·3 ml. of aniline in 30 ml. of 10% aqueous sodium hydroxide in a boiling-tube, shaking the corked tube vigorously after each addition. Finally add if necessary 10–15 ml. of water to obtain a clear solution. Chill the solution and acidify with 1:1 hydrochloric acid, when the *N*-benzenesulphonamide will usually separate as an oil which rapidly solidifies on cooling. Filter at the pump, wash well with water, drain and recrystallise from aqueous-ethanol until pure. (M.ps. of sulphonamides, p. 548.)

This method of sulphonamide formation may obviously be invalidated by the presence of nuclear —NH₂ or —OH groups, which could react with the phosphorus pentachloride or with the subsequent —SO₂Cl group.

The preparation of the phenacyl-, *p*-bromophenacyl or *p*-nitrobenzyl esters of sulphonic acids is usually unsatisfactory.

Section 15. Esters. −COOR. (*cf.* Tables, pp. 543–547)

Methyl, ethyl, n-*propyl,* iso*propyl,* n-*butyl, benzyl, cyclohexyl esters of formic, acetic, oxalic, succinic, tartaric, citric, benzoic, salicylic* (and other substituted benzoic acids), *phthalic and cinnamic acids; phenyl esters of acetic, benzoic and salicylic acids.*

Physical Properties. All colourless. Most are liquids, but a few are solids at room temperature. (See Table on p. 546.) The following crystalline solids should be noted: methyl oxalate (m.p. 54°), methyl tartrate (m.p. 48°), methyl succinate (m.p. 18°, liquid in hot weather), methyl cinnamate (m.p. 36°), phenyl benzoate (m.p. 70°), phenyl salicylate or "salol" (m.p. 42°).

Most are very sparingly soluble in water; note however that methyl formate, methyl oxalate, methyl succinate, methyl and ethyl tartrate, methyl and ethyl citrate are soluble in water.

GENERAL REACTIONS.

1. Many esters possess characteristic odours.
2. Esters form hydroxamic acids which give colorations with ferric chloride.
3. All esters are hydrolysed by sodium hydroxide to the alcohol (or sodium phenoxide) and the sodium salt of the acid from which they are derived.
4. Form (a) amides with ammonia;
   (b) benzylamides with benzylamine.
5. Undergo "ester interchange" with 3,5-dinitrobenzoic acid.

1. *Odours.* As it is impossible to describe the odours of esters in absolute terms, the student should familiarise himself with the odours of the above esters and decide for himself how much reliance he can place on this test.

As a general guide, however, it may be noted that the following have fairly easily recognisable odours: methyl and ethyl formate; methyl and ethyl acetate (apples); methyl and ethyl benzoate; methyl salicylate (oil of wintergreen) and ethyl salicylate; methyl and ethyl cinnamate. (It is however usually impracticable to distinguish by odour alone between the methyl and ethyl esters of a particular acid.) Methyl and ethyl oxalate, and methyl and ethyl phthalate are almost odourless. Succinic and tartaric esters have faint odours.

2. *Hydroxamic acid formation* (*cf.* Section 9, p. 334). To a few drops of an ester, add 0·2 g. of hydroxylamine hydrochloride and about 5 ml. of 10% NaOH solution and *gently* boil the mixture for 1–2 minutes. Cool and acidify with dil. HCl and then add a few drops of ferric chloride solution. A violet or deep red-brown colour develops immediately.

A similar coloration is given by acid chlorides, acid anhydrides and many amides, but these classes of substances are readily detected by other means and cannot be confused with esters.

3. *Hydrolysis.* Place 2 ml. of the ester in a 50 ml. round-bottomed flask fitted with a reflux water-condenser, or use the reflux-distillation apparatus shown in Fig. 38, p. 63. Add about 20 ml. of 10% aqueous NaOH solution, and some fragments of unglazed porcelain, and reflux gently for 20–30 minutes. (Note that methyl oxalate is hydrolysed rapidly by water alone. Phenyl esters on the other hand hydrolyse comparatively slowly even with hot NaOH solution, and should be heated

under reflux for *at least* 30 minutes.* Phenyl esters when heated with
soda-lime (Section 3) give an odour of phenol, and their identity will
have already been suspected.) At the end of this time, all oily drops†
of unchanged ester should have disappeared, and the solution now
contains the free alcohol and the sodium salt‡ of the acid: in the
case of the phenyl esters, the solution will contain sodium phenate and
the sodium salt of the acid.

Now disconnect the condenser and re-attach it to the flask by a knee-
tube for distillation (Fig. 59, p. 100), unless the apparatus in Fig. 38 has
been used. Distil off about 5 ml. of the liquid.

(*a*) The aqueous distillate may be clear, and may contain methanol or ethanol. Test for each of these, as described on pp. 335–
337.

(*b*) If the distillate is clear and contains neither methanol nor
ethanol, then only water has distilled over and the original substance is a phenyl ester (sodium phenoxide being non-volatile).
Treat according to the special directions for phenyl esters given
below.

(*c*) A cloudy distillate, separating later into two layers, may be
obtained. This indicates benzyl alcohol or cyclohexanol which are
insoluble in water: separate and apply special test (pp. 335–337).
(Obviously it is important that the ester should have been completely hydrolysed, otherwise unchanged ester will distil over,
giving a cloudy distillate.)

Next cool the alkaline residue in the flask and add dil. H_2SO_4 until
definitely acid.

(*a*) If a precipitate is formed, the acid is aromatic (benzoic,
salicylic, cinnamic or phthalic). Cool, filter through a small
Buchner funnel, wash thoroughly with water, drain well, and
(i) perform the tests for these acids (pp. 352, 353), or (ii) recrystallise from water and take the m.p.

(*b*) If no precipitate is formed, the acid is soluble in water and is
aliphatic. It may be volatile (formic and acetic acids), or non-
volatile (oxalic, succinic and tartaric acids). Therefore reconnect
the flask to the condenser and distil off about 8–10 ml. Test the distillate for formic and acetic acids (pp. 350–351). If a negative result
is obtained, test the residue in the flask for the non-volatile acids
(pp. 351–352), taking care to make an exactly neutral solution where
required.

* See, however, footnote, p. 245.

† Any benzyl alcohol or cyclohexanol formed by hydrolysis of a benzyl or
cyclohexyl ester will, however, remain as an oil.

‡ Some sodium salts (particularly sodium oxalate) may be precipitated, due
to their low solubility in NaOH solution. The salt should be redissolved by
the addition of water before the subsequent distillation.

Treatment of phenyl esters. (See also p. 248.) The alkaline solution containing phenoxide and the sodium salt of the acid should now be worked up by the following method.

Cool the solution in ice-water, and then add dil. H_2SO_4 with stirring until the solution is acidic to litmus-paper and the acid, if aromatic, begins to separate as a faint but *permanent* precipitate. Now add dil. Na_2CO_3 solution with *vigorous* stirring until the solution becomes definitely alkaline to litmus-paper and any precipitate entirely redissolves. Finally extract the clear solution twice with ether. Transfer the ethereal layer to an evaporating-basin, and evaporate on a previously heated water-bath. (*No flames must be near.*) Identify the phenol which remains in the basin (p. 337). Acidify the aqueous solution with dil. H_2SO_4 and investigate the organic acid as above.

Hydrolysis of methyl oxalate. The exceptionally rapid hydrolysis of methyl oxalate can be followed thus: Dissolve 0·2 g. of finely powdered methyl oxalate in 10 ml. of water, and add 1 drop of phenolphthalein. Then add very dil. NaOH solution (1%) drop by drop until the solution *just* turns pink: it will be noticed that the colour rapidly fades, but is restored on the further addition of 1–2 drops of NaOH solution. The colour fades again and the addition can be repeated until hydrolysis is complete. Oxalic acid (with which methyl oxalate may be confused) gives a precise end-point when treated with NaOH solution in this way.

4. (*a*) *Amide formation.* The only esters which give insoluble amides *rapidly* with concentrated ammonia solution are methyl and ethyl oxalate.

Dissolve 0·2 g. of methyl oxalate in 10 ml. of water, add without delay 1 ml. of ammonia (*d*, 0·880) and shake: a fine white precipitate of the insoluble oxamide is produced. A precipitate of oxamide is similarly produced when 2–3 drops of ammonia are added directly to 0·5 ml. of ethyl oxalate.

Ethyl oxalate is the only *liquid* ester which gives this rapid separation of the amide, which is therefore characteristic. Methyl and ethyl formate react rapidly with ammonia, but the soluble formamide does not separate: methyl succinate gives crystalline succinamide after about 1 hour's standing, other esters only after a much longer time. The solid esters, other than methyl oxalate, are either soluble in water and remain so when treated with ammonia, or alternatively are insoluble in water and hence clearly not methyl oxalate.

(*b*) *Benzylamide formation.* Many methyl and ethyl esters react with benzylamine, in the presence of ammonium chloride as a catalyst, to give crystalline *N*-benzylamides.

$$C_6H_5COOCH_3 + HNH \cdot CH_2C_6H_5 \rightarrow C_6H_5CONH \cdot CH_2C_6H_5$$

Heat together under reflux 1 g. of the ester, 3 ml. of benzylamine and 0·15 g. of ammonium chloride for ½ hour. Cool, add about 10 ml. of water to dissolve up the excess of benzylamine and filter off the benzylamide. Recrystallise from ethanol and take the m.p.

(M.ps., pp. 543–545.)

It should be noted that this test gives information about the nature of the "acid" component of the original ester.

In general the method is more satisfactory with esters of aromatic acids than with esters of aliphatic acids. Esters of alcohols other than methyl and ethyl are best treated by first converting them into methyl esters thus: Heat together under reflux 1 ml. of the higher ester, 5 ml. of methanol and 0·2 g. of sodium methoxide. [In place of the sodium methoxide, it suffices to add 0·1 g. of metallic sodium to the methanol.] After refluxing, distil off the excess of methanol (b.p. 65°). The residue is then heated under reflux with benzylamine as described above.

5. *3,5-Dinitrobenzoates.* The 3,5-dinitrobenzoate of the alcohol portion of the ester may be obtained by "ester interchange." Thus an ester, R'·COOR, when heated with 3,5-dinitrobenzoic acid and sulphuric acid gives $(NO_3)_2C_6H_3COOR$.

To about 1·0 ml. of the ester add about 0·5 g. of 3,5-dinitrobenzoic acid and 0·25 ml. of conc. H_2SO_4. Heat the mixture gently under reflux for 5 minutes. Add *very carefully* about 10 ml. of water, make alkaline with NaOH and filter at the pump. Recrystallise the solid 3,5-dinitrobenzoate from benzene and take the m.p. (M.ps., pp. 536–538.)

It should be noted that this test gives information only about the nature of the "alcohol" component of the original ester, whereas test 4 (*b*) gives information about the "acid" component.

CRYSTALLINE DERIVATIVES FOR IDENTIFICATION.

(A) Hydrolyse with dil. NaOH and then prepare suitable derivatives of alcohol and of acid.

(B) *Benzylamides* (see 4(*a*) above) can often be prepared directly from the ester, particularly if a methyl or ethyl ester. Usually works best with esters of aromatic acids. (M.ps., pp. 543–545.)

(C) *3,5-Dinitrobenzoates* (see 5 above) can usually be prepared directly from the ester, provided that the alcohol component is not destroyed too rapidly by hot sulphuric acid. (M.ps., pp. 546–548.)

NOTE. Many esters reduce Fehling's solution on warming. This reduction occurs rapidly with the alkyl esters of many aliphatic acids, but scarcely at all with similar esters of aromatic acids (*e.g.*, ethyl oxalate reduces, but ethyl benzoate does not). Note also that this is a property of the ester itself: thus both methyl and ethyl oxalate reduce Fehling's solution very rapidly, whereas neither oxalic acid, nor sodium oxalate, nor a mixture of the alcohol and oxalic acid (or sodium oxalate), reduces the solution.

Methyl and ethyl salicylate give a violet coloration with $FeCl_3$.

Section 16. Ammonium salts, amides, imides, and nitriles. (*cf.* Tables XI, XII, pp. 543–545)

(A) AMMONIUM SALTS. R·COONH$_4$. *Ammonium salts of formic, acetic, oxalic, succinic, tartaric, citric acid; benzoic, salicylic* (and other substituted benzoic acids); *phthalic and cinnamic acids.*

(B) AMIDES. R·CONH$_2$. *Formamide, acetamide, oxamide, urea, benzamide, salicylamide. Thiourea.*

(C) IMIDES. R$\diagdown$$\overset{CO}{\underset{CO}{}}$$\diagup$NH. *Succinimide, phthalimide.*

(D) NITRILES. R·CN. *Acetonitrile, benzonitrile* (and substituted benzonitriles).

Physical Properties.

(A) *Ammonium salts.* All colourless solids readily soluble in cold water.

(B) *Amides.* All colourless solids except formamide, HCONH$_2$, a liquid which decomposes on boiling at atmospheric pressure.* Formamide, acetamide, CH$_3$CONH$_2$, and urea, CO(NH$_2$)$_2$, are readily soluble in water; thiourea, CS(NH$_2$)$_2$, is moderately soluble; oxamide,† (CONH$_2$)$_2$, benzamide, C$_6$H$_5$CONH$_2$, and salicylamide, HOC$_6$H$_4$CONH$_2$, are almost insoluble in cold water; salicylamide is readily soluble in cold NaOH solution. All are odourless: acetamide, however, has an odour of mice unless it has been purified by recrystallisation.

(C) *Imides.* Both colourless solids: succinimide is readily soluble, and phthalimide sparingly soluble, in cold water.

(D) *Nitriles.* Acetonitrile, CH$_3$CN, b.p. 82°, is miscible with water, but benzonitrile, C$_6$H$_5$CN, b.p. 191°, is insoluble. Acetonitrile, unless specially purified, retains the mouse-like odour of acetamide: benzonitrile has an odour resembling both that of benzaldehyde and of nitrobenzene (bitter almonds).

(A) GENERAL REACTIONS FOR AMMONIUM SALTS.

   1. Give off ammonia freely when treated with aqueous NaOH solution *in the cold* (distinction from amides, imides and nitriles).
   2. Aqueous solutions give with ferric chloride the characteristic reactions of the neutral salt of the acid (p. 348). Identify the carboxylic acids by the tests already given (Section 14, p. 347), or by the preparation of one of the crystalline derivatives below.

---

* Note that some *N*-alkyl-formamides such as dimethylformamide, are also liquid.

† Cf. p. 118.

CRYSTALLINE DERIVATIVES FOR IDENTIFICATION.

(A) *Acids.* The ammonium salts of *aromatic* acids when acidified in cold aqueous solution will deposit the crystalline acid.

(B) *Benzylthiouronium salts.* Cold aqueous solutions of ammonium salts, when treated with benzylthiouronium chloride, usually deposit the benzylthiouronium salt (*cf.* p. 349), and the intermediate formation of the sodium salt is unnecessary. (M.ps., pp. 543–545.)

(C) *Phenacyl and* p-*Bromophenacyl esters.* Ammonium salts in aqueous-ethanolic solution do not however usually condense satisfactorily with phenacyl and *p*-bromophenacyl bromide. The aqueous solution of the ammonium salt should therefore be boiled with a slight excess of sodium hydroxide to remove ammonia, and the solution then cooled, treated with hydrochloric acid until *just* alkaline to phenolphthalein, and then evaporated to dryness. The sodium salt is then treated as described (p. 349) to give the ester. Filter the ester, and wash with water to remove sodium halide before recrystallisation.

The preparation of the benzylthiouronium salt is clearly the more satisfactory.

(D) *N-Benzylamides.* Ammonium salts are readily converted into the

$$R \cdot COONH_4 + H_2N \cdot CH_2C_6H_5 \rightarrow R \cdot CO \cdot NH \cdot CH_2C_6H_5$$

benzylamides by heating with benzylamine.

Example. Heat under reflux 0·5 g. of ammonium benzoate and 1·5 ml. of benzylamine for 1 hour. Shake with water to remove unchanged benzylamine and filter off the benzylamide. Recrystallise from ethanol: m.p., 105°.

(M.ps., pp. 543–545.)

(B) GENERAL REACTIONS FOR AMIDES,* IMIDES AND NITRILES.

1. *Boiled* with aqueous NaOH solution yield ammonia and the sodium salt of the corresponding acid.

2. Aqueous solutions (when obtainable) give no reaction with ferric chloride. This is an important distinction from ammonium salts (see above). Salicylamide, being also a phenol, is however an exception (p. 344).

   1. *Hydrolysis by sodium hydroxide.* Classes (B), (C) and (D) hydrolyse thus:

---

* In addition to General Reactions 1 and 2, all amides react with nitrous acid evolving nitrogen:

$$CH_3CONH_2 + HNO_2 = CH_3COOH + N_2 + H_2O$$

The evolution of nitrogen is not always entirely satisfactory as a test owing to the possible evolution of gaseous decomposition products of nitrous acid itself. The test may be performed as follows. To 1 ml. of chilled concentrated sodium nitrite solution add 1 ml. of dilute acetic acid. Allow any preliminary evolution of gas to subside, and then add the mixed solution to a cold aqueous solution (or suspension) of the amide: note the *brisk* effervescence.

(B) $RCONH_2 + NaOH = RCOONa + NH_3$

(C) $R\!\!<^{CO}_{CO}\!\!>\!\!NH + 2NaOH = R\!\!<^{COONa}_{COONa} + NH_3$

(D) $RCN + NaOH + H_2O = RCOONa + NH_3$

Place together in a 50 ml. conical flask about 1 g. of the substance and 10 ml. of 10% NaOH solution (or use apparatus in Fig. 38, p. 63). Add a few pieces of unglazed porcelain, fit a reflux water-condenser, and boil gently for about 20 minutes. Nitriles require longer heating than amides, usually about 30 minutes. The completion of the hydrolysis of an insoluble nitrile (*e.g.*, benzonitrile) is indicated by the disappearance of oily drops in the liquid. Cool the flask, add an excess of dil. H_2SO_4 and cool thoroughly.

(*a*) A white precipitate indicates an aromatic acid: filter off, wash well with water and (i) carry out tests for benzoic, salicylic and phthalic acids (Section 14, p. 347), or (ii), recrystallise from water and take m.p. Phthalic acid is moderately soluble in cold water, and is therefore precipitated only if the volume of the liquid is kept small.

(*b*) A brisk effervescence of CO_2 without the formation of a precipitate indicates urea (if the NaOH used is free from carbonate).

(*c*) If no precipitate is obtained and there is no marked effervescence, connect a knee-tube and water-condenser to the flask (Fig. 59, p. 100) (unless apparatus in Fig. 38 has been used) and distil off about 5 ml. of the liquid. Test the distillate for formic and acetic acids (pp. 350–351). If a negative result is obtained, cool the residue in the flask and carry out tests for oxalic and succinic acids (p. 351), taking care to neutralise the solution where necessary.

NOTE. Thiourea hydrolyses slowly under the above conditions. With 25-30% NaOH solution it gives ammonia, sodium sulphide and some sodium thiocyanate.

CRYSTALLINE DERIVATIVES FOR IDENTIFICATION.

Amides (except urea and thiourea), *imides* and *nitriles*, after the above alkaline hydrolysis, give derivatives similarly to those from the alkaline solution obtained from ammonium salts (p. 360). (A) If the original compound is aromatic, acidification of the cold solution deposits the crystalline acid. (B) The cold solution, when carefully neutralised (p. 332) and treated with benzylthiuronium chloride, deposits the thiuronium salt.

(*Note.* The treatment of amides with nitrous acid, to obtain the free acid more rapidly than by alkaline hydrolysis, is in general inadvisable when preparing the thiuronium salts.)

If the amide is an N-(mono- or di)-substituted amide, or the imide an N-substituted imide, the above alkaline hydrolysis will give a solution of the sodium salt of the corresponding acid, and also the free amine. If the latter is aromatic, it will be insoluble and can be extracted with ether from the cold hydrolysis mixture, and then identified (p. 347). If the amine is aliphatic, it will probably remain dissolved in the cold mixture: a portion of this mixture may then be shaken with benzoyl chloride (p. 243), and the benzoyl derivative of the amine thus isolated and identified.

(C) *N-Benzylamides.*   *Amides* readily react by interchange with

$$R \cdot CONH_2 + H_2N \cdot CH_2C_6H_5 \rightarrow R \cdot CO \cdot NH \cdot CH_2C_6H_5$$

benzylamine to give benzylamides.

Example. Heat together under reflux 0·5 g. of ammonium tartrate and 1·5 ml. of benzylamine for ½ hour. Shake with water to remove the excess of benzylamine and filter off the benzylamide. Recrystallise from ethanol; m.p. 199°.   (M.ps., pp. 543–345.)

Urea.   Prepare the nitrate or oxalate (see below).

Thiourea.   Boil in ethanolic solution with benzyl chloride to prepare the crystalline benzylthiouronium chloride, m.p. 170–174° (p. 126).

SPECIAL REACTIONS.

Formamide.

Boil 1 ml. of formamide in a test-tube and note that ammonia is freely evolved. Carbon monoxide is also produced, but cannot usually be ignited in the presence of the ammonia.

Urea.

1. *Formation of Biuret, and Biuret reaction.* Place 0·2 g. of urea in a dry test-tube, heat very gently just above the m.p. and note the production of ammonia. After 1–2 minutes the liquid suddenly solidifies with the formation of biuret:

$$2NH_2CONH_2 = NH_2CONHCONH_2 + NH_3$$

Dissolve the solid residue in a few ml. of warm 10% NaOH solution, cool and add 1 drop of very dilute copper sulphate solution. A purple coloration is obtained.*

2. *Action of hypobromite.* To a solution of urea add sodium hypo-

$$NH_2CONH_2 + 3NaOBr = N_2 + CO_2 + 3NaBr + 2H_2O$$

bromite solution and note the brisk effervescence.

3. *Urea nitrate and oxalate.* Prepare a concentrated aqueous solution of urea. (*a*) To one portion, add a few drops of conc. HNO_3: the white

---

* A purple or rose-pink coloration is produced when sodium hydroxide and dilute copper sulphate solution are added to compounds containing two –CONH– groups attached *either* to one another, *or* to the same nitrogen atom, *or* to the same carbon atom. It is therefore also given by oxamide, $NH_2CO \cdot CONH_2$, malonamide, $NH_2CO \cdot CH_2 \cdot CONH_2$ and by proteins and peptides. In fact the –CONH– is often spoken of as the "peptide" linkage.

crystalline urea nitrate, m.p. 163°, is precipitated. (*b*) To another portion, add concentrated aqueous oxalic acid solution: white crystals of urea oxalate, m.p. 171°, separate, particularly on scratching. Both salts dissolve in an excess of water.

4. *Urease test.* The enzyme *urease* hydrolyses urea to ammonium carbonate (p. 519). The reaction is sp⸌cific and is frequently used for solutions of urea to which the biuret test cannot be applied. Add about 5 drops of phenol-red to 0·2 g. of urea dissolved in 5 ml. of water. To this yellow solution, add 0·2 g. of jack bean meal suspended in 2 ml. of water containing also 5 drops of phenol-red. The colour changes to red as the solution becomes alkaline.

Oxamide.

1. *Biuret test.* Oxamide, having two ·$CONH_2$ groups, will give this test without any preliminary treatment (*cf.* urea). Shake 0·1 g. of oxamide with 1 ml. of 10% NaOH solution, add 1 drop of very dilute $CuSO_4$ solution and mix well. A rose-pink coloration is produced.

2. *Sulphuric acid test.* Heat 0·5 g. of oxamide with conc. H_2SO_4. CO and CO_2 are evolved.

Salicylamide.

Ferric chloride coloration. To a trace of the solid add ferric chloride solution and shake: an intense violet coloration is produced, owing to the presence of the phenolic grouping.

Succinimide.

1. *Reduction.* Mix together intimately in a dry hard-glass test-tube 0·1 g. of succinimide and an equal amount of zinc dust. Heat strongly, and in the mouth of the tube place a pinewood splinter which has been soaked in conc. HCl. Note that the splinter is turned red by the vapour of pyrrole which is formed by reduction.

$$\begin{array}{c} CH_2CO \\ | \quad\quad >NH \\ CH_2 \cdot CO \end{array} \longrightarrow \begin{array}{c} CH:CH \\ | \quad\quad >NH \\ CH:CH \end{array}$$

2. *Fluorescein reaction.* Fuse together in a dry test-tube 0·1 g. of succinimide, 0·1 g. of resorcinol and 2 drops of conc. H_2SO_4. Cool, add water and then NaOH solution in excess. A green fluorescent solution is obtained.

Phthalimide.

1. *Phthalein reaction.* Fuse together very gently in a dry test-tube 0·1 g. of phthalimide, 0·1 g. of phenol and 2 drops of conc. H_2SO_4. Cool, add water and then NaOH solution in excess. A red coloration is produced which is decolorised by acids. (NOTE. Succinimide gives no definite coloration in these circumstances.)

2. *Fluorescein reaction.* Repeat the above test, but use resorcinol instead of

phenol and fuse *very gently*. A green fluorescent solution is produced on the addition of NaOH solution.

Section 17. (A) Acid chlorides. R·COCl. (*cf.* Tables, pp. 543–545)
(B) Acid anhydrides. R·CO·O·CO·R

(A) ACID CHLORIDES. *Acetyl chloride; benzoyl chloride* (and substituted benzoyl chlorides).

(B) ACID ANHYDRIDES. *Acetic anhydride, succinic anhydride; phthalic anhydride* (and substituted derivatives).

(A) ACID CHLORIDES.

Physical properties. Colourless liquids when pure, benzoyl chloride, C_6H_5COCl, is frequently pale yellow. Acetyl chloride, CH_3COCl, has a pungent odour, fumes in moist air and is immediately hydrolysed by cold water. Benzoyl chloride also has a pungent odour, is lachrymatory, and is hydrolysed only slowly by cold water, in which it is insoluble.

(B) ACID ANHYDRIDES.

Physical properties. Acetic anhydride, $(CH_3CO)_2O$, is a colourless liquid with a sharp pungent odour, decomposed slowly by water, in which it is only slightly soluble.

Succinic anhydride and phthalic anhydride (of structure $\begin{matrix} H_2C\cdot CO \\ | \qquad \rangle O \\ H_2C\cdot CO \end{matrix}$

and $C_6H_4 \left\langle \begin{matrix} CO \\ \rangle O \\ CO \end{matrix} \right.$ respectively) are both colourless crystalline solids almost insoluble in cold water.

The chemical reactions of the acid chlorides and anhydrides are so closely parallel that they are considered together.

GENERAL REACTIONS.

1. Acid chlorides (but not acid anhydrides) precipitate silver chloride on treatment with aqueous $AgNO_3$ acidified with HNO_3.
2. Hydrolysed by water or (more rapidly) by alkalis to corresponding carboxylic acid or salt.
3. Form esters with alcohols.
4. Acid chlorides, and some anhydrides, condense with aniline to give anilides.
5. Acid chlorides and anhydrides give hydroxamic acids with

$$R\cdot COCl + H\cdot NHOH \rightarrow R\cdot CO\cdot NH\cdot OH + HCl$$
$$(R\cdot CO)_2O + H\cdot NHOH \rightarrow 2R\cdot CO\cdot NH\cdot OH + H_2O$$

hydroxylamine (see p. 332).

N.B. In all these reactions acetyl chloride reacts with much greater vigour than the other compounds, and accordingly tests with this substance must be carried out *with extreme care.*

1. *Action of silver nitrate.* Acidify 2 ml. of aqueous $AgNO_3$ solution with dil. HNO_3 and add the acid chloride drop by drop with shaking. Acetyl chloride and benzoyl chloride give a precipitate of AgCl. Filter, wash with water, and then with methylated spirit to remove any benzoic acid: the AgCl remains.

2. *Hydrolysis.* If the substance is a liquid, add 1 ml. very carefully to 5 ml. of distilled water:

(*a*) Acetyl chloride reacts almost immediately with the evolution of HCl and of heat. Cool, and to one portion of the solution add dil. HNO_3 and then aqueous $AgNO_3$ solution: a copious precipitate of AgCl is formed. Test the remainder of the solution for acetic acid (p. 347).

(*b*) Acetic anhydride is almost insoluble in water. Warm the mixture gently and note that a completely homogeneous solution is rapidly obtained. No precipitate is obtained with dil. HNO_3 and $AgNO_3$. Carry out tests for acetic acid (p. 347).

(*c*) Benzoyl chloride does not dissolve even on warming. Transfer to a boiling-tube and add several ml. of 10% aqueous NaOH solution and a few pieces of unglazed porcelain: boil *gently* until all the oil has dissolved. Cool and add conc. HCl carefully: a white precipitate is formed. Filter, wash with water and identify the benzoic acid (p. 347).

3. *Ester formation.* Add carefully 1 ml. of the liquid to 1 ml. of ethanol and then warm gently for 1 minute. Pour into water, make alkaline with aqueous Na_2CO_3 solution (to remove HCl and other acid fumes), and note the odour of ethyl acetate or ethyl benzoate.

$$CH_3COCl + HOC_2H_5 = CH_3COOC_2H_5 + HCl$$
$$CH_3 \cdot CO \cdot O \cdot CO \cdot CH_3 + HOC_2H_5 = CH_3COOC_2H_5 + CH_3COOH$$
$$C_6H_5COCl + HOC_2H_5 = C_6H_5COOC_2H_5 + HCl$$

4. *Anilides.* (*a*) To 1 ml. of aniline in a small conical flask add very slowly and *carefully* about 1 ml. of acetyl chloride. A vigorous reaction occurs and a solid mass is formed. Add just sufficient water (about 15 ml.) to dissolve the solid completely on boiling. On cooling, crystals of acetanilide separate out: filter and determine the m.p. (113°).

(*b*) To 1 ml. of aniline in a small conical flask add about 2 ml. of acetic anhydride and heat on a boiling water-bath for 5 minutes. Now add just sufficient water to dissolve the product on boiling. On cooling, crystals of acetanilide separate out.

(*c*) Prepare benzanilide from benzoyl chloride and aniline according to the directions given on p. 245. The reaction can be carried out conveniently on a small scale using 1 ml. aniline, 15 ml. 10% aqueous NaOH solution and 1·5 ml. of benzoyl chloride.

5. *Hydroxamic acid formation.* To 0·1 g. of acetic anhydride, add 0·1 g. of hydroxylamine hydrochloride and 5 ml. of 10% NaOH solution. Boil the mixture for 1 minute, cool and acidify with dilute

HCl. Cool again and add a few drops of FeCl$_3$ solution. A deep brown-red coloration is produced immediately.

Succinic Anhydride and Phthalic Anhydride.

To distinguish these anhydrides from the corresponding acids, note that succinic anhydride (m.p. 120°) is almost insoluble in cold water, whereas succinic acid (m.p. 185°) is readily soluble. Phthalic anhydride has m.p. 132° and phthalic acid has m.p. 196–199° with decomposition. Each of these anhydrides when heated with water hydrolyses to the corresponding acids.

Both succinic and phthalic anhydride respond to the hydroxamic acid test (see 5 above).

The fluorescein test for succinic acid (p. 349) and the phthalein and fluorescein tests for phthalic acid (p. 351) are obviously given also by succinic anhydride and phthalic anhydride, as these tests depend upon the initial formation of the anhydride in each case.

CRYSTALLINE DERIVATIVES FOR IDENTIFICATION.

The choice of type of derivative should be based on whether the chloride or anhydride is aliphatic or aromatic, because this factor largely determines the reactivity. Aliphatic acid chlorides are best converted into their anilides, as in 4 above; aromatic acid chlorides may be similarly converted into their anilides, or they may be converted into their amides by shaking with an excess of ammonia (p. 120). (M.ps., pp. 544–545.) Aliphatic acid anhydrides should be converted into their crystalline anilides, but aromatic acid anhydrides are best hydrolysed to the acid, which can then be converted into one of the standard derivatives (p. 349).

Section 18. Carbohydrates. C$_x$(H$_2$O)$_y$.

Glucose and *fructose* (C$_6$H$_{12}$O$_6$, monosaccharides); *sucrose*, *maltose* and *lactose* (C$_{12}$H$_{22}$O$_{11}$, disaccharides); *starch*, (C$_6$H$_{10}$O$_5$)$_n$, a polysaccharide.

Before proceeding with this section the student should read pp. 134–137 very carefully in order to understand the nature of the reactions which substances of this type undergo.

Physical Properties.

All colourless solids, which decompose on heating and therefore have no definite m.p.s. All insoluble in ether (like most poly-hydroxy-compounds). All except starch are soluble in water and have a sweet taste.* Starch as ordinarily supplied is insoluble in

* Students are strongly advised not to attempt identification of the soluble carbohydrates by taste—quite apart from the fact that other compounds (*e.g.*, saccharin) also have a sweet taste, the tasting of an imperfectly identified organic compound is too dangerous an operation.

water. So-called "starch solution" or "starch paste" is prepared as follows: Place about 1 g. of starch in a test-tube, add about 10 ml. of water, and mix well. Pour this suspension with stirring into 100 ml. of boiling water and continue to boil the mixture for 1 minute.

A soluble starch is obtainable which dissolves slightly in cold water and readily in hot water to give a clear solution. Concentrated solutions of both "soluble starch" and "ordinary starch" set to a jelly on cooling.

GENERAL REACTIONS.

  1. Respond to Molisch's Test.
  2. Blackening and effervescence when warmed with conc. H_2SO_4.
  3. Certain carbohydrates give yellow colorations when boiled with NaOH solution.

  1. *Molisch's Test.* Dissolve about 0·1 g. of the carbohydrate in 2 ml. of water (for starch use 2 ml. of "starch solution"), add 2–3 drops of a 1 % alcoholic solution of 1-naphthol (ignoring traces of the latter precipitated by the water) and then carefully pour 2 ml. of conc. H_2SO_4 down the side of the test-tube so that it forms a heavy layer at the bottom. A deep violet coloration is produced where the liquids meet. This coloration is due apparently to the formation of an unstable condensation product of 1-naphthol with furfural (an aldehyde produced by the dehydration of the carbohydrate).

  2. *Sulphuric acid.* *Warm* about 0·2 g. of the carbohydrate with 1 ml. of conc. H_2SO_4, using a *small* flame. Observe the immediate blackening. As the temperature is raised, CO_2, CO and SO_2 are evolved.

  3. *Action of sodium hydroxide.* Boil about 0·2 g. of glucose with 5 ml. of 10% NaOH solution: the mixture turns yellow, then brown, and emits the odour of caramel. Fructose, maltose, lactose and soluble starch behave similarly: sucrose and ordinary starch do not give colorations.

SPECIAL REACTIONS.

  A 1% solution is suitable for most of the following reactions.

Glucose. (Dextrose or grape sugar.)

  1. *Reduction of ammoniacal silver nitrate.* Place 2 ml. of dilute silver nitrate solution in a clean test-tube. Add 1 drop of NaOH solution and then add dil. ammonia drop by drop until the precipitate formed by the NaOH is *just* not redissolved. Now add 1–2 ml. of glucose solution and place the test-tube in a water-bath at 50–60°: a silver mirror is produced in 1–2 minutes.

  2. *Reduction of Fehling's solution.* Add 5 ml. of the glucose solution to 5 ml. of Fehling's solution and boil. Reduction takes place and a precipitate of cuprous oxide is formed; the latter is at first yellow but may become red on standing.

3. *Osazone formation.* The preparation of glucosazone has already been given (p. 137). It may be carried out on a small scale by either of the following methods, according as (*a*) the phenylhydrazine base, or (*b*) one of its salts, is used.

(*a*) Dissolve 1 g. of the sugar in 10 ml. of water in a boiling-tube, add 2·5 ml. of phenylhydrazine and 3 ml. of glacial acetic acid. Mix well, cork the tube loosely and place in a beaker of boiling water. Yellow crystals of the osazone appear after 10–15 minutes. Examine some of the crystals under the microscope as described on p. 139, and note the sheaves of fine needles (Fig. 63(A), p. 139). Filter off the remainder, wash well with water, dry and take the m.p. (204°).

(*b*) To 10 ml. of a 1% solution of glucose, add about 0·2 g. of phenylhydrazine hydrochloride, about 0·5 g. of sodium acetate and a few drops of glacial acetic acid. Warm gently to dissolve and then filter if necessary through a small fluted filter-paper (to remove impurities) into a boiling-tube. Proceed as in (*a*) above. (Glucose can thus be identified in biological fluids.)

4. *"Rapid furfural test."* If in Molisch's test conc. HCl is used instead of H_2SO_4, the violet coloration is produced at different rates according to the carbohydrate used. Take 1 ml. of a dilute solution of glucose, add 1 ml. of a 1% alcoholic solution of 1-naphthol and then 6–8 ml. of conc. HCl and boil. In the case of fructose and sucrose a violet coloration is produced *immediately* the solution starts to boil: with glucose the coloration is delayed and may not be produced until after 1 minute's boiling. In this way glucose may be distinguished from fructose.

*Fructose.** (Laevulose or fruit sugar.)

1. *Reduction of ammoniacal silver nitrate.* As for glucose.
2. *Reduction of Fehling's solution.* As for glucose.
3. *Osazone formation.* Fructose forms an osazone identical with that obtained from glucose. It is, however, usually formed more quickly

* In an analytical laboratory, glucose (dextrorotatory) would be conclusively differentiated from fructose (laevorotatory) by using a polarimeter: in the present scheme, however, chemical tests are primarily considered. There are various other chemical tests for differentiating between glucose and fructose, but these are frequently vitiated by the fact that fructose as ordinarily supplied almost invariably contains traces of glucose. The student is recommended, when once the sugar is recognised as a monosaccharide, to base the final identification primarily on the Rapid Furfural test, and also on rate of osazone formation under parallel conditions.

Fructose can be distinguished from glucose, *if both sugars are pure,* by the Ammonium Molybdate test which is carried out as follows. To about 10 ml. of a 1% solution of the sugar in a boiling-tube, add an equal volume of a freshly prepared 4% aqueous solution of ammonium molybdate, and then 4–5 drops of glacial acetic acid. Heat the boiling-tube in a beaker of boiling water. Fructose gives a greenish-blue coloration within 3–4 minutes. *Pure* glucose gives only a very faint coloration after about 10 minutes, and other sugars give no coloration. All ordinary samples of glucose contain sufficient fructose, however, to give a coloration after about 4–5 minutes. Free mineral acids interfere with the test.

from fructose (about 5 minutes under above conditions) than from glucose, but little reliance can be placed on this difference unless the two reactions are carried out side by side under strictly parallel conditions.

4. *"Rapid furfural test."* Fructose gives an *immediate* violet coloration on boiling (see Test 4 for glucose).

Sucrose. (Cane sugar).

1. Does not reduce ammoniacal silver nitrate or Fehling's solution. If, however, the sucrose solution is warmed for some time with the reagent in question, slight hydrolysis to glucose and fructose does take place and reduction then occurs: occasionally samples of sucrose will rapidly give a silver mirror, presumably owing to impurities.

2. Does not form an osazone.

3. *"Rapid furfural test."* A violet coloration is produced *immediately* on boiling (as for fructose).

4. *Hydrolysis by acids.* Sucrose is readily hydrolysed by *dilute* acids. Dissolve 0·5 g. of sucrose in 5 ml. of water, add 2 ml. of dil. H_2SO_4 and heat *in* a boiling water-bath for 5 minutes. Cool and show that the solution has reducing properties, and will form glucosazone. Note that the excess of acid must be neutralised before carrying out the reduction tests.

Maltose. (Malt sugar.)

1. Reduces ammoniacal silver nitrate, and Fehling's solution.

2. *Osazone formation.* Forms an osazone, m.p. 206° (see however footnote, p. 140); this osazone, unlike glucosazone, is soluble in hot water. See p. 139 for preparation. Examine the crystals under the microscope and note the sheaves of plates, not needles (Fig. 63(B), p. 139).

3. *"Rapid furfural test."* The violet coloration is produced only after boiling for about 1 minute (as for glucose).

Lactose. (Milk sugar.)

1. Reduces ammoniacal silver nitrate, and Fehling's solution.

2. *Osazone formation.* Forms a yellow osazone, m.p. 208°; soluble in hot water. See p. 137 for preparation. If examined under the microscope very characteristic clusters of "hedge-hog" crystals will be seen (Fig. 63(c), p. 139). The difference in the crystalline appearance of lactosazone and maltosazone should be very carefully noted, as this difference forms the chief and most reliable method of differentiating between these two sugars.

3. *"Rapid furfural test."* Violet coloration after about 1 minute's boiling, as for glucose and maltose.

Starch.

1. Does not reduce ammoniacal silver nitrate or Fehling's solution, and does not form an osazone.

2. *Starch Iodide coloration.* To a small volume of "starch solution"

add 1–2 drops of dilute iodine solution. A deep blue colour is produced which disappears on boiling and reappears on cooling.

3. *Hydrolysis by acids.* Place 15 ml. of starch solution in a boiling-tube, add 1 ml. of conc. HCl, mix well and place in a boiling water-bath for 20 minutes. Cool and add 2 drops of iodine solution to 1 ml. of the solution: no blue coloration is produced. On the remainder, perform tests for glucose: in particular show that glucosazone can be formed. Neutralise the excess of acid before carrying out these tests. (Note that a more concentrated acid is required to hydrolyse starch than to hydrolyse the disaccharides, such as sucrose.)

4. *Microscopic appearance.* Place a small amount of dry starch on a microscope slide, add a drop of water, cover with a slip and examine under the microscope. Characteristic oval grains are seen which have concentric rings round a hilum which is towards one end of the grain. Run a drop of *very* dilute iodine solution under the slip from a fine dropping-tube: the grains become blue.

5. *Hydrolysis with diastase and ptyalin.* See pp. 512, 514.

Section 19. Quinones. O:C< >C:O. (*cf.* Table XV, p. 549)

Benzoquinone, p-toluquinone, 1,2-naphthoquinone, 1,4-naphthoquinone, anthraquinone, 9,10-phenanthraquinone, alizarin.

Physical Properties. All yellow or orange-yellow solids except 1,2-naphthoquinone which is red. Benzoquinone (I), slightly soluble in cold water, readily soluble in hot water and volatile in steam. Toluquinone (II), sparingly soluble in water, volatile in steam, odour resembles that of benzoquinone. 1,2-Naphthoquinone (III), red, insoluble in water, odourless, non-volatile in steam. 1,4-Naphthoquinone (IV), yellow, sparingly soluble in water, volatile in steam. Anthraquinone (V), yellow, insoluble in cold and in hot water, almost insoluble in ethanol, non-volatile in steam. Phenanthraquinone (VI), orange, sparingly soluble in water. Alizarin (VII), orange, insoluble in water. (Note that phenanthraquinone is not a true quinone, but a 1,2-diketone: *cf.* p. 304.)

GENERAL REACTIONS.

1. Many quinones are volatile in steam.
2. Give characteristic reduction products depending upon reagent used.
3. Give colorations with NaOH solution.
4. Oxidation depending upon oxidising agent used.

1. *Volatility in steam.* Add about 0·1 g. of benzoquinone to 3 ml. of water in a test-tube and boil gently. The benzoquinone dissolves to give a yellow solution, which rapidly darkens in colour. Note the irritating and characteristic odour of benzoquinone which has volatilised in the steam. Also given by *p*-toluquinone and 1,4-naphthoquinone but not by the other quinones mentioned above.

2. *Reduction.* (*a*) *By sulphurous acid.* Benzoquinone, *p*-toluquinone, 1,2-naphthoquinone are readily reduced by SO_2 ultimately to the dihydroxy-compound. Thus benzoquinone gives colourless hydroquinone or quinol, p-$C_2H_4(OH)_2$.

To a cold aqueous solution of benzoquinone, add 1 drop of sulphurous acid solution (SO_2-water): the solution turns deep green-brown owing to the intermediate formation of quinhydrone, $C_6H_4O_2,C_6H_4(OH)_2$. Now add excess of sulphurous acid: the solution becomes colourless owing to the formation of hydroquinone. Add a few drops of $FeCl_3$ solution: the reaction is reversed and the deep yellow colour (distinct from that of $FeCl_3$) is restored.

Anthraquinone and alizarin are unaffected by sulphurous acid. Phenanthraquinone is reduced in warm ethanolic solution by SO_2-water to hydrophenanthraquinone, m.p. 147°. 1,2-Naphthoquinone gives the corresponding hydronaphthoquinone, m.p. 60°. Toluquinone gives toluhydroquinone, m.p. 124°.

(*b*) *By Zn and NaOH.* Formation of oxanthranol from anthracene. Heat 0·2 g. of anthraquinone with 5 ml. of 10% NaOH solution, and add a small quantity of Zn dust: an intense red colour is produced. On shaking in contact with air (after the Zn has dissolved) the solution is slowly decolorised and the anthraquinone reappears as an almost colourless flocculent precipitate.

The red colour is due to oxanthranol, C_6H_4 — CO — C_6H_4 which is red in alkaline solution.

$$\diagdown \diagup$$
$$\text{CH(OH)}$$

(*c*) *By acetic anhydride, Zn and pyridine. Reductive acetylation of anthraquinone.* Heat under reflux 0·2 g. of anthraquinone, 0·2 g. of zinc dust, 1 ml. of acetic anhydride and 0·5 ml. of pyridine for 20 minutes. While still hot, pour the liquid product into water, taking care to leave the zinc behind in the flask. On scratching, anthrahydroquinone diacetate separates and can be recrystallised from ethanol: m.p. 260°.

(*d*) *By acidified potassium iodide.* To an aqueous KI solution containing a few drops of dil. H_2SO_4, add 1 ml. of aqueous benzoquinone solution: iodine is liberated, the quinone simultaneously undergoing reduction.

Anthraquinone does not liberate iodine from KI solution.

3. *Sodium hydroxide.* Dissolve a few crystals of benzoquinone in 10% aqueous NaOH solution and shake gently. The solution turns rapidly brown and then almost black owing to atmospheric oxidation.

Alizarin dissolves in aqueous NaOH solution giving a purple solution. Calcium hydroxide will precipitate a blue salt from this solution. Anthraquinone is unaffected by NaOH solution.

Oxidation. (a) *Ammoniacal silver nitrate.* To a few ml. of ammoniacal $AgNO_3$ (preparation, p. 525), add a few drops of cold aqueous benzoquinone solution: a silver mirror or (more generally) a dark precipitate of metallic silver is formed in the cold.

(b) *Alkaline permanganate.* Heat under reflux 1 g. of 1,2-naphthoquinone, 50 ml. of saturated aqueous $KMnO_4$ solution and 2 g. of anhydrous Na_2CO_3 for 30 minutes. Then proceed as for oxidation of benzyl chloride (p. 393). 1,2-Naphthoquinone gives phthalic acid, m.p. 195°. Phenanthraquinone gives diphenic acid, $HOOC \cdot C_6H_4 \cdot C_6H_4 \cdot COOH$, m.p. 229°.

CRYSTALLINE DERIVATIVES FOR IDENTIFICATION.

(A) *Semicarbazones.* Prepared according to the directions given for acetophenone semicarbazone (p. 258), but use twice the amount of semicarbazide hydrochloride and sodium acetate. (M.ps., p. 549.)

(B) *Oximes.* Dissolve 1 g. of the quinone in 5 ml. of glacial acetic acid. Dissolve 1 g. of hydroxylamine hydrochloride in 10 ml. of 10% aqueous sodium acetate solution and shake the mixture for 5 minutes. Cool, filter off the dioxime and recrystallise from ethanol. (M.ps., p. 549.)

(C) *Reductively acetylated products.* See 2(c) above.

SPECIAL REACTION FOR PHENANTHRAQUINONE.

Formation of a Quinoxaline. Heat together for 5 minutes under reflux 0·2 g. of phenanthraquinone dissolved in 1 ml. of glacial acetic acid and 0·2 g. of o-phenylene diamine also dissolved in 1 ml. of glacial acetic acid. The yellow substituted quinoxaline (p. 305) separates rapidly. Cool, filter and recrystallise from benzene: m.p. 225°.

Section 20. Amines. *(cf.* Tables XVI–XVIII, pp. 550–553)

(A) PRIMARY AROMATIC AMINES. RNH_2.* *Aniline,* o-, m-, *and* p-*toluidine* (and other nuclear-substituted anilines); 1- *and* 2-*naphthylamines.* (For note on Aliphatic Amines, cf. p. 375.)

(B) SECONDARY AMINES. (i) *Aromatic amines.* R_2NH. *Monomethyl- and monoethylaniline, diphenylamine.* (ii) *Aliphatic and other amines. Diethylamine, di-n-propylamine, di-isopropylamine. Also Piperidine; piperazine (diethylene diamine).*

* Only the mono-amines are described here. The diamines are more frequently encountered as reduction products of dinitrobenzenes and nitroanilines, and the chief reactions of the phenylenediamines are therefore given in Section 23, pp. 384–388.

(C) **TERTIARY AMINES.** R$_3$N. The tertiary amines which the student is likely to encounter can be conveniently subdivided:

(i) *Aliphatic amines. Triethylamine, tri-n-propylamine, and tri-isopropylamine.*

(ii) *Dialkylarylamines. Dimethylaniline, diethylaniline.*

(iii) *Triarylamines. Triphenylamine.*

(iv) *Heterocyclic amines. Pyridine, the picolines* (1-, 2-, and 3-*methylpyridine), quinoline, 2-methylquinoline (quinaldine), 4-methylquinoline (lepidine).*

(v) *Special compounds, e.g., Hexamethylenetetramine.*

(A) PRIMARY AROMATIC AMINES.

Physical properties. Majority are liquids except *p*-toluidine and 1- and 2-naphthylamine. All are colourless when pure, but rapidly darken on exposure to air and light. All are very sparingly soluble in water, but dissolve readily in dilute mineral acids (except the naphthylamines, which are only moderately soluble in acids). They form colourless crystalline salts (*e.g.*, C$_6$H$_5$NH$_2$,HCl) which are soluble in water; these aqueous solutions usually have an acid reaction owing to hydrolysis, and give the reactions of both the amine and the acid from which they are derived. Addition of alkali to the acid solution liberates the amine.

GENERAL REACTIONS.

1. Give the isocyanide (or carbylamine) reaction.
2. Give acetyl derivatives.
3. Give benzoyl and toluene-*p*-sulphonyl derivatives (Schotten-Baumann reaction) (p. 243): also benzene-sulphonyl derivatives.
4. Form diazonium compounds which couple with alkaline 2-naphthol to give red dyes (p. 339).
5. Give coloured oxidation products, depending on the amine and the oxidising agent used.

For the following experiments the amine or one of its salts may be used.

1. *Isocyanide reaction.* Add a few drops of chloroform to about 0·2 g. of the substance, and then 2–3 ml. of ethanolic NaOH solution. Mix well and warm gently: the foul odour of isocyanide (carbylamine) is produced. *Immediately* the odour of isocyanide is detected, cool the tube and add carefully an excess of conc. HCl: the isocyanide is thus hydrolysed to the odourless amine.

Note. When this test is applied to amino-acids, *e.g.* glycine, anthranilic acid, sulphanilic acid, no odour is detected owing to the non-volatility of the acidic isocyanide in the alkaline solution.

2. *Acetylation.* Place 1 ml. of the substance (or, if solid, 1 g. of the *powdered* amine) in a small flask fitted with a reflux condenser (or in a test-tube fitted with a "cold-finger," as in Fig. 35, p. 62), add 5 ml. of an acetic anhydride-acetic acid mixture (equal volumes) and reflux

gently for 15 minutes. Pour into water: the solid anilide separates. Filter off, wash with water, and recrystallise from water or dilute methylated spirit. Note the m.p. (M.ps., pp. 550–551.)

3. (a) *Benzoylation* (p. 243). Mix together in a strong boiling-tube 1 ml. (or 1 g.) of the substance and 20 ml. of 10% NaOH solution. Add 1–1·5 ml. of benzoyl chloride (0·5 ml. at a time) until shaking the mixture vigorously in the securely corked boiling-tube gives no further separation of the semi-solid benzoyl derivative. Then continue the shaking for 5 minutes, and finally filter off the solid, wash well with water, and recrystallise from methylated spirit. Take the m.p.

(M.ps., pp. 550–551.)

(b) *Toluene-p-sulphonylation* (p. 247). Proceed as in 3(a), but using 1·5 g. of toluene-p-sulphonyl chloride, either finely powdered or in concentrated acetone solution. *Note.* The sulphonyl derivative of a primary amine is soluble in aqueous sodium hydroxide, and the final solution must be diluted and acidified to precipitate the product. Recrystallise and take the m.p. (M.ps., pp. 550–551.)

Benzene-sulphonylation. Benzene-sulphonyl chloride, which can be used in place of toluene-p-sulphonyl chloride, is liquid at room temperature and consequently reacts rapidly when the reaction mixture (as in 3(a)) is vigorously shaken. In general, however, the toluene-p-sulphonyl derivatives crystallise even more readily than the benzene-sulphonyl analogues, and have lower solubilities and higher m.ps.

(M.ps., pp. 550–551.)

4. *Diazotisation.* Dissolve 0·2 g. of the substance in 1 ml. of conc. HCl: dilute with about 3 ml. of water, cool in ice, and add a few drops of sodium nitrite solution. Now add this cold diazonium solution slowly to a cold solution of 2-naphthol in a considerable excess of 10% NaOH solution: a brilliant red dye is produced.

5. (a) *Action of bleaching powder.* Shake 1–2 drops of aniline with 10 ml. of water and add a few drops of bleaching-powder solution A transient purple coloration is produced which soon turns brown.

o-Toluidine and m-Toluidine give a brown coloration immediately, p-toluidine gives a yellow-brown colour, 1-naphthylamine gives a pale purple coloration and 2-naphthylamine is unaffected.

(b) The colour reactions with the enzyme *peroxidase* and H_2O_2 permit all the above amines to be distinguished from one another in very dilute solution (p. 523).

Note. All but the purest samples of monomethylaniline contain sufficient aniline to give positive (although possibly weak) reactions to certain tests for aniline (particularly Tests 1 and 4). If it is suspected that aniline is present solely as an impurity, the positive tests for monomethylaniline (particularly Test 4 below) should be applied.

CRYSTALLINE DERIVATIVES FOR IDENTIFICATION.

(A) *Picrates.* Attempt precipitation of picrates by (a) mixing cold ethanolic solutions of the amine and of picric acid (saturated); or

(b) aqueous or ethanolic solutions of the amine salt and of sodium picrate (saturated). (M.ps., pp. 550–551.)

(B) *Acetyl Derivatives.* Proceed as in (2) above. Use only for aromatic amines, since acetyl derivatives of aliphatic amines are usually soluble in cold water. (M.ps., pp. 550–551.)

(C) *Benzoyl and Toluene-p-sulphonyl Derivatives.* Proceed as in (3) above, using benzoyl or toluene-p-sulphonyl chlorides: benzene-sulphonyl chloride can be similarly used (see 3 above). (M.ps., pp. 550–551.)

(D) *Phenylurea Derivatives.* This reaction usually proceeds readily when cold solutions of the *dried* amine and of phenyl isocyanate, each in petroleum (b.p. 100–120°), are mixed; if no reaction is obvious, heat under reflux for 30 minutes. (*Care* in using the isocyanate, p. 336.)

$$R \cdot NH_2 + C_6H_5NCO = RNH \cdot CO \cdot NHC_6H_5$$

Traces of water will contaminate the product with diphenylurea (p. 336) if the solution is boiled: hence the need for anhydrous conditions. 1-Naphthylisocyanate reacts more slowly with water, and the 1-naphthylurea derivative can often be obtained using a cold aqueous solution of an aliphatic amine: it is particularly necessary in such cases to purify the product by recrystallisation from, or extraction with, boiling petroleum, leaving behind any insoluble di-1-naphthylurea. Note that the amine must also be free from alcohols (p. 335) and phenols (p. 337).

(M.ps., pp. 550–551.)

Note. PRIMARY ALIPHATIC AMINES. The lower amines are gases or low-boiling liquids (b.ps.; CH_3NH_2, −7°; $C_2H_5NH_2$, 17°; $CH_3(CH_2)_2NH_2$, 49°; $(CH_3)_2CHNH_2$, 34°) but may be encountered in aqueous or alcoholic solution, or as their crystalline salts. They are best identified as their benzoyl, or toluene-p-sulphonyl derivatives (*cf.* (C) above), and as their picrates when these are not too soluble. This applies also to benzylamine, $C_6H_5CH_2NH_2$, b.p. 185°; also to ethylenediamine, usually encountered as the hydrate, $NH_2 \cdot (CH_2)_2 \cdot NH_2, H_2O$, b.p. 116°, for which a moderate excess of the reagent should be used to obtain the di-acyl derivative. (M.ps., pp. 550–551.)

(B) SECONDARY AMINES.

Physical Properties. (i) *Aromatic.* Colourless when freshly prepared, but usually brown. Monomethylaniline, $C_6H_5NHCH_3$, b.p. 193°, and monoethylaniline, $C_6H_5NHC_2H_5$, b.p. 206°, diphenylamine, $(C_6H_5)_2NH$, m.p. 54°, are all insoluble in water, the two alkylanilines having well-marked basic properties, diphenylamine being feebly basic and insoluble in dilute mineral acids.

(ii) *Aliphatic, etc.* Diethylamine, $(C_2H_5)_2NH$, b.p. 56°, is freely soluble in water: di-*n*-propylamine, $(CH_3CH_2CH_2)_2NH$, b.p. 111°, and diisopropylamine, $[(CH_3)_2CH]_2NH$, b.p. 83°, are very sparingly soluble in water. Piperidine, (I) b.p. 106°, and piperazine (II), m.p. 104° (hexa-hydrate, m.p. 44°) are freely soluble.

GENERAL REACTIONS.

1. Do not give the isocyanide reaction.
2. Give acetyl derivatives.
3. Give benzoyl and toluene-*p*-sulphonyl derivatives.
4. With nitrous acid give nitrosamines.
5. Give coloured oxidation products.

2. *Acetylation.* Proceed as in 2 (p. 373). Pour the final acetylation mixture into 10 ml. of water, and add 10% NaOH solution, with stirring, until no more anilide is precipitated (acetyl-monoethylaniline is very soluble even in dil. acetic acid: acetyl-diphenylamine readily separates without the addition of alkali). Filter, wash with water and recrystallise.

Note. The acetyl derivatives in Class (ii) are usually water-soluble and some are liquid.   (M.ps., p. 552.)

3. *Benzoyl and Toluene-p-sulphonyl derivatives.* Proceed as in 3 (p. 374). The benzene-sulphonyl derivatives can be similarly prepared.

Note. The sulphonyl derivatives of secondary amines are neutral and insoluble in alkali, and separate on formation.   (M.ps., p. 552.)

4. *Formation of nitrosamine,* $R_2N \cdot NO$. (*a*) *From monomethylaniline.* Dissolve 1 ml. of monomethylaniline in about 3 ml. of dil. HCl and add sodium nitrite solution gradually with shaking until the yellow oil separates out at the bottom of the solution. Transfer completely to a small separating-funnel, add about 20 ml. of ether and shake. Run off the lower layer and wash the ethereal extract first with water, then with dil. NaOH solution, and finally with water to free it *completely* from nitrous acid. Evaporate the ether in a basin over a previously warmed water-bath, *in a fume-cupboard with no flames near.* Apply Liebermann's reaction to the residual oil (p. 340).

(*b*) *From diphenylamine* (p. 204). Prepare as on p. 204, using 1 g. of diphenylamine.

Note. The nitrosamines in Class (ii) do not give the Liebermann reaction.

5. *Coloured oxidation products.* (*a*) Dissolve a few small crystals of diphenylamine in 1 ml. of conc. H_2SO_4.* Add 2 drops of conc. HNO_3 to about 10 ml. of water, shake, and add 1 drop of this diluted HNO_3 to the diphenylamine solution: an intense purple-blue coloration is produced. Monomethylaniline merely turns a dirty brown when treated in this way.

(*b*) Neither monomethylaniline nor diphenylamine when pure gives colorations with bleaching powder. The former, however, almost invariably contains aniline and so gives a purple-brown coloration.

CRYSTALLINE DERIVATIVES FOR IDENTIFICATION.

(A) *Picrates* (except diphenylamine). (B) *Acetyl Derivatives.* (C) *Benzoyl, Toluene-p-sulphonyl* and *Benzenesulphonyl Derivatives.* (D)

---

* A slight green coloration is usually noticed at this stage, due presumably to traces of impurities.

Phenylurea Derivatives. These are prepared precisely as those from primary amines, except that the toluene-*p*-sulphonyl and benzene-sulphonyl derivatives are insoluble in aqueous sodium hydroxide and therefore separate on formation.   (M.ps., p. 552.)

Note. Secondary amines, *etc.*, in Class (ii) can be identified by their derivatives (C) and (D) above, and by their picrates when these can be readily isolated. The preparation of derivatives (D) requires the dry amine, whereas water does not affect that of derivatives (C).

(C) TERTIARY AMINES.

For division into Classes (i), (ii), (iii) and (iv), see p. 373.

Physical Properties. (i) Triethylamine, b.p. 90°, tri-*n*-propylamine, b.p. 156°, tri-*n*-butylamine, b.p. 212°, are liquids with a fishy odour, and with decreasing solubility in water.

(ii) Dimethylaniline, b.p. 193°, and diethylaniline, b.p. 216°; liquids which are colourless when pure, but rapidly darken in air; insoluble in water: characteristic odour. Moderately strong bases, dissolve in dilute mineral acids.

(iii) Members of this class are stable solid compounds, with very weak basic power: their chemical inertness renders rapid identification difficult. Triphenylamine, m.p. 127°, is colourless when pure, but usually pale brown: insoluble in water. Does not dissolve in conc. HCl, but dissolves in conc. H_2SO_4.

(iv) Pyridine,* b.p. 116°, is soluble in water; the three picolines have lower solubility; quinoline,* b.p. 238°, quinaldine, b.p. 247°, and lepidine, b.p. 260°, are insoluble. Pyridine has a marked odour, that of the picolines being similar but less intense.

GENERAL REACTIONS.

1. Do not give the isocyanide reaction.
2. Do not give acetyl, benzoyl or toluene-*p*-sulphonyl derivatives.†
3. Members of Classes (i), (ii) and (iv) usually react readily with methyl iodide to give methiodides, *i.e.*, quaternary ammonium iodides.
4. Members of Class (ii) give bright green *p*-nitroso derivatives with nitrous acid (p. 204).
5. Certain members, particularly those in Class (iii), give coloured products with oxidising agents.

3. *Methiodide formation.* Place 2 drops of dry pyridine in a dry test-tube, add 4–5 drops of methanol, and 2–3 drops of methyl iodide.

---

* Pyridine and quinoline are usually sold each in two grades, "technical" and "pure." The "technical" grade may contain various impurities which can hinder the identification of the base.

† "Derivatives" of the type given by primary and secondary amines. Pyridine can combine with acyl chlorides to give unstable salts of type $[C_5H_5N \cdot COC_6H_5]Cl$, which are often formed as intermediates in the acylation of primary and secondary amines, when pyridine is used in place of aqueous sodium hydroxide solution (*cf.* p. 339).

The mixture becomes hot, and on cooling the colourless crystals of the methiodide separate.

4. p-*Nitroso derivative*. Dissolve 0·5 ml. of dimethylaniline in about 4 ml. of dil. HCl, chill in ice and then add carefully drop by drop about 2 ml. of a 20% sodium nitrite solution. A reddish solution is obtained, but no oil separates (*cf*. methylaniline). Allow to stand for 5 minutes in the cold and then add dil. NaOH solution. A green precipitate of p-nitrosodimethylaniline is obtained. Shake with a few ml. of ether and note that the ethereal layer becomes deep green in colour.

5. *Coloured oxidation products*. (*a*) Dissolve a few small crystals of triphenylamine in 1 ml. of conc. H_2SO_4 (*cf*. footnote, p. 376). Add 2 drops of conc. HNO_3 to about 10 ml. of water, mix, and add 1 drop of this diluted HNO_3 to the triphenylamine solution: an intense greenish-blue coloration is produced. Dimethylaniline when treated in this way turns a deep dichromate colour.

(*b*) Neither dimethylaniline nor triphenylamine gives colorations with bleaching powder.

CRYSTALLINE DERIVATIVES FOR IDENTIFICATION.

(A) *Picrates*. These are usually precipitated when ethanolic solutions of picric acid and of the amine, in Classes (i), (ii) and (iv), are mixed. (Occasionally acetone or benzene solutions of the acid and the amine give better results, or even aqueous solutions for the water-soluble amines.) Class (iii) do not form picrates.   (M.ps., pp. 553–554.)

(B) *Methiodides*. Members of Classes (i), (ii) and (iv) combine with methyl iodide (some very vigorously) to form quaternary methiodides. It is best to add the amine to an excess of methyl iodide dissolved in about twice its volume of methanol, allow any spontaneous reaction to subside, and then boil under reflux for 30 minutes (extend to 1 hour for Class (iv) except pyridine and quinoline). The methiodide may crystallise when the reaction-mixture cools: if not, evaporate the latter to small bulk or to dryness, and recrystallise. (M.ps., pp. 553–554.)

Some methiodides may separate initially as sticky syrups: in this case, redissolve a portion in ethanol and add to an ethanolic solution of picric acid, when the yellow methopicrate is usually precipitated, and when filtered off and recrystallised, has often a sharp m.p.   (M.ps., pp. 553–554.)

Some less reactive tertiary amines can be mixed with an excess of methyl toluene-p-sulphonate, m.p. 28°, and the mixture (without a solvent) heated to a much higher temperature. The mixture is allowed to cool, but before solidification occurs, it is thoroughly stirred with ether to extract unused sulphonate, and the insoluble quaternary metho-toluene-p-sulphonate may then crystallise. If crystallisation does not occur, dissolve this residue in ethanol and treat one portion with ethanolic picric acid (to precipitate the methopicrate) and another portion with cold concentrated ethanolic sodium iodide (to precipitate the methiodide).* (M.ps. of the sulphonates, pp. 553–554.)

* Cf. p. 392.

Members of Class (iii) do not form quaternary salts. (M.ps., *cf.* methiodides and methopicrates, pp. 553–554.)

(C) p-*Nitroso derivatives*. These derivatives are obtained only from Class (ii): for preparation, see p. 204.   (M.ps., p. 553.)

(D) No *general* reaction can be cited for the preparation of crystalline derivatives of Class (iii). Triphenylamine, when nitrated in acetic acid with fuming nitric acid, gives tri-*p*-nitrophenylamine, m.p. 280°. The presence of substituents in the phenyl groups may however complicate or invalidate nitration.

Note. Tribenzylamine $(C_6H_5CH_2)_3N$, b.p. 380–390°, can be identified as indicated in (A) and (B).

SPECIAL REACTION FOR QUINOLINE.

Dissolve 1 drop of quinoline in 1 ml. of dil. HCl and add a few drops of a saturated solution of potassium dichromate. A copious orange-yellow precipitate of quinoline dichromate, $(C_9H_7N)_2,H_2Cr_2O_7$, is formed; pyridine does not give a crystalline dichromate under these conditions.

SPECIAL REACTIONS FOR HEXAMETHYLENETETRAMINE.

1. *Hydrolysis.* Warm 0·5 g. with a few ml. of dil. HCl. The pungent odour of formaldehyde, produced by the hydrolysis of the tetramine, is readily detected:

$$(CH_2)_6N_4 + 6H_2O + 4HCl = 6CH_2O + 4NH_4Cl$$

2. *Action of nitrous acid.* Dissolve 0·5 g. in a few ml. of dil. HCl. Add slowly 2 ml. of a 20% solution of sodium nitrite. A brisk effervescence takes place and almost colourless crystals of trimethylenetrinitrosamine, m.p. 105°, separate out.

Section 21. Anilides. R·CONHC₆H₅. (*cf.* Tables, pp. 543–545)

Acetanilide, benzanilide and their nuclear- and N-substituted derivatives.

Physical Properties: All colourless odourless crystalline solids. Acetanilide, $CH_3CONHC_6H_5$, and benzanilide, $C_6H_5CONHC_6H_5$ are both sparingly soluble in cold water, but acetanilide has the greater solubility in hot water.

GENERAL REACTIONS.

1. Give the isocyanide (carbylamine) reaction, if the anilide is an acylated *primary* amine.

2. Hydrolyse readily with 70% H_2SO_4.

1. *Isocyanide reaction .* Heat together *gently* 0·2 g. of the anilide, 3 ml. of ethanolic NaOH solution and 1 ml. of chloroform: hydrolysis of the anilide occurs, and the odour of the isocyanide can be detected after about 1 minute's heating. [This test clearly differentiates an anilide of type $R·CONHC_6H_5$ from one of type $R·CO·N(CH_3)C_6H_5$.]

2. *Hydrolysis with 70% H_2SO_4.* Hydrolyse about 2 g. of the

* See footnote, p. 370.

compound by boiling with 70% H_2SO_4 under reflux as described for acetanilide (p. 108) and benzanilide (p. 246). Then cool the mixture and dilute with water. The hydrolysis will furnish an aliphatic or an aromatic acid, and a primary or secondary amine. An aromatic acid will separate almost completely from the diluted solution, and the remainder of the acid can be extracted with ether: an aliphatic acid will remain in solution and can usually be isolated by steam-distillation. The amine will remain in solution as its sulphate (unless the latter has a very low solubility): on basification, the amine will be liberated, and if liquid can be extracted with ether, and if solid can be collected by filtration.

CRYSTALLINE DERIVATIVES FOR IDENTIFICATION.

These are not essential if the acid and amine obtained on hydrolysis are crystalline: but crystalline derivatives of the acid and amine can be prepared by the standard methods for acids (p. 349) and amines (pp. 374, 376) respectively.

Section 22. Amino-acids. NH_2RCOOH and NH_2RSO_3H.
(*cf.* Table XIX, p. 555)

(A) AMINO-ALIPHATIC CARBOXYLIC ACIDS.*
Glycine or *amino-acetic acid*, NH_2CH_2COOH;
tyrosine, $p\text{-}HOC_6H_4CH_2CH(NH_2)COOH$;
cystine, $[\cdot SCH_2CH(NH_2)COOH]_2$.

(B) AMINO-AROMATIC CARBOXYLIC ACIDS. *Anthranilic* or
o-*amino-benzoic acid*, $NH_2C_6H_4COOH$.

(C) AMINO-AROMATIC SULPHONIC ACIDS. *Sulphanilic* or
p-*amino-benzene sulphonic acid*, $NH_2C_6H_4SO_3H$.

(A) AMINO-ALIPHATIC CARBOXYLIC ACIDS. *Glycine, tyrosine, cystine.*

Physical Properties. Glycine is a colourless crystalline solid soluble in water. Owing to the almost equal opposing effects of the amino and the carboxylic groups, its aqueous solution is almost neutral (actually, slightly acidic to phenolphthalein) and glycine is therefore known as a "neutral ampholyte."† It exhibits both acidic and basic properties.

---

* All the amino-acids of physiological importance are α-amino-acids, *e.g.* (in addition to the above compounds), alanine or α-amino-propionic acid, $CH_3CH(NH_2)COOH$, and leucine or α-amino-γ-dimethyl-*n*-butyric acid, $(CH_3)_2CHCH_2CH(NH_2)COOH$, and naturally occurring samples (except glycine) are therefore optically active.

† Some amino-acids, *e.g.*, aspartic acid, $HOOC\cdot CH_2\cdot CH(NH_2)COOH$, also exhibit acidic and basic properties, but the acidic properties predominate owing to the presence of the two carboxylic groups. These are known as "acid ampholytes." A third class of amino-acids contain more basic than carboxylic groups and are consequently known as "basic ampholytes."

Tyrosine and cystine are colourless solids almost insoluble in water and in ethanol (tyrosine dissolves in hot water). They are readily soluble in dilute caustic alkali solution, in ammonia and mineral acids, but not in acetic acid. They are also classed as "neutral ampholytes."

GENERAL REACTIONS.

1. Soluble in Na_2CO_3 solution, with very slow evolution of CO_2 on heating.
2. React with nitrous acid to give nitrogen and the corresponding hydroxy-carboxylic acid.
3. Formaldehyde converts the basic NH_2 group into the neutral $CH_2{:}N$ group (Sørenson's reaction).
4. Form derivatives with benzoyl chloride and (more rapidly and conveniently) with 3,5-dinitrobenzoyl chloride.
5. Form deep blue copper salts usually sparingly soluble in water.

1. *Solubility in Na_2CO_3 solution.* See Section 5 (p. 330), and also Test 2 for carboxylic acids (p. 347).

2. *Action of nitrous acid.* To a few ml. of 20% $NaNO_2$ solution add a few drops of cold dil. acetic acid. Pour the mixture into a cold aqueous solution of glycine, and note the brisk evolution of nitrogen. $NH_2{\cdot}CH_2COOH + HNO_2 = HO{\cdot}CH_2COOH + N_2 + H_2O$. Owing to the insolubility of cystine in acetic acid use a suspension in dil. acetic acid for this test. In each case care must be taken not to confuse the evolution of nitrogen with any possible thermal decomposition of the nitrous acid (*cf.* footnote, p. 360).

3. *Sørensen's reaction.* First read carefully the "Estimation of Glycine," p. 463. Dissolve 0·2 g. of glycine in a few ml. of water in a test-tube **A**, add 2 drops of phenolphthalein and then *very dilute* NaOH solution drop by drop until the solution *just* turns pink. In a second test-tube **B** place 2 ml. of 40% formalin solution, add 2 drops of phenolphthalein solution and then the dil. NaOH solution until the solution *just* turns pink. Pour the contents of **B** into **A** and note the immediate decolorisation of the phenolphthalein, the solution now being acid. Observe also that several drops of dil. NaOH solution can now be added before the pink colour is restored.

Tyrosine and cystine are insoluble in water: therefore place about 0·2 g. in the test-tube **A**, dissolve in the dil. NaOH solution, add phenolphthalein as before and then add dil. HCl until pink colour is *just* not discharged: then proceed as above.

4. 3,5-*Dinitrobenzoyl-glycine.** Dissolve 0·4 g. of glycine in 10 ml. of *N*.NaOH solution in a small stoppered bottle. And 1·1 g. of finely powdered 3:5-dinitrobenzoyl chloride (preparation, p. 242) and shake vigorously for about 1 minute. Filter if necessary and acidify with dil.

---

* Many amino-acids are easily identified as their 3,5-dinitrobenzoyl derivatives (Saunders, *Biochem. Jour.*, 1934, **28**, 580; 1942, **36**, 368). Cystine, however, forms a gelatinous derivative, but is readily identified by special tests. Tyrosine does not form a derivative under these conditions.

HCl. The derivative crystallises out immediately: filter off, wash with cold water and recrystallise from boiling water. Long colourless silky needles, m.p. 179°.

5. *Copper salt.* (*a*) Add aqueous copper acetate solution to an aqueous solution of glycine. Note the formation of a blue colour which is considerably deeper than the colour of the original copper acetate solution. On heating the solution, blue needles of the copper salt usually separate.

(*b*) Dissolve about 0·5 g. of glycine in about 40 ml. of water and add an excess of freshly precipitated well-washed cupric hydroxide. Boil for 5 minutes and filter while hot into a small evaporating-basin. Concentrate to about half-bulk on a boiling water-bath and then allow to cool: fine blue needles of the copper salt, $(NH_2CH_2COO)_2Cu$, crystallise out (*cf*. p. 130).

Prepare the cupric hydroxide by dissolving 2 g. of copper sulphate in about 100 ml. of water, and adding with stirring 16 ml. of *N*.NaOH solution. Filter off the precipitate and wash thoroughly with water.

CRYSTALLINE DERIVATIVES FOR IDENTIFICATION.

(A) 3,5-*Dinitrobenzoyl derivatives.* For preparation, see 4 above. These are the most readily prepared derivatives. (M.ps., p. 555.)

(B) *Benzoyl derivatives.* Most amino-acids can be benzoyl-ated when their solutions in 10% aqueous sodium hydroxide are shaken with a small excess of benzoyl chloride until a clear solution is obtained (Schotten-Baumann reaction, p. 243). Acidification of the solution then precipitates the benzoyl derivative and the excess of benzoic acid, and the mixture must be filtered off, washed with water, and recrystallised (usually from ethanol) to obtain the pure derivative.   (M.ps., p. 555.)

(C) *Sulphonylation.* If the benzoyl chloride in (B) is replaced by toluene-*p*-sulphonyl chloride or naphthalene-2-sulphonyl chloride, a clear solution will again be obtained, although several hours' shaking may sometimes be required: on acidification of the solution only the sulphonyl derivative will separate, for the sulphonic acid is soluble in water.   (M.ps., p. 555.)

SPECIAL REACTIONS FOR TYROSINE.

1. *Mercuric nitrite reaction* (*Millon's reaction*). Dissolve a very small crystal of tyrosine in 1 ml. of water, add 1–2 drops of mercuric nitrate* solution, and 1 drop of dil. H_2SO_4, and then boil. Cool, add 1 drop of sodium nitrite solution and warm again: a red coloration is obtained.

2. *Formalin coloration.* To a small crystal of tyrosine, add 1 drop of 40% formalin, 1 ml. of water, and 1 ml. of conc. H_2SO_4. Boil gently: a deep green coloration is developed.

---

* Mercuric sulphate may be used instead of the nitrate: mercuric chloride must not be used, however, as chlorides interfere with the formation of the red coloration.

SPECIAL REACTIONS FOR CYSTINE.

1. *Removal of sulphur as sodium sulphide.* Dissolve about 0·1 g. of cystine in a few ml. of 10% NaOH solution. Add a few drops of lead acetate solution and boil for 1 minute. The solution darkens owing to the formation of lead sulphide.

2. *Nitroprusside test.* Dissolve about 0·1 g. of cystine in a few ml. of dilute ammonia and then add a few drops of potassium cyanide solution. This reduces cystine to cysteine.

$$S·CH_2CH(NH_2)COOH + 2H = 2HS·CH_2CH(NH_2)COOH$$
$$\qquad\qquad\qquad\qquad\qquad\qquad\qquad\qquad (Cysteine)$$
$$S·CH_2CH(NH_2)COOH$$
$$(Cystine)$$

Now add a few drops of a freshly prepared solution of sodium nitroprusside. A purple coloration is obtained (test for – SH Group).

(B) AMINO-AROMATIC CARBOXYLIC ACIDS. *Anthranilic acid.*

Physical Properties. Colourless solid when pure, usually pale brown. Sparingly soluble in cold water, soluble in hot water: soluble also in cold mineral acids and caustic alkalis. Dissolves readily in cold alcohol, and solution possesses a faint blue fluorescence.

REACTIONS.

1. Soluble in Na_2CO_3 solution with evolution of CO_2.
2. Gives aniline on heating with soda-lime.
3. Gives diazonium derivative which:
    (a) couples with alkaline 2-naphthol to give an azo-dye;
    (b) decomposes on heating to give a phenolic derivative.

1. *Solubility in Na_2CO_3 solution.* See Section 5 (p. 330), and also Test 2 for carboxylic acids (p. 347).

2. *Heating with soda-lime.* See Section 3, p. 327. Condense the aniline which distils over in a test-tube, dilute with water and add bleaching powder (or NaClO) solution. Note the violet coloration.

3. *Diazotisation.* Dissolve 0·2 g. of anthranilic acid in about 4 ml. of dil. HCl and cool in ice-water. To this solution, add slowly about 1 ml. of cold 20% sodium nitrite solution and divide the cold diazonium solution thus prepared into two portions A and B.

(a) Pour A into a cold alkaline solution of 2-naphthol and note the formation of a brilliant red dye.

(b) Boil B until the evolution of nitrogen ceases, cool the solution and shake. Note the separation of salicylic acid.

$$NH_2C_6H_4COOH \longrightarrow ClN_2C_6H_4COOH \longrightarrow HOC_6H_4COOH$$

To the contents of the test-tube, add about 1 ml. of methanol and 1 ml. of conc. H_2SO_4, and heat for 1 minute. Pour the solution into cold water in a boiling-tube and note the characteristic odour of methyl salicylate (oil of wintergreen).

(C) AMINO-AROMATIC SULPHONIC ACIDS. *Sulphanilic acid.*

Physical Properties. Colourless crystalline solid, soluble in boiling water, very sparingly soluble in cold water: crystallises $+ 2H_2O$. The strongly acidic $-SO_3H$ group suppresses the normal basic properties of the $-NH_2$ group: the acid therefore dissolves readily in alkalis, but not in dilute mineral acids.

REACTIONS.

1. Soluble in Na_2CO_3 solution with the evolution of CO_2.
2. Gives aniline when heated with soda-lime.
3. Forms diazonium derivative which can be coupled with 2-naphthol or with dimethylaniline to form azo-dyes.

1. *Solubility in sodium carbonate solution.* See Section 5 (p. 330), and also Test 2 for carboxylic acids (p. 347).

2. *Heating with soda-lime.* See Test 2 for anthranilic acid (p. 383) and also Section 3, p. 327.

3. *Formation of methyl-orange (cf.* p. 214). Dissolve about 0·3 g. of sulphanilic acid in 2 ml. of 10% aqueous Na_2CO_3 solution. Cool in ice-water and add 2 to 3 drops of 20% $NaNO_2$ solution. Now add about 1 ml. of cold dil. HCl, shake and leave for 2–3 minutes. Meanwhile dissolve 1 drop of dimethylaniline in a few drops of dil. HCl, cool thoroughly in ice-water and then add to the cold diazo solution. Shake well and make alkaline with aqueous NaOH solution: note the formation of a deep orange-yellow coloration or precipitate. On the addition of HCl, a bright red coloration is produced.

CRYSTALLINE DERIVATIVES FOR IDENTIFICATION.

Benzylthiouronium salts. Add 0·5 g. of sulphanilic acid to 10 ml. of water and 5 ml. of 10% NaOH solution, and *gently* warm the shaken mixture until a clear solution is obtained. Cool, add 1 drop of phenol-phthalein solution, and then add dilute HCl dropwise with shaking until the pink colour is just discharged. Now add very dilute NaOH solution until the pink colour *just* returns. Cool and add with shaking a solution of 0·5 g. of benzylthiouronium chloride in 5 ml. of water. The thiouronium salt rapidly separates: filter at the pump, wash with water, drain and recrystallise from ethanol. Colourless crystals, m.p. 185°. (M.ps., p. 548.)

These salts are by far the most readily prepared derivatives (having sharp m.ps.) of the amino-aromatic sulphonic acids.

Section 23. Nitro-compounds.* $R \cdot NO_2$. (*cf.* Table XXI, p. 557)

(A) NITRO-HYDROCARBONS. *Nitrobenzene, p-nitrotoluene, m-dinitrobenzene.*

* Most nitro-compounds react vigorously with metallic sodium during the tests for elements present (p. 321).

(B) NITRO-PHENOLS. o- and p-*Nitrophenols*.

(C) NITRO-ANILINES, o-, m- and p-*Nitro-anilines*.

A) NITRO-HYDROCARBONS.

Physical Properties. Nitrobenzene, $C_6H_5NO_2$, pale yellow liquid, insoluble in and heavier than water, characteristic odour of bitter almonds, (similar to that of benzaldehyde and benzonitrile). *p*-Nitrotoluene, $C_6H_4(CH_3)NO_2$, usually pale yellow solid, insoluble in water. *m*-Dinitrobenzene, $C_6H_4(NO_2)_2$, colourless solid when pure, but often pale yellow: insoluble in water.

GENERAL REACTION.

Reduced in acid solutions to primary amines.

Place about 1 g. of the nitro-hydrocarbon in a boiling-tube and add 5 ml. of conc. HCl and several pieces of granulated tin. Warm the mixture and shake continuously to break up the oily drops of the nitro-compound. When all the oil has disappeared (about 3 minutes' heating) pour off the liquid from any undissolved tin into a 100 ml. conical flask. Cool and add cautiously 30% aqueous NaOH solution until the precipitate formed redissolves to give a dark-coloured solution. Cool the latter thoroughly and shake well with about 15 ml. of ether. Separate the ethereal layer in a separating-funnel, wash with water and evaporate the ether in a basin on a previously heated waterbath in a fume-cupboard *away from all flames*. The residue is either (*a*) aniline (from nitrobenzene), *p*-toluidine (from *p*-nitrotoluene), or (*b*) *m*-phenylenediamine, $C_6H_4(NH_2)_2$, (from *m*-dinitrobenzene).

(*a*) Carry out tests for aniline and *p*-toluidine (p. 373).

(*b*) Carry out the following tests for *m*-phenylenediamine. Usually dark coloured, sticky solid, soluble in hot water, slightly soluble in cold water.

(i) Dissolve a small quantity of the substance in about 1 ml. of dil. HCl. Cool and add a few drops of NaNO$_2$ solution. A deep brown solution is produced, and a brown precipitate of the dye Bismarck Brown separates out: the latter is best observed by pouring the mixture into a small porcelain basin and stirring it around.

(ii) To a very dilute aqueous solution of the substance, add a few drops of FeCl$_3$ solution. A reddish coloration is produced.

CRYSTALLINE DERIVATIVES FOR IDENTIFICATION.

In general, nitro-hydrocarbons are most readily identified by reduction to the corresponding amine (above), which is then identified as its benzoyl or other derivative (p. 374).   (M.ps., pp. 550–551.)

SPECIAL TEST FOR NITROBENZENE.

Nitration. Mix together in a boiling-tube 2 ml. of conc. HNO$_3$ and 2 ml. of conc. H$_2$SO$_4$. Add 1 ml. of nitrobenzene with shaking and then heat the mixture over a small flame with constant shaking in a fume-cupboard for a few minutes. Pour into cold water and note the separation of solid *m*-dinitro-benzene, m.p. 90°.

SPECIAL TEST FOR *m*-DINITROBENZENE.

Acetone-Alkali coloration. Dissolve a few crystals in 1–2 ml. of acetone and add a few drops of aqueous NaOH solution. A deep violet coloration is produced, and is turned red by acetic acid but destroyed by mineral acids (see Test 4(*b*) for Ketones, p. 346, and also Test 2(*a*) p. 274).

(B) NITROPHENOLS.

Physical Properties. Both solids, freely soluble in hot water, sparingly in cold water. *o*-Nitrophenol, bright yellow, volatile in steam,* odour resembling both that of phenol and of nitrobenzene: *p*-nitrophenol, colourless when pure, non-volatile in steam, odourless.

GENERAL REACTIONS.

1. Soluble in aqueous NaOH solution, giving yellow or red solutions.
2. Sufficiently strongly acidic to liberate CO_2 from Na_2CO_3 solution.
3. Reduced to primary aminophenols.
4. Some nitrophenols give colorations with ferric chloride.
5. Do not give the Liebermann reaction (p. 340).
6. Give acetyl derivatives, but that from *o*-nitrophenol is not so readily obtained.

1. *Coloured salts with alkalis.* Dissolve a few crystals of *o*-nitrophenol in a few ml. of 10% NaOH solution. An orange-coloured solution is produced, and becomes almost colourless on the addition of acids. Alkali restores the orange coloration, and so the solution exhibits the properties of an indicator.

p-Nitrophenol gives similarly a bright yellow coloration with NaOH solution.

2. *Reaction with sodium carbonate.* Boil about 0·5 g. of *o*- and of *p*-nitrophenol in turn with Na_2CO_3 solution, using the method described in Section 5, p. 330, and note the evolution of CO_2.

3. *Reduction to aminophenol.* Reduce about 0·5 g. of *o*-nitrophenol with conc. HCl and tin as described on p. 385. After a few minutes the yellow molten *o*-nitrophenol disappears completely, the solution becoming homogeneous and colourless due to the formation of *o*-aminophenol (which is soluble in HCl). Cool and add 30% aqueous NaOH solution: note that a white precipitate is first formed and then redissolves in an excess of NaOH, and that the solution does not develop an orange coloration, indicating that the nitro-group has been reduced.

---

* Volatility in steam is readily observed by boiling a small quantity of the substance with water in a test-tube, and noting the appearance of drops of condensed yellow oil on the upper and cooler portions of the tube.

p-Nitrophenol is reduced similarly and the product does not give a yellow coloration with alkali.

4. *Ferric chloride coloration.* Add $FeCl_3$ solution to a few crystals (or to an aqueous solution) of p-nitrophenol: a violet-red coloration is produced. o-Nitrophenol does not give a coloration.

6. *Acetylation.* Heat 1 g. of p-nitrophenol with 5 ml. of an acetic acid-acetic anhydride mixture under reflux for 15 minutes. Pour into water: the solid acetate separates. Filter, wash with water and recrystallise from ethanol: m.p. 77·5°. This treatment usually leaves o-nitrophenol unchanged. The addition, however, of about 0·5 ml. of conc. H_2SO_4 to the acetylating mixture gives the o-derivative, m.p. 40°.

CRYSTALLINE DERIVATIVES FOR IDENTIFICATION.

(A) *Benzoyl Derivative.* Since acetylation and benzoylation do not always proceed smoothly with nitrophenols, it is best to reduce them to the aminophenol as in (3) above. Add an excess of 20% aqueous sodium hydroxide to the reaction mixture after reduction, cool and then add a small excess of benzoyl chloride, and shake in the usual way. The *dibenzoyl* derivative will separate. Filter, wash with water and recrystallise. (M.ps., p. 551.)

(C) NITROANILINES.

Physical Properties. All solid, sparingly soluble in cold water, freely soluble in hot water. o-Nitroaniline, $NO_2C_6H_4NH_2$, orange, volatile in steam; m-nitroaniline, yellow, also volatile in steam; p-nitroaniline, yellow, non-volatile in steam.

GENERAL REACTIONS.

1. Form colourless diazonium compounds which couple with alkaline 2-naphthol to give red dyes.
2. Reduced to colourless diamines.
3. Give (*a*) acetyl derivatives, (*b*) benzoyl derivatives.
4. No odour is detectable in the isocyanide reaction.
5. No colour reaction with bleaching powder (*cf.* amines).

1. *Diazotisation.* Dissolve 0·2 g. of the substance in about 5 ml. of dil. HCl, warming if necessary. Cool in ice-water* and add sodium nitrite solution drop by drop: the end of the diazotisation is marked by the complete decolorisation of the solution. Pour the diazonium solution into a cold solution of 2-naphthol in a considerable excess of NaOH solution: a brilliant red dye is produced.

2. *Reduction.* Reduce 0·5 g. of the nitroaniline with HCl and tin, as described on p. 385. Note that after a few minutes the original yellow colour has entirely disappeared. Cool and add 20% aqueous NaOH solution: a white precipitate is formed which redissolves to give

---

* The hydrochloride of the nitroaniline may separate out at this stage, but this does not interfere with the reaction as the hydrochloride separates in fine, feathery crystals which readily redissolve and hence are very reactive.

a dark-coloured solution. Cool and extract with about 15 ml. of ether. Separate the ethereal layer, wash with water and evaporate the ether in a basin on a previously heated water-bath in a fume-cupboard *away from all flames*.

The residue may be:

(a) *o*-Phenylene diamine from *o*-nitroaniline. Colourless crystals. Dissolve in a *small* quantity of dil. HCl and add several drops of FeCl₃ solution: a deep red coloration is produced and increases in intensity on standing.

(b) *m*-Phenylenediamine from *m*-nitro-aniline. Usually dark-coloured, semi-solid mass. Carry out the two tests described on p. 385. Note that although both *o*- and *m*-phenylenediamines give reddish colorations with FeCl₃, only the *m*-phenylenediamine on diazotisation gives a *deep* brown solution with separation of the solid Bismarck Brown. *o*-Phenylenediamine similarly treated gives a very pale brown (almost colourless) solution with only a trace of solid matter separating, while *p*-phenylenediamine is unchanged.

(c) *p*-Phenylenediamine from *p*-nitroaniline. Colourless solid, but soon becomes coloured on exposure to air. Dissolve in cold water and add 1 drop of FeCl₃ solution: a deep green coloration is produced and rapidly turns brown.

The above diamines can alternatively be identified as their *diacetyl* derivatives. Heat under reflux 0·5 g. of the diamine with 3 ml. of acetic acid—acetic anhydride mixture for 30 minutes. Pour into water, when the diacetyl derivative usually separates. If there is no precipitate, the careful addition of dilute NaOH solution will cause the separation of the diacetyl derivative. Recrystallise from ethanol. M.ps. of the diacetyl derivatives of *o*-, *m*-, and *p*-phenylene diamine are 185°, 191°, and 304° respectively (p. 551).

The dibenzoyl derivatives can be prepared by the normal Schotten-Baumann method, using 10% aqueous sodium hydroxide and an excess of benzoyl chloride, but the m.ps. of the dibenzoyl derivatives are inconveniently high (p. 551).

3. (a) *Acetylation.* Proceed exactly as for the acetylation of amines, (Test 2, p. 373). *o*-Nitroacetanilide, pale yellow crystals from water, m.p. 92°; *m*- and *p*-nitroacetanilides, colourless crystals from methylated spirit, m.p. 155° and 214° respectively.

(b) *Benzoylation.* Proceed exactly as for benzoylation of amines (Test 3 (a), p.374), but use a suspension of the finely ground nitroaniline in the 10% NaOH solution. This preparation of the benzoyl derivatives is rarely necessary, however, as the above acetylation proceeds very satisfactorily. (M.ps., p. 550.)

CRYSTALLINE DERIVATIVES FOR IDENTIFICATION.

Prepare acetyl or benzoyl derivatives as in (3) above.

(M.ps , p. 550.)

Section 24. Purines.

Uric acid or 2,6,8-*trihydroxypurine*, $C_5H_4N_4O_3$.

$$
\begin{array}{ccc}
\text{HN} & \text{—C:O} & \\
| & | & \\
\text{O:C} & \text{C——NH} & \\
| & \| & \rangle\text{C:O} \\
\text{HN} & \text{—C——NH} &
\end{array}
\quad \rightleftharpoons \quad
\begin{array}{ccc}
\text{N} & =\!\!=\text{C·OH} & \\
| & | & \\
\text{HO.C} & \text{C——N} & \\
\| & \| & \rangle\text{C·OH} \\
\text{N} & \text{—C——NH} &
\end{array}
$$

(A) *Keto* or *lactam* form.   (B) *Enol* or *lactim* form.

Physical Properties. White solid almost insoluble in water and in ethanol. It is a weak acid and exists in the tautomeric forms (A) and (B) above. It dissolves in alkali hydroxide solutions, giving salts of the type $C_5H_2Na_2N_4O_3$, the free acid being reprecipitated from such solutions on the addition of HCl or acetic acid: it is also soluble in solutions of borates, phosphates, carbonates and acetates of the alkali metals. It dissolves in conc. H_2SO_4, and is reprecipitated on addition of water.

REACTIONS.

1. Chars on being heated.
2. Gives murexide on treatment with conc. HNO_3 and then ammonia.
3. Solution in aqueous Na_2CO_3 reduces silver nitrate (Schiff's test).
4. Reduces Fehling's solution.
5. Reduces alkaline $KMnO_4$ in the cold.

1. *Action of heat.* Heat about 0·2 g. of uric acid in a hard-glass test-tube. Note the charring and also the formation of a white sub-limate on the cooler parts of the tube.

2. *Murexide test.* Place about 0·1 g. of uric acid in a small evapor-ating-basin and moisten with 2–3 drops of conc. HNO_3. Heat *very gently* to dryness, and then add 1 drop of aqueous NH_3 from a glass rod: a purple coloration is produced due to the formation of ammonium purpurate or murexide.* Now add a drop of NaOH solution: the coloration changes to blue.

3. *Schiff's test.* Dissolve about 0·1 g. of uric acid in Na_2CO_3 solution and pour some of this solution on to a filter-paper which has been moistened with $AgNO_3$ solution: a black stain of metallic silver results.

4. *Reduction of Fehling's solution.* Dissolve 0·1 g. of uric acid in Na_2CO_3 solution, and to the clear solution add Fehling's solution drop by drop. Note the formation of a white precipitate of copper

* Murexide is probably

$$
\begin{array}{ccccc}
 & \text{H} & & \text{H} & \\
 & \text{N} & \text{O}^- & \text{N} & \\
\text{O:C} & & \text{C} & & \text{C:O} \\
\| & & & & | \quad +\\
\text{HN} & & \text{C} & & \text{NH} \quad NH_4 \\
 & \text{C} & \text{N} & \text{C} & \\
 & \text{O} & & \text{O} &
\end{array}
$$

urate. Now add a slight excess of Fehling's solution and boil for several minutes: reduction occurs with the precipitation of cuprous oxide.

5. *Reduction of potassium permanganate.* To a solution of uric acid in aqueous Na_2CO_3 add $KMnO_4$ solution drop by drop: a brown precipitate of MnO_2 is produced immediately in the cold.

Section 25. Halogeno-hydrocarbons. (*cf.* Table XXVI, p. 559)

Methyl iodide, ethyl bromide, ethyl iodide, higher alkyl halides, chloroform, iodoform, carbon tetrachloride, chlorobenzene, bromobenzene, iodobenzene, benzyl chloride (and nuclear substituted derivatives)

Physical Properties. All heavier than, and insoluble in water. All liquids, except iodoform, CHI_3, which is a yellow crystalline solid with a characteristic odour. The remainder are colourless liquids when pure: ethyl iodide, C_2H_5I, and iodobenzene, C_6H_5I, are, however, usually yellow or even brown in colour. Methyl iodide, CH_3I, ethyl bromide, C_2H_5Br, ethyl iodide, chloroform,* $CHCl_3$, and carbon tetrachloride,* CCl_4, have sweetish odours, that of chloroform being particularly characteristic.

Chlorobenzene, C_6H_5Cl, bromobenzene, C_6H_5Br, and iodobenzene possess aromatic odours. Benzyl chloride, $C_6H_5CH_2Cl$, has a sharp irritating odour and is lachrymatory.

GENERAL REACTIONS.

1. Aliphatic mono-halides, and aromatic hydrocarbons with halogen in side-chain, precipitate silver halide on treatment with cold aqueous silver nitrate solution.
2. Aliphatic halides, and aromatic hydrocarbons with halogen in side-chain, are readily hydrolysed by boiling with alcoholic NaOH solution.
3. Aromatic halides can, in virtue of their aromatic character, be nitrated, *etc.*
4. Alkyl and aryl-alkyl halides form 2-naphthyl ethers with 2-naphthol.

1. *Reaction with cold silver nitrate solution.* Add 2 ml. of 10% aqueous $AgNO_3$ solution to 1 ml. of methyl iodide and shake vigorously: a yellow precipitate of AgI is formed in the cold. Add an excess of dil. HNO_3 to show that the precipitate does not dissolve.†

Ethyl bromide and ethyl iodide behave similarly. Benzyl chloride gives a faint precipitate in the cold, but the precipitation is complete on gentle warming.

---

* Chloroform and carbon tetrachloride must not be heated with metallic sodium as an explosive reaction is likely to take place (see footnote, p. 321).

† The identity of the silver *iodide* may be confirmed in the usual way, but this is unnecessary at this stage as the halide should already have been identified during the Preliminary Tests, p. 325.

Chloroform, carbon tetrachloride, iodoform and the halogeno-benzenes do not give precipitates with cold aqueous silver nitrate solution.

2. *Hydrolysis with alcoholic NaOH solution.* Boil together in a small conical flask, fitted with a reflux water-condenser, 1 ml. of chloroform and 10 ml. of alcoholic NaOH solution for 10 minutes. Then dilute with water to dissolve any NaCl which may have separated, add dil. HNO_3 until acid and then $AgNO_3$ solution. A copious precipitate of AgCl is produced.

Similar results are obtained with methyl iodide, ethyl bromide, ethyl iodide, iodoform, carbon tetrachloride, and benzyl chloride.

Chloroform and iodoform give also sodium formate in this reaction: $CHCl_3 + 4NaOH = HCOONa + 3NaCl + 2H_2O$. A portion of the solution, before the addition of the HNO_3, should therefore be tested for formic acid (Tests, p. 350): ensure however that the solution is neutralised where necessary during these tests.

Methyl iodide, ethyl bromide and ethyl iodide also evolve small amounts of ethylene when treated as above. If this is suspected, a small quantity of the substance should be heated with alcoholic NaOH solution in a small flask, fitted with a "knee" delivery-tube. Pass the gas evolved through a very dilute solution of $KMnO_4$ which has been made alkaline with aqueous Na_2CO_3 solution. If ethylene has been formed, a brown precipitate of MnO_2 will be produced (a transient green colour may appear).

3. *Nitration.* Place 1 ml. of chlorobenzene in a boiling-tube and add 2 ml. of conc. HNO_3 and then 2 ml. of conc. H_2SO_4. Warm *gently** with continuous shaking for about 4 minutes. Pour into about 50 ml. of water; an oil separates and, on cooling and scratching with a glass rod, solidifies to a pale yellow crystalline mass: the characteristic odour of "bitter almonds" also becomes noticeable.

Bromobenzene, iodobenzene and benzyl chloride behave somewhat similarly. The *p*-nitro-derivatives of the first two compounds frequently crystallise out even before pouring into water: *p*-nitrobenzyl chloride usually remains as an oil for several minutes before solidifying.

4. *Formation of 2-naphthyl ethers.* Alkyl halides and aryl-alkyl halides (e.g. benzyl chloride) are converted into 2-naphthyl ethers thus:

$$C_6H_5CH_2Cl + C_{10}H_7OH + NaOH \rightarrow$$
$$C_6H_5CH_2OC_{10}H_7 + NaCl + H_2O.$$

Heat together under reflux 1 g. of 2-naphthol, 3 ml. of 10% NaOH solution and 0·5 ml. of the halide (e.g. benzyl chloride) for 30 minutes. Cool, shake with about 10 ml. of water and filter off the solid ether. Recrystallise from ethanol: m.p. 101·5°.

* Although these nitrations proceed smoothly, attempted nitration of an unidentified substance should always be carried out *with extreme care*, *e.g.*, by working in a fume-cupboard and pointing the boiling-tube *away* from the operator. Many organic substances (*e.g.*, alcohols and phenols) react with great violence with a mixture of nitric and sulphuric acids.

If desired, the crude naphthyl ether can be identified as its crystalline picrate (p. 397). (M.ps., p. 561).

SPECIAL REACTIONS.

Methyl iodide and ethyl iodide.

Pyridine methiodide and ethiodide. Place 2 drops of dry pyridine in a test-tube, add 2 drops of methyl iodide and mix. A vigorous reaction occurs and on cooling, a colourless crystalline mass of pyridine methiodide, C_5H_5N,MeI, is formed (*cf.* p. 377): when recrystallised from methylated spirit, the methiodide has m.p. 117°.

The reaction with ethyl iodide is less rapid and it is necessary to warm the mixture *gently* until cloudy. On cooling, crystals of the ethiodide are formed, and after recrystallisation from methylated spirit have m.p. 84°.

Chloroform.

1. *Isocyanide (or carbylamine) reaction.* Dissolve 1 ml. of chloroform in 2–3 ml. of alcoholic NaOH solution, add a few drops of aniline, mix well and warm *gently*: the foul odour of isocyanide is produced.

$$CHCl_3 + C_6H_5NH_2 + 3NaOH = C_6H_5NC + 3NaCl + 3H_2O$$

Immediately the odour is detected, cool the tube and add carefully an excess of conc. HCl: the isocyanide is thus hydrolysed to the odourless amine.

2. *Colorations with resorcinol and naphthol.* Dissolve about 0·2 g. of resorcinol in 1 ml. of 30% aqueous NaOH solution, add 1 ml. of chloroform and warm gently: the aqueous layer turns red and shows a slight fluorescence.

Repeat using using 1- or 2-naphthol in place of resorcinol: the aqueous layer becomes deep blue, fading to green.

3. *Reduction of Fehling's solution.* Boil 1 ml. of chloroform *gently* with 3 ml. of Fehling's solution with constant shaking for 3–4 minutes. Reduction occurs and reddish cuprous oxide slowly separates.

Iodoform.

1. *Liberation of iodine on heating.* On heating in a dry tube, iodoform gives off copious violet vapours of iodine. This will have been observed during the Preliminary Tests, p. 319.

2. *Isocyanide reaction.* Repeat Test 1 for chloroform (above) using 0·5 g. of iodoform instead of 1 ml. of chloroform: the foul odour of isocyanide is produced as before.

Carbon tetrachloride.

1. *Isocyanide reaction.* Repeat Test 1 for chloroform using 1 ml. of carbon tetrachloride in place of the chloroform. The odour of isocyanide can be detected only after heating gently for several minutes.

2. Does not give a coloration with alkaline solutions of resorcinol or 1- or 2-naphthol (difference from chloroform).

Benzyl chloride.

1. *Oxidation to benzoic acid.* Boil a mixture of 1 ml. of benzyl chloride, 50 ml. of saturated aqueous $KMnO_4$ solution and 2 g. of anhydrous Na_2CO_3 under reflux for 30 minutes. Acidify with conc. HCl and then add 25% Na_2SO_3 solution until the brown precipitate of MnO_2 has dissolved. On cooling, benzoic acid crystallises out. Filter through a small Buchner funnel, wash with water and identify (p. 347). When recrystallised from water, benzoic acid has m.p. 121°.

Section 26. Hydrocarbons. C_xH_y. (*cf.* Table XXVII, p. 560)

Benzene, toluene, naphthalene, anthracene, phenanthrene, biphenyl, petroleum.

Physical Properties. Benzene, C_6H_6, toluene, $C_6H_5 \cdot CH_3$, and petrol (a mixture of aliphatic hydrocarbons, *e.g.*, pentane, hexane, *etc.*) are colourless liquids, insoluble in and lighter than water. Benzene and toluene, which have similar odours, are not readily distinguishable chemically, and their physical constants should therefore be carefully noted: benzene, m.p. 5° (solidifies when a few ml. in a dry test-tube are chilled in ice-water), b.p. 81°; toluene, m.p. − 93°, b.p. 110°. Petroleum* has a characteristic odour.

Naphthalene, $C_{10}H_8$, colourless solid, m.p. 80°, insoluble in water, soluble in alcohol, characteristic odour. Anthracene, C_6H_4:C_2H_2:C_6H_4, m.p. 216°, white crystals when pure, with a faint blue fluorescence, but often very pale yellow crystals; insoluble in water, slightly soluble in alcohol. Phenanthrene, m.p. 98°, and biphenyl, m.p. 69°, are white solids.

The aliphatic hydrocarbons are extremely unreactive and do not respond to any of the following tests for aromatic hydrocarbons.

GENERAL REACTIONS FOR AROMATIC HYDROCARBONS.

1. Can be nitrated.
2. Can be sulphonated.
3. Form picrates: that of naphthalene can be readily isolated.

1. *Nitration.* (*a*) To 5 ml. of a mixture of equal volumes of conc. HNO_3 and conc. H_2SO_4, add gradually 1 ml. of benzene or toluene with shaking; cool if the reaction tends to become too violent. After shaking the mixture well for about 2 minutes, pour into cold water: the nitro-compound will separate out as a yellow oil or solid. Separate the product, wash once with water, and then prove the presence of the nitro-group by reduction with tin and conc. HCl as described for nitro-benzene (p. 385).

(*b*) To nitrate naphthalene: dissolve 1 g. in 5 ml. of glacial acetic acid by gentle warming, cool, add 1 ml. of conc. HNO_3 and heat to about 80°

---

* Petroleums or "petrols" are used as solvents and are usually supplied as fractions boiling over the following ranges: 40–60°, 60–80°, 80–100°, 100–120°.

for 1 minute, a clear yellow solution being obtained. Pour into water: the yellow 1-nitro-compound, m.p. 61°, solidifies.

(c) Biphenyl gives 4,4'-dinitrobiphenyl, m.p. 237°.

The nitration of anthracene is more difficult to perform and is not recommended as a test.

2. *Sulphonation.* To 1 ml. of benzene or toluene, add slowly 1 ml. of 20% fuming H_2SO_4. Shake well and note that a homogeneous solution is obtained. [If this is repeated using petrol, the latter does not react, but merely floats unchanged on the surface of the H_2SO_4 (a slight darkening may take place due to traces of impurities).] Now pour the reaction mixture carefully with stirring into about 20 ml. of cold water: a clear solution of the sulphonic acid is obtained. Usually, however, a small amount of the corresponding sulphone, R_2SO_2, separates as fine colourless crystals.

3. *Picrates.* The picrates of benzene and toluene are isolated only with extreme difficulty and are not used for purposes of identification.

(a) *Naphthalene picrate.* Make a concentrated solution of picric acid in cold acetone,* and add about 2 ml. of this solution to 2 ml. of a cold concentrated solution of naphthalene also in acetone. Shake well: on standing for about 1 minute long yellow needles of naphthalene picrate crystallise out. After recrystallisation from ethanol the picrate has m.p. 152°.

(b) *Anthracene picrate.* This picrate has a characteristic red colour. It is, however, far more soluble than that of naphthalene: therefore proceed thus:

Make a concentrated solution of anthracene in hot acetone. To about 2 ml. of this solution add a cold concentrated acetone solution of picric acid drop by drop, and note the formation of a red coloration which becomes deeper on further addition of the acid. If excess of picric acid is added, however, the solution becomes paler in colour, and this is to be avoided if possible. Boil to ensure that both components are in solution and then transfer to a small porcelain basin or watch-glass: ruby-red crystals of anthracene picrate separate out on cooling. The product, however, is often contaminated with an excess of either anthracene or of picric acid, which appear as yellowish crystals.

CRYSTALLINE DERIVATIVES FOR IDENTIFICATION.

No very general rules can be given with regard to the formation of crystalline derivatives of aromatic hydrocarbons. Their reactivities towards a particular reagent vary considerably and complications often arise owing to the production of isomers.

(A) *Nitrohydrocarbons.* With few exceptions these are solids. Whenever possible, mild conditions of nitration should be attempted (see 1(a) and 1(b) above), and the product recrystallised to constant m.p. to eliminate isomers.   (M.ps., p. 560.)

* Picric acid is usually stored damp for safety, and acetone is therefore a better solvent than benzene or this test: the solutions *must* be almost saturated, however.

(B) *Picrates.* Many picrates are unstable. (See 3 above.)

(M.ps., p. 560.)

(C) *Oxidation of side chains.* Aromatic hydrocarbons with side chains are oxidised by alkaline $KMnO_4$ to carboxylic acids. Proceed as for the oxidation of benzyl chloride (p. 393), using 1 g. of the hydrocarbon in place of the chloride. Thus toluene and ethylbenzene give benzoic acid, *o*-, *m*- and *p*-xylene give phthalic acid, isophthalic acid, and terephthalic acid respectively (M.ps., p. 544). If desired, these crystalline acids can be further identified by making suitable crystalline derivatives according to the directions given under acids (p. 353).

Aromatic hydrocarbons with unsaturated side-chains.

Styrene, stilbene.

Physical Properties. Styrene, $C_6H_5CH = CH_2$, is a pleasant smelling liquid, lighter than and insoluble in water, b.p. 146°. Stilbene, $C_6H_5CH = CHC_6H_5$, is a colourless solid, m.p. 125°, b.p. 306°, insoluble in water.

GENERAL REACTIONS.

 1. Decolorise bromine.

 2. Oxidised by acid or by alkaline permanganate.

 1. *Dibromide formation.* Dissolve 0·2 ml. of styrene in 0·5 ml. of CCl_4 in a test-tube. Add slowly, drop by drop, a 10% solution of bromine in CCl_4. Note the decolorisation of the bromine and absence of HBr fumes (therefore reaction by addition and not by substitution). Continue to add the bromine solution until a faint brown colour persists. Scratch the sides of the tube and cool it in ice-water. Filter off the crystals that separate and recrystallise the styrene dibromide from methanol: m.p. 72°.

Stilbene decolorises bromine only on heating. Proceed as above, but keep the stilbene solution hot during the addition of the CCl_4 solution of bromine. Stilbene dibromide has m.p. 237°.

 2. *Oxidation.* (*a*) Oxidise 1 g. of styrene with $KMnO_4$ and Na_2CO_3 (for details see oxidation of benzyl chloride, p. 391). Benzoic acid, m.p. 121° is obtained. Stilbene similarly gives benzoic acid, but requires longer heating—about 1 hour.

(*b*) Heat about 0·1 g. of either styrene or stilbene with 5 ml. of saturated $KMnO_4$ solution and 1 ml. of dil. H_2SO_4 under reflux. Note the decolorisation of the $KMnO_4$ and the marked odour of benzaldehyde produced by oxidation.

SPECIAL TEST FOR STYRENE.

Polymerisation. To 0·5 ml. of styrene add 1 drop of conc. H_2SO_4. Note the formation of a solid glassy mass of polystyrene.

Section 27. Ethers. ROR. (*cf*. Table XXVIII, pp. 560–561).

Diethyl ether, b.p. 35°. *Di*-n-*propyl ether*, b.p. 90°. *Di*-iso-*propyl ether*, b.p. 67·5°. *Anisole (methyl phenyl ether)*, b.p. 154°. *Phenetole (ethyl phenyl ether*), b.p. 172°. *Guaiacol* (1-*hydroxy-2-methoxybenzene*), b.p. 205°. *Nerolin* (*methyl 2-naphthyl ether*), m.p. 72°, b.p. 273°.

Physical Properties. All these ethers are insoluble in water. The aliphatic ethers have strong characteristic odours, have anaesthetic properties and are extremely inflammable.

GENERAL REACTIONS.

Ethers are, in general, inert compounds and their identification presents difficulties. Further complications also arise with mixed ethers.

1. Iodine dissolves in liquid ethers giving brown solutions.
2. Esters are formed with sulphuric acid and acetic acid.
3. Many ethers dissolve in conc. HCl.
4. Aliphatic ethers are broken down by heating with $ZnCl_2$.
5. Usually ruptured by hydrogen iodide.
6. Aryl ethers form picrates.

1. *Iodine solutions.* Dissolve 1 crystal of iodine in diethyl ether and note the brown colour. Aromatic hydrocarbons (*e.g.* benzene) give purple solutions.

2. *Ester formation.* Heat under *very efficient* reflux 1 ml. of diethyl ether, 4 ml. of glacial acetic acid and 1 ml. of conc. H_2SO_4 for 10 minutes. Distil off 2 ml. of liquid. Use a few drops of this liquid for the hydroxamic acid test for esters (p. 334). Use the remainder for other tests for esters (p. 354).

$$2CH_3COOH + C_2H_5OC_2H_5 = 2CH_3COOC_2H_5 + H_2O$$

3. *Oxonium salt formation.* Shake up 0·5 ml. of ether with 1 ml. of conc. HCl and note that a clear solution is obtained owing to the formation of a water-soluble oxonium salt. Note that aromatic and aliphatic hydrocarbons do not behave in this way. In general diaryl ethers and alkyl aryl ethers are also insoluble in conc. HCl.

$$C_2H_5OC_2H_5 + HCl = [(C_2H_5)_2\overset{+}{O} - H]\overset{-}{C}l$$

4. *Formation of 3,5-dinitrobenzoates.* Aliphatic ethers are broken up by heating with $ZnCl_2$, and a 3,5-dinitrobenzoate of the residue can then be prepared. This is suitable only for symmetrical ethers.

$$CH_3CH_2OCH_2CH_3 \xrightarrow{ZnCl_2} CH_3CH_2OH + [CH_2 = CH_2]$$

Heat together under *very efficient* water reflux 1 g. of freshly fused *dry* powdered $ZnCl_2$, 2 ml. of diethyl ether and 0·5 g. of 3,5-dinitrobenzoyl chloride for 2 hours. Shake the product with 5 ml. of water and then add 10% NaOH solution until all the $ZnCl_2$ and excess of 3,5-dinitrobenzoyl chloride and 3,5-dinitrobenzoic acid have gone into solution. Filter at the pump and recrystallise from petroleum (b.p. 40–60°) to obtain ethyl 3,5-dinitrobenzoate, m.p. 93°. (M.ps. of other 3,5-dinitrobenzoates, p. 536.)

5. *Rupture by hydrogen iodide.* Ethers are usually broken up by hot hydrogen iodide thus:

$$C_2H_5OC_2H_5 + 2HI = 2C_2H_5I + H_2O$$
$$CH_3OC_6H_5 + HI = CH_3I + C_6H_5OH$$

Heat under reflux 1 g. of anisole and 10 ml. of constant-boiling hydrogen iodide for 30 minutes. Now distil off the volatile methyl iodide and identify it in the distillate (see pp. 390–391).

6. *Picrate formation.* Dissolve 0·1 g. of anisole in 10 ml. of hot ethanol and add this solution to a solution of 0·25 g. of picric acid in 10 ml. ethanol. Set aside until separation of the picrate (1:1 compound) is complete. Filter off the solid and recrystallise from ethanol: m.p. 80°.   (M.ps., p. 560.)

CRYSTALLINE DERIVATIVES FOR IDENTIFICATION.

As stated above, ethers do not lend themselves to the ready formation of crystalline derivatives. The following however, are recommended.

(A) 3,5-*Dinitrobenzoates.* Only suitable for symmetrical aliphatic ethers. Preparation, see above. The yields are usually very low.

(M.ps., p. 536.)

(B) *Picrates.* Very useful for ethers containing an aromatic group. Preparation, see above.   (M.ps., p. 560.)

SCHEME FOR THE SEPARATION OF SIMPLE BINARY MIXTURES OF ORGANIC COMPOUNDS

The successful separation of a mixture of the two organic substances will depend largely upon the student's general knowledge of organic chemistry and in particular upon his acquaintance with the reactions of the substances given in the previous sections. It is impossible to give more than an outline of the methods employed, as the mode of separation depends upon the actual substances present as well as the classes to which they belong.

Three types of mixtures will be considered:

(1) *Two neutral substances.*
(2) *A neutral and an acidic substance.*
(3) *A neutral and a basic substance.*

(1) **Two neutral substances.** The separation is usually based upon one of the following:

> (a) difference in volatility (*i.e.*, fractional distillation, steam-distillation, sublimation);
> (b) difference in solubility, including Soxhlet extraction;
> (c) the formation of a crystalline derivative of one or of both the substances;
> (d) by chromatographic methods (pp. 48–58).

(a) Two liquids may be separated by fractional distillation provided that they do not form a constant-boiling mixture and that their boiling-points are sufficiently far apart. For instance, carbon tetrachloride (b.p. 77°) and toluene (b.p. 110°) can be separated in this way, but difficulty may be experienced in separating substances with much closer boiling-points, unless an efficient fractionating column is used.

Two components can often be separated if one is volatile, and the other non-volatile, in steam, e.g., o-nitrophenol and p-nitrophenol (p. 170).

Frequently one component of a mixture is readily sublimed and so can be obtained in a highly purified condition by this process.

Solutions of solids in liquids can sometimes be separated by distilling off the liquid and leaving a residue of the solid, e.g., acetone and acetamide.

(b) This depends entirely upon the nature of the particular compounds present, and no general rule can be given. The method of separation ultimately adopted must be based solely on experimental tests, e.g., a mixture of starch and cane sugar can be separated by making use of the fact that the latter is soluble in cold water whereas the former is completely insoluble. The components of other mixtures can sometimes be separated by fractional crystallisation: this is often a long process, as it must be repeated until each component is pure, i.e., entirely free from the other component.

For separation by Soxhlet extraction, see p. 38.

(c) In a mixture of toluene and benzaldehyde, for example, the latter may be separated as the bisulphite compound. It must be pointed out, however, that a derivative of one component may prove to be very soluble in the other component. In such a case it may be necessary to make some less soluble derivative.

Special methods are available for particular classes of compounds, e.g., Hinsberg's method of separating primary, secondary and tertiary amines (p. 249).

(2) A neutral and an acidic substance.

Only those mixtures in which the neutral substance is insoluble in water will be considered.* The method of separation consists in extracting the mixture with aqueous sodium hydroxide solution, whereby the acidic component dissolves in the form of its sodium salt, while the neutral component remains undissolved and can thus be separated.

First carry out a small-scale test, placing about 0·5 g. of the mixture in a test-tube, adding about 5 ml. of 10% aqueous NaOH solution, and shaking the mixture well. It will be readily seen whether the neutral substance (which remains undissolved) is solid or liquid. Then repeat the extraction on a larger scale as follows:

(a) *Neutral Component is solid.* Place about 5 g. of the original mixture (if solid) or 10–15 ml. (if liquid) in a small conical flask,

---

* For very small quantities, ion exchange processes may be utilised (p. 55) even with water-soluble neutral substances.

add excess of NaOH solution as before, and thoroughly shake the securely corked flask. Then dilute somewhat with water, and filter off the solid neutral component at the pump. Reserve the filtrate for subsequent identification of the acidic component (see below). Wash the solid residue on the filter thoroughly with very dilute NaOH solution to ensure complete extraction of the acidic component, then wash with water, drain, and dry by pressing between sheets of drying-paper as usual. Then identify.

(b) *Neutral Component is liquid.* Place the above quantities of the original mixture in a separating-funnel, add excess of the NaOH solution and shake thoroughly. Run off the aqueous layer and reserve as before for the identification of the acidic component. Then again extract the neutral liquid remaining in the funnel with more NaOH solution. Run off and reject the latter, and extract the neutral liquid finally with water. Separate the liquid, dry it with anhydrous sodium sulphate, and distil if considered necessary. Alternatively, if the volume is very small, extract with ether, dry the ethereal extract, filter, and then evaporate the solvent. Then identify the pure neutral component.

Acidic Component. The filtrate from (a) or the first alkali extract from (b) will contain the acidic component, which will be either an acid or a phenol. Continue as follows:

Add dil. H_2SO_4 until the solution is acid to litmus. Cool, and scratch the sides of the vessel with a glass rod: a white precipitate indicates an aromatic carboxylic acid* or uric acid, or a solid phenol insoluble in water (*e.g.*, 1- or 2-naphthol). If a precipitate is obtained, filter off through a Buchner funnel, wash with water, recrystallise if necessary and identify.

If no solid precipitate is obtained but the solution becomes cloudy, a low-melting or liquid phenol is indicated: this will, of course, be revealed also by the characteristic phenolic odour. Transfer to a separating-funnel and extract with an equal volume of ether. Separate and dry with anhydrous sodium sulphate. Distil off the ether and identify the residue.

If a phenol is not indicated, the solution may contain an aliphatic acid. Transfer to a distilling-flask, make definitely acid with dil. H_2SO_4, and distil: the volatile formic and acetic acids if present will distil over. If the distillation gives negative reactions, test the residual solution in the flask for oxalic, succinic, lactic, tartaric and citric acids and glycine, remembering that the solution is strongly acid.

---

* An amino-acid, although insoluble in water (*e.g.*, anthranilic acid), is usually soluble in excess of mineral acid: in such a case it is important to make the solution only very slightly acid. This applies also to a mixture of a neutral and a basic substance, from which dil. HCl will extract an amino-acid: the solution must then be carefully treated with NaOH to precipitate the amino-acid.

(3) A neutral and a basic substance.

It is again assumed that the neutral substance is insoluble in water (see, however, the footnote on p. 389). The separation now consists in extracting the mixture with dil. HCl, which dissolves the basic component, leaving the undissolved neutral component.

Again, first carry out a small-scale test, extracting about 0·5 g. of the mixture with about 5 ml. of dil. HCl in a test-tube, in order to determine whether the neutral component is solid or liquid.

(*a*) *Neutral Component is solid.* Continue precisely as in 2(*a*) above, except that the mixture must now be extracted with an excess of dil. HCl instead of NaOH. Filter at the pump, reserve the filtrate, and then wash the residue on the filter thoroughly with dil. HCl, then wash with water, and finally drain, dry and identify as before.

(*b*) *Neutral Component is liquid.* Proceed as in 2(*b*) above, extracting the mixture with dil. HCl: reserve the HCl extract, and then wash the neutral insoluble liquid with dil. HCl, then with water. Continue as in 2(*b*) to identify the neutral component.

Basic Component. The filtrate from (*a*), or the HCl extract from (*b*), now contains the basic component in the form of its hydrochloride. Add 30% aqueous NaOH solution until alkaline to litmus. Cool, and scratch the sides of the vessel with a glass rod: a white precipitate indicates a solid amine, *e.g.*, *p*-toluidine or a naphthylamine. Dilute, filter off, wash well with water (recrystallise if necessary), dry and identify.

If no solid precipitate is obtained, an oil or an oily suspension, may be produced. Allow to stand, and then, if possible, separate the oil directly in a separating-funnel and dry with solid KOH. If the volume of the oil is too small for such separation, extract with ether* and then separate the ethereal solution, dry as before, filter, and distil off the ether. Distil the amine (if considered necessary) and identify.

In the separations (2) and (3) above, it is often advisable to dissolve the original mixture in a water-insoluble solvent. Select a solvent which will dissolve the *entire* mixture, and then shake the solution with either (i) dil. NaOH or (ii) dil. HCl. Separate the aqueous layer, and to it add either (i) dil. HCl or (ii) dil. NaOH to liberate the organic acid or the organic base, as the case may be. The non-aqueous layer now contains the neutral component. Re-extract this layer with either (i) dil. NaOH or (ii) dil. HCl to ensure removal of traces of the non-neutral component.

---

* Or alternatively add powdered sodium chloride with stirring in order to "salt out" the amine, and then run off the lower aqueous layer.

SCHEME FOR THE IDENTIFICATION OF AN ORGANIC COMPOUND.

General Remarks. In the following pages an account is given of the results which may be observed when an unknown organic compound is subjected to the following tests:

A. Physical characteristics.
B. Heating on a crucible lid.
C. Identification of the elements present.
D. Heating with soda-lime.
E. Treatment with 10% aqueous NaOH solution.
F.   ,,   dil. Na_2CO_3 solution.
G.   ,,   conc. H_2SO_4.
H.   ,,   dil. HCl.
I (i)   ,,   Fehling's solution.
  (ii)   ,,   Ammoniacal silver nitrate solution.
J. Reactions and colorations with ferric chloride.
K. Treatment with 2,4-dinitrophenylhydrazine.
L. Treatment with hydroxylamine and ferric chloride.

Proceed through Tests A, B and C. Carry out Test C (identification of the elements present) *with great care*, as a mistake at this stage will invalidate much of the subsequent analysis. Then proceed, in general, through Tests D—L, keeping in mind the results obtained in Test C. (If, for example, the substance is found not to contain nitrogen, then it is obvious that neither ammonia nor aniline can be produced when treating the substance with sodium hydroxide in Test E. In such a case the student should keep a sharp lookout for a positive reaction characteristic of a non-nitrogenous substance.)

From the cumulative evidence given by Tests A—L, the student will probably have a strong indication of the type of compound which he is investigating. He should then refer back to the table given under Test C (p. 405), and with the information that he has gained (and in particular with the knowledge of the elements present) he should select the most likely class to which the compound belongs. He should then consult the appropriate section giving the reactions of this class of compound, and carry out the tests there mentioned, when it should soon become apparent whether he has selected the correct class to which the compound belongs. If the results obtained are conflicting, the student should then select the next likely class of compounds, and then proceed in this way until the behaviour of the substance investigated agrees closely with those given in a particular section.

After some experience, an able student will find that it is frequently unnecessary to carry out all the Tests A—L. If, for example, the substance is found to contain only carbon and hydrogen, and chars on ignition giving a smell of burnt sugar, then confirmatory tests (given in

PRACTICAL ORGANIC CHEMISTRY

the appropriate section) can be carried out immediately for carbohydrates and aliphatic hydroxy-acids.

Furthermore, Tests D–L need not necessarily be carried out in the order given. As elementary students often experience difficulty with the interpretation of Test D, it is often convenient to relegate it to a lower position in the order of Tests.

Derivatives. The precise identification of a compound normally depends upon the preparation of a derivative and the determination of physical constants such as m.p. in the case of a solid. Many simple compounds can, however, be identified with a fair degree of certainty by intelligently-selected qualitative tests alone, *e.g.*, formates, oxalates, succinates, lactates, tartrates, chloral hydrate. In general, derivatives should be easily-prepared crystalline solids with sharp m.ps. In this book no attempt has been made to describe derivatives which go beyond the theoretical knowledge that a student of this standard might be expected to possess. Useful derivatives are as follows:

Alcohols. 3,5-Dinitrobenzoates (pp. 247, 335), Phenyl and 1-naphthylurethanes (p. 336), Carboxylic acids (p. 337).

Phenols. Benzoates (pp. 244, 338), *p*-Nitrobenzoates (p. 339), 3,5-Dinitrobenzoates (p. 338), Phenylurethanes (p. 340), Toluene-*p*-sulphonates (pp. 249–254).

Aldehydes. Phenylhydrazones (pp. 341, 343), 2,4-Dinitrophenylhydrazones (pp. 342–343), Semicarbazones (pp. 342–343), Carboxylic acids (p. 343).

Ketones. Phenylhydrazones (p. 346), 2,4-Dinitrophenylhydrazones (p. 346), Semicarbazones (p. 346).

Carboxylic Acids. Benzylthiouronium salts (p. 349), Phenacyl esters (p. 349), *p*-Bromophenacyl esters (p. 349), *N*-Benzylamides (p. 350), *p*-Nitrobenzyl esters (p. 350).

Esters. 3,5-Dinitrobenzoates (p. 358), *N*-Benzylamides (p. 357).

Ammonium Salts. Benzylthiouronium salts (p. 360), Acids if aromatic (p. 360), Benzylamides (p. 360).

Amides. Benzylamides (p. 362).

Sulphonic Acids. Benzylthiouronium salts (p. 359), Sulphonamides and sulphonanilides (p. 354).

Acid chlorides. Anilides (p. 365).

Acid anhydrides. Anilides (p. 367).

Sulphonyl chlorides. Sulphonamides (p. 354), Sulphonanilides (p. 354).

Carbohydrates. Osazones (pp. 137–141, 368–369).

Primary and Secondary Amines. Picrates (pp. 374, 376), Acetyl derivatives (pp. 373, 376), Benzoyl derivatives (pp. 374, 376), Toluene-*p*-sulphonyl and benzene-sulphonyl derivatives (pp. 374, 376), Phenylurea derivatives (pp. 374, 377).

Tertiary Amines. Picrates (p. 378), Methiodides (p. 377), *p*-Nitroso-derivatives (p. 378).

Quinones. Semicarbazones (pp. 258, 372).

Amino Aliphatic Carboxylic Acids. 3,5-Dinitrobenzoyl derivatives (p. 381), Benzoyl derivatives (p. 382), Sulphonyl derivatives (p. 382).

Amino Aromatic Sulphonic Acids. Benzylthiouronium salts (p. 384).

Nitrophenols. Acetates (p. 386).

Nitroanilines. Acetyl derivatives (p. 388), Benzoyl derivatives (p. 388).

Diamines. Diacetyl derivatives (p. 388), Dibenzoyl derivatives (p. 388).

Halogeno-hydrocarbons. 2-Naphthyl ethers (from reactive halogen compounds, p. 391, and their Picrates, p. 394), Nitro-derivatives (p. 391), Carboxylic acid (if oxidisable side chain) (p. 393).

Ethers. 3,5-Dinitrobenzoates (p. 396), Picrates (with aryl ethers) (p. 397).

A. Physical characteristics.

Note the obvious physical properties: appearance, colour, state, odour, solubility in (or reaction with) water, whether aqueous solution is neutral or otherwise.

Colour.

Yellow. Quinones, *m*- and *p*-nitroaniline, *o*-nitrophenol, and many other nitro-compounds. [Note that some nitro-compounds often appear yellow (*e.g.* *m*-dinitrobenzene and 3,5-dinitrobenzoic acid), but are colourless when absolutely pure.] Iodoform.

Orange. *o*-Nitro-aniline, phenanthraquinone, alizarin.

Red. 1,2-Naphthoquinone.

Blue. Copper salts.

Odour.

Pleasant (often fruity) odour. Esters, ethers.

Pungent odour. Formic acid, acetic acid, acetyl chloride, acetic anhydride, benzoyl chloride, benzyl chloride, pyridine. Benzoquinone (when warmed with water).

Phenolic (carbolic) odour. Many phenols, some derivatives of salicylic acid (*e.g.*, salicylaldehyde).

Odour of almonds. Benzaldehyde, benzonitrile, nitrobenzene.

The following substances possess odours which, although not necessarily characteristic, often aid identification considerably: Monohydric alcohols, aldehydes (including chloral hydrate), ketones, cinnamic acid, amines (2-naphthylamine* is odourless), nitrophenols (resemble both phenol and nitro-compound), halogeno-hydrocarbons, aliphatic hydrocarbons, liquid aromatic hydrocarbons, naphthalene.

Acetamide and acetonitrile, unless specially purified, possess a mouse-like odour.

Solubility in water and action of solution on litmus-paper.

(*a*) *Soluble in cold water.* Lower aliphatic alcohols (including glycerol), some phenols, lower aliphatic aldehydes (including chloral hydrate), lower aliphatic ketones, aliphatic acids, sulphonic

---

* This amine is very seldom encountered because of its carcinogenic properties.

acids, ammonium salts and alkali salts of all acids, methyl esters of certain acids (*e.g.*, formic, oxalic, succinic, tartaric), ethyl tartrate, some aliphatic amides (including urea) and imides (*e.g.*, succinimide), lower aliphatic nitriles, lower aliphatic acid chlorides (with hydrolysis), mono- and di-saccharides, hexamethylene-tetramine, lower aliphatic amines, pyridine, salts of amines, glycine.

(*b*) *Almost insoluble in cold water.* Higher alcohols (including benzyl alcohol), higher phenols (*e.g.*, naphthols), metaformaldehyde, paraldehyde, aromatic aldehydes, higher ketones (including acetophenone), aromatic acids, most esters, ethers, oxamide and aromatic amides, sulphonamides, aromatic imides, aromatic nitriles, aromatic acid anhydrides, aromatic acid chlorides, sulphonyl chlorides, starch, aromatic amines, anilides, tyrosine, cystine, nitro-compounds, uric acid, halogeno-hydrocarbons, hydrocarbons.

(*c*) *Acid reaction in aqueous solution*, or when hydrolysed with water. Acids, esters which hydrolyse easily (*e.g.*, methyl oxalate), acid chlorides, acid anhydrides, salts of amines, nitrophenols.

(*d*) *Weakly acidic.* Phenols.

Note. Phenols (unless nitrated) do not liberate CO_2 from Na_2CO_3 solution.

(*e*) *Weakly alkaline.* Alkali salts of some weak acids, pyridine.

Note. Useful information can often be obtained by adding (i) dilute H_2SO_4, or (ii) dilute NaOH solution to an aqueous solution of the substance under investigation. A precipitate with (i) usually indicates an aromatic carboxylic acid from a metallic or from an ammonium salt. A precipitate or oil with (ii) usually indicates an aromatic amine from an amine salt.

B. Heating on a crucible lid (p. 319).

(*a*) *Almost non-luminous flame.* Aliphatic compounds containing a low percentage of carbon.

(*b*) *Smoky flame.* Aromatic compounds.

(*c*) *Non-inflammable.* Compounds rich in halogen or containing a metal.

(*d*) *Residual ash.* Compounds containing a metal.

(i) Metallic salts of carboxylic acids give carbonate, oxide or metal. Apply usual tests of qualitative inorganic analysis to this residue.

Note that some of the metals frequently encountered in simple organic compounds give characteristic flame colorations: Na, yellow; K, lilac through blue glass; Ca, brick-red; Ba, apple-green; Cu, bright blue-green. Ag and Pb, no characteristic flame.

(ii) The bisulphite compounds of aldehydes or ketones leave sodium sulphite and sodium sulphate.

(iii) The alkali salts of sulphanilic acid leave alkali sulphide.

(*e*) *Charring.* Many organic compounds char, more particularly the following: carbohydrates (odour of burnt sugar); tartaric acid and its salts, citric acid and its salts (odour somewhat resembling burnt sugar); uric acid. (Salts of some acids char, although the free acids do not, *e.g.*, sodium succinate, lactate, and salicylate.)

(*f*) *Violet vapours.* Iodoform.

C. Identification of elements present.

(i) *Beilstein's Test* (p. 323). Note that this test is of negative value only, and the *absence* of a green colour proves that the compound does *not* contain halogen.

(ii) *Lassaigne's Test for nitrogen, halogens and sulphur* (pp. 321–327). Perform with great care. If only a faint indication of a particular element is obtained, repeat, using a slightly larger amount of material and longer heating.

Elements present	Substances	Section	Page
C.H.[O]	Alcohols	10	335
	Phenols	11	337
	Aldehydes	12	341
	Ketones	13	345
	Carboxylic acids (and metallic salts)	14	347
	Esters	15	354
	Acid anhydrides	17(B)	364
	Carbohydrates	18	366
	Quinones	19	370
	Hydrocarbons	26	393
	Ethers	27	395
C.H.[O].Halogen	Chloral hydrate	12	341
	Acid halides	17(A)	364
	Halogeno-hydrocarbons	25	390
C.H.[O].N	Ammonium salts ⎫		
	Amides, imides ⎬	16	359
	Nitriles ⎭		
	Amines	20	372
	Anilides	21	379
C.H.[O].N	Amino-carboxylic acids	22	380
	Nitro-compounds	23	384
	(*a*) Nitro-hydrocarbons		
	(*b*) Nitro-phenols		
	(*c*) Nitro-anilines		
	Uric Acid	24	389
C.H.[O].N.Halogen	Salts of amines, nitro-amines and amino-carboxylic acids with halogen acids (HCl, *etc.*). (*Note.* The halogen is ionic and can be tested for directly with $HNO_3 +$ $AgNO_3$).	20, 23(C) 22	372, 387 380

Elements present	Substances	Section	Page
C.H.[O].S	Alkali bisulphite compound of (a) aldehyde, (b) ketone	12, 13	341, 345
	Sulphonic acids.	14(B)	353
C.H.[O].S.Halogen	Aryl sulphonyl chlorides	14(B)	354
C.H.[O].N.S	Salts of amines and nitro-amines with H_2SO_4. (Note. The SO_4 radical can be tested for directly in solution with $HCl + BaCl_2$).	20, 23(C)	372, 387
	Amino-aromatic sulphonic acid (sulphanilic acid)	22(C)	384
	Cystine	22(A)	380

NOTE.—1. If C and H only have been detected and the substance is soluble in water, then O must also be present.

2. If C, H, and a halogen (but no nitrogen) have been detected, and the substance is *freely* soluble in (or readily hydrolysed by) cold water, then O must also be present.

3. It should be noted that only representative substances are indicated in the above list. Substituted derivatives of the compounds in most classes may be encountered, *e.g.*, nitrobenzoic acid in the aromatic carboxylic acids (p. 347). This acid will contain CH(O)N, but the salient properties are still those of a carboxylic acid, CH(O), Section 14, although the properties of an aromatic nitro-compound (*e.g.*, reduction to an amino-compound) will also be evident.

D. Heat with an excess of soda-lime (p. 327).

(a) *Ammonia or ammoniacal vapours evolved.* Ammonium salts, amides, imides; amino-aliphatic acids, uric acid. (Certain polynitro-compounds, *e.g.*, *m*-dinitrobenzene, sometimes give ammonia on strong heating.)

(b) *Hydrogen evolved.* Formate, oxalate.

(c) *Hydrocarbon evolved.* Carboxylic acid or salt of carboxylic acid:

methane from acetate;
ethane from succinate;
benzene from benzoate or phthalate;
styrene and benzene from cinnamate.

(d) *Phenol produced.* Salicylic acid and salts; phenyl esters of carboxylic acids; tyrosine also produces a phenolic odour.

Note. Phenols distil unchanged.

(e) *Odour of burnt sugar.* Carbohydrates; some aliphatic hydroxy-acids (*e.g.*, tartaric acid) and their salts.

(f) *Aromatic amine produced.* Amine salts; anilides; aromatic amino-carboxylic acids; sulphanilic acid, sulphanilamide.

(g) *Chloroform produced.* Chloral hydrate.

Note. A compound may yield more than one product, *e.g.*, salicyl-amide, $HO \cdot C_6H_4CONH_2$, will give ammonia and phenol. Sulphanilamide will give ammonia and aniline.

E. Treat with 10% aqueous NaOH solution, then heat (p. 329).

(a) *Dissolves easily in cold NaOH solution although insoluble in cold water.* Some phenols*; aromatic carboxylic acids; some amino-acids; uric acid.

(b) *Dissolves easily in cold NaOH solution (although only slightly soluble in cold water), at the same time forming deep yellow or orange alkaline solution.* Nitrophenols. (Salicylaldehyde gives a yellow coloration in the cold: *m*-dinitrobenzene gives a reddish-brown coloration on warming.)

(c) *Dissolves easily, giving yellow solution which rapidly darkens on shaking.* Benzoquinone. Polyhydric phenols, *e.g.*, resorcinol, rapidly darken.

(d) *Ammonia evolved in the cold.†* Ammonium salts.

(e) *Ammonia evolved on heating.* Amides, imides, nitriles (slowly).

(f) *Brown resinous product formed.* Aliphatic aldehydes (except formaldehyde); carbohydrates and soluble starch (sucrose and ordinary starch only faintly coloured).

(g) *Reacts slowly on heating without evolution of gas.* Esters; some acid chlorides and anhydrides; benzaldehyde (undergoes Cannizzaro's reaction, p. 342).

(h) *Chloroform produced.* Chloral and chloral hydrate.

(i) *Aromatic amine liberated rapidly* (as an oil, if liquid or of low m.p.). Salts of amines.

(j) *Aromatic amine liberated slowly* on prolonged heating. Anilides.

(k) *Hydrogen sulphide evolved.* Cystine.

(l) *Purple solution.* Alizarin.

F. Treat with dil. Na$_2$CO$_3$ solution and boil (p. 330).

CO$_2$ liberated. All acids; esters which hydrolyse easily, *e.g.*, methyl oxalate (p. 357); salts of amines; nitrophenols.

G. Treat with conc. H$_2$SO$_4$, then heat (p. 331).

(a) *Gives a clear solution on gentle heating, dilution then precipitating the unchanged substance.* Uric acid.

(b) *No blackening, CO evolved.* Formates.

(c) *No blackening, CO + CO$_2$ evolved.* Oxalates.

(d) *Turns yellow, no charring, evolution of CO and CO$_2$.* Citrates.

(e) *No blackening, no marked effervescence, pungent vapour evolved.* Certain acids and their salts, *e.g.*, acetic, succinic, and benzoic acid.

---

* Many phenols are of course freely soluble in cold water as well as in NaOH solution.

† This distinction is not absolute, as some amides decompose slightly even in cold 10% NaOH solution.

(*f*) *Blackening with effervescence.* Carbohydrates; tartrates and lactates.

(*g*) *Blackening without effervescence.* Certain polyhydric phenols. Succinates (strong heating).

(*h*) *Gelatinous polymeric product.* Benzyl alcohol.

Note. A large variety of organic compounds darken to some extent (without actual blackening) when heated with conc. H_2SO_4.

H. Treat with dil. HCl, then warm.

Substance insoluble in cold water, readily soluble in warm dil. HCl. Various basic substances, such as aromatic amines (naphthylamines dissolve with difficulty in dil. HCl, diphenylamine only in conc. HCl, triphenylamine insoluble); nitro-anilines; some amino-carboxylic acids.

I. (*a*) Heat with Fehling's solution.

Disappearance of the deep blue colour and precipitation of cuprous oxide indicates reducing agents such as:

Aldehydes (including chloral hydrate); formates and lactates; some esters; chloroform and iodoform; reducing sugars; some phenols.

Uric acid first gives white precipitate of copper urate and then reduces.

(*b*) Treat with ammoniacal silver nitrate solution and warm.

Formation of silver mirror or precipitate of silver indicates reducing agent. (This is often a more sensitive test than I (*a*) above, and some compounds reduce ammoniacal silver nitrate but are without effect on Fehling's solution.) Given by aldehydes and chloral hydrate; formates, lactates and tartrates; reducing sugars; benzoquinone; many amines; uric acid.

J. Treat with neutral ferric chloride solution (p. 332).

Colorations or precipitates given by phenols and many derivatives of phenols; by neutral salts of acids; by some amines. (The $FeCl_3$ solution can be added directly to a *small quantity* of the phenol or to its aqueous solution: free acids must first be neutralised.)

(*a*) *Red coloration.* Formate and acetate.

(*b*) *Yellow coloration.* Lactates, tartrates and citrates. (Oxalates give very faint yellow.)

(*c*) *Violet coloration.* Phenol, resorcinol, *o*-, *m*-, and *p*-cresol; salicylates; methyl and ethyl salicylate; salicylamide; salicyl-aldehyde.

(*d*) *Violet-red coloration.* *p*-Nitrophenol.

(*e*) *Buff or pale-brown precipitate.* Succinate, benzoate, phthalate and cinnamate. (Add dil. H_2SO_4: basic ferric succinate dissolves giving a clear solution; the others dissolve but are rapidly replaced by white precipitate of free acid.)

(*f*) *Green coloration.* Catechol (colour rapidly darkens). [Aniline (pale green), *o*-toluidine (pale green initially), monomethylaniline, and diphenylamine, each in dil. HCl.]

(*g*) *Bluish precipitate.* 1-Naphthylamine.

K. Treat with 2,4-dinitrophenylhydrazine reagent (pp. 263, 334).

Yellow or orange-yellow precipitates given by most aldehydes and ketones.

L. Treat with hydroxylamine and ferric chloride (pp. 334, 353).

Violet or red colorations given particularly by esters. Deep colorations also given by acid chlorides, acid anhydrides and by some acid amides (usually aliphatic) and by a few of the simpler anilides.

On pp. 410–415 Tables are given showing some of the properties of the simpler members of certain classes of organic compounds. These tables should be useful to the elementary student working with a limited range of compounds. It must be emphasised that these tables serve primarily to summarise some of the detailed descriptions given in the foregoing sections, and should be used when the student is familiar with these sections.

Tables IV–XXVIII (pp. 560–561) record the m.ps. of crystalline derivatives of a much wider range of compounds, and are intended primarily for the more advanced student.

Section II. Phenols (pp. 337, 538)

TEST	Phenol	Resorcinol	Catechol	Hydroquinone	o-Cresol	m-Cresol	p-Cresol	1-Naphthol	2-Naphthol
FeCl₃ (coloration)	←—— violet ——→		green	red, green crystals then yellow	←—— violet ——→			—	—
Phthaleins (Phthalic anhydride + H_2SO_4)	red	green fluorescence	usually blue	purple	red	blue-purple	—	green	faint green fluorescence
Benzoates m.ps.	69°	117°	84°	204°	liquid	54°	71°	56°	107°
p-Nitrobenzoates m.ps.	126°	182°	169°	250°	94°	90°	98°	143°	169°
3,5-Dinitrobenzoates m.ps.	146°	201°	152°	317°	138°	165°	189°	217°	210°
Phenylurethanes m.ps.	126°	164°	169°	224°	145°	121°	115°	178°	155°
1-Naphthylurethanes m.ps.	133°	206°	175°	247°	142°	128°	146°	155°	157°

Section 12. Aldehydes (pp. 401, 539,–540)

TEST	Formaldehyde (solution)	Acetaldehyde (solution)	Paraldehyde	Chloral hydrate	Benzaldehyde	Salicylaldehyde
Schiff's reagent (pink)	+	+	+		+	—
NaOH	Cannizzaro's reaction	←——— yellow resin ———→		chloroform on heating	Cannizzaro's reaction	yellow coloration
Ammoniacal AgNO₃ (reduction)	+	+	+	+	+	—
Fehling's solution (reduction)	+	+	+	+	very faint reduction	—
Special Tests		(i) Nitroprusside + NaOH (red). (ii) Iodoform	Nitroprusside + NaOH (red)		(i) NaHSO₃, immediate ppt.	(i) FeCl₃ (violet) (ii) NaHSO₃, ppt. on standing.
2,4-Dinitrophenyl-hydrazones, M.ps.	166°	147° (see p. 537)	—	—	237°	252°(d.)

Section 13. Ketones (pp. 345, 541, 542)

TEST	Acetone	Acetophenone	Benzophenone
Iodoform (KI + NaClO)	+	+	—
Na Nitroprusside + NaOH (red coloration)	+	+	—
m-Dinitrobenzene + NaOH (purple coloration)	+	+	—
Na Bisulphite (addition)	+	—	—
2,4-Dinitrophenyl-hydrazones	126°	250°	239°

Section 14. Carboxylic Acids (pp. 347, 543, 544-555)

NOTE. The tests marked * must be performed with a neutral salt of the acid.

TEST	Formic	Acetic	Oxalic	Succinic	Lactic	Tartaric	Citric	Benzoic	Salicylic	Phthalic	Cinnamic
Soda-lime	H_2	CH_4	H_2	C_2H_4	←— odour of burnt sugar —→			benzene	phenol	benzene	styrene, benzene
FeCl$_3$	←—— red ——→		v. pale yellow	buff ppt.	←—— yellow ——→			←——— buff ppt. ———→	violet		
Conc. H_2SO_4	CO	—	CO + CO$_2$	darkens on strong heating	blackens, effervescence	chars, effervescence	yellow, effervescence	—	darkens slightly	—	—
KMnO$_4$ + dil. Na$_2$CO$_3$	de-colorisation in the cold	—	slight fading	—	←——— reduction on heating ———→			—	de-colorisation in the cold	—	de-colorisation in the cold
Ammoniacal AgNO$_3$ (reduction)	+	—	—	—	+	+	—	—	—	—	reduction on boiling
Special reactions	—			Fluorescein	Iodoform* (KI + NaClO)	FeSO$_4$ + H$_2$O$_2$ + NaOH violet				(a) Fluorescein (b) Phthalein	
Benzylthiouronium salts, m.ps.	152°	134°	196°	154°	153°	—	—	167°	148°	158°	183°
Phenacyl esters, m.ps.	Liq.	50°	244°d	148°	96°	130°	104°	119°	110°	154°	146°
p-Bromophenacyl esters, m.ps.	99°	85°	244°d	211°	112°	216°	148°	119°	140°	153°	140°
Benzylamides, m.ps.	60°	60°	223°	206°	—	199°	169°	105°	137°	178°	226°
p-Nitrobenzyl esters, m.ps.	31°	78°	204°	88°	Liq.	163°	102°	89°	98°	155°	117°

Section 15. Esters (pp. 354–358, 546). *Summary of Hydrolysis.*

Hydrolyse by boiling with 10% aqueous NaOH solution for about 30 minutes:

Substance.	Products.	
Ester of an alcohol	Alcohol (volatile)	Na salt of a carboxylic acid (non-volatile).
Ester of a phenol	a Na phenoxide (non-volatile)	,,

Distil.

(A) (i) *Distillate.* Test for the alcohol, *e.g.*, methyl, ethyl, benzyl, or **cyclohexyl** alcohol.

(ii) *Residual solution.* If test in (A) (i) is *positive*, proceed with tests for organic acid in residual solution: acidify with dil. H_2SO_4.

　　(*a*) white ppt.: aromatic acid.

　　(*b*) no ppt.: aliphatic acid. Distil off 5 ml. and test distillate for **volatile acids,** *e.g.*, formic and acetic acids. If negative results are obtained, test residual solution for **non-volatile acids,** *e.g.*, oxalic, succinic, tartaric and citric acids.

(B) If test in (A) (i) is *negative*, an alcohol is absent and the residual solution must contain a Na phenoxide as well as the Na salt of a carboxylic acid.

　　Residual solution. Make just acid with dil. H_2SO_4, and then just alkaline to litmus-paper with Na_2CO_3 solution. Extract phenol with ether, distil off latter and identify the residue. Identify the organic acid in the aqueous layer, as in (A) (ii).

Section 18. Carbohydrates (water-soluble) (pp. 336)

TEST	Glucose	Fructose	Sucrose	Maltose	Lactose
Molisch's (1-naphthol + H_2SO_4)	←————————— violet coloration —————————→				
Rapid furfural (1-naphthol + HCl)	delayed	←—— immediate ——→		←——— delayed ———→	
NaOH (Conc.)	←——— yellow resin ———→		—	←——— yellow resin ———→	
Ammoniacal $AgNO_3$ (reduction)	+	+	—	+	+
Fehling's solution (reduction)	+	+	—	+	+
Osazone	+ ←——— (identical, insol. in hot water) ———→ +		—	+ (freely sol. in hot water)	+ (moderately sol. in hot water)

Section 20. Aromatic (mono)amines (pp. 372, 550-554)

TEST	Aniline	o-toluidine	m-toluidine	p-toluidine	1-naphthyl-amine	2-naphthyl-amine *	mono-methyl-aniline	diphenyl-amine	dimethyl-aniline	triphenyl-amine
Isocyanide (carbylamine)	+	+	+	+	+	+	—	—	—	—
Nitrous acid (NaNO$_2$ + HCl)	diazotises — Pour into alkaline 2-naphthol: red dye						yellow — nitrosamine →		green nitroso compound (NaOH)	—
Acetyl deriv., m.p.	113°	112°	65°	· 152°	159°	134°	102°	103°	No deriv.	No deriv.
Benzoyl deriv., m.p.	163°	143°	125°	158°	160°	162°	63°	180°	No deriv.	No deriv.
Benzenesulphonyl deriv., m.p.	112° ← Sol. in NaOH →	124°	95° Sol. in NaOH	120° Sol. in NaOH	167°	102° →	79° ← Insol. in NaOH →	124° Insol. in NaOH →	No deriv.	No deriv.
Toluenesulphonyl deriv., m.p.	103° ←	110°	114° Sol. in NaOH	118° Sol. in NaOH	157°	133°	94° ← Insol. in NaOH →	142° Insol. in NaOH →	No deriv.	No deriv.
Picrate, m.p.	165°	214°	195°	181°	163°	195°	145°	182°	163°	No deriv.

* Cf. footnote, p. 403.

PART IV

QUANTITATIVE ANALYSIS

THE analyses which follow are arranged in the order in which they would be applied to a newly discovered substance, the estimation of the elements present and molecular weight determinations (*i.e.*, determination of empirical and molecular formulae respectively) coming first, then the estimation of particular groups in the molecule, and finally the estimation of special classes of organic compounds. It should be noted, however, that this systematic order differs considerably from the order of experimental difficulty of the individual analyses. Consequently many of the later macro-analyses, such as the estimation of hydroxyl groups, acetyl groups, urea, *etc.*, may well be undertaken by elementary students, while the earlier analyses, such as estimation of elements present in the molecule, should be reserved for more senior students.

The estimation of carbon and hydrogen, of nitrogen and of methoxy groups has now however been transferred to Section B (Semi-microanalysis) (p. 465). In this connection it should be noted that the macro-estimation of nitrogen in foodstuffs, *etc.*, by the Kjeldahl method is still often employed because of the low nitrogen content and the non-homogeneous nature of the material. Full details of this method on the macro-scale will be found in *An Introduction to Practical Organic Chemistry* by Mann and Saunders, 4th ed., p. 148 (Longman Group Ltd.).

SECTION A

MACROANALYSIS

Estimation of Halogens. Carius's Method.

Principle. A known weight of the substance is heated with fuming nitric acid and silver nitrate in a sealed tube. The organic material is thus oxidised to carbon dioxide and water, whilst the halogen is converted quantitatively into the corresponding silver halide. The latter is subsequently washed out of the tube, filtered and weighed.

The method is general for all organic halogen compounds and is the standard method for almost all such compounds, except of course those water-soluble compounds (*e.g.*, halide salts) in which the halogen is ionic. The method, although long, is simple, the main difficulty for students being the preparation and sealing of the glass tube.

Carius tubing is normally supplied in lengths of about 15 dcm. (5 ft.), sufficient for two tubes: the tubing is usually of about 2 cm. external diameter, whilst the thickness of the wall is about 3 mm. Carius tubing of good quality soft glass, if carefully prepared and sealed, is amply strong enough and has the great advantage of being easily worked in the ordinary air-gas blowpipe flame. Hard-glass tubing gives a much stronger sealed tube, but the latter has to be worked in an oxygen-gas blowpipe flame.

For the actual estimation, heat the middle portion of a double length* of Carius tubing cautiously in the blowpipe flame, starting first with a smoky flame and then increasing the proportion of air until a flame of maximum temperature is obtained, meanwhile rotating the horizontal tube (using both hands simultaneously, and not each hand in turn, for the rotation) in order to secure uniform heating. When the middle portion of the tube is quite soft, draw the two portions of the tube apart, so that two tubes similar to **A** (Fig. 72) are obtained, each being open at one end and drawn out to a fine tail at the other. Two Carius tubes can thus be made, although only one will be

---

* A practical demonstration of the preparation and sealing of Carius tubes is of vastly greater value than any written description.

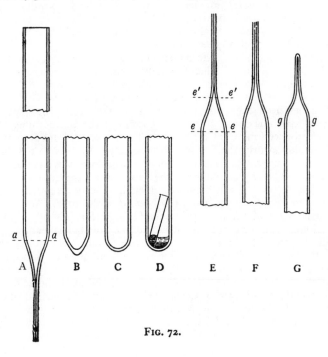

FIG. 72.

considered further. The tube, throughout the whole of its subsequent manipulation in the blowpipe flame, *must* be kept steadily and regularly rotated
in order to ensure uniform heating and treatment: this point will not therefore
be further emphasised. Now heat the tube in a small hot flame about the
portion *aa* until the pointed tail, which has hitherto been used as a handle,
can be drawn off, leaving the tube closed as shown in **B**. By using this method,
the formation of a heavy blob or button of glass at the extreme end of the
tube (a source of great subsequent weakness) can easily be avoided. Now
heat the closed end of the tube in a rather larger flame until the end is uniformly
soft, and then carefully blow down the tube, keeping the latter rotated gently
in the mouth whilst the pressure is applied. By these means, a rounded end
of uniform thickness, as in **C**, is obtained. The heating and subsequent
blowing down the rotating tube should be repeated until a really satisfactory
seal has been obtained. Allow the tube to cool (away from draughts) for at
least 45 minutes. Then ensure that the interior of the tube is quite clean and
free from dust, *etc.* For this purpose, pour a few ml. of concentrated nitric
acid into the tube, cork securely and then invert several times: finally wash
the tube out thoroughly with distilled water, and then in turn with methylated spirit and dry ether. Remove the last traces of ether by blowing air
right down to the closed end of the Carius tube by means of a length of clean
glass quill-tubing temporarily attached to the blowpipe bellows.

It is now necessary to place about 1 g. of finely powdered pure
silver nitrate in the closed end of the tube: at the same time, care
should be taken to avoid dusting the internal walls of the tube with
silver nitrate, as it is a great advantage to have the silver halide subsequently collected at the extreme end of the tube, and not scattered in
specks over the walls. Therefore roll a narrow strip of clean glazed
paper around the quill-tubing originally used for drying the tube and
then insert the roll of paper and the quill-tube into the Carius tube
(which has been clamped in a vertical position) until the paper roll
reaches within about 5 cm. of the bottom of the Carius tube. Now
remove the central quill-tube, when the paper will tend to unroll
slightly and so grip the Carius tube securely. Add about 1 g. of the
powdered silver nitrate, tap the tube to shake down the last fragments
of the nitrate, and then withdraw the paper roll. Insert into the tube a
clean thistle-funnel, the stem of which has been extended until it
reaches to about 10 cm. from the bottom of the tube. Add 1·5–2·0
ml. (*not more*) of fuming nitric acid (*d*, 1·5): for this and the next
estimation, a sample of fuming nitric acid free from halogen and sulphur
should be used. If there is any doubt with regard to the purity of the
acid, the latter should be well shaken with a small quantity of powdered
silver nitrate, and the mixture allowed to stand (preferably overnight)
until all the solid matter has collected at the bottom, the acid being
subsequently withdrawn for the analysis by means of a short dropping-
tube. When the nitric acid has thoroughly drained from the thistle-
funnel, the latter should be cautiously withdrawn so that the upper
portion of the Carius tube is not wetted.

Meanwhile, the organic compound can be prepared for analysis whilst the sealed end **C** (Fig. 72) of the Carius tube has been cooling down. For this purpose, thoroughly clean and dry a small tube, which is about 6 cm. long and 8–10 mm. wide. Weigh it carefully, supporting it on the balance pan either by means of a small stand of aluminium foil, or by a short section of a perforated rubber stopper (Fig. 73 (A) and (B)

respectively): alternatively the tube may be placed in a small beaker on the balance pan, or suspended above the pan by a small hooked wire girdle. Place in the tube sufficient organic compound to give subsequently about 0·3 g. of the silver halide, and weigh again. Now allow the small tube to slide carefully down the inclined Carius tube until it finally adopts the position

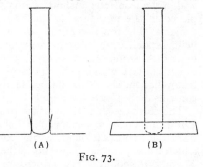

(A) (B)

Fig. 73.

shown in **D** (Fig. 72). If the compound readily loses halogen in the presence of nitric fumes, the Carius tube should first be rotated in an oblique position to wet the tube for about 10 cm. from the bottom: the small tube, if cautiously inserted into the Carius tube, will now come to rest when it first reaches the wet portion of the tube and will thus be held above the main bulk of the acid until the tube is sealed.

Before sealing the Carius tube, the length desired for the final sealed tube should first be decided. The tube has to be placed in a heavy iron tube, and its length should be roughly adjusted so that the final capillary end of the sealed tube will project about 2 cm. beyond the mouth of the iron tube. Now heat the upper portion of the Carius tube at a suitable place to obtain this length, holding the rotated tube in an oblique position meanwhile. When the glass is soft, draw off the unrequired end, leaving the top of the tube drawn out into a long tail as in **E** (Fig. 72): break off this tail so that it is about 15 cm. long and can thus serve as a handle, and ensure that the end is open. (If the tube is not sufficiently long to enable the extreme top to be held in the hand whilst it is being drawn off, first fuse a piece of stout rod on to the extreme end, taking care that the end of the tube is not closed thereby.) Now heat the tapering portion of the tube, approximately between *ee* and *e'e'* (**E**, Fig. 72) in a rather small and not too hot flame until the walls have thickened uniformly and very considerably, and can be slowly drawn out into a thick-walled capillary, as in **F**. Allow to cool slightly and then with a very small hot flame close the capillary, as shown in **G**: rotate the closed tip rapidly for a few seconds in the flame until the sealed end is of uniform thickness, and then place in a smoky, air-free blowpipe flame for a few seconds to ensure an even temperature-distribution over the heated end. Finally allow the tube to cool slowly in a vertical position in a place free from draughts: as a further precaution, a handful of cotton-wool may be loosely tied around the upper end of the tube as it cools. The tube whenever possible should be left over-night before being heated in the furnace: failing this, at least 3 hours should elapse between sealing and heating in the furnace.

Now roll up the Carius tube (while still in a vertical position) in a strip of ordinary thick drying-paper, and then place it in the heavy iron protector tube: if the Carius tube is too short and tends to disappear within the iron tube, a short section of old glass tubing should first be placed in the iron tube so that the capillary of the Carius tube just projects. The function of the paper is to protect the Carius tubing from being scratched, and also (more important) to prevent the local overheating which would otherwise occur at places where the Carius tube is in direct contact with the iron tube. The sealed tube, throughout its manipulation, should be left as nearly vertical as possible, so that the contents do not leave the rounded end.

The furnace (Fig. 74) consists primarily of an iron box **A**, having 3 or 4 tubes (*e.g.*, **B**) arranged in a horizontal row, and dipping slightly from the open (left-hand) to the closed (right-hand) end. The top, which usually forms a loose lid to the rest of **A**, carries a thermometer **T**, and care should be taken to ensure that the bulb of the thermometer is not touching any part of the metal box. The Carius tube encased in

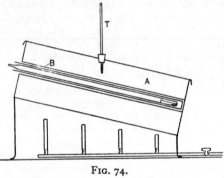

its iron protector tube is then placed as shown in one of the wide tubes **B** of the box, and the latter can then be heated either by the burners below, or in a suitable electric furnace. The box **A** is usually per-manently fitted inside a much larger iron or brick-work oven having sliding doors on one of the longer sides: this oven and its doors have necessarily to

FIG. 74.

be large enough to allow the introduction of the Carius tube into the box **A** without moving the latter. Occasionally no oven is used, and instead the ends of the box **A** are covered with heavy iron flaps hinged horizontally along the top: in the event of a tube bursting during the heating, these flaps lift sufficiently to allow immediate release of the gases, but not sufficiently to permit fragments of glass being blown away from the apparatus.

Now heat the furnace, so that the temperature rises slowly in the course of about 2 hours to 260–270°, and then maintain this tempera-ture for at least another 4 hours. Then turn off the heating, and allow the furnace to cool and remain untouched overnight. A considerable pressure will now exist in the cold tube, and must be released *before* the tube is removed from the box **A**: *on no account* must the unopened tube be removed from the furnace, nor must any attempt be made to crack open the capillary end by means of a file, *etc.*, even when the tube is still in position. To release the pressure, first gently warm the capillary end of the Carius tube (which projects just beyond the mouth of the iron tube) with a small smoky Bunsen flame. The extreme end of the cold capillary will always contain some condensed liquid, which under the influence of this preliminary warming will be forced back into the wider portion of the tube: this step is particularly necessary in the estimation of sulphur (p. 423). Finally increase the heating of the extreme tip of the capillary until softening of the glass finally allows the compressed gases to blow out.

Now remove the tube from the furnace and make a deep file-mark completely round the tube about 15 cm. from the bottom: then wash the outside of the tube to remove any powdered glass from the file-mark, and also all traces of charred paper, *etc.* Then, whilst holding the tube securely in a vertical position, press the molten end of a fine glass rod on to the file-mark, when the tube should crack cleanly around the scratch: finally pull the two portions of the tube *away* from one another, so that the two ends have no opportunity of grating against one another and so causing fine splinters of glass to fall into the tube. Then wipe the two cut ends of the tube carefully in an outwards direction to remove any splinters which, in spite of these precautions, may have formed. (Cutting the tube in this way about 15 cm. from the bottom has the advantage that the silver halide is now readily accessible, but has the disadvantage that the tube is usually too short to be used again. It is not advisable, however, to use soft-glass tubing a second time, as it often devitrifies on further heating and in any case usually gives an unsatisfactory sealed tube. Hard-glass tubing can sometimes be used for several consecutive estimations, and if this is intended the tube should be cut across *gg* (Fig. 72): the silver halide is now, however, not so readily removed from the tube.) Now smear a trace of vaseline around the outside portion of the cut ends of the two portions of the tube (to prevent drops of the liquid from subsequently running down the outside of the tube). Pour some distilled water into the portion of the tube containing the silver halide, loosen the contents by stirring them gently with a rod, and then tip the contents carefully into a beaker. If any fragments of silver halide still adhere to the Carius tube, loosen them further by means of a glass rod the end of which is covered with a short length of rubber tubing, and then finally wash out the inside of the tube (whilst the latter is inclined downwards over the beaker) with a fine jet of water from a wash-bottle. Now remove the small tube from the beaker (preferably with a pair of forceps), again loosen any adhering particles of silver halide, and wash the tube thoroughly whilst it is held over the beaker. Similarly wash the longer portion of the Carius tube, which however should not contain any particles of silver halide. Then boil the liquid in the covered beaker until the silver halide has thoroughly coagulated, and formed a heavy amorphous mass at the bottom of the beaker: for silver chloride and bromide 20–30 minutes' boiling is usually sufficient for this purpose, but for silver iodide at least $2\frac{1}{2}$ hours' boiling (with occasional addition of more water) is required to ensure complete decomposition of a stable addition product of silver iodide and nitrate.

Then cool the solution, and filter, wash and weigh the silver halide by any of the standard methods of gravimetric analysis: the most usual method is to filter the solution through a weighed Gooch crucible, wash the contents thoroughly with *very* dilute nitric acid, and then dry the crucible in an oven at 130°. The value obtained for the percentage of halogen should be within $\pm$ 0·2 of the theoretical value.

ESTIMATION OF HALOGENS IN LIQUID ORGANIC COMPOUNDS. If the liquid is of high boiling-point and not deliquescent, it may be weighed in the small tube precisely as for solid compounds. The tube may be corked during the two weighings, but in this case great care should be taken to place the liquid in the tube so that the neck is not moistened: the use of a fine dropping-tube is of particular value for this purpose.

Volatile, deliquescent, or unstable liquids should be weighed in a small, thin-walled sealed bulb-tube **T** (Fig. 75). This is made by blowing a delicate bulb of about 1–2 ml. capacity on the end of a piece of fine, thin-walled quill tubing, the neck of which is then drawn out into a long thin taper. For use,

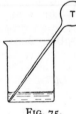

first weigh the clean dry tube, then place it upside-down as shown in a small beaker or bottle containing the organic liquid. Now place the beaker in a vacuum desiccator, and gently evacuate. After a few minutes, remove the desiccator from the pump and slowly admit air, dried if necessary beforehand by passage through a calcium chloride tube. The liquid will now rise in the tube **T**. If the amount which enters is insufficient, repeat the evacuation in the desiccator for a longer period. Then reverse the tube, carefully dry the tapered neck, and seal the extreme tip in a small flame.

FIG. 75.

Weigh the tube, place it in the Carius tube and seal the latter as before. The weighed tube must now be broken in the Carius tube *before* the latter is heated—on no account should the fracture of the small tube be left to the expansion of its contents during the heating. The bulb-tube can usually be broken by holding the Carius tube in a vertical position, and then vigorously jerking the bottom of the tube to one side: it should not be fractured by shaking the Carius tube up and down its long axis, as this will fling both silver nitrate and glass into the capillary end. If the organic material is readily oxidised, wrap the Carius tube in several thicknesses of iron gauze and then in a duster before shaking, in case the vigorous oxidation which will occur on fracture of the bulb-tube also causes the Carius tube to burst. After heating the Carius tube in the furnace, transfer the contents as before to a beaker, and with a pair of forceps pick out the larger pieces of broken glass, wash them carefully free from silver halide, dry in an oven and weigh when cold. The weight of the remaining smaller pieces of glass, which will be subsequently weighed with the silver halide in the crucible, is thus known.

Example of Calculation.

Estimation of Cl in chloral hydrate.

0·1872 g. chloral hydrate gave 0·4856 g. silver chloride

Factor for Cl in AgCl, 0·2474. (Table III, p. 531.)

∴ 0·1872 g. chloral hydrate contains 0·4856 × 0·2474 g. chlorine

∴ 100 g. chloral hydrate contain $\dfrac{0·4856 \times 0·2474 \times 100}{0·1872}$ g. chlorine

$$= 64·16\%$$

Theoretical for $C_2H_3Cl_3O_2$; 64·33% chlorine.

Estimation of Halogens, Carius's Method. Semi-micro Scale.

For a description of the Carius Method on a semi-micro scale, see pp. 502. *et seq.*

Estimation of Sulphur. Carius's Method.

Principle. A known weight of the substance is heated with fuming nitric acid in a sealed tube, the organic material being oxidised to carbon dioxide and water, and the sulphur to sulphuric acid. The latter is subsequently washed out of the tube, precipitated as barium sulphate, and estimated as such

The method is general for all organic compounds, although some require prolonged heating to ensure complete oxidation (see later).

Proceed precisely as in the estimation of halogen (p. 416), but omitting the silver nitrate: take sufficient of the organic compound to give 0·2–0·3 g. of barium sulphate. Before opening the cold Carius tube, pay particular attention to the initial gentle warming of the capillary end of the tube to ensure that the liquid which has condensed in the capillary is driven back well into the wide portion of the tube, otherwise it will be lost with the escaping gases. Then cut open the tube as already described, wash out the contents into a beaker and, should any trace of glass splinters be observed, filter carefully, finally washing the filter thoroughly with water.

The precipitation of the barium sulphate must be performed with care, otherwise high results are obtained owing to occlusion of barium chloride in the barium sulphate. This is avoided by the following method, which has the further advantage that the tedious initial removal of the excess of nitric acid by evaporation is unnecessary.

Dilute the solution (if necessary) to about 150 ml., add 1 ml. of concentrated hydrochloric acid, and then heat in a covered beaker almost to boiling. Meanwhile dissolve a small excess (0·4–0·5 g.) of barium chloride in about 50 ml. of water, bring to the boil, and then transfer to a clean 50 ml. burette. Now run this solution slowly *drop by drop* into the sulphuric acid solution, keeping the latter steadily stirred throughout the addition. Then boil the solution *gently* in the covered beaker for about 1 hour in order to increase the size of the barium sulphate particles: if the solution tends to "bump," transfer it to a hot plate and keep it just below the boiling-point for about 2 hours. Then cool, filter and estimate the barium sulphate by any of the standard methods, e.g., by filtering the liquid through a weighed Gooch crucible, washing the barium sulphate thoroughly with water, and then drying in an oven at about 130°. The value obtained for the percentage of sulphur should be within $\pm$ 0·2 of the theoretical value.

NOTE. (1) Most sulphur compounds are completely oxidised if the tube is heated under the conditions described for the estimation of halogens. Sulphonic acids and sulphones are more difficult to oxidise completely and the tube should be slowly heated to 300° and maintained at this temperature for at least 6 hours. The oxidation may be facilitated by adding a few crystals of sodium or potassium bromide to the organic material in the small tube, so that bromine shall be present to intensify the oxidation during the heating.

(2) Liquid sulphur compounds should be weighed and introduced into the Carius tube by precisely the same methods as those described for liquid halogen compounds (p. 442).

Example of Calculation.

Estimation of S in thiocarbanilide.

0·2563 g. of thiocarbanilide gave 0·2655 g. barium sulphate.

Factor for S in $BaSO_4$ = 0·1374 (Table III, p. 534).

∴ 0·2563 g. of thiocarbanilide contains 0·2655 × 0·1374 g. sulphur

∴ 100 g. of thiocarbanilide contain $\dfrac{0·2655 \times 0·1374 \times 100}{0·2563}$ g. sulphur

$$= 14·23\%.$$

Theoretical for $C_{13}H_{12}N_2S$, 14·05%.

Determination of Molecular Weights.

The chief methods available for the determination of the molecular weight of organic compounds are:

A. *Physical Methods.*

   I. Determination of Vapour Density.
       Victor Meyer's Method.

  II. Depression of the Freezing-point (Cryoscopic Method).
       (a) Macro-scale, (b) Semi-micro scale.

 III. Depression of the Freezing-point of Camphor (Rast's Method).

 IV. Elevation of the Boiling-point (Ebullioscopic Method).
       (a) Macro scale, (b) Semi-micro scale (e.g., Sucharda-Bobranski method).

B. *Chemical Methods.*

   I. Molecular Weight of Acids by Analysis of Silver Salts.
  II. Molecular Weight of Acids by Titration with Standard Alkali.
 III. Molecular Weight of Bases by Analysis of Chloroplatinates.

The practical limitations of the above methods are indicated in their detailed description.

Although certain of the above methods give results of high accuracy, it should be emphasised that very accurate determinations of molecular weights are not *usually* required in organic chemistry, where the chief purpose of such determinations is to fix the molecular formula of a compound. Thus the quantitative estimation of the elements in a particular compound may show that the empirical formula is $(C_3H_5Cl)_n$, and the molecular weight is then required in order to fix the value of n and hence the molecular formula.

Molecular Weight Determinations by Physical Methods. Vapour Density. Victor Meyer's Method.

Victor Meyer's method is almost universally employed for the determination of the vapour density of organic compounds. It has the advantages of requiring a very small quantity of the organic material, giving accurate results, and of being applicable to compounds the boiling-points of which lie over a wide range. It cannot however be applied to compounds which decompose on attempted volatilisation at atmospheric pressure. In principle, Victor Meyer's method consists in volatilising a known weight of the organic compound at the lower closed end of a hot tube: an equivalent volume of hot air is therefore displaced from the upper portion of the tube through a side delivery-tube (where it cools to room temperature) into a calibrated vessel, in which its volume is measured under known conditions of temperature and pressure. The volume of this cold air is clearly equal to the volume of vapour which the known weight of the organic liquid would evolve, assuming that this vapour could exist without condensation under the same conditions of temperature and pressure as those of the cold air.

The apparatus consists of a tube **T** (Fig. 76) usually of total height about 75 cm.: the upper portion of the tube has an internal diameter of about 1 cm., whilst the lower portion is blown out as shown into a bulb of about 100 ml. capacity. Near the top of **T** is the delivery-tube **D** of coarse-bored capillary, bent as shown. The tube **T** is suspended in an outer glass jacket **J** which contains the heating liquid: this jacket is fitted around **T** by a split cork **F** which has a vertical groove cut or filed in the side to allow the subsequent expansion of the air in **J**. The open end of the side-arm **D** can be placed in a trough **W** containing water, and a tube **C**, calibrated in ml. from the top downwards, can be secured as shown over the open end of **D**.

For an actual determination, first place in **J** some stable liquid the boiling-point of which is at least 50° above that of the organic liquid the vapour density of which is to be measured. This difference in boiling-point is important, because it is essential that the organic liquid, when subsequently dropped into the bottom of **T**, should volatilise rapidly and so push out an equivalent volume of air before the organic vapour itself can diffuse up the tube **T** and possibly condense in the cooler upper portion of the tube. Suitable liquids for use in the jacket are water, chlorobenzene (132°), *sym*-tetrachloro-ethane (147°), *p*-

chlorotoluene (156°), aniline (184°), nitrobenzene (210°), 1-chloro-naphthalene (260°) and 1-bromonaphthalene (281°). Finally add a few fragments of unglazed porcelain to the liquid in **J** to ensure smooth steady boiling.

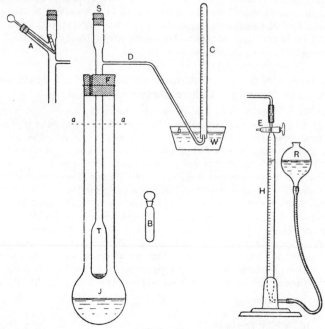

FIG. 76.

Thoroughly clean and dry the tube **T**, blowing air through a long piece of quill tubing to the lower end of **T** to ensure complete removal of any organic liquid remaining from a previous determination. Place a small quantity of clean *dry* sand at the bottom of **T**, and adjust the tube in position within the jacket **J**. Close the top of **T** securely with a rubber stopper **S**, and place the end of the tube **D** in the trough of water **W**, omitting at this stage the tube **C**. Now boil the liquid in **J** until it is refluxing up to a level *aa*. The air in **T** expands and escapes through **D**: allow the boiling to continue steadily so that eventually the expansion of the air is complete and no more bubbles escape from the end of **D**.

Meanwhile clean, dry and weigh a small bottle **B** made specially for this purpose: it has a ground-glass stopper, and a capacity of about 0·5 ml. Then by means of a fine dropping-tube, place about 0·2 ml. of the organic liquid in the bottle and weigh again. Fill the calibrated tube **C** with water and invert it in the trough **W** over the end of **D**. After loosening the stopper, quickly drop the bottle **B** down the tube **T**, where its fall is broken by the sand below: *at once* replace firmly the rubber stopper **S** at the top of **T**.

The liquid in **B** rapidly volatilises at the bottom of the tube **T**, the stopper being thrown off, and bubbles of air escape from **D** into the tube **C**. Continue boiling the liquid in **J** steadily until no more bubbles escape into **C**. Then carefully slip the end of **D** from under the tube **C**, close the end of **C** securely with the finger, and then transfer the tube to a gas-jar of water, so that the level of the water inside and outside **C** can be equalised. Measure the volume of air in **C**, and note the room temperature and the barometric pressure. The vapour density can now be calculated (see p. 428).

NOTE. The above represents the simplest form of Victor Meyer's apparatus. The following modifications may however be applied:

(1) A small error is introduced in the above method of working when the stopper **S** is removed from **T** in order to admit the bottle **B**, because water at once enters the lower end of the delivery-tube **D** and rises slightly above the normal level (*b*) of the water in the trough **W**. When **S** is replaced and the organic liquid volatilises, this water has to be expelled before any air can escape into **C**. The tube **D** is made of coarse capillary tubing so that this error is reduced to a minimum, and so that the air can escape readily through **D**. The error may be overcome by storing the bottle **B** (when filled and weighed) in the upper cold portion of **T**, and allowing it to fall when required into the lower portion. Various devices are available for this purpose. One of the simplest consists of a short wide tube **A** (Fig. 76) fused at an angle to the tube **T**, as shown, a few cm. above the delivery-tube **D**. **A** is closed by a rubber stopper containing a short thick glass rod, the upper end of which is flattened to allow ready rotation. The central hole of the rubber stopper is well lubricated with vaseline or some other non-volatile grease, so that the rod can be readily pushed up and down, at the same time making a satisfactorily air-tight fit in the stopper. Before starting the experiment, the rod is pushed down (as shown) so that the tube **T** is partly obstructed and the bottle **D** containing the organic liquid is placed so that it is held loosely in position by the end of the rod. The stopper **S** is replaced, the liquid in **J** boiled as before, and the tube **C** placed in position. The rod in **A** is then partly withdrawn until the bottle **B** falls, and is then replaced in its former position.

(2) The air may be collected directly into a Hempel gas-burette (Fig. 76) and there measured. This burette consists of a glass tube **H** calibrated in ml. from the tap **E** downwards, and connected by a piece of rubber tubing to the reservoir **R**, the height of which can be adjusted. The tap **E** is a 3-way tap, by which the tube **H** can be connected directly through to the capillary tube above, or either tube can be connected through the left-hand end of the tap to the atmosphere.

In use, the burette **H** and the reservoir **R** are partly filled with water. The delivery-tube **D** of the Victor Meyer apparatus is now horizontal, and is connected by a further piece of coarse capillary tubing at least 30 cm. long to the burette **H** as shown. The tubing is made of this length partly to ensure that the warm air passing along **D** becomes cooled to room temperature before being collected and partly to ensure that the burette itself is not heated by the boiling liquid in **J**: for the latter purpose it is advisable in addition to place a metal or asbestos screen vertically between **J** and **H** during the experiment.

In the actual determination, the tap **E** is adjusted to give direct access from **D** to the open air during the initial boiling of the liquid in **J**, so that the expanding air in **T** can readily escape. To determine when the air in **T** has been heated until no further expansion occurs, equalise the water levels in **H** and **R** (**H** containing a few ml. of air) and then adjust **E** to give access between the capillary **D** and the tube **H**: no change in the level of the water should occur. Now rotate **E** so that **H** is open to the air, and raise **R** so that the water completely fills the tube **H** up to **E**. Drop the bottle **B** containing the weighed liquid into **T**, and *at once* replace **S** and rotate **E** to give access again from **D** to **H**. As the air passes into **H**, drop **R** steadily so that the levels remain approximately equal. When no more air passes into **H**, close **H** (by rotating **E** so that **D** is open to the air) and allow the air in **H** to stand for about 10 minutes to attain a uniform temperature. Meanwhile suspend a thermometer from the tap **E**. Then readjust the two water levels accurately, and note the volume of air in **H**, the temperature, and also the barometic pressure.

Example of Calculation.

Vapour Density of Carbon Tetrachloride, chlorobenzene being used as the heating liquid.

Weight of carbon tetrachloride taken . . . . . 0·2120 g.
Volume of air collected . . . . 32·8 ml.
   Temperature, 14·5°. Barometic Pressure, 744·5 mm.
   Vapour Pressure of water at 14·5°, 12·3 mm. (Table II, p. 534.)

$$\text{Therefore volume of air at S.T.P.} = 32\cdot8 \times \frac{273}{287\cdot5} \times \frac{(744\cdot5 - 12\cdot3)}{760}$$

$$= 30\cdot00 \text{ ml.}$$

$$30\cdot00 \text{ ml. of vapour weigh } 0\cdot2120 \text{ g.}$$

$$\therefore\ 11{,}210 \text{ ml.* of vapour weigh } \frac{0\cdot2120 \times 11{,}210}{30\cdot00} = 79\cdot2 \text{ g.}$$

    Therefore Vapour Density = 79
    and Molecular Weight   = <u>158</u>
  Theoretical for CCl₄; 154.

Molecular Weight Determinations in Solution.

Before describing the chief methods by which the molecular weight of an organic compound in solution may be determined, a description is given of the Beckmann thermometer, and of the Tabloid Press, both of which are frequently used in the above determinations.

* NOTE. (1) 1 G. of hydrogen (taken as standard) occupies 11,210 ml. at N.T.P., therefore the density of any gas is that weight of it which occupies 11,210 ml. at N.T.P. (2) By Avogadro's hypothesis, the Molecular Weight of any gas = 2 × Vapour Density. Therefore the molecular weight of any gas is that weight which occupies 22,420 ml. at S.T.P. It is usual, therefore, to ignore the actual vapour density in organic chemistry and calculate the molecular weight directly on the 22,420 ml. basis.

The Beckmann Thermometer.

For determining the depression of the freezing-point, or elevation of the boiling-point, of a solvent when a solute is added, a thermometer is required which measures accurately a small change in temperature, the absolute value in degrees Centigrade of the limits of this change being immaterial. The Beckmann thermometer (Fig. 77(A)) is therefore constructed with a very large mercury bulb so that a change in temperature of a few degrees causes a considerable movement of the mercury in the capillary: consequently the scale **S** can be so larg: that readings to 0·01° can easily be made with the unaided eye. Since this scale **S** usually covers only 5–6°, it is necessary that the amount of mercury in the bulb should be capable of adjustment, so that, irrespective of the *actual* temperature at which the thermometer is being used, the readings will come conveniently on the scale. For this purpose the thermometer has a reserve supply of mercury in the reservoir **R**. For working at low temperatures, more mercury is required in the bulb, and an extra supply is brought down from **R**: for working at higher temperatures, less mercury is required in the bulb to enable readings to be made on the scale **S**, and therefore a suitable quantity of mercury is detached from that in the bulb and deposited in the reservoir.

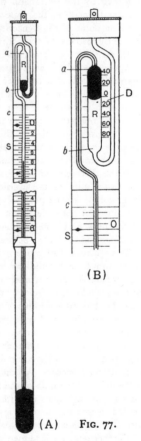

(B)

Therefore before the thermometer can be used in a particular experiment, it must be "set," *i.e.*, the amount of mercury must be adjusted so that the readings fall conveniently upon the scale **S**. As an example of this process, suppose the thermometer is required for determining the depression of the freezing-point of benzene (m.p. 5·5°), on the addition of a particular solute. First place the bulb of the thermometer in a beaker of water the temperature of which has been adjusted by the careful addition of ice to 7–8°C., this temperature being registered of course by an independent thermometer: this difference of 2–3° (above the true freezing-point of the solvent) corresponds to rather more than the length of the capillary between *c* (the highest calibrated point on the scale **S**) and the point *a*, where the capillary widens out into the reservoir **R**. If the thermometer has (A)   FIG. 77.

previously been used at some higher temperature, the mercury will now fall well below the scale **S**. Now momentarily invert the thermometer and tap it gently, so that the mercury in the reservoir **R** falls to *a*, where it remains when the thermometer is again carefully restored to its normal position. Place the bulb of the thermometer in a *warm* water-bath (avoid if possible the use of *hot* water) so that the mercury in the bulb rises up beyond the scale **S** and joins up with the mercury at *a*. Now replace the thermometer in the beaker of water at 7-8°C., and when the contraction of the mercury is complete, tap the thermometer sharply at **R** so that the mercury remaining in the upper part of **R** breaks sharply at the constriction *a* and falls to *b*. Finally place the dry thermometer in a boiling-tube containing about 25 ml. of the benzene to be used, and chill the tube in ice-water so that the benzene when stirred with the thermometer undergoes partial crystallisation to a semi-solid mass. The temperature recorded by the Beckmann thermometer should now be about 1° below the highest point *c* on the scale **S**: consequently subsequent depressions of the freezing-point of the benzene on the addition of the solute can now be conveniently read on the scale **S**.

If, on the other hand, the thermometer has previously been used at some temperature below the freezing-point of benzene, when the bulb is originally placed in the beaker of water at 7-8°C., the mercury will rise in the capillary and ultimately collect in the upper part of the reservoir at *a*. When the expansion is complete, again tap the thermometer sharply at **R** so that this excess of mercury drops down into *b*, and then as before check the success of the "setting" by placing the thermometer in some partly frozen benzene. In either case, if the adjustment is not complete, repeat the operations, making a further small adjustment, until a satisfactory result is obtained.

If the thermometer is to be used to determine the elevation of the boiling-point of a liquid on the addition of a solute, it must be remembered that at the boiling-point of the pure solvent the mercury must now be about 1-2° *above the bottom* of the scale **S**, and hence for adjustment purposes the temperature of the beaker of water should be 6-7° above the boiling-point of the liquid itself, instead of 1-2° as before.

The "setting" of modern Beckmann thermometers has been made much more simple and rapid by having the reservoir itself calibrated in degrees Centigrade as shown (much enlarged) in Fig. 77(B). Owing to the position of the scale **D**, the readings are necessarily inverted: readings at the top of the scale **D** above the zero mark represent degrees *below* 0°C., and *vice-versa*. Its use is best illustrated by a particular example. Suppose the thermometer is again to be used to determine the depression of the freezing-point of benzene: it is required therefore that at 5°C., the thermometer itself should give a reading about 1° below the top point *c* on the major scale **S**, *i.e.*, a reading near the 0° mark on this scale. All the mercury in the reservoir at *b* is transferred to *a* as before, and the bulb of the thermometer again gently warmed until the mercury in the bulb joins up with that at *a*. The bulb of the thermometer is now cooled so that the mercury at *a* contracts and the meniscus in the reservoir **R** rises. When this meniscus reaches the +5° mark on the small scale **D**, the top of the thermometer is tapped as before to break the mercury thread at *a* so that the remainder of the mercury in *a* falls to *b*: it will now be found that if the bulb is cooled to 5°C. (*e.g.*, by immersion in crystalline benzene as before) the thermometer will give a reading at the 0° mark on the major scale **S**. Stated in general terms, therefore, to "set" this type of Beckmann thermometer for use at a particular temperature, it is necessary merely to join the mercury in the bulb to the whole of the reservoir-mercury collected at *a*, and then to cool or warm the bulb until the reservoir-mercury reads the required temperature on the small scale **D**. The mercury thread is then broken at *a*, and at the desired temperature, the thermometer will then read 0° on the major scale **S**.

When actually taking a reading on the scale **S** during an experiment, a small lens is used, and the usual precautions must be taken to avoid an error by "parallax."

It is always advisable to use a particular Beckmann thermometer either solely for freezing-point determinations or solely for boiling-point determinations. If a thermometer which has been used at low temperatures for some time is reset for boiling-point determinations, it will be found that the glass bulb of the thermometer (as distinct from the mercury) does not adjust itself at once to the higher temperature: a slow "settling-down" process occurs, during which the reading of the thermometer steadily changes. This effect is of course negligible when the thermometer is reset over a range of only a few degrees.

The Tabloid or Pellet Press. When determining the molecular weight of a solid substance in solution, it is often most convenient to add a weighed pellet or tabloid of the substance to the solvent. A tabloid press is therefore used to compress the powdered substance into a pellet of suitable weight. The press consists essentially of a cylinder **C** (Fig. 78), having a circular bore through its long axis. The cylinder **C** fits over a metal base **B**, and a plunger **P** fits closely into the circular bore: the plunger **P** and the cylinder **C** have side-arms to limit rotation in the frame **F**.

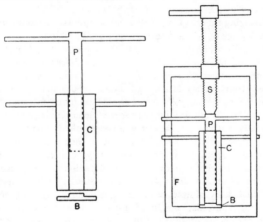

FIG. 78.

In use, the cylinder **C** is fitted over the base **B**, and the powdered compound is placed in **C** in small quantities at a time, and pressed firmly down (by hand) with the plunger **P**. When sufficient material has been placed in **C**, the whole unit is fitted into the frame **F** as shown, and the screw-plunger **S** screwed down first until **P** is held in position, and then more firmly until the material in **C** has formed a compact pellet. The cylinder **C** is then removed from **F**, and the pellet ejected from the lower end by thrusting **P** completely down the circular bore.

NOTE. For most compounds, the circular bore in **C** should have a diameter of not less than 1 cm.: otherwise the final ejection of the pellet may prove very difficult. Some powdered substances do not "bind" well in the press however, and for these compounds a cylinder having a narrower bore (3–5 mm.) is desirable.

It is of great advantage, however, to have available a second cylinder similar to, but much shorter than, **C**, and of wider internal bore. When the pellet has been formed inside **C**, the plunger **S** is released and the shorter cylinder inserted between **C** and the base **B**. The plunger **S** is again screwed down, and the pellet is thus slowly forced out of **C** into the shorter cylinder below. In this way the pellet, even if originally firmly fixed in **C**, can be removed without risk of fracture.

Molecular Weight by Depression of the Freezing-point.

When a substance is dissolved in a solvent, the freezing-point of the latter is depressed, this depression (for dilute solutions) being directly proportional to the number of molecules of the solute in unit weight of the solvent. It follows therefore that for a particular solute, the depression of the freezing-point will be directly proportional to the concentration of the solute in the solution: and also equimolecular quantities of different solutes, each dissolved separately in the same weight of the solvent, will cause equal depressions of the freezing-point. The **Molecular Depression Constant** (K) of a solvent is the depression of the freezing-point produced when 1 gram-molecule of a substance is dissolved in 100 grams of the solvent. This Constant may be calculated thermodynamically, but is more usually determined experimentally, using in turn a number of solutes of known molecular weight, the solutes being selected from those compounds which show neither ionisation nor association in the particular solvent. It should be borne in mind that in the majority of cases the conditions defined for the Molecular Depression Constant are not physically realisable, because 1 gram-molecule of a compound is rarely soluble in 100 grams of a solvent, and moreover when soluble, would give far too concentrated a solution for the physical laws underlying the process to apply accurately. In the experimental determination of the constant, however, only very dilute solutions (rarely exceeding 5%) are used, and the Constant calculated by simple proportion: in using this Constant in turn to determine the molecular weight of a new solute, the depression of the freezing-point once again of a very dilute solution is measured, and the weight of the solute, which when dissolved in 100 grams of the solvent would give a depression equal to the Constant, is then calculated. Therefore only dilute solutions are used both in the determination and in the subsequent application of the Molecular Depression Constant.

Since ice-water is the cheapest and most convenient cooling agent available in the laboratory, it is best to use for Freezing-point determinations the following solvents, which freeze a few degrees above 0°C.

Solvent	Freezing-point	Molecular Depression Constant (K)
Benzene	5·5°	50
Nitrobenzene	5·0	69
Cyclohexane	6·5	201
Bromoform	7·8	144
1,2-Dibromoethane	8·0	118
Water	0°	18·6
Acetic acid	17	39·0

Certain practical points concerning the use of these solvents are discussed after the description of the experimental method: water and acetic acid are also included, although the former is rarely used in organic work, and the latter presents certain experimental difficulties which are also discussed later.

The apparatus (Fig. 79) used consists of a glass tube **T** (usually about 18 cm. in length and 2·5–3·0 cms. in diameter), having a short side-arm **A**, as shown. Into the top of **T** are fitted through a cork the Beckmann thermometer **B** (already "set" for the required solvent) and the stirrer **S** made of thin glass rod. It is advisable for the hole in the cork carrying the stirrer **S** to be protected by a short collar **C** of glass tubing, the handle of the stirrer being bent after threading through the collar. The tube **T** fits into an outer tube **J**, which acts as an air-jacket to prevent too rapid cooling of the contents of **T**. **J** in turn is held in a metal lid covering a large glass jar of ice-water: a much heavier and stronger stirrer **D** passes through this lid to enable the ice-water mixture to be thoroughly stirred from time to time.

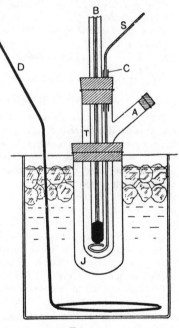

Fig. 79.

Weigh the clean dry tube **T**, then add about 25 ml. of the pure solvent (*i.e.*, sufficient to ensure that the bulb of the thermometer is subsequently well covered) and weigh again. Place the thermometer and stirrer in position, and, to save time, dip **T** directly into some ice-water: stir the solvent occasionally, when crystallisation will soon occur. Remove **T** from the ice-water, dry it thoroughly, and then stir the semi-solid solvent whilst holding the bottom of **T** in the hand: directly the last trace of crystals disappears, fit **T** into the jacket **J** and assemble the apparatus as shown in Fig. 79. Now stir the solvent in **T** by moving **S** up and down *slowly and at uniform speed*. The temperature of the solvent falls steadily, and ultimately drops slightly below its freezing-point: crystallisation then occurs and the latent heat causes the temperature to rise a few degrees, when it then becomes stationary for several minutes. Note the highest temperature reached, maintaining a steady stirring throughout this process. Now remove **T** and warm it in the hand until all crystals disappear. Repeat the process until *three consistent* readings of the freezing-point have been obtained.

Then again remove **T**, and drop a weighed pellet of the solute through the side-arm **A**. Stir the mixture until a clear solution is obtained, and then repeat the above process until three consistent readings of the freezing-point of the solution have been obtained. Then add a second weighed pellet of the solute, and determine the freezing-point of this more concentrated solution in the same way.

Then if:

g. g. of solute in G g. of solvent depress F.P. by T°C.

$$\frac{g. \times 100 \times K}{G \times T}$$ g. of solute in 100 g. of solvent depress F.P. by K°C.

= Molecular Weight of the solute.

NOTE. (1) It is often found on determining the freezing-point of a solution that considerable super-cooling occurs, with the result that crystallisation, when it does take place, is considerable, and the temperature of the solution rises possibly several degrees. This is always to be avoided, because the freezing-point now measured is that of the more concentrated solution remaining after the crystallisation of a large proportion of the solvent, and a marked error may be thus incurred. If the solution shows signs of super-cooling, chill 1-2 ml. of the pure solvent in a test-tube in ice-water, and stir with a glass rod until crystallisation occurs. Now, when the solution is only slightly super-cooled, lift the stirrer **S** until its base is opposite the side-arm **A**, and then quickly transfer some of the crystals from the test-tube by means of the rod on to the stirrer. At once lower the stirrer into the solution and continue stirring, when crystallisation should occur within a few seconds.

(2) This method of Molecular Weight determination should be used only with solvents in which the particular substance is freely soluble, since it is essential that, on cooling, the *solvent*, and not the solute, should crystallise out.

(3) If the solute is a liquid, introduce it into the apparatus from an ordinary pyknometer tube (Fig. 80), weighing the tube before and after. For this purpose, insert the delivery-tube of the pyknometer carefully down the side-arm **A** (Fig. 79) so that the liquid falls well into the body of **T**. Force the liquid

out of the pyknometer by blowing gently down the right-hand inlet tube by means of a piece of rubber tubing carrying a short calcium chloride tube.

(4) Molecular weight determinations by depression of the freezing-point are more accurate and far less troublesome than those by the elevation of the boiling-point (p. 440), and the former method should always be preferentially employed if the solubility of the organic compound in the solvent is sufficiently high.

(5) Certain solvents, particularly benzene, cause many organic compounds to form bi-molecular associates in solution, with the result that the experimental molecular weight is twice the true value. If association is suspected, the determination should be repeated in one or more other solvents, in order to ascertain whether consistent results are obtained.

The following practical points in the choice and use of the solvents mentioned in the above table should be noted:

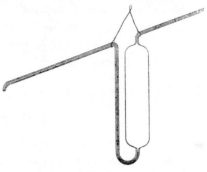

Fig. 80.

Benzene. Pure benzene (free in particular from toluene) must be used, otherwise the freezing-point is too low, and crystallisation may not occur with ice-water cooling alone. On the other hand, this benzene should not be specially dried immediately before use, as it then becomes slightly hygroscopic and does not give a steady freezing-point until it has been exposed to the air for 2–3 hours. Many compounds (particularly the carboxylic acids) associate in benzene, and molecular weights determined in this solvent should therefore be otherwise confirmed.

Nitrobenzene. Usually rather a troublesome solvent, as it is markedly hygroscopic and the freezing-point of the solvent itself tends to fall steadily: moreover it is, like benzene, an associating solvent. For a modification of the above freezing-point apparatus, by which the determination may be made in the absence of water-vapour, the student should consult an advanced text-book of practical physical chemistry.

Cyclohexane. An excellent solvent for many determinations, particularly as, owing to the high value of K, a large fall in the freezing-point is obtained, and the accuracy of the determination is therefore correspondingly increased. Care should be taken to avoid super-cooling, however, as it has a marked effect on the true freezing-point of cyclohexane solutions.

Bromoform. Commercial bromoform should be shaken thoroughly with water, separated, dried over powdered anhydrous sodium sulphate and then fractionally distilled under reduced pressure using a water-condenser. It should be stored in a dark cupboard. It is an excellent solvent, has the advantage of a high Constant, and very seldom causes association of the solute.

1, 2-Dibromoethane dibromide. Also has a very high Constant, but some-times causes association of the solute. It usually gives excellent consistent results.

Water. When water is used as a solvent, an ice-salt mixture should be employed for cooling purposes.

Glacial Acetic Acid. Acetic acid is very hygroscopic, and its freezing-point is considerably affected by the water absorbed. Satisfactory results cannot be obtained with the apparatus shown in Fig. 79, p. 433, and a specially modified apparatus must be employed (see Nitrobenzene).

Example of Calculation.

Molecular Weight of Naphthalene in Benzene.

Weight of benzene used . . . . . 19·40 g.
F.P. of benzene . . 5·056, 5·057, 5·057. Mean, 5·057°
(i) Weight of first pellet of Naphthalene added, 0·2107 gg.
F.P. of solution . . 5·496,* 5·497, 5·497. Mean, 5·497°

Depression of F.P. = 0·440°

$$\therefore \text{Molecular Weight of naphthalene} = \frac{0\cdot2107 \times 100 \times 50}{19\cdot40 \times 0\cdot440} = \underline{123}$$

(ii) Weight of second pellet of naphthalene added, 0·1385 g.
Total weight of naphthalene present, 0·3942 g.
F.P. of solution . . 5·776, 5·775, 5·776. Mean, 5·776°
Depression of F.P. = 0·719°

$$\therefore \text{Molecular Weight of naphthalene} = \frac{0\cdot3492 \times 100 \times 50}{19\cdot40 \times 0\cdot719} = \underline{125}$$

Theoretical for $C_{10}H_8$; 128.

SEMI-MICRO MODIFICATION OF THE ABOVE METHOD.

If a small Beckmann thermometer, similar to that used in the Sucharda-Bobranski method (p. 442) is available, the above method can be readily modified by replacing the tube **T** (Fig. 79) by an ordinary small boiling-tube without the side-arm **A**. The thermometer **B** and the stirrer **S** are fitted as in Fig. 79. The volume of solvent (usually *ca* 5 ml.) must of course cover the bulb of the thermometer.

To determine the molecular weight of a solid compound, it should be powdered and then weighed by difference from a weighing-cup similar to that shown in Fig. 90 (p. 503): it is convenient, but not essential, for the cup to have a ground-glass stopper. The bung carrying the thermometer and stirrer is lifted just clear of the tube, and the compound dropped carefully down the vertical tube: when the bung is replaced, any powder which may have adhered to the walls of the tube can be brought down into solution by vigorous action of the stirrer.

* The degrees of the thermometer are numbered from the top downwards; hence the apparent rise in the F.P.

For liquid compounds, a very thin-walled glass bulb, of *ca.* 3–5 mm. diameter, similar to that shown in Fig. 75 (p. 422) is prepared, and the stem cut off about 5 mm. from the bulb. The bulb is then weighed, and the liquid introduced through a fine capillary tube inserted down the stem into the bulb. If the liquid is not appreciably volatile, the bulb can then be weighed: if the liquid is volatile, the bulb before weighing should be held in light tongs or tweezers, and the stem quickly sealed in a small flame. When the freezing-point of the pure solvent has been determined, the bung with the thermometer and stirrer must be lifted out of the tube, and the bulb dropped in. The stirrer may not be sufficiently robust subsequently to break the bulb: in this case, the bulb should be broken by a thick glass rod, the solution well stirred, the rod withdrawn, and the thermomenter and stirrer promptly replaced. Although in general a Beckmann thermometer should not be withdrawn from the liquid at any time during the determination, the above brief withdrawal does not usually affect the accuracy of the determination.

The weight of solute employed, usually 20–50 mg. will depend on the nature and weight of the solute, the solubility of the solute, and the order of molecular weight expected.

Molecular Weight by Depression of the Freezing-point of Camphor. (Rast's Method.)

Camphor possesses the very high Molecular Depression Constant of 400, and therefore a given weight of a particular solute will give a much greater depression in camphor solution than in solutions of the usual organic solvents at the same concentration. Consequently the chief advantages arising from the use of camphor as a solvent, compared with the usual liquid solvents, are (1) much smaller quantities of the solute and of the solvent are required, so that the method amounts almost to a semi-micro determination, (2) an ordinary thermometer can be used instead of a Beckmann thermometer, (3) because of the high melting-point of camphor, no special apparatus is required, the ordinary melting-point apparatus (Figs. 1(A) and 1(B), p. 3) giving excellent results, (4) the method is much more rapid, particularly in the hands of an experienced worker.

On the other hand, molten camphor can exist as either the *keto* or the *enol* form, and it is essential that the substance the molecular weight of which is required should (*a*) dissolve freely in molten camphor without thermal decomposition, and (*b*) not react chemically with either form of the solvent.

$$C_8H_{14}\Big\langle\begin{array}{c}CH_2\\|\\CO\end{array} \rightleftharpoons C_8H_{14}\Big\langle\begin{array}{c}CH\\\|\\C(OH)\end{array}$$

keto   *enol*

Moreover, it is important that a determination of the Molecular Depression Constant of the camphor should always precede that of the molecular weight of a particular solute: the precise value of the constant depends largely on the "personal equation" of the observer,* and the two determinations should therefore always be made by the same observer to ensure identical conditions of manipulation.

The capillary tubes used for the melting-point determinations should be both longer and wider than those normally used: they should be at least 10 cm. long (to decrease the chance of slipping off the thermometer during the determination) and 2–3 mm. in diameter (in order to have sufficient semi-molten material in the tube to observe accurately the process of melting).

(1) DETERMINATION OF THE MELTING-POINT OF THE PURE CAMPHOR.

Pulverise some pure camphor on a piece of unglazed porcelain using a clean spatula: transfer some of this camphor to a capillary tube and press it firmly down by means of a second capillary tube sealed at the end and fitting snugly into the larger tube. Sufficient camphor should be taken to give a column of pressed material about 15 mm. in height. Place the capillary in the usual melting-point apparatus and raise the temperature fairly rapidly until the camphor melts to a clear liquid (about 180°). Now allow the temperature to fall until the camphor resolidifies, and then increase the temperature *very slowly* again. The camphor slowly remelts: take as the melting-point of the camphor that temperature at which the last trace of crystalline material *just* disappears. Allow to cool and redetermine the melting-point of the solidified camphor. Three *consistent* determinations should be made in this way: an accurate determination cannot be obtained unless the temperature rises very slowly (not more than 1 degree in 1 minute), therefore use a *very* small flame protected from draughts by a windscreen.

(2) DETERMINATION OF MOLECULAR DEPRESSION CONSTANT OF CAMPHOR, using Solute of Known Molecular Weight (Naphthalene, $C_{10}H_8$).

Weigh accurately a small clean specimen-tube directly on the balance. Add about 0·2 g. of pure naphthalene and reweigh: finally add about 2·0 g. of finely divided camphor and weigh again. The two substances have now to be melted together to obtain a clear homogeneous solution, and for this purpose *the tube should be sealed to prevent loss of either substance by volatilisation*. It is usually sufficiently accurate, however, to cork the tube *loosely* and then to melt the camphor by direct *gentle* heating: this should be done very carefully and slowly, the aim of the operation being to get a clear solution of the naphthalene in the molten camphor *at as low a temperature as possible*. Swirl the molten material gently around the bottom of the tube to ensure good mixing, and then

* This is clearly seen in large classes, where the values obtained for the "Constant" may vary over a wide range, but the values for the molecular weight of a given substance, with each student using his own "Constant", are (usually) remarkably consistent.

allow to cool. When quite cold, either remove the contents of the tube with a spatula, or, if this is not possible, break the tube, removing all fragments of glass from the solid camphor. Grind up the camphor in a mortar in order further to ensure a homogeneous mixture, and then fill a melting-point tube precisely as in (1) above. The melting-point is determined precisely as before—namely, by first rapidly melting the entire contents of the capillary tube in the melting-point apparatus, allowing to cool until resolidification occurs, and then increasing the temperature *very slowly*, again noting as the melting-point the temperature at which the last trace of crystalline matter just disappears. Repeat with a further portion of the same material until consistent results are obtained.

Molecular Weight of Naphthalene, 128. Then if:

g g. of naphthalene in G g. of camphor depress F.P. by t°C., 128 g. of naphthalene in 100 g. of camphor depress F.P. by

$$\frac{t \times 128 \times G}{g \times 100} °C.$$

This value is the Molecular Depression Constant (K) of Camphor.

(3) DETERMINATION OF MOLECULAR WEIGHT OF A GIVEN SUBSTANCE, *e.g.*, ACETANILIDE, using the above Molecular Depression Constant of Camphor.

Proceed precisely as in (2), but use pure powdered acetanilide instead of naphthalene.

Then if:

g^1 g. of acetanilide in G^1 g. of camphor depress F.P. by T°C.,

then $\dfrac{g^1 \times 100 \times K}{G^1 \times T}$ g. acetanilide in 100 g. of camphor depress F.P. by K°C.

= Molecular Weight of Acetanilide.

Example of Results Obtained.

F.P. of Camphor . . 176·0, 176·0, 176·0°. Mean, 176·0°

Determination of Constant, using Naphthalene

Weight of naphthalene used . . . . 0·1990 g.
Weight of camphor used . . . . . 2·0590 g.
F.P. of mixture . . 146·5, 146·5, 146·4°. Mean, 146·5°
∴ Depression of F.P. . . 29·5°

Molecular Depression Constant = $\dfrac{29·5 \times 128 \times 2·0590}{0·1990 \times 100}$ = 391

Molecular Weight of Acetanilide.

Weight of acetanilide used . . . . 0·2053 g.
Weight of camphor used . . . . . 2·0750 g.
F.P. of mixture . . 147·1, 147·0, 147·0°. Mean, 147·0°
∴ Depression of F.P. . . 29·0°

Molecular Weight of acetanilide = $\dfrac{0·2053 \times 100 \times 391}{2·0750 \times 29·0}$ = 133

Theoretical for acetanilide, $C_6H_5NHCOCH_3$; 135.

Molecular Weight by Elevation of the Boiling-point.

This method is strictly parallel in principle to that for the determination of molecular weight by depression of the freezing-point. When a substance is dissolved in a solvent, the boiling-point is raised, and the **Molecular Elevation Constant** (K) of a solvent is the elevation of the boiling-point produced when 1 gram-molecule of a substance is dissolved in 100 grams of the solvent. This Constant again can be either calculated, or determined experimentally using a number of solutes of known molecular weight.

The solvents most frequently employed are:

SOLVENT	BOILING-POINT	MOLECULAR ELEVATION CONSTANT (K)
Ether	35°	21·0
Acetone	56	17·0
Chloroform	61	36·6
Ethyl Acetate	77	27·5
Rectified Spirit* (95·6%)	78	11·5
Carbon Tetrachloride	78	48·0
Benzene	80	27·0
Cyclohexane	81	27·5
Water	100	5·2
1,2-Dibromoethane	130	64·0

The method is used to determine the molecular weight primarily of those compounds which are too slightly soluble in the usual cold solvents for the more efficient freezing-point method to be employed.

The apparatus is shown in cross-section in Fig. 81. **T** is a glass tube similar to that used for freezing-point determinations, except that a short piece of stout platinum wire should be fused through the base as shown. A Beckmann thermometer **B** is fitted to the tube **T**, and a condenser (either a short light water-condenser or a spiral air-condenser) to the side-arm. The tube **T** is supported within a glass jacket **J** which carries a similar condenser: a supply of the pure solvent is boiled in **J** during the determination to ensure a uniform temperature and to protect the contents of **T** from loss of heat by radiation. The jacket **J** stands on an asbestos tray **A**, which has in the centre a small hole covered with fine wire gauze: the tray **A** has in addition at diagonally opposite corners two asbestos chimneys **D** and **E** to conduct away the hot air. The apparatus is heated by means of a Bunsen burner, and the supply of gas must be capable of delicate adjustment by a screw-clip or some similar means.

For use, clean and dry the tube **T** and weigh it with both necks corked. Now add about 20-25 ml. of the solvent, and weigh again. Add

---

* Rectified spirit should always be used in preference to absolute ethanol which is strongly hygroscopic.

either a number of glass beads or (preferably) some fragments of unglazed porcelain, and adjust the thermometer **B** in position: the bulb of
B should be amply covered by the solvent and should just not touch the
beads. It is advisable now
to wrap some asbestos
cord **CC¹** loosely in a
spiral round the lower
portion of **T**, and then
fit **T** into the jacket **J**,
finally plugging the top
of the annular space be-
tween **T** and **J** loosely
with the upper end of the
cord: by these means the
direct ascent of hot gases
in the annular space is
prevented, and the tube
T cannot come in direct
contact with **J**. Place
sufficient solvent in **J** to
bring it approximately
level with the top of the
beads in **T**. Adjust the
condenser, and then sur-
round the whole appar-
atus with wind-screens
so that it is completely
protected from draughts.
Now start the heating so

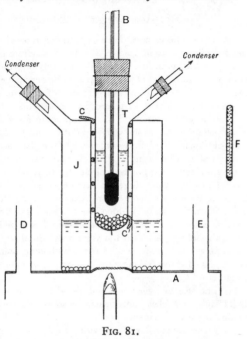

FIG. 81.

that the solvent in both **T** and **J** is boiling steadily, and that the condensed liquid is falling back into **T** from the condenser at about 1
drop per second. When the boiling is quite steady, take readings on the
Beckmann thermometer every 2–3 minutes, tapping it gently about 5
seconds before each reading to ensure that the mercury meniscus is not
"sticking" and so giving an inaccurate reading.

When three consistent readings are obtained, add a weighed pellet of
the solute to **T**: for this purpose it is important that the thermometer is
not withdrawn, and the boiling is not interrupted. It is best to hold the
pellet ready in a pair of forceps near the mouth of the side-arm of **T**,
and then momentarily to remove the condenser, drop in the pellet and
replace the condenser: when the condenser is removed a small quantity
of cold air entering the side-arm will cause slight condensation of the
hot vapour, none of which will therefore escape.

Wait a few minutes after the pellet has completely dissolved, and
then continue taking readings as before until three consistent values are
obtained. A second weighed pellet may then be added if desired, and
the process repeated.

Then as before if:

g g. of solute in G g. of solvent elevate B.P. by T°C.,

$$\frac{g \times 100 \times K}{G \times T}$$ g. of solute in 100 g. of solvent elevate B.P. by K°C.

= Molecular Weight of the solute.

NOTE. (1) The success of this method depends primarily on obtaining smooth steady boiling of the liquid in **T** with an absolute minimum of superheating. It is advisable before starting the determination to roughen the end of the platinum wire inside **T** by means of a piece of emery paper wrapped around the end of a glass rod. If, in spite of the presence of this wire and the glass beads, steady boiling is not obtained, better results can sometimes be obtained by preparing a fine roll (2–3 mm. diameter) of thin platinum foil **F** (Fig. 81), and then cutting it completely across (as shown on the dotted lines) to make a number of triangular cross-sections: add about ten of these to the glass beads.

(2) It should be borne in mind that any variation of the rate of heating will affect appreciably the boiling-point of the solvent or that of the solution, and the rate of heating must therefore remain constant throughout the experiment. Students frequently make the mistake of boiling the pure solvent *too gently*: hence when the solute is added, the temperature of the solution barely reaches the new boiling-point, and the gas pressure has to be increased. If, on the other hand, the solvent is boiled too vigorously, slight superheating alternating with "bumping" will occur, and an irregular boiling-point will result. The rate of boiling noted above (giving 1 drop of condensate per second) is usually the most suitable.

(3) The use of water as a solvent should be avoided whenever possible, as its Molecular Elevation Constant is so low that only a small elevation of the boiling-point is obtained.

(4) The same considerations with regard to association in solution apply here as in the freezing-point method (p. 435).

Example of Calculation.

Molecular Weight of Benzoic Acid in Benzene.

Weight of benzene used . . . . . 29·30 g.
B.P. of benzene . . 4·162, 4·163, 4·160. Mean, 4·162°
Weight of benzoic acid added . . . . 1·133 g.
B.P. of solution . . 3·720, 3·725, 3·722. Mean, 3·722°
Elevation of B.P. = 0·440°

∴ Molecular Weight of benzoic acid $= \dfrac{1·133 \times 100 \times 27}{29·3 \times 0·440} = \underline{237}$

Theoretical for $C_7H_6O_2$; 122.

Hence benzoic acid forms bi-molecular associates in benzene solution.

Molecular Weight by the Sucharda-Bobranski Method. (Semi-micro Scale).

This method has the advantages that (*a*) the boiling is much steadier than that in the previous method and consistent readings of the thermometer can therefore be rapidly obtained, (b) the determination requires less time, and (c) excellent results can be obtained using 20-50 mg. pellets of the compound the molecular weight of which is being determined.

The apparatus (Fig. 82), which is constructed throughout of glass, consists of a pear-shaped bulb **A** (of about 5 ml. capacity) in which the solution is boiled, and which has a short length of platinum wire fused through its lowest point to assist steady boiling. The bulb **A** is connected near its base by a curved narrow tube **B** to a vertical condenser **C**, and from its apex by a similar tube **D**, undulating as shown, to the cup **E**. A larger outer cup **F** is fused to the lower neck of **E** as shown. The cup **F** carries a third cup **G** which fits inside **E**, and which subsequently carries a small Beckmann thermometer having a rather narrow bulb. Finally the cup **F** is connected by a wider tube **H** to the base of the condenser **C**. It is essential that when the condenser **C** is vertical, the tube **H** slopes gently downwards as shown from the cup **F** to the condenser **C**. Since high-boiling solvents are rarely used in this apparatus the condenser **C**

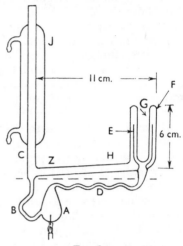

FIG. 82.

requires a water-jacket **J**. This water-jacket should either be fused to the condenser **C**, or have narrow necks which just slide over **C** and which can be held in position by short lengths of rubber tubing which provide watertight seals. The jacket **J** can be a plain glass cylinder held in position by rubber bungs at each end, but the condenser is then comparatively heavy.

General Dimensions. As a guide to the general dimensions of the apparatus for semi-micro determinations, the volume of **A** may be abut 05 ml., the external diameter of the tubes **B** and **D** 5 mm., that of the tube **H** 10-11 mm., and that of the condenser **C** 12-14 mm. The diameter of the cup **F** (external) and of the cup **G** (internal) may be 24 mm. and 11 mm. respectively. The diameter of **G** is determined by the Beckmann thermometer, the bulb of which should fit reasonably snugly (but not tightly) into the cup **G**.

Clean and dry the apparatus and then clamp the condenser

securely in a vertical position, and connect up the water supply to the condenser. Place sufficient clean mercury in **G** so that when the Beckmann thermometer is inserted, the bulb is just covered with the mercury and good thermal contact thus ensured: clamp the top of the thermometer, to relieve the cup **G** of its weight. Using a semi-micro pipette, which should be inserted well down the condenser **C**, run in a suitable volume (*e.g.*, 5 ml.) of solvent into the apparatus. (The most suitable volume, to ensure steady circulation of the boiling solvent, can readily be found by trial: normally, the cold solvent fills **A** and **B** up to about the level **L**.)

Now carefully screen the apparatus from draughts, and heat the platinum wire at the base of **A** with the small hot flame of a semi-micro Bunsen burner, so that the solvent boils fairly vigorously in **A**: a stream of boiling solvent interspersed with vapour consequently passes along **D**, rises upwards through the annular space between **E** and **G**, and then descends through the space between **E** and **F**, and then finally the hot solvent returns down the tubes **H** and **B** to the bulb **A**. (The construction of the tube **D**, combined with the relative sizes of the component parts of the apparatus, prevents any back-flow through **D**.) It is essential to adjust the heating to obtain this steady circulation of boiling liquid.

Meanwhile, prepare a pellet of the substance, using a pellet press of the type shown in Fig. 78 (p. 431), but having the cylinder **C** of about 3 mm. internal bore to enable a pellet of 20–50 mg. to be compressed and then ejected. (Do not compress the pellet more than is necessary for manipulation, otherwise it may dissolve too slowly in the boiling solvent.) Transfer the pellet to a watch-glass, which preferably should be kept in a small desiccator before and after weighing.

To test whether the Beckmann thermometer has attained thermal equilibrium with the circulating boiling solvent, tap the thermometer *gently* with a pencil and take a reading, preferably using a small lens. Repeat this twice more at 2–3 minute intervals until three consistent readings are obtained. From this point onwards, there should be no change whatsoever in the rate of heating, or the position of the Bunsen burner, or even in the rate of flow of water in the condenser. Now grasp the weighed pellet gently with a pair of tweezers, and drop it down the condenser tube **C**. If a suitable solvent has been chosen, the pellet should rapidly dissolve without interrupting the circulation of the boiling liquid.

It may occasionally happen, particularly if the solution is approaching saturation, that a small quantity of the crystalline solute separates at the top of the tube **H** in the zone **Z**, *i.e.*, immediately above the source of the heat. This may be prevented by placing a narrow oblong piece of asbestos paper, with slots cut in each end, horizontally between the tubes **H** and **D**, the slots fitting over the lower narrow ends of the condenser **C** and the cup **F**.

Wait 2–3 minutes after the pellet has dissolved, and then again read the tapped thermometer. If three consistent readings are obtained, the heating can be stopped. It should be emphasised that the most accurate results are obtained if the thermometer readings are thus noted shortly after the rise in the boiling-point, as registered by the thermometer, is complete. An appreciably longer delay may produce inaccurate or inconsistent readings.

Now calculate the molecular weight of the substance precisely as described on p. 442. The weight of the solvent employed may be calculated from the following densities: methanol, 0·810; rectified spirit, 0·807; acetone, 0·797; ethyl acetate, 0·905; chloroform, 1·504; carbon tetrachloride, 1·582; benzene, 0·880; toluene, 0·871; cyclohexane, 0·724; 1, 2–dichloroethane, 1·252.

The molecular elevation constants given on p. 440 can be used, but it is advisable to check the constant of the solvent, using a pure sample of a known compound under precisely the same conditions as those of the first determination.

The use of solvents having boiling-points below or much above the range indicated by the above examples is inadvisable, for the maintenance of a steady circulation of the boiling liquid may prove difficult.

Molecular Weights by Chemical Methods.
Molecular Weight of an Acid by Analysis of its Silver Salt.

The silver salts of most carboxylic acids are only sparingly soluble in cold water, and hence are readily prepared. Moreover they very rarely contain water of crystallisation, and therefore when dried can be analysed without further treatment. The analysis itself is simple, rapid and accurate, because gentle ignition of a weighed quantity of the silver salt in a crucible drives off the organic matter, leaving a residue of pure metallic silver.

Since the silver salts of the carboxylic acids are usually soluble in dilute nitric acid, they must be prepared by treating an aqueous solution of a *neutral salt* of the acid (and not the free acid itself) with silver nitrate solution. It is not practicable to attempt to neutralise the acid with sodium or potassium hydroxide solution, because the least excess of alkali would subsequently cause the white silver salt to be contaminated with brown silver oxide. The general method used therefore to obtain a neutral solution is to dissolve the acid in a small excess of ammonia solution, and then to boil the solution until all free ammonia is driven off. The solution of the pure ammonium salt is now cooled and treated with a small excess of silver nitrate solution, when the silver salt of the acid is precipitated.

Dissolve 1·5 ml. of glacial acetic acid in about 50 ml. of distilled water and then* add dilute ammonia solution until the well-stirred mixture smells of ammonia. Boil the solution *gently* until no odour of ammonia can be detected in the steam and until a red litmus-paper placed in the steam gives no blue coloration. Then cool and add dilute (*e.g.*, 10%) silver nitrate solution with stirring until no further precipitation of the white silver acetate occurs. Filter through a *small* Buchner funnel, drain well and then wash at least three times with small quantities of water to remove excess of silver nitrate. Then drain thoroughly, transfer to a small evaporating-basin, cover with a watch-glass and dry either in a steam oven or in a vacuum desiccator. Powder the cold dry salt in a small clean mortar: if the salt does not readily form a fine dry powder, continue the drying for a further period.

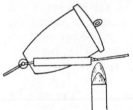

Meanwhile clean and dry a porcelain crucible and lid, selecting for this purpose a crucible of the tall narrow type (Fig. 83): heat the crucible and lid on a pipe-clay triangle over a Bunsen flame and allow to cool in an atmospheric desiccator. Weigh the crucible and lid when quite cold, add about 0·5 g. of the powdered silver salt, and weigh again. Place the crucible and lid in an inclined position (Fig. 83) in a pipe-clay triangle, and then gently heat the upper portion of the crucible with a very small Bunsen flame as shown. After 5–10 minutes, increase the size of the flame somewhat in order to heat the whole of the upper portion of the crucible and the lid. The silver salt below becomes heated by conduction and largely decomposes at this stage. Now slowly bring the flame down to the base of the crucible, and then after several minutes heat far more strongly until eventually the whole crucible becomes red hot. Then stop the heating, allow the crucible to cool somewhat and replace it in the desiccator until quite cold. Weigh again. Repeat the ignition until the weight of the crucible and its metallic contents is constant (if the first heating has been carefully performed, one reheating should be sufficient).

FIG. 83.

Then, since Atomic Weight of silver = 107·9,
if *g* g. silver is obtained from G g. silver salt,

107·9 g. silver are obtained from $\dfrac{G \times 107\cdot9}{g}$ g. silver salt

= Molecular Weight of silver salt.

Alternatively, to prevent undue hydrolysis, make the solution just alkaline to phenolphthalein with sodium hydroxide, then *just* acid with dilute nitric acid, and finally, add a slight excess of ammonia.

The Molecular weight of the acid itself is clearly equal to that of the silver salt *minus* the atomic weight of silver *plus* the weight of hydrogen displaced by the silver, *i.e.*, to $\left(\dfrac{G \times 107{\cdot}9}{g} \right) - 107{\cdot}9 + 1$.

Silver acetate is one of the most soluble of the silver salts of the carboxylic acids. When determining the molecular weight of one of the aromatic acids, *e.g.*, benzoic acid, a larger volume of water should be taken for the preparation of the silver salt, otherwise a thick cream of precipitated material is obtained and is difficult to filter and wash efficiently. For benzoic acid, therefore, add 1 g. of the powdered acid to about 50 ml. of water, and then add dilute ammonia until the acid has dissolved and the solution smells of ammonia. Boil and cool as before, and then dilute (if necessary) so that the solution has a volume of at least 75 ml. Precipitate the silver salt as before, filter, drain, and wash *thoroughly* before drying. Use 0·6–0·7 g. for the analysis. The silver salts of the aromatic acids give much free carbon on heating in a crucible, and the ignition must therefore be carefully and thoroughly performed.

Note. (1) It is clear that the above calculation is based on the knowledge that the acid is monobasic. If the acid had been dibasic, one gram-molecule of the silver salt would have contained two atoms of silver and the calculation, based on this fact, would have given twice the previous value. The method can therefore be used to determine molecular weights *only* if the basicity of the acid is already known: otherwise only the *equivalent weight* of the acid (*i.e.*, the weight in grams of the acid equivalent to 1 gram-atom of silver) can be calculated from the above analysis.

(2) The method cannot be applied to acids which contain halogens or sulphur: the silver salts of the former on ignition would give silver halide and those of the latter would give silver sulphide containing some silver sulphate, *etc.* Certain acids moreover give silver salts which on being heated decompose too vigorously for accurate results, *e.g.*, silver oxalate, which decomposes suddenly with the evolution of carbon dioxide: $(COOAg)_2 = 2Ag + 2CO_2$.

(3) The above method of preparing a neutral solution of the ammonium salt cannot be applied to *extremely* weak acids (*e.g.*, some amino-acids), the ammonium salts of which dissociate in boiling aqueous solution.

Molecular Weight of an Acid by Titration with Standard Alkali Solution.

The molecular weight of many carboxylic acids which are freely soluble in cold water (*i.e.*, chiefly the aliphatic acids) can readily be obtained by titrating a known weight of the acids in aqueous solution with standard sodium or potassium hydroxide solution, using phenolphthalein as an indicator. To avoid the use of unduly large quantities of the acid, it is advisable to use $M/2$ caustic alkali solution, and in order to obtain a sharp end-point, this alkali solution should be prepared from CO_2-free water* and pure (ethanol-washed) **caustic alkali free from carbonate.**

Weigh out accurately about 2·5 g. of pure powdered succinic acid, transfer to a 100 ml. graduated flask, dissolve in distilled water, make the solution up to the graduation mark and mix well. Now, by means of a pipette, transfer 25 ml. of the solution to a 150 ml. conical flask, add a drop of phenolphthalein solution and titrate with $M/2$ NaOH or KOH solution to obtain consistent results.

If the acid had been monobasic, then clearly the molecular weight would be the weight in grams which neutralises 1000 ml. of *normal* alkali solution: the molecular weight of the dibasic succinic acid is the weight which neutralises 2000 ml. of the normal alkali solution. Hence this method, like the preceding silver salt method, presupposes a knowledge of the basicity of the acid concerned: if the basicity is unknown, then only the equivalent weight (*i.e.*, the weight which neutraises 1000 ml. of the normal alkali solution) can be calculated.

Example of Calculation.

Weight of succinic acid taken . . . . 2·627 g.
Solution made up to 100 ml.
25 ml. of this solution required 22·2, 22·1, 22·1

$$= 22·1 \text{ ml. } M/2 \text{ NaOH solution}$$

∴ 100 ml. of this solution require 88·4 ml. $M/2$ NaOH solution

$$= 44·2 \text{ ml. } M.\text{NaOH solution}$$

2·627 g. succinic acid (dibasic) are equivalent to 44·2 ml. $M.\text{NaOH}$

∴ $\dfrac{2·627 \times 2000}{44·2}$ g. succinic acid (dibasic) are equivalent to 2000 ml. $M.\text{NaOH}$

$$= \underline{119}$$

Theoretical for succinic acid, $C_4H_6O_4$; 118.

Molecular Weight of a Base by Analysis of its Chloroplatinate.

When platinum is dissolved in aqua regia it is first converted to platinic chloride, $PtCl_4$, and the latter at once unites with the excess of hydrochloric acid to give the stable soluble dibasic chloroplatinic acid, H_2PtCl_6.†

* To prepare CO_2-free water, almost fill a large aspirator or bottle with distilled water, and then securely close the neck with a rubber stopper carrying two delivery-tubes, one passing just through the stopper into the aspirator and the other passing right down to the bottom: connect the former delivery-tube to a water-pump. Join three wash-bottles in series, the first two containing 50% aqueous KOH solution and the third containing distilled water to a depth of at least 10 cm.: connect this wash-bottle to the long delivery-tube of the aspirator. When the water-pump is in operation, air is drawn through the two KOH wash-bottles (where CO_2 and all other acid gases are absorbed), then through the water wash-bottle (which absorbs any alkali spray) and finally through the distilled water in the aspirator, from which all CO_2 is slowly extracted. Using a moderately vigorous stream of air, about 12 litres of CO_2-free water can be prepared in 3 hours with this apparatus.

† "Chloroplatinic acid" is an accepted abbreviation for "Tetrachloroplatinic (IV) acid".

When an amine, or a solution of its hydrochloride, is added to an aqueous solution of chloroplatinic acid, a salt of the base with the chloroplatinic acid, of general formula B_2,H_2PtCl_6 (where B is one molecule of the base) is formed and usually crystallises out, for these chloroplatinates have normally a rather low solubility in cold water. The chloroplatinate can be filtered off, dried, and then analysed by direct ignition, when only the metallic platinum ultimately remains. Knowing the percentage of platinum in the chloroplatinate, the molecular weight of the latter, and hence of the constituent base, can readily be calculated.

Dissolve 0·2 ml. of pure aniline (or 0·2 g. of powdered p-toluidine) in 5 ml. of dilute hydrochloric acid (warming if necessary to obtain a clear solution). Pour this solution with stirring into a slight excess of chloroplatinic acid solution, e.g., into about 10 ml. of a solution containing 5% of platinum as the chloroplatinic acid. The orange-yellow chloroplatinate of the amine at once crystallises out. Cool in ice-water for about 10 minutes, and then filter through a small Buchner funnel (preferably one of the cone-shaped type). Drain the chloroplatinate and then wash it twice, using about 5 ml. of ice-cold distilled water for each washing. Again drain thoroughly, transfer to a small basin,* cover with a watch-glass and dry either in a steam oven or (preferably) in a vacuum desiccator.

Now analyse 0·2-0·25 g. by ignition *precisely* as described for the ignition of silver salts (p. 446).

Then, since Atomic Weight of platinum = 195·2,
if g g. platinum is obtained from G g. chloroplatinate,

195·2 g. platinum are obtained from $\dfrac{G \times 195\cdot2}{g}$ g.

$$= \text{Molecular Weight of chloroplatinate}$$

Then, since $B_2,H_2PtCl_6 = \dfrac{G \times 195\cdot2}{g}$, and $H_2PtCl_6 = 410$.

$$2B = \dfrac{G \times 195\cdot2}{g} - 410$$

* When the chloroplatinate has been transferred to the basin, wash out the Buchner funnel, filter-paper and flask with hot water until all remaining traces of the chloroplatinate have been dissolved: add the united washings to the original filtrate and place in the platinum residue bottle. The platinum can be readily recovered from these aqueous residues as follows. Heat the solution in a large beaker on a water-bath, and then add a coil of pure magnesium ribbon, pressing the latter to the bottom of the beaker with a heavy glass red. Cover the beaker with a watch-glass. After several minutes, the colour of the solution begins to fade, and spongy platinum is deposited: the process then rapidly becomes complete and, on stirring, the platinum settles to the bottom of the colourless solution. Filter off the metal at the pump, wash with very dilute hydrochloric acid, and then thoroughly with water. Drain, and dry in a desiccator (and *not* by washing with alcohol and ether, as these solvents may ignite in contact with the finely divided platinum).

Alternatively, the bulk of the platinum in the aqueous residues can be precipitated by ammonium chloride as ammonium chloroplatinate, the latter filtered off, and the filtrate evaporated to dryness. The chloroplatinate and the residue from the evaporation are then ignited.

NOTE. (1) The above calculation (similarly to that of the silver salt of an acid) is based on the knowledge that the amine is monacidic and therefore forms a chloroplatinate of formula B_2,H_2PtCl_6. If the amine is diacidic (e.g., ethylene diamine, phenylene diamine, etc.), the chloroplatinate would have the general formula B,H_2PtCl_6, and the calculated result would have twice the above value. Hence the molecular weight of an amine can be determined by this method only if the acidity of the amine is known: otherwise, the calculated result gives only the *equivalent weight* of the base (i.e., the weight in grams equivalent to 1 gram-atom of platinum).

(2) The chloroplatinates prepared as above are sufficiently pure for direct analysis without recrystallisation. The chloroplatinates of the amines are usually freely soluble in hot water, but recrystallisation (when required) should not be attempted until the process has been found to be successful with a small test-portion of the chloroplatinate. The chloroplatinates of many primary and secondary amines decompose in hot water, the amine being oxidised, and the chloroplatinate reduced to the metal: some amines furthermore co-ordinate readily with the metal when the chloroplatinate is boiled with water and a mixed product is obtained on cooling.

(3) Many chloroplatinates separate from aqueous solution with water of crystallisation. If this is suspected, the chloroplatinate should be dried to constant weight in the oven before analysis, to ensure elimination of water of crystallisation. Aniline, p-toluidine and pyridine all give anhydrous chloroplatinates, and can be conveniently used in the above determination: no attempt should be made to recrystallise their chloroplatinates.

Estimation of the Number of Hydroxyl Groups in a given Polyhydric Alcohol or Phenol.

Method. A known weight of the alcohol is heated with a definite volume of a mixture of acetic anhydride and pyridine until acetylation is complete:

$$R(OH)_n + nCH_3CO\cdot O\cdot COCH_3 = R(O\cdot COCH_3)_n + nCH_3COOH$$

The excess of unchanged acetic anhydride is then hydrolysed by the addition of water, and the total free acetic acid estimated by titration with standard NaOH solution. Simultaneously a control experiment* is performed identical with the above except that the alcohol is omitted. The difference in the volumes of NaOH solution required in the two experiments is equivalent to the difference in the amount of acetic acid formed, i.e., to the acetic acid used in the actual acetylation. If the molecular weight of the alcohol is known, the number of hydroxyl groups can then be calculated.

* Control or blank experiments have frequently to be employed in organic estimations. Their value is twofold:

(1) The *absolute* concentration of a reagent (e.g., the exact amount of acetic anhydride in the above pyridine solution) need not be determined, since if the same amount of the reagent is used in the actual and in the control experiments, the *difference* gives at once the actual amount used.

(2) Adventitious losses of the reagent, due, e.g., to the chemical action of the alkaline glass vessels, slight absorption by the corks, etc., are almost identical for the actual and the control experiments and therefore do not affect the *difference* in result between the two experiments.

1. DETERMINATION OF NUMBER OF HYDROXYL GROUPS IN PHENOL. C_6H_5OH. Molecular Weight, 94.

Prepare the acetylating mixture by adding 1 volume of acetic anhydride to 4 volumes of pure anhydrous pyridine, and shaking thoroughly. Immediately before use, transfer the mixture to a clean dry burette having a well-fitting glass tap, and then close the top of the burette by means of a soda-lime tube.

Fit two similar 100 ml. conical flasks, **A** and **B**, with reflux water-condensers, using ground-glass joints or rubber stoppers. Connect up the water-condensers in series. Weigh the flask **A**, add about 1 g. of pure *dry* powdered phenol and weigh again. Now add 10 ml. of the acetylating mixture to the flask **A**, and also to the control flask **B**. Connect the flasks to the reflux condensers and heat both flasks on briskly boiling water-baths for 30 minutes. Then remove the water-baths, and pour 20 ml. of distilled water down each condenser, shaking the contents of each flask gently to ensure complete hydrolysis of the unchanged acetic anhydride. Finally cool each flask thoroughly in cold water and allow to stand for 10 minutes. Then titrate the contents of each flask with N.NaOH solution, using phenolphthalein as an indicator. A fine emulsion of phenyl acetate will form when the contents of the flask **A** are diluted, and should therefore be vigorously stirred throughout the titration to ensure that all the free acetic acid is extracted by the N.NaOH solution.

Example of Calculation.

Weight of phenol used	. .	0·956 g.
Flask **A** requires .	. . .	33·9 ml. M.NaOH solution
Flask **B** (Control) requires	. .	43·85 ml. M.NaOH solution

Difference in M.NaOH solution required for **A** and **B** = 9·95 ml.

1000 ml. M.NaOH $\equiv$ 1 G.Mol.NaOH $\equiv$ 1 G.Mol.CH_3COOH $\equiv$ 1 Hydroxyl group.

$\therefore$ 9·95 ml. M.NaOH $\equiv$ 9·95/1000 Hydroxyl group

$\therefore$ 1·930 g. phenol contain 9·95/1000 Hydroxyl group

and 94 g. (1 G.Mol.) phenol contain $\dfrac{9·95}{1000} \times \dfrac{94}{0·965}$ Hydroxyl group

= 0·97 Hydroxyl group.

NOTE. (1) In view of the large volume of M.NaOH solution required in the above titrations, the contents of the flask **A** after hydrolysis may alternatively be washed carefully into a 100 ml. graduated flask, and the solution made up to the mark and well mixed. 25 ml. of the solution are then withdrawn with a pipette, and titrated with the M.NaOH solution. The 100 ml. flask is then washed out repeatedly with distilled water, and used similarly for the contents of the flask **B**.

(2) The use of reflux condensers during the acetylation is not absolutely essential, since very little evaporation of the acetylating mixture from an open conical flask would occur during heating on the water-bath. The use of

the condensers is desirable however, both for training in sound analytical practice, and also to protect the contents of the flask from condensed steam, *etc.*

2. DETERMINATION OF THE NUMBER OF HYDROXYL GROUPS IN (ii) GLYCOL. $C_2H_4(OH)_2$. Molecular Weight, 62.

Carry out the determination precisely as for phenol, but add about 0·5 ml. (approximately 0·5 g.) of glycol to the flask **A**, and weigh as before by difference.

(iii) GLYCEROL. $C_3H_5(OH)_3$. Molecular Weight, 92.

Use approximately 0·5 ml. of glycerol, and cork the flask **A** securely when weighing the glycerol by difference, owing to the very hygroscopic nature of the latter. Heat on the water-bath for 60 minutes instead of 30 minutes. Excellent results are obtained by this method if a freshly opened sample of anhydrous glycerol is available: a sample which has been exposed to the air for even a short period will absorb sufficient water to give inaccurate results.

(iv) MANNITOL. $C_6H_8(OH)_6$. Molecular Weight, 182.

Take approximately 0·5 g. of the finely powdered mannitol, using either a weighing bottle, or else weighing directly in the flask **A** as before. Heat on the water-bath for 60 minutes. During the titration with the NaOH solution, a fine precipitation of the hexacetyl-mannitol may occur, but will not affect the titration. The results are excellent.

(v) GLUCOSE. $C_6H_7O(OH)_5$. Molecular Weight, 180.

Use approximately 0·5 g. of the finely powdered *anhydrous* glucose, heating for 60 minutes. Slightly low results (*e.g.*, 4·7–4·8 Hydroxyl groups) are usually obtained.

NOTE. (1) It is clear that the molecular weight of the alcohol or phenol must be known before the above determinations are carried out. The molecular weight if unknown must be determined by one of the methods given on pp. 428–345.

(2) The method can be used to determine the amount of a known alcohol or phenol present in a crude sample, provided that the impurities do not themselves contain hydroxyl groups.

Estimation of the Number of Amino Groups in Aniline. First Method.

This method is precisely similar to the previous method used for the estimation of the number of hydroxyl groups in a polyhydric alcohol. A known weight of aniline is heated with a mixture of acetic anhydride and pyridine until acetylation is complete; the excess of acetic anhydride remaining is

$$C_6H_5NH_2 + CH_3CO\cdot O\cdot COCH_3 = C_6H_5NHCOCH_3 + CH_3COOH$$

then hydrolysed with water and the total free acetic acid estimated by titration with standard NaOH solution, the result being compared with that obtained in a control or blank experiment.

If the molecular weight of the aniline is known, the number of amino groups can be calculated: alternatively, if the aniline is known to be a monacidic base, its molecular weight can be calculated. If the molecular weight and the acidity of the aniline are both known, then clearly the method can be used to estimate the amount of aniline in a given sample. The method is general for many primary and secondary amines, aniline being used solely as a typical member of the former class.

Proceed *precisely* as in the Determination of the Number of Hydroxyl Groups in Phenol, except that after weighing the flask **A**, run in about 1 ml. of pure aniline, and weigh again. Then continue exactly as before. The acetanilide which is formed usually remains in solution when the contents of the flask **A** are diluted with water for hydrolysis.

Example of Calculation.

Weight of aniline used	. . .	1·007 g.
Flask **A** requires	. . .	31·7 ml. M.NaOH solution
Flask **B** (Control) requires	.	42·6 ml. M.NaOH solution

Difference in M.NaOH solution required for **A** and **B** = 10·9 ml

To calculate number of amino groups, knowing Mol. Weight of aniline (93):

1000 ml. M.NaOH $\equiv$ 1 Gm. Mol. $CH_3COOH \equiv$ 1 NH_2 group

$\therefore$ 10·9 ml. M.NaOH are equivalent to 10·9/1000 NH_2 group

$\therefore$ 1·007 g. aniline contain   10·9/1000 ,, ,,

$\therefore$ 93 g. aniline contain $\dfrac{10\cdot9 \times 93}{1000 \times 1\cdot007}$ = 1·01 NH_2 group.

Alternatively, to calculate Molecular Weight of aniline, knowing latter to be a monacidic amine:

10·9 ml. M.NaOH are equivalent to 1·007 g. aniline

1000 ml. M.NaOH are equivalent to $\dfrac{1\cdot007 \times 1000}{10\cdot9}$ = 92·4 g. aniline.

Second Method.

Although the above method gives excellent results and is to be strongly recommended, its use in large classes entails the consumption of large quantities of the comparatively costly pyridine. This difficulty can be overcome by acetylating the aniline with a mixture of acetic anhydride and glacial acetic acid. For this purpose a mixture of 2 volumes of the anhydride and 1 volume of acetic acid is used: this mixture contains more acetic anhydride than that previously used for acetylations (p. 107) in order to ensure that quantitative acetylation occurs in a reasonably short time. If acetic anhydride alone is used high results are obtained, presumably owing to the formation of diacetyl-aniline.

Fit two similar 250 ml. conical flasks, **A** and **B**, with reflux water-condensers (using ground-glass joints or rubber stoppers) and connect the condensers in series as before over two water-baths. Prepare a mixture of 2 volumes of acetic anhydride and 1 volume of glacial acetic acid, and shake it thoroughly. Weigh the flask **A**, run in about 1·5 ml. of pure aniline, and weigh again. Now chill the flask **A** in ice-water, and then carefully run in 4 ml. of the acetylating mixture, using for this purpose either an accurate burette or (better) a small pipette: unless the aniline is thus kept chilled during the addition, the heat of the reaction may send up a fine spray of the acetylating mixture which will be largely lost. Run 4 ml. of the acetylating mixture also into the control flask **B**. Fit the flasks to the condensers and heat on the briskly boiling water-baths for 30 minutes, occasionally shaking the contents of the flasks gently around. Then pour about 50 ml. of hot water down each condenser. (In spite of the cooling action of the condenser, the water enters the flask **A** sufficiently hot to precipitate the acetanilide as an oil, which subsequently forms a suspension of fine crystals: if cold water is added, the acetanilide may separate as a hard crystalline lump, which will interfere with the subsequent titration.) Continue heating the flasks on the water-baths for a further 10 minutes to ensure complete hydrolysis of unchanged acetic anhydride. Then remove the water-baths, wash the condensers again with a small quantity of cold water, detach the flasks and wash the base of the corks also with water, allowing all washings to fall into their respective flasks.

Cool the flasks in cold water, and then titrate the contents of each with M.NaOH solution, using phenolphthalein as an indicator. Shake the contents of the flask **A** repeatedly during the titration in order to keep the fine crystals of acetanilide dispersed in the aqueous solution.

The acetylations may alternatively be performed in 100 ml. conical flasks, and the contents after dilution and hydrolysis with water can then be carefully washed into 250 ml. beakers for the titration with alkali. The calculation is precisely similar to that of the first method. Excellent results are obtained.

Estimation of Aniline Hydrochloride.

Aniline hydrochloride, being a salt formed from a very weak base and a strong acid, undergoes considerable hydrolysis in aqueous solution to aniline

$$C_6H_5NH_2,HCl \rightleftharpoons C_6H_5NH_2 + HCl$$

and hydrochloric acid. The latter can be titrated with standard alkali solution, in which case the progressive neutralisation of the free hydrochloric acid causes the hydrolysis of the aniline hydrochloride to be ultimately complete. If phenolphthalein is used as an indicator, the end-point is unaffected by the free aniline present.

The method can therefore be used to estimate the percentage of aniline hydrochloride in a crude sample, provided the impurities are not themselves salts of other similar amines. Alternatively, if aniline is known to be a monacidic base (forming therefore a mono-hydrochloride) the molecular weight of aniline can be determined, since the molecular weight of the aniline hydrochloride is clearly that weight which is neutralised by 1000 ml. of M.NaOH solution.

Weigh out accurately about 3 g. of the finely powdered aniline hydrochloride on a watch-glass. Place a small funnel (having preferably only a very short stem) in the neck of a 100 ml. graduated flask, and transfer the hydrochloride through the funnel into the flask, pushing the powder if necessary gently down the stem of the funnel with a fine glass rod. Rinse the watch-glass, rod and funnel with distilled water, dissolve the hydrochloride completely, make the solution up to the mark and mix well. Withdraw 20 ml. of the solution with a pipette, and titrate with $M/5$ NaOH solution, the latter having been prepared by diluting M.NaOH solution with CO_2-free water (see footnote, p. 448). Repeat the titration with a further 20 ml. of the solution to ensure consistent results.

Estimation of the Number of Acetyl Groups in an Acetyl Ester.

Method. This method is essentially the reverse of the estimation of the number of hydroxyl groups in a polyhydric alcohol by quantitative acetylation (p. 450). A known weight of the acetyl compound is hydrolysed by boiling with a known volume of M.NaOH solution, this volume being in excess of that required for complete hydrolysis. The excess of NaOH is then estimated

$$R(O \cdot COCH_3)_n + nNaOH = R(OH)_n + nCH_3COONa$$

by titration with M.HCl or $M/2H_2SO_4$ solution, and the volume of M.NaOH solution used actually to hydrolyse the acetyl compound thus determined. If the molecular weight of the acetyl compound is known, the number of acetyl groups in the molecule can then be calculated.

1. DETERMINATION OF NUMBER OF ACETYL GROUPS IN TRIACETIN (TRIACETYL-GLYCEROL) $C_3H_5(O \cdot COCH_3)_3$. Molecular Weight, 218.

Fit two 200 ml. conical flasks, **A** and **B**, with reflux water-condensers, again using ground-glass joints or rubber corks. Weigh the flask **A**, add about 1 ml. of triacetin, and weigh again. (Alternatively, in large classes it is sufficiently accurate to run in 1·0 ml. of triacetin, *i.e.*, 1·15 g., from a burette.) Then by means of a pipette add 25 ml. of M.NaOH solution to each flask (the flask **B** acting as a control), and finally add a few *minute* fragments* of unglazed porcelain to each flask to ensure steady boiling subsequently. Boil each solution under reflux *very gently* for 30 minutes, heating the solutions over a gauze with a small flame for this purpose. Then stop the heating, pour about 10 ml. of distilled water down each condenser to wash any solution back into the flasks, and then remove the latter and cool in cold water. Titrate the contents of each flask with M.HCl solution, using phenolphthalein as an indicator.

* Larger fragments of porcelain would absorb appreciable quantities of the sodium hydroxide, which would be only slowly extracted by the acid during the subsequent titration; hence finely divided carborundum may well be used (p. 8).

Example of Calculation.

Weight of triacetin taken = 1·150 g.

Flask **A** requires . . . . 9·15 ml. M.HCl solution

Flask **B** (Control) requires . . . 24·85 ml. M.HCl solution

Difference in volume of M.HCl required = 15·70 ml.

1000 ml. M.HCl ≡ 1000 ml. M.NaOH ≡ 1 G. Mol. NaOH ≡ 1 Acetyl group

∴ 15·7 ml. N.HCl ≡ 15·70 ml. M.NaOH ≡ 15·70/1000 G. Mol. NaOH

≡ 15·70/1000 Acetyl groups

Thus 1·150 g. triacetin contain 15·70/1000 Acetyl groups,

218 g. (1 G. Mol.) triacetin contain $\dfrac{15 \cdot 70}{1000} \times \dfrac{218}{1 \cdot 150}$ Acetyl groups

= 2·97 Acetyl groups.

2. DETERMINATION OF THE NUMBER OF ACETYL GROUPS IN:

(ii) HEXACETYLMANNITOL. $C_6H_8(O \cdot COCH_3)_6$. Molecular Weight, 434.

Continue precisely as for triacetin, but since hexacetyl-mannitol (p. 142) is a crystalline compound, weigh out 1·0–1·2 g. of the finely powdered substance, either from a weighing-bottle, or by direct weighing in the flask **A**. The results are excellent.

(iii) PENTACETYLGLUCOSE. $C_6H_7O(O \cdot COCH_3)_5$. Molecular Weight, 390.

A modification of the above method is required for acetylated sugars, because on alkaline hydrolysis the liberated sugar, *e.g.*, glucose, under-goes slight resinification by the alkali present, giving a brown solution, in which the end-point of the titration is difficult to detect accurately. If however $M/2.H_2SO_4$ solution is used instead of M.NaOH solution, hydrolysis occurs rapidly, and the acidic solution remains colourless, giving therefore an excellent end-point when the mixture of acetic acid and unchanged sulphuric acid is back-titrated with M.NaOH solution, using phenolphthalein as an indicator.

Weigh out approximately 1·5 g. of powdered pentacetylglucose (p. 141) in the flask **A**, and then add 25 ml. of M/H_2SO_4 solution to each of the flasks **A** and **B**, together with a fragment of porcelain. Boil under reflux gently for 30 minutes, then wash each condenser down as before with 10 ml. of distilled water, cool, and titrate the solutions with M.NaOH solution.

Example of Calculation.

Weight of pentacetylglucose taken = 1·500 g.

Flask **A** requires . . . . 44·3 ml. M.NaOH solution

Flask **B** (Control) requires . . 25·1 ml. M.NaOH solution

Difference in volume of M.NaOH required = 19·2 ml.

1000 ml. M.NaOH solution = 1 Acetyl group

19·2 ml. M.NaOH solution = 19·2/1000 Acetyl group

1·500 g. pentacetylglucose contain 19·2/1000 Acetyl group

$\therefore$ 390 g. (1 G. Mol.) pentacetylglucose contain $\dfrac{19\cdot2}{1000} \times \dfrac{390}{1\cdot500}$ Acetyl group

$$= 4\cdot99 \text{ Acetyl groups}$$

NOTE. (1) The above method (pp. 455–457) is sometimes used in preference to that given on p. 450 in order to determine the number of hydroxyl groups in an unidentified polyhydric alcohol. The alcohol is acetylated by any of the standard methods, a marked excess of the acetylating reagent being used to ensure complete acetylation of all hydroxyl groups present. The polyacetyl compound is then purified and its molecular weight determined: the number of acetyl groups present (and therefore the number of hydroxyl groups in the original alcohol) is then estimated by the above method. The advantage of this longer method is chiefly that the estimation of the number of acetyl groups by quantitative hydrolysis is more accurate (particularly for a substance of unknown constitution) than that of the number of hydroxyl groups by quantitative acetylation.

(2) The same method can clearly be applied to the quantitative saponification or hydrolysis of most esters. Hence it may equally well be used for the quantitative estimation of a known ester in a crude sample.

Estimation of Formaldehyde.

Method. Formaldehyde may be estimated in solution by oxidising it to formic acid by means of a known quantity (in excess) of iodine dissolved in an excess of NaOH solution. The oxidation is, in effect, carried out by the sodium hypo-iodite formed by the action of the iodine on the alkali, the formic acid being then neutralised by the alkali present:

$$I_2 + 2NaOH = NaI + NaIO + H_2O$$
$$HCHO + NaIO = HCOOH + NaI$$

When the oxidation is complete, the excess of hypo-iodite is estimated by acidifying the solution, and then titrating the iodine thus formed against

$$NaIO + NaI + 2HCl = 2NaCl + H_2O + I_2$$

standard sodium thiosulphate solution. It will be seen that each molecule of iodine used in the original oxidation corresponds to one molecule of formaldehyde.

Formalin Solution. The method has frequently to be applied to the estimation of formaldehyde in commercial formalin solution. The latter must, however, first be diluted until it contains about 0·2% of formaldehyde, before the above method is applied. Therefore first weigh accurately a corked conical flask of about 75–100 ml. capacity. Then run in about 2·5 ml. of the formalin using preferably a dropping-tube or a pipette for this purpose, to ensure that the neck of the flask is kept free from the solution. Re-weigh the corked flask. Now add about 50 ml. of water to the formalin in the flask, and then pour the mixed solution carefully through a small funnel into a 500 ml. graduated flask. Rinse out the conical flask and then the funnel thoroughly with water, make the solution in the graduated flask up to the mark and mix well.

Transfer 25 ml. of this dilute solution by means of a pipette to a conical flask, and add similarly 50 ml. of $M/10$ iodine solution. Now add 10% sodium hydroxide solution until the liquid becomes pale yellow in colour, and allow the solution to stand, with occasional shaking, at room temperature for at least 10 minutes. Then acidify with dilute hydrochloric acid (free from chlorine) in order to liberate the remaining iodine. Titrate the latter with $M/10$ sodium thiosulphate solution, using starch as an indicator in the usual way.

From the above equations, it will be seen that 1 ml. of the $M/10$ iodine solution used in the oxidation is equivalent to 0·00150 g. of formaldehyde.

Example of Calculation.

Weight of formalin solution used . . . 2·520 g.

Diluted to 500 ml.

50 ml. of $M/10$ I_2 solution added to 25 ml. of this dilute formalin solution. After oxidation in the presence of sodium hydroxide, and subsequent acidification, the excess of iodine liberated required 17·3 ml. $M/10$ $Na_2S_2O_3$ solution.

$$17\text{·}3 \text{ ml. } N/10 \text{ } Na_2S_2O_3 \equiv 17\text{·}3 \text{ ml. } M/10 \text{ } I_2 \text{ solution}$$

Therefore the iodine used to oxidise the formaldehyde

$$= 50 - 17\text{·}3 = 32\text{·}7 \text{ ml. } M/10 \text{ } I_2 \text{ solution}$$
$$\equiv 32\text{·}7 \times 0\text{·}00150 \text{ g. HCHO}$$

25 ml. of the dilute formalin contain $32\text{·}7 \times 0\text{·}00150$ g. HCHO

∴ 500 ml. of the dilute formalin contain $32\text{·}7 \times 0\text{·}00150 \times 20$ g. HCHO

i.e., 2·520 g. of the original formalin contain $32\text{·}7 \times 0\text{·}00150 \times 20$ g. HCHO

∴ 100 g. of the orig. formalin contain $\dfrac{32\text{·}7 \times 0\text{·}00150 \times 20 \times 100}{2\text{·}520}$ g. HCHO

$$= \underline{38\text{·}9\%} \text{ HCHO.}$$

NOTE. The above method can be successfully applied only to dilute solutions of formaldehyde which are free in particular from other aliphatic aldehydes, since the latter, if present, would undergo a similar oxidation. Formaldehyde, if mixed with other aldehydes, should be estimated by quantitative addition of potassium cyanide: for details, see advanced text-books of quantitative organic analysis.

Estimation of Urea (Hypobromite Method).

Method. There are two standard methods for the estimation of urea, (i) the hypobromite method, (ii) the urease method (p. 519). The chief merit of the hypobromite method is the rapidity of the analysis: the results obtained are considered sufficiently accurate for most medical requirements, *e.g.*, for the estimation of urea in urine. For accurate metabolic work, however, the urease method should be employed.

Urea is decomposed by alkaline sodium hypobromite solution according to the equation:

$$CO(NH_2)_2 + 3NaBrO + 2NaOH = 3NaBr + N_2 + Na_2CO_3 + 3H_2O$$

Thus 1 gram-molecule of urea (60 g.) should give 22·4 litres of nitrogen at S.T.P., or 1 g. of urea should give 373 ml. of nitrogen. Actually however urea in solution always gives a small amount of ammonium cyanate with which it is in equilibrium, and consequently the full amount of nitrogen (in accordance with the above equation) is not evolved: it is found that 1 g. of urea gives actually 357 ml. of nitrogen at S.T.P. (*i.e.*, 95·7% of the theoretical), and all calculations should therefore be based on this value.

A convenient form of apparatus, particularly for large classes, is shown in Fig. 84; it is identical with that used for the determination of the equivalent weight of metals by hydrogen evolution. **A** and **H** are

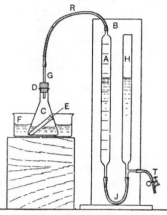

FIG. 84.

glass tubes connected together by the rubber tubing **J** and securely fastened to the board **B**. The tube **A** is graduated from the top downwards. The tube **H** carries near its base a short outlet tube, to which is connected a piece of rubber tubing closed by the clip **T**. A gas-tight rubber tube **R** joins **A** to a short length of glass tubing **G**, which can be fitted securely by the rubber stopper **D** to the 250 ml. conical flask **C**. **F** is a bath containing water at the temperature of the laboratory. Care must be taken to ensure that all connections are gas-tight.

The estimation may be made to determine the amount of urea in a crude sample, or the amount of urea in a sample of urine. Place about 30 ml. of freshly prepared sodium hypobromite solution (p. 525) in the flask **C**. Now weigh out accurately about 0·15 g. of urea into a small test-tube **E**, and then place the latter as shown in the flask **C**. (Alternatively, if the estimation is being carried out on urine, which usually contains about 2% of urea, measure out exactly 5 ml. of the sample into the tube **E**.) In each case, take great care not to spill any of the contents of **E** into the hypobromite solution. Now fit the stopper **D** securely into **C** and immerse the latter in the water-bath **F**. When thermal equilibrium is attained, run water from **T** or add it through the open end of **H** until the level of the water is the same in both limbs of the U-tube. Note the volume in **A**, reading the bottom of the meniscus. Now tilt **C** so that the urea and hypobromite are thoroughly mixed: a copious evolution of nitrogen follows. Allow water to run from **T** so that approximately the same level is maintained in the tubes **A** and **H**. After the evolution of nitrogen has ceased, allow **C** to cool to the temperature of the bath by moving the flask about in the water. Next bring the water to the same level in each limb **A** and **H** as before. Again note the reading in **A**, and so determine the volume of gas evolved. Note the temperature of the water in **F** and the barometric pressure.

A Hempel gas-burette (Fig. 76, p. 426) may be used in place of the tubes **A** and **H**: for this purpose it is manipulated precisely as described on p. 427.

Example of Calculation.

Weight of urea taken	0·144 g.
Volume of nitrogen obtained	53·2 ml.

Barometric pressure, 757 mm. Temperature, 18°C.

Vapour pressure of water at 18°C., 15·4 mm. (Table II, p. 534).

53·2 ml. of nitrogen reduced to S.T.P. become

$$\frac{53\cdot2 \times 273 \times (757 - 15\cdot4)}{291 \times 760} = 48\cdot7 \text{ ml.}$$

357 ml. of nitrogen are given by 1 g. of pure urea.

∴ 48·7 ml. of nitrogen are given by 48·7/357 g. of pure urea

i.e., 0·144 g. of urea contains . 48·7/357 g. of pure urea

∴ 100 g. of urea contain . $\frac{48\cdot7 \times 100}{357 \times 0\cdot144}$ g. of pure urea

≈ 94·7% urea.

Estimation of Sugars.

Three methods are in use for the estimation of sugars:

(i) Chemical, depending upon the reducing properties of certain sugars.

(ii) Polarimetric, depending upon the optical activity of the sugars concerned.

(iii) Fermentation methods.

The third method is of limited application and is used only in special cases. The second is the most accurate and rapid method, and is of considerable technical importance. The chemical method (described below), although less accurate than the polarimetric method, is of great value for the estimation of sugars in biological fluids. In fact, for such purposes, it is often to be preferred to the polarimetric method owing to the probable presence of other substances having high optical rotations.

Several variations of the chemical method are in use. In the one described below, a freshly prepared Fehling's solution is standardised by titrating it directly against a standard solution of pure anhydrous glucose: when the end-point is reached, *i.e.*, when the cupric salt in the Fehling's solution is completely reduced to cuprous oxide, the supernatant solution becomes completely decolorised. Some difficulty is often experienced at first in determining the end-point of the reaction, but with practice accurate results can be obtained. The titrations should be performed in daylight whenever possible, unless a special indicator is used (see under Methylene-blue, p. 463).

The standardised Fehling's solution can then be used to determine, for example, the percentage amount of glucose in a crude sample. The method clearly can be applied only to reducing sugars: hence those disaccharides and polysaccharides which are non-reducing must first be hydrolysed to mono-saccharides, and the estimation carried out on the hydrolysed product. It should be noted that solutions containing about 0·5% of reducing sugar give the most consistent and accurate results, and all sugar solutions should there-fore be made up to approximately this concentration.

PREPARATION AND STANDARDISATION OF FEHLING'S SOLUTION.

Solution A. Dissolve 17·320 g. of powdered crystalline copper sulphate, $CuSO_4,5H_2O$, in water and make the solution up to 250 ml. in a graduated flask.

Solution B. Dissolve 86·5 g. of crystalline sodium potassium tartrate ("Rochelle salt," $C_4H_4O_6NaK,4H_2O$) in warm water. Dissolve 30 g. of pure sodium hydroxide in water. Mix the tartrate and hydroxide solutions, cool and make up to 250 ml. in a graduated flask.

When the Fehling's solution is required, transfer equal volumes of solutions A and B (at room temperature) to a dry flask, and mix thoroughly by shaking. Since however Fehling's solution deteriorates slowly on keeping, only sufficient of the solutions A and B should be mixed together to meet immediate requirements.

To standardise this solution, weigh out accurately about 1·25 g. of pure anhydrous glucose ("Analar"), dissolve in water and make up the solution to 250 ml. in a graduated flask. By means of a pipette, place 25 ml. of the freshly prepared Fehling's solution in a porcelain evapora-ting-basin, dilute with an equal volume of distilled water and boil *very gently* over a gauze. Now run the standard glucose solution from a burette, 1 ml. at a time, into the boiling Fehling's solution until the blue colour has entirely disappeared. Do this by allowing the solution to cool at intervals and so permitting the precipitate of cuprous oxide to settle: then tip the basin on one side and look through the supernatant liquid on to the white background of the basin. Bring the solution to the boil again during each addition of the sugar solution. Having thus determined approximately how much sugar solution is required, carry out more accurate titrations, running the glucose solution steadily into the boiling Fehling's solution until the end-point is approached, and then continuing by adding 0·1 ml. of the glucose solution at a time.

Repeat the titrations until consistent values (*i.e.*, values which do not differ by more than 0·1 ml. of glucose solution) are obtained. Then calculate the weight of glucose equivalent to 1 ml. of the Fehling's solution.

It is usually found that 1 ml. of the above Fehling's solution ≡ 0·0050 g. of glucose.

The weights of other monosaccharides and reducing disaccharides which will reduce 1 ml. of this standard Fehling's solution are: galactose, 0·00511 g.; fructose, 0·00514 g.; mannose, 0·00431 g.; lactose, 0·00678 g.; maltose, 0·00807 g.

ESTIMATION OF GLUCOSE IN A GIVEN SAMPLE.

This is clearly the reverse of the standardisation of the Fehling's solution described above.

Weigh out accurately about 1·25 g. of the sample, dissolve it in water and make the solution up to 250 ml. Titrate this solution against 25 ml. of the standard Fehling's solution, precisely as before.

Example of Calculation.

Weight of sample taken, 1·250 g. Dissolved in 250 ml. of water.

25 ml. of Fehling's solution required 26·7 ml. of glucose solution.

But 1 ml. of Fehling's solution $\equiv$ 0·005 g. of pure glucose.

i.e., 26·7 ml. of glucose solution contain 25 $\times$ 0·005 g. of pure glucose.

$\therefore$ 250 ml. of glucose solution contain $\dfrac{25 \times 0\cdot005 \times 250}{26\cdot7}$ g. pure glucose

$\therefore$ Sample contains $\dfrac{25 \times 0\cdot005 \times 250 \times 100}{26\cdot7 \times 1\cdot250}$ % of pure glucose

$= \underline{93\cdot7\%}$ glucose.

ESTIMATION OF CANE SUGAR (SUCROSE).

This is done by estimating the reducing power of the sugar after hydrolysis (or "inversion") by acid, the glucose and fructose thus formed having very nearly the same reducing power.

The calculation is based on the equation:

$$C_{12}H_{22}O_{11} + H_2O = 2C_6H_{12}O_6$$

$\therefore$ 342 g. of cane sugar $\equiv$ 360 g. of invert sugar

$\therefore$ 0·00475 g. of cane sugar $\equiv$ 0·005 g. of invert sugar

$\equiv$ 1 ml. of the Fehling's solution

Weigh out accurately about 1·3 g. of the sample of cane sugar, dissolve it in about 15 ml. of distilled water in a boiling-tube, add 5 ml. of M.HCl and stand the tube in a briskly boiling water-bath for 10 minutes. Cool, add 5 ml. of M.NaOH solution, and transfer to a 250 ml. graduated flask. Rinse out the boiling-tube thoroughly with water, transfer the washings to the graduated flask and make the solution up to the mark. Place 25 ml. of the standardised Fehling's solution in a porcelain basin, bring to the boil and add the "invert" sugar from a burette until the Fehling's solution is decolorised, observing all the precautions described above. Repeat the titrations until consistent results are obtained.

Example of Calculation.

Weight of sample = 1·310 g. Dissolved in 250 ml. of water.

25 ml. of Fehling's solution required 23·4 ml. of invert sugar solution.

But 1 ml. of Fehling's solution $\equiv$ 0·005 g of invert sugar.

$\equiv$ 0·00475 g. of cane sugar.

i.e., 23·4 ml. of the sugar solution contain 25 $\times$ 0·00475 g. of cane sugar.

. 250 ml. of the sugar solution contain $\dfrac{25 \times 0\cdot00475 \times 250}{23\cdot4}$ g. of the cane sugar

∴ Sample contains $\dfrac{25 \times 0\cdot00475 \times 250 \times 100}{23\cdot4 \times 1\cdot310}$ % cane sugar

$= 96\cdot8\%$ cane sugar.

NOTE. The use of methylene-blue has been recommended to mark more accurately the complete reduction of Fehling's solution by a reducing sugar. This indicator is prepared by dissolving 1 g. of powdered methylene-blue in water and diluting to 500 ml. It is used as an internal indicator, a few drops of the methylene-blue solution being added to the Fehling's solution just before reduction is complete. The end-point is indicated by the disappearance of the methylene-blue colour, the dye being reduced to a colourless substance immediately an excess of sugar is present. The use of this indicator enables a sharper end-point to be obtained, and its use is specially recommended if the titrations have to be carried out by artificial light.

Estimation of Amino-acids, e.g., Glycine.

Method. An amino-acid such as glycine, NH_2CH_2COOH, cannot be estimated by direct titration with standard alkali solution, owing to the opposing effects of the basic and the acidic groups. If, however, the amino-acid is first

$$HCHO + H_2NCH_2COOH \rightarrow CH_2:NCH_2COOH + H_2O$$

treated with neutral formaldehyde solution, it can be titrated directly with standard sodium hydroxide solution.

Glycine is present in aqueous solution as the "zwitterion" $\overset{+}{N}H_3CH_2CO\overset{-}{O}$ which is incapable of reacting with formaldehyde. When, however, sodium hydroxide solution is added, the glycine is converted into $NH_2CH_2CO\overset{-}{O}$ which condenses with formaldehyde to give a stable cation. The overall changes may be represented by the following equations, although the precise reactions are probably more complicated:

$$\overset{+}{N}H_3CH_2CO\overset{-}{O} + O\overset{-}{H} \rightleftharpoons NH_2CH_2CO\overset{-}{O} + H_2O$$

$$CH_2O + H_2NCH_2CO\overset{-}{O} \longrightarrow CH_2:NCH_2CO\overset{-}{O} + H_2O$$

Since formaldehyde solutions almost invariably contain formic acid, and amino-acids themselves are seldom exactly neutral,* it is very important that both the formaldehyde solution and the glycine solution should before mixing be brought to the same pH (see footnote, p. 509), and for this purpose each solution is first made *just* alkaline to phenolphthalein by means of dilute sodium hydroxide solution. This preliminary neutralisation must not be confused with

---

* Glycine itself is almost neutral, and requires very little sodium hydroxide to give a pink colour with phenolphthalein; some other amino-acids, *e.g.*, glutamic acid, aspartic acid, *etc.*, are definitely more acidic and consequently require more alkali for this purpose (*cf.* footnote, p. 380).

the subsequent *titration* with standard sodium hydroxide, using phenolphthalein as an indicator.

Place about 50 ml. of 40% "formalin solution" in a conical flask and add *at least* 10 drops of phenolphthalein solution. Now add very carefully from a burette dilute sodium hydroxide solution ($M/10$ will serve the purpose) until the solution is *just* faintly pink. Weigh out accurately about 2 g. of glycine, transfer to a 250 ml. graduated flask, dissolve in distilled water, make up to the mark, and mix well. Transfer 25 ml. of the solution to a conical flask, add 2 drops of phenolphthalein, and then again add dilute sodium hydroxide very carefully until the solution is *just* faintly pink. Now add about 10 ml. (*i.e.*, an excess) of the neutralised formaldehyde solution: the pink colour of the phenolphthalein disappears immediately and the solution becomes markedly acid. Titrate with $M/10$ sodium hydroxide solution until the pink colour is just restored. Repeat the process with at least two further quantities of 25 ml. of the glycine solution in order to obtain consistent readings.

The calculation depends simply on the fact that 1000 ml. M.NaOH $\equiv$ 1 g. mol. of glycine. The method can clearly be used either to determine the molecular weight of an amino-acid of known basicity, or to estimate an amino-acid of known molecular weight.

Example of Calculation. Glycine, Molecular Weight, 75.

Weight of glycine taken = 2·029 g. Glycine solution made up to 250 ml.
25 ml. require 26·5 ml. $M/10$ NaOH solution.

∴ 250 ml. glycine solution require 26·5 ml. M.NaOH solution.

But 1000 ml. M.NaOH = 75 g. glycine.

$$\therefore 26 \cdot 5 \text{ ml. } M.\text{NaOH} = \frac{75 \times 26 \cdot 5}{1000} \text{ g. glycine.}$$

$$\therefore \text{ Sample used contains } \frac{75 \times 26 \cdot 5 \times 100}{1000 \times 2 \cdot 029} \% \text{ glycine}$$

$$= 98 \cdot 0\% \text{ glycine.}$$

The above method, due to Sørensen, is of great importance in following the course of hydrolysis of proteins by enzymes (p. 516). For example, if the protein and its hydrolysis are represented thus:

$$H_2N \cdot CHR_1CO\text{--}NH \cdot CHR_2CO\text{--}NH \cdot CHR_3COOH$$
$$\downarrow 2H_2O$$
$$H_2N \cdot CHR_1COOH + H_2N \cdot CHR_2COOH + H_2N \cdot CHR_3COOH$$

it will be clear that if the above estimation is carried out on the original protein and on the hydrolysis product, then the latter will require three times as much sodium hydroxide for neutralisation as the former.

SECTION B
SEMI-MICROANALYSIS
The Balance* and Weighing.

Precautions. Undoubtedly the most important factor in carrying out semi-micro determinations effectively is to have a balance that is sufficiently accurate. For such determinations it is necessary to weigh to not less than the nearest o·1 mg. An ordinary analytical balance of good quality can often be adjusted to such a sensitivity but it is necessary to keep the case and pans scrupulously clean, to shield the balance from draughts, vibration and direct sunlight and to operate the balance with considerable care. A true semi-micro balance is certainly less likely to give trouble but is not essential; a prismatic recording ring-rider balance is almost ideal for the purpose, particularly for rapidity of weighing, but it is expensive.

Provided that the balance is functioning correctly, the main source of error is in the weights themselves; these should be calibrated by one of the standard methods so that their relative values are known, and they should be carefully cleaned with tissue paper and checked from time to time. To make the best use of the balance, weighing should be carried out by the method of swings, but for this purpose it is necessary first to determine the sensitivity of the balance.

The sensitivity of the balance. The sensitivity of the balance may conveniently be defined as the deflection of the balance pointer over the scale caused by an excess of 1 mg. on one of the pans. This factor differs according to the actual load on the pans, and it is usual to plot the sensitivity at a series of loads over the range within which the balance is to be used; the sensitivity at any particular load may then be determined at once by reference to the curve.

Assume for purposes of illustration that the whole balance beam corresponds to 10 mg. and is graduated over its whole length in 10 divisions; on such a beam a 5 mg. rider is used. It is very important that the rider should sit exactly upright on any notch-mark on the beam and it should, if necessary, be bent to ensure this position. The balance pointer-scale is commonly graduated in 10 divisions on each side of the centre, and it is conventional mentally to divide each of these main divisions into 10 parts; deflections to the left are written −, those to the right +. Thus a deflection of 5 whole divisions to the left is written as −50, and one of nearer 4 than 3 whole divisions to the right may, perhaps, be estimated as +37. It is important that the swings of the balance should not be too large and a deflection of 50 is probably sufficient for most purposes.

It is necessary first to determine the rest-point of the balance. This may be done by setting the balance swinging (it is essential that the balance case should be closed when the balance is swinging and when the rider is being used), with the rider on the zero mark on the beam, ignoring the first three swings, then taking the average deflection of two swings to the left and adding it (*i.e.*,

* The type of balance referred to above has now been superseded by far more accurate and more rapid balances which do not require the method of weighing described (p. 466). This book may, however, be used in laboratories which do not possess these balances, or use 'single-pan' balances.

algebraically, the signs being taken into account) to the deflection of the intermediate swing to the right; the result is the rest-point of the balance. Thus if the swings are − 47, +40, − 45, the rest-point is 0·6 of a large division on the left of the zero mark on the pointer-scale (*i.e.*, − 6). The rest-point of the balance need not be exactly at the zero mark on the pointer-scale but it should not be more than one large scale division off. If necessary, adjustment should be made with the screws at the ends of the balance beam.

For determining the sensitivity of the balance, the rider is now moved to the 1 mg. notch on the beam (*i.e.*, the first large beam division), the balance pans being without load. The balance is set swinging and the rest-point again determined, as described above; it will now, of course, have moved further to the left. If it is now − 48 (*i.e.*, − 4·8 large divisions), then the sensitivity is − 48 − (− 6) = − 42 units of deflection per mg. when the balance is unloaded. A sensitivity in the neighbourhood of 50 units per mg. is convenient, and if the observed value is widely different from this it may be adjusted by raising or lowering the "gravity" screw on the balance, the sensitivity being increased by raising the screw or nut. The sensitivity should be checked after each adjustment (the rest-point with the rider at zero and on the 1 mg. notch being determined each time), until a satisfactory value is obtained. The determination is then repeated with 1 g., 2 g., 5 g., 10 g., and 20 g. weights on each pan and the sensitivity plotted against load.

Weighing by swings. Before any series of weighings the rest-point should be determined (the rider being on the zero notch on the beam); the object to be weighed is then placed on the left-hand pan of the balance and the weights on the right. It is important that the weights should be placed as centrally as possible on the pan. Weights are added in the usual way until their sum is seen to be within 10 mg. of the weight of the object; the rider is then used in the normal way until the milligram division nearest to the point of balance is found (this may be the division above or below the point of balance, depending on which is nearest). The beam is then allowed to swing and after neglecting the first three swings, the deflection of two swings to the left is noted (and their average taken), and of the intermediate swing to the right, and their algebraic sum determined. The difference between this and the original rest-point gives the mean deflection; looking up the sensitivity at this load from the graph, this may be translated into a weight in mg., thus, in conjunction with the weights on the pan and the rider reading, giving the weight of the object. It is very important to check the sum of the weights whilst on the balance pan and again as they are put away into their box.

Example. Suppose for illustration that the weights on the pan amount to 18·54 g. and that the rider is balanced on the 7 mg. graduation on the beam and that the observed rest-point is +17 units, the original rest-point of the balance, before weighing was started, being +4 units. Then the mean deflection is +13 units and if the sensitivity of the balance at a load of *ca.* 18 g. (read off from the load/sensitivity curve) is 39 units per mg., then this deflection corresponds to a weight of $\frac{13}{39}$ = 0·3(3) mg. Thus the total weight of the object is 18·54 g. (weights on pan) + 0·007 g. (rider on beam scale) + 0·0003(3) g. (calculated from swings) = 18·54733 g. If the rider reading had been on the notch above the weight of the object, and a similar-sized deflection to the left (the original rest position of the balance still being $+ 4$ units) had been obtained, then the mean deflection would have been $- 21$ units, corresponding to a weight of $-\frac{22}{39} = - 0\cdot5(6)$ mg., and this would have to be *subtracted* from the weight indicated on the pan and rider. Thus the weight of the object would be $18\cdot54$ g. $+ 0\cdot007$ g. $- 0\cdot0005(6)$ g. $= 18\cdot5464(4)$ g.

Conclusion. It is unnecessary to correct the weight of the object for the original rest-point of the balance where only weighings by difference are being carried out, unless there has been an actual change in the rest-point over the period during which the weighings have been made; this is very unlikely to happen if the balance is properly situated and functioning correctly. Any necessary correction, derived from the calibration of the weights, should, however, be applied where, as usually happens, the weights on the pan are not identical at the initial and final weighings, when weighing by difference. It should finally be emphasised that the secret of accurate weighing is care and patience; weighing cannot be rushed!

Estimation of Carbon and Hydrogen.

Principle. A definite amount of substance (*ca.* 25 mg.) is weighed into a small boat, placed in a combustion tube and heated in a stream of oxygen with a bunsen flame; the resulting products of incomplete combustion are passed through a part of the tube packed with an oxidising filling heated in a furnace. The resulting products of complete combustion, water and carbon dioxide, are absorbed in weighed tubes containing anhydrous magnesium perchlorate and soda-lime respectively, and these are weighed again after absorption is complete, thus giving the weight of water and carbon dioxide produced, and hence the percentages of carbon and hydrogen in the original compound.

It will be apparent that this method depends for its success on the fact that all organic compounds, if oxidised under sufficiently vigorous conditions, may be converted quantitatively to water and carbon dioxide.

Apparatus.

The oxygen used in the combustion is supplied by a small cylinder (120 Atm.) fitted with a pressure reduction valve, pressure gauge (to avoid the risk of the cylinder becoming exhausted during an actual determination) and fine control knob. It is important that the valve is kept free from oil or grease of any kind. In order to ensure the complete purity of the oxygen it is first passed through a purification train.

The purification train. The oxygen is led from the cylinder through ordinary flexible rubber condenser tubing to the constant level device **A** (Fig. 85). This consists of two concentric tubes (approximately 2 cm. and 0·5 cm. respectively, in diameter; the inner tube being narrowed and curved at the bottom as shown) immersed in 50% aqueous potassium hydroxide contained in the outer vessel (diameter 3·5 cm.). Then by adjusting the liquid level in **A** the pressure of oxygen may be kept constant, and at a maximum of about

8 cm. of water. The constant pressure stream of oxygen is delivered to the apparatus through the side-arm **B**, and any excess from the cylinder escapes around the outside of the outer tube and through the hole **C**. When the apparatus is in use there should be a small but regular excess of bubbles escaping through the liquid and out at **C**. The potash in **A** serves to remove any traces of carbon dioxide that may remain in the oxygen.

The side-arm **B** is connected by a length of narrow-bore pressure tubing to a small open-ended manometer **D**. This rubber tubing, and all the rest employed up to the point **V**, have previously been impregnated with paraffin wax by immersing the lengths of tubing in paraffin wax boiling under reduced pressure. By these means the wax is driven into the pores of the tubing, which is rendered quite impermeable to the passage of gas through its walls. The orifice of the tube is usually found to be blocked with wax, and after removal of the obvious blockage, the tubing should be thoroughly cleared by the use of a narrow glass rod, followed by pipe cleaners; otherwise when the rubber is used to connect glass tubes, these will scrape slivers of wax from the tube-pores and will become blocked. All joints in the apparatus, except that between **B** and **D**, are made so that the two glass portions are touching inside the rubber tube and the latter acting only as a sleeve to hold them together—this avoids any possibility of minute particles of wax being carried over into the combustion tube.

The manometer **D** contains a small quantity of dilute sodium hydroxide solution coloured with phenolphthalein and is backed by a scale graduated in cm. The length of impregnated pressure-tubing joining **B** and **D** passes through a rigidly mounted pinch-cock **E** fitted with a fine adjustment screw. This is used to reduce the oxygen pressure slightly so that about 6 cm. head is indicated on **D**.

The manometer **D** is connected with impregnated pressure-tubing, and by a glass-to-glass joint, with the side-arm **F** of a U-tube (each limb being about 1 cm. in diameter and 12 cm. long). Before filling, the U-tube should be washed with distilled water, alcohol, then ether and finally dried in an oven. The first limb of the U-tube contains soda-lime (B.D.H. Micro-analytical reagent grade Carbasorb is very convenient) whose purpose is to remove any carbon dioxide from the oxygen stream. A drawback of the soda-lime is that it readily takes up water vapour (a little comes from the pressure gauge) becoming first sticky and then forming a hard impermeable crust that greatly slows the oxygen stream. This difficulty may be overcome by putting a small quantity of magnesium perchlorate (Anhydrone—M.A.R. grade) in the top of the U-tube limb; this also absorbs water, but tends to contract as it does so, drawing away from the wall of the tube and hence not impeding the oxygen flow. Thus in filling the U-tube a small plug of glass wool is put at the bottom of the limb, the limb two-thirds filled with soda-lime, a further plug of glass wool inserted, the top third of the tube filled with magnesium perchlorate and topped with a plug of glass wool that comes just opposite the side-arm. The open end of the limb which projects (5 cm.) above the side-arm is then sealed off. Sealing off the limb has been found to be most satisfactory, as stoppers, taps, *etc.*, tend to leak or to give other trouble. (Glass stoppers, each previously ground to fit its own neck, are reasonably satisfactory if carefully sealed with glass cement: for subsequent recharging, the cement is softened by warming and the stopper released.) After being used for many determinations the absorbent gradually "cakes," seriously impeding the passage of oxygen, and has to be replaced. This is easily effected by carefully cutting the top off the limb, cleaning it out, refilling and sealing once again. By having the projecting length above the side-arm in the first instance this process may be repeated several times without modifying the tube; when the edge finally gets too near to the side-arm a fresh length of tube may be fused on and the whole series repeated.

The second limb of the U-tube is similarly filled with magnesium perchlorate and sealed off; this packing ensures the final removal of any traces of water vapour from the oxygen stream. It is essential when the limbs are being filled and sealed that the operations are carried out as rapidly as possible and that the side-arms are stoppered (by means of a short length of impregnated tubing blocked with a glass rod) as both substances absorb water vapour from the air very readily. The two limbs of the U-tube are separated by a ground-glass tap T_2. This keeps the two absorbents out of contact with each other except when oxygen is flowing and also shuts the oxygen stream off from the combustion tube.

It is an advantage to have all the components of the purification train mounted on a small rigid framework. Thus pure, dry oxygen is delivered at the combustion tube.

The combustion tube. The oxygen is led through the side-arm **G** (Fig. 85) into the combustion tube **L** via the horizontal side-arm **H** which is fused into the combustion tube about 4 cm. from the end (the joint between **G** and **H** is also made with impregnated rubber tubing with the two glass tubes touching inside the rubber). The position of **H** thus allows the combustion

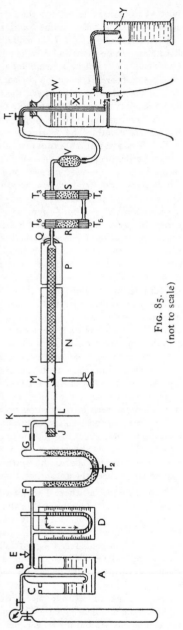

FIG. 85.
(not to scale)

boat **M** to be introduced into the combustion tube through the end (normally sealed by a tight-fitting rubber bung **J**) while oxygen is flowing.

The combustion tube **L** is made preferably of transparent silica (though hard glass can be used) and is 60 cm. long and 1 cm. in diameter; at the further end it has a short fine beak (2 cm long, *ca*. 0·25 cm. in diameter). A small square of asbestos board **K**, having a slit cut to fit the combustion tube, is placed up against the side-arm **H** to screen the rubber bung **J** from heat and thus avoid any possibility of its evolving volatile carbon compounds during the combustion.

The combustion tube is empty, with the exception of the boat, up to the furnace mouth. The packing of the tube is considered in detail below.

The furnace and thermostatic mortar. For heating the tube packing, a small electric furnace **N** has been found to be more satisfactory than a row of gas burners. The type used consists of a silica tube (1·5 cm. in diameter and 25 cm. long) wound with nichrome wire and contained in an asbestos cylinder, the annular space being lagged; the ends of the asbestos cylinder being closed by asbestos semi-circles built round the porcelain furnace tube. The furnace is controlled by a Simmerstat that has been calibrated at 680° against a bimetal pyrometer, and the furnace temperature is checked by this method from time to time. The furnace is equipped with a small steel bar attached to the asbestos and is thus mounted on an ordinary laboratory stand; the Simmerstat may then be placed immediately underneath it on the baseplate of this stand, or alternatively the furnace may be built on to the top of the Simmerstat box.

The thermostatic mortar **P**, whose function is described below, is a small electrical heating unit (1·5 cm. in diameter and 7 cm. long) kept constant at 180°. The temperature is kept constant by another Simmerstat. The mortar may be supported on its Simmerstat box; or alternatively screwed on to the end of the furnace, a gap of 1 cm. being left between the furnace and the mortar in each case. The right-hand end of the mortar bore is only wide enough to take the drawn-out beak end of the combustion tube, which is thus held in place.

There is a tendency for the water produced by the combustion to condense in the narrow neck of the combustion tube, instead of passing right over into the absorption tube. To avoid this, two movable copper hooks **Q** are mounted on a copper rod, which can slide in and out of a hole cut in the mortar **P**; these may be placed over the beak of the combustion tube and conduct sufficient heat from the mortar to vaporise the water once again so that it is driven over by the oxygen stream into the absorption tube **R**.

The absorption tubes. The water from the combustion is absorbed by magnesium perchlorate (anhydrone) in the tube **R** and the carbon dioxide by sodalime (Carbasorb) in the tube **S**. It is convenient to use absorption tubes having two taps each, which may be closed at the end of the experiment. The tubes may then be immediately weighed full of oxygen, thus avoiding the necessity for sweeping them out with air before weighing. Before filling, both tubes are washed in turn with distilled water, alcohol, then ether and finally dried in the oven.

In filling the tube **R**, one tap is inserted after being carefully greased with a high-vacuum or silicone grease. The taps are provided with scored grooves (that run completely around them near their outer end) which act as a trap to prevent any grease reaching the uncovered portion of the tap where it may attract dirt, or be wiped off during weighing or otherwise change the weight of the tube. The taps are, in effect, hollow stoppers having at the side a small hole of approximately the same bore as the side-arms of the absorption tube (cf. T_4, Fig. 86). A small plug of glass wool is inserted into the tube which is then filled nearly to the end with perchlorate and topped with a second plug of glass wool. The second tap is then greased and inserted; both taps are kept closed when the tube is not in use. It is important that the same end of the water absorption tube is always attached to the beak of the combustion tube so that the oxygen always flows through in the same direction, and absorption takes place evenly from one end. After some absorption has taken place it is easy to recognise the "absorbing end" as the perchlorate contracts from the sides of the tube and congeals. In order to label the absorbing end previous to this indication, the perchlorate packing is not continued quite to the top of the tube so that the ends are distinguishable. Absorption of water indiscriminately at either end tends to cause "channelling" in the packing with consequent risk of some water escaping absorption.

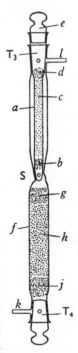

FIG. 86.

The type of carbon dioxide absorption tube **S** (Fig. 85) which is recommended is shown in detail in Fig. 86. In this tube the composite filling of soda-lime and a small packing of magnesium perchlorate are kept in separate chambers which are put in contact only while gas is flowing, by rotating a ground-glass joint tap T_3 which divides the tube into two compartments; the perchlorate being packed in what is virtually an enlarged hollow tap-stopper **a** (Fig. 86) at one end of the tube. By keeping these two elements of tube-packing out of contact with each other except when the tube is being used to absorb carbon dioxide, the "life" of the tube, before repacking becomes necessary, is much increased. In filling the carbon dioxide absorption tube **S** of this type (Fig 86), the hollow stopper **a**, having a small hole at the lower end, is charged in turn with a glass-wool plug **b**, perchlorate **c**, and a second glass-wool plug **d**, and the glass stopper **e** is then fixed into **a** with warm glass cement. The absorption stopper **a** is carefully greased at the neck T_3 and at the lower end opposite **S**, and then fitted into the main absorption tube **S** like an ordinary tap: the unit now constitutes the tap T_3. The main soda-lime chamber **f** is then filled from the other end of **S** with a glass-wool plug **g**, soda-lime **h**, and a second glass-wool plug **j**, and the greased tap T_4 finally inserted. The presence of perchlorate is necessary as the soda-lime contains a little moisture which is driven off by the continued passage of oxygen, and this would cause low results for carbon if the water were not prevented from leaving the tube by the "safety" layer of perchlorate.

When in position, the side-arm **k** of the carbon dioxide absorption tube is attached to the T_5 side-arm of the water absorption tube **R** (Fig. 85) by impregnated rubber pressure tubing over a glass-to-glass joint. The side-arm l (Fig. 86) of the carbon dioxide absorption tube is attached by a similar joint to a small guard-tube V containing perchlorate to prevent any water vapour reaching the perchlorate in the absorption tube. This end of the absorption train is supported by a small wire hook attached to a stand.

The Mariotte bottle. The perchlorate guard tube is attached by a length of ordinary rubber condenser tubing to the Mariotte bottle W. This is, in effect, a siphon bottle, and the lead-in tube X is a capillary provided with a tap T_1. The bent capillary Y (drawn off slightly at the end) serves as exit tube; it is fitted into W by a rubber bung and its level may be adjusted.

By the time the oxygen stream has reached the absorption tubes its initial excess pressure (*ca.* 6 cm. of water) has been almost completely dissipated by the resistance afforded to its passage by the packing of the combustion tube. The purpose of the Mariotte bottle is not only to indicate the rate of flow of gas through the apparatus, but also to create a slightly reduced pressure on the far side of the absorption train and so to draw the gas through the absorption tubes. The fact that the pressure inside the apparatus is equal to atmospheric pressure at the place where absorption begins, reduces the chance of leakage of carbon dioxide out of the apparatus and of leakage of water vapour into it. The reduced head in the Mariotte bottle is the difference in level between the bottom of X and the tip of Y, and is adjusted so as to give an initial flow of oxygen through the apparatus of 5 ml./min.

Packing of combustion tube. The exact filling used in the combustion tube depends on the elements other than carbon, hydrogen and oxygen that are present in the substances to be analysed. On combustion, halogens and sulphur, and to some extent nitrogen, all produce acid gases that would be absorbed by the soda-lime in the carbon dioxide absorption tube; thus if reliable results are to be obtained the packing of the combustion tube must be of such a nature that these products are not permitted to emerge from the tube.

(a) *For compounds containing carbon, hydrogen, oxygen, nitrogen and halogens.* Before filling, the combustion tube is washed with conc. nitric acid, distilled water, alcohol, ether and finally dried in an oven. A 15 mm. roll of silver gauze, which has been etched in pure nitric acid, washed with distilled water, dried and heated to dull redness, is first introduced into the tube; it should be of such a diameter that it just fits in the tube and slides easily down to the "beak" end. The purpose of this, and of another roll of silver gauze to be inserted later, is to convert any halogens or hydrogen halides produced in the combustion to non-volatile silver halides. Next a small plug (2–3 mm.) of ignited asbestos is inserted; this should be pushed in firmly, but not tightly, by means of a glass rod. These asbestos plugs, of which there are a number of others yet to be mentioned, serve to confine the elements of tube-filling in small separate compartments. Next comes 30 mm. of M.A.R. grade lead peroxide (it is very important that this reagent is of high quality), care being taken that this is not tightly packed otherwise too much resistance will be offered to the passage of oxygen when the combustion tube is in use. Any lead peroxide adhering to the walls of the tube is pushed down by an asbestos wool plug fastened to a copper wire. These elements of tube-filling will be heated, not by the furnace but by the thermostatic mortar which is maintained at 180°. The main purpose of the lead peroxide is to absorb any oxides of nitrogen produced in the combustion of nitrogen-containing substances. It is maintained at 180°, which is about its optimum temperature for this purpose. Lead peroxide also absorbs appreciable quantities of water at this temperature but it is allowed to absorb its complement before an actual determination is carried out in the tube. When an actual combustion is then carried out there is a smooth exchange of water through the lead peroxide, provided the temperature of the mortar is kept constant, and the theoretical amount of water vapour emerges from the combustion tube and is absorbed in the absorption tube. Lead peroxide also absorbs some CO_2 but this is at a minimum around 180° and again it is allowed to absorb its complement before an actual determination is carried out. The remainder of the filling of the combustion tube is heated to 680° by the furnace.

Another small asbestos plug is then inserted to confine the lead peroxide (it is very important that the lead peroxide is not tamped down or it will almost completely prevent passage of gas through the tube) followed by a 30 mm. roll of silver gauze, treated in the same way as the first one inserted. This is the main halogen-absorbent, the one already inserted serving as a trap (at 180°) to catch any halogen lost by the hot (680°) silver halide first formed. Next about 25–30 mm. of ignited asbestos is added; this is known as a "choking plug" as it is this element of filling that offers the major part of the resistance to the flow of oxygen in the apparatus. The exact dimensions and compression of the choking plug are determined by trial and error. The amount of asbestos is so adjusted that, when the combustion tube is completely packed, the apparatus assembled, the absorption tubes in place, the furnace and thermostatic mortar at their equilibrium temperatures, and also when there is a pressure of 60 mm./water registered on the pressure gauge and a reduced head of about 20 mm. of water on the Mariotte bottle, the rate of flow of oxygen through the apparatus is about 5 ml. per min. It is essential to have the furnace and mortar on while this adjustment is being made as temperature greatly affects the rate at which gas will flow at a given pressure difference (hot tubes generally "run" noticeably faster than cold).

The choking plug is followed by 200 mm. of M.A.R. "wire-form" copper oxide; this is the main oxidative packing of the tube. Partially combusted material reacts with the heated copper oxide to form carbon dioxide and water, leaving copper behind which is re-oxidised by the oxygen passing over the heated metal. The copper oxide is confined by a small plug (2–3 mm.) of ignited asbestos, followed by a 10 mm. roll of silver gauze. This just protrudes from the furnace and acts as a catalytic surface on which most of the initial combustion takes place, the heated vapour of the substance reacting with the stream of hot oxygen. The remainder of the combustion tube is empty except for the boat holding the material to be analysed.

A tube filled in this fashion will last for about a hundred combustions of substances containing C, H, O, N, and halogens.

(b) *For compounds containing carbon, hydrogen, oxygen, nitrogen, halogens and sulphur.* If the compound to be analysed contains sulphur in addition to the elements considered above, then oxides of sulphur will be formed, and a new substance will have to be introduced into the combustion tube in order to prevent these acid oxides from reaching the soda-lime in the absorption tube. This is effected by replacing the 200 mm. length of M.A.R. "wire-form" copper oxide with a 1:1 mixture of the oxide with M.A.R. lead chromate in fine granules. The oxides of sulphur are then converted to non-volatile lead sulphate and so prevented from passing out of the tube and reaching the absorption train.

Burning out of combustion tube. The combustion tube **L** and also the materials with which it has been filled, have not been specially dried in any way and it is now necessary to burn out the combustion tube and packing till no more water vapour or carbon dioxide can be driven off. To do this the side-arm **H** (Fig. 85) is attached to the end of the purification train **G** in the usual way (the bung **J** being in place). This joint should be made really tight fitting and there should be no need to disturb it subsequently until either the purification train or combustion tube need repacking. The beak of the combustion tube is then attached to the bottle **W** via the guard-tube **V**—the absorption tubes **R** and **S** not being put on at this stage. The oxygen is then turned on, all the taps opened, the gauge **D** adjusted to 60 mm. of water and the furnace and thermostatic mortar then turned on. It generally requires about 20 minutes for the two heated portions of the combustion tube to reach their equilibrium temperatures; at the end of this period the side-arm **Y** of the bottle may be adjusted so as to give a rate of flow of 5 ml./min. This can be tested sufficiently accurately by collecting the flow over one minute in a 5 or 10 ml. measuring cylinder.

The board **K** is now placed over the end of the combustion tube (Fig. 85) and the tube is heated with the hottest part of a Bunsen flame, starting just to the right of **K**. The burner should be put only gradually under the tube otherwise the sudden expansion of hot gas will blow the fluid out of the gauge **D**. It is an advantage to have a small metal cone held by a wire support fixed to the top of the burner; this serves to concentrate the flame and the combustion tube may be kept "cupped" in the hottest part of the flame. The flame is slowly moved to the right along the tube until it reaches the furnace mouth, the complete transit taking about 15 minutes. The process should then be repeated, heating the tube with the burner from **K** up to the furnace mouth. After the heating is complete, a further 250 ml. of oxygen, as measured by the water displaced from **W** and collected directly in a 250 ml. measuring cylinder below, is passed through the apparatus. The tap **T₁** is then closed, the furnace and mortar shut off, and the apparatus allowed to cool down with the end **H** of the combustion tube open to the oxygen supply. The tap **T₂** and the oxygen supply are turned off when the combustion tube is cold.

The whole process is then repeated exactly as described above. The absorption tubes are then weighed and attached to the apparatus (full details will be given below when a complete combustion is described), and the above process repeated. The absorption tubes are detached and reweighed. They should not have gained in weight by more than 0·1 mg. If either or both have changed by more than this amount, the whole process is repeated until each shows no further gain in weight (of more than 0·1 mg.).

One of the dangers in burning out a combustion tube is that of burning it out too thoroughly; so that when a substance is then ignited in it, the results obtained will be low as the tube filling will take up as much carbon dioxide and water vapour as it requires in order to come to equilibrium at the furnace and thermostatic mortar temperatures. This difficulty is overcome by doing two or three "equilibrium" combustions of known substances in a new combustion tube, after it has been burnt out and before a real estimation is carried out in it. The combustion tube thus has opportunity to come to equilibrium and the water absorption tube may also pick up the very small quantity of carbon dioxide that it normally retains. The operations leading up to the carrying out of a combustion will now be described.

Weighing of absorption tubes. During the processes of attaching the tubes **R** and **S** to the apparatus and subsequently detaching them after a combustion, they will pick up a certain amount of grease and water vapour from the fingers of the operator. This would be no drawback if the amount that was wiped on or off was the same in every case, *i.e.*, if there was no resultant change in weight. This is found not to be the case, and as the water absorption tube **R** usually gains less than 20 mgm. as the result of a combustion, steps have to be taken to avoid what would otherwise be a very considerable source of error.

In practice the closed tubes are carefully polished to remove all grease, moisture, *etc.*, and are then allowed to stand for a definite period of time in the air, to pick up a definite amount of water vapour—this process is known as maturing. Unless the atmospheric conditions change very considerably during the experiment (about 2 hours), the amount of water vapour deposited on the polished tubes before and after the combustion will be the same and any systematic error will have been avoided. Unless the tubes have been used in the combustion tube burning-out process, and so are full of oxygen, they must be filled with oxygen before weighing by connecting to the apparatus (both furnace and mortar being cold) and passing oxygen through for 20 minutes. (It is very important not to forget this when a spent absorption tube is replaced by a freshly-packed one.)

Chamois cloths are used to polish the tubes and it is essential to have a carefully controlled scheme of polishing, so that any tube is always polished in the same way and for the same length of time. Before polishing is started, one of the taps of the absorption tube should be opened momentarily in order to equalise the gas pressure inside and outside the tube. It is probably simplest to use two cloths and start polishing in the middle of the tube, outwards, first towards one end and then towards the other (always starting towards the same end first) and including the side-arms and taps, care being taken not to dislodge the latter. Once polishing has started, the tubes should no on account be touched with the fingers.

The polishing process should take between thirty seconds and one minute and the tube should then be placed on a small stand. The time at which polishing ended should be noted. The other tube is then treated similarly and the time at which polishing was completed again noted; the two tubes should always be polished in the same order.

The tubes are left on their rack until ten minutes have elapsed since the completion of polishing of the first one; the latter is then transferred to a small aluminium rider which holds it firmly and evenly on the balance pan. This transfer may best be accomplished by using a pair of thin metal tweezers of wide aperture, whose ends have been slightly bent inwards, to grip the tube firmly and easily. The time at which the final counterpoising and reading is made is noted. At the end of the combustion when the tubes have been momentarily opened to the air, repolished exactly as before and are reweighed, their weight will be known to within a few milligrams and the weighing will therefore be rather more rapid in the second case than in the first; hence the tube is allowed to mature for a slightly longer time in the second case so that exactly the same length of time elapses, between the end of polishing and the final counterpoising, as before the combustion.

Some authorities recommend that the inside of the side-arms of the absorption tubes should also be polished by rubbing with "pipe-cleaner." This, however, is unsatisfactory with the type of absorption tube that has greased taps as there is always a risk of removing traces of grease from the tap and hence of changing the weight of the tube. Although the side-arm interiors are not, therefore, specially polished, care should be taken that no minute pieces of rubber or wax from the impregnated tubing find their way into them. If this does take place, the offending particles should be carefully removed with a piece of very fine copper wire.

A little practice in polishing and weighing the absorption tubes is desirable before an actual analysis is carried out. It is important that when the taps on the absorption tubes are "off," they should be as far "off" as possible (*i.e.*, hole in tap is 180° away from side-arm hole).

Weighing out the sample. The combustion is carried out in a flat-bottomed boat (30 mm. × 5 mm.) provided with a small lip at one end for easy handling. It is an advantage to have a long, narrow boat both for ease of introduction into the combustion tube and also for smooth combustion. The boat is preferably made of platinum but one of hard glazed porcelain is satisfactory. The boat is ignited in a Bunsen flame (using crucible tongs which have themselves just been ignited), so that all of it has been heated red-hot and then placed on an aluminium block in a desiccator over perchlorate; the block has preferably a narrow groove into which the boat just fits. The block is used so that the heat is very rapidly conducted away from the hot boat, which thus attains the temperature of its surroundings almost instantaneously.

The boat is then transferred to the balance pan (narrow-ended meta tweezers are most suitable for this purpose) and weighed: the weight of the empty boat should never vary by more than 0·1 mg. during its working life. The boat is transferred to the grooved block (removed from the desiccator) and 20–25 mg. of the sample to be analysed are then transferred to it. This is best carried out using a very small, narrow-ended spatula, and it is essential that only a small amount of material is put in the boat at a time—the 20–25 mg. should be transferred in several operations. The boat is then gripped firmly with the tweezers and carefully tapped on the aluminium block; this serves to remove any small particles of substance that may possibly be adhering to the outside of the boat and also to settle the charge of substance thinly and evenly along the whole length of the boat. The face and groove of the block are then carefully wiped with a polishing cloth. The boat is transferred to the balance pan and reweighed. It is then returned to the block and both replaced in the desiccator.

This operation of weighing out the sample of substance to be analysed may conveniently be carried out while waiting for the absorption tubes to mature after polishing.

Carrying out a combustion. The apparatus (Fig. 85, p. 469) will have been left with the bottle **W** connected to the beak of the combustion tube via the guard tube **V** and with all the taps shut; the combustion tube, which is always allowed to cool down while connected to the oxygen source, will therefore be full of oxygen at slightly above atmospheric pressure, thus preventing any leaking in of carbon dioxide or water vapour from the air.

The oxygen is turned on, tap T_2 carefully opened and the furnace **N** and the thermostatic mortar **P** then turned on. The apparatus can conveniently be allowed to attain its equilibrium temperature over the period of about 20 minutes while the absorption tubes are being polished and weighed and the specimen for analysis weighed out: it is thus ready for immediate use as soon as the weighings have been completed.

The bung **J** is then removed from the combustion tube and the charged combustion boat inserted. This is best carried out by raising the aluminium block, with the boat in place, to the level of the combustion tube floor and then gently pushing the boat, the lip pointing away from the furnace, into the combustion tube with a length of stout, rigid, copper wire. The boat should be inserted till its front end is about 8 cm. away from the furnace; the boat may be guided by leverage of the copper rod on the lip, thus keeping it flat on the floor of the combustion tube and avoiding any chance of its being overturned. The rubber bung is then firmly inserted. It is an advantage to remove the asbestos square **K** during this operation to leave a little more room for manipulation, but it should be replaced as soon as the bung has been reinserted. By having the oxygen turned on and the far end of the system closed by the tap T_1 oxygen is flowing out of the open back-end of the combustion tube all the time the above operation is in progress, and the risk of any carbon dioxide or water vapour getting into the tube from the air is thus very small.

The absorption tubes **R** and **S** are next joined together by a 20 mm. length of impregnated rubber tubing, the side-arms forming a glass-to-glass join inside the rubber; the side-arm at the "non-absorbing" end of the tube **R** being attached to the side-arm of the "absorbing" end of the tube **S**. The exit of the tube **S** is now attached to the guard tube **V** in the usual way and the pair of tubes finally attached by a 15 mm. piece of impregnated tubing, and glass-to-glass joint, to the beak of the combustion tube. As short a piece of tubing as is compatible with a gas-tight join is used for this connection so that as much as possible of the beak of the combustion tube and of the side-arm of **R** may be heated directly by the heating hooks **Q** attached to the thermostatic mortar. These hooks are next placed in position, both initially being on the combustion tube beak between the mortar and the rubber connection to the tube **R**.

The tap **T₂** is now turned off and the apparatus tested for leaks. If no bubbles appear at the end of the capillary **X** there is no leak between **Y** and the tap **T₁** of the bottle **W**. The best way of observing **X** is to shake off any bubbles at its end and then to observe the water meniscus inside the capillary. If it continues to move, there is a leak. The tap **T₁** is now opened and **X** observed again: rapid cessation of flow indicates no leak up to the first tap **T₃** on the carbon dioxide absorption train. The process is repeated for the other taps, **T₄**, **T₅**, and **T₆**, of the absorption tubes; water may flow for a few seconds on opening **T₆** as the Mariotte bottle has then been put in contact with with the whole length of the hot combustion tube up to the tap **T₂** of the purification train. If any leak is encountered at any stage all the taps should be closed, the faulty tap or tube adjusted, and the process repeated. The tap **T₂** is then opened and the oxygen stream allowed to pass through the apparatus. If necessary the level on the pressure gauge **D** is adjusted to 6 cm. by the micro screw-clip **E**, and then the side-arm **Y** of the Mariotte bottle lowered until there is a rate of flow of 5 ml./min. If it is found necessary to lower **Y** more than a few centimetres there is an obstruction in the system. This is nearly always caused by one or more of the taps on the absorption tubes being not quite completely open; when opening the taps it is essential to ensure that side-arm and hole in the tap are exactly in line, as the thumb-grip on the top of the tap is not always set exactly at right-angles to the tap-hole. A 5 or 10 ml. measuring cylinder should be used when adjusting the rate of flow so that the value is measured with reasonable accuracy.

A beaker is placed under **Y** and the combustion may now be started. The Bunsen burner,* with the air-hole wide open, and the

---

* Various small moving electric heaters and other devices have been developed for carrying out the combustion, including methods by which it is done

cone in place, is carefully introduced under the combustion tube so that liquid is not driven out of the pressure gauge by the sudden thermal expansion. The heating is started about 2 cm. to the right of the asbestos square **K**; care should be taken that the burner is not left at this end of the tube long enough for the bung **J** to become appreciably warmed, otherwise errors will arise due to the evolution of volatile carbon-containing compounds. The Bunsen should be moved slowly along the combustion tube so that each part of the tube is heated to a bright red heat. Particular care should be taken as the burner approaches the boat.

When burning the majority of organic compounds, an attempt should be made to drive the substance out of the boat, by heating, in an only partially combusted state, the greater part of the combustion taking place catalytically on the piece of silver gauze just protruding from the furnace mouth. Exceptions to this are non-volatile substances such as glucose which may largely be oxidised in the boat.

The chief danger and main source of error in a combustion is that of moving the Bunsen forward a little too rapidly and so causing much of the substance to burn very rapidly, so that a "flash-back" occurs. This usually causes an explosion wave to travel back along the tube towards the purification train, some carbon dioxide and water vapour being carried with it. If these reach the packing of the purification train they will, of course, be absorbed there and the results of the estimation will necessarily be low.

There are two main warning signs of a "flash-back" which, if observed, allow sufficient time for remedial measures. During the combustion, the height of the pressure gauge fluctuates very little, but as soon as a flash-back, due to over-heating, is imminent the pressure begins to rise. Immediately this is seen to occur the Bunsen should be moved back several cm. along the tube, and if the pressure still rises, right back to where heating was originally started.

The second indication is a faint smoke-like cloudiness in the zone of the tube which is being heated by the Bunsen; this is readily visible as the interior of the tube is normally quite clear and bright. This is a later stage of development of the flash-back than the rise of pressure, already mentioned, and should be counteracted by moving the Bunsen immediately to the point of the combustion tube where heating was commenced. In either case the Bunsen should then be moved slowly forwards as before. A flash-back is attended by the deposition of carbon particles, carried back by the explosion wave, on the cold walls of the tube. Care should be taken that these are completely burnt off as the Bunsen is slowly moved forward again.

As the substance is heated in the boat—it usually melts before the Bunsen quite reaches the boat itself and runs forward to the front end—

---

automatically, but it should be remembered that all substances behave differently and each combustion is, in the strict sense of the word, a new experiment. For this reason, a Bunsen burner is preferred as it allows great sensitivity of control and, more important, allows the student to see exactly what is taking place at each stage.

it distils out and forms a ring round the combustion tube and finally a clearly visible drop of liquid on the floor of the tube. The boat is carefully heated bright red-hot throughout its length to ensure that any particles of carbon left by partial combustion are completely burned away in the stream of oxygen. Care should be taken not to heat too rapidly when the boat is reached or the substance is rapidly vaporised, may catch fire, and a flash-back result. As the burner approaches the far end of the boat, the drop of partially burnt material will move slowly down the tube in front of it. As the material approaches the silver gauze at the furnace mouth it is being driven forward into a heated zone, instead of a cold one as previously, and its rate of progress is slowed down; this means that the chance of the Bunsen catching up the material with the consequent danger of a "flash-back" is increased, and great care should be taken. During the whole of the passage of the Bunsen it is important that the combustion tube should be cupped evenly in its flame; there is a danger of the operator moving the Bunsen slightly towards himself all the time, and the position of the burner should therefore be occasionally checked by looking at it from above.

Finally the material is driven on to the silver gauze and the combustion of the partially broken-down substance begins to take place catalytically. The Bunsen should not now be moved forward for several minutes and then only very slowly. At this point a drop in the rate of flow of water from the siphon will be noticed as a considerable proportion of the oxygen passing into the tube will be used up in the combustion and will thus not pass the absorption tubes. It is important that the flow of water should never actually stop and if it becomes very slow the burner should be moved slightly away from the furnace mouth; it should be realised that there is a time lag between the actual "over-combustion" taking place and the arrival of the products of combustion at the absorption tubes with consequent fall in the rate of flow; thus the Bunsen should be moved back slightly as soon as any really noticeable fall in the rate of flow takes place.

The end of the combustion is nearly always marked by the difference of levels registered on the pressure gauge sinking momentarily to zero. When this takes place the Bunsen is gently moved forward until it is on the silver gauze and this is then heated to bright redness. The catalytic combustion that has taken place nearly always leaves some particles of unburnt carbon on the gauze and these now burn off in the oxygen stream with tiny flashes of light. When the burner has heated the tube right up to the furnace mouth it is removed and carefully replaced at the far end of the combustion tube where heating began. At the same time the beaker is removed from under the siphon of the Mariotte bottle and replaced by a 250 ml. measuring cylinder. The Bunsen is now moved slowly along the exposed length of the combustion tube as before; the second heating taking about 15 minutes. It is then removed and extinguished. The passage of oxygen through the apparatus is continued until a total of 250 ml. have been passed. This operation is designed to ensure that the carbon dioxide and water vapour are swept out of the combustion tube and transferred quantitatively to the absorption tubes. The carbon dioxide is swept out and absorbed more rapidly than the water vapour. This is due in large part to the tendency of the water vapour to condense in the beak of the combustion tube and/or the side-arm of the water absorption tube **R**. The two heating hooks **Q** are left in their original position until 120 ml. of water have been collected, they are then separated and placed one on each side of the piece of rubber tube which connects beak and side-arm, and just touching it. They remain here until a total of 190 ml. has been collected, and are finally placed on the absorption tube side-arm while the last 60 ml. pass, thus ensuring that all the water is driven over from the side-arm into the absorption tube **R**. If all the water has not been driven over when 250 ml. of oxygen have passed, this sweeping-out process should be continued until this has been achieved.

At the end of the sweeping out, the tap T_1 is first closed, and then the taps T_3, T_4, T_5 and T_6 in this order. The tubes **R** and **S** are then detached from the beak of the combustion tube, the guard tube **V** is then detached from them and replaced on the combustion tube beak. The furnace and thermostatic mortar are then switched off and the combustion tube allowed to cool with the tap to the oxygen supply open. The bung **J** is removed, and the boat withdrawn by means of a piece of rigid copper wire with a small hook in the end that fits into the small hole in the lip at the back of the boat; the bung is then replaced and the boat transferred to its block in the desiccator.

The absorption tubes are then detached from each other, transferred to their stand, and polished, matured and weighed exactly as at the beginning of the experiment, taking care that no particles of rubber or wax are left in the side-arms. They must be repolished, matured and reweighed before they are used for a further determination. Finally when the tube is cool, the tap T_2 of the purification train may be closed and the oxygen supply shut off.

Example of Calculation.

Estimation of C and H in acetanilide.

0·0217 g. of acetanilide gave 0·0565 g. CO_2 and 0·0127 g. H_2O

$\therefore$ 0·02170 g. of acetanilide contains $\dfrac{0·0565 \times 12}{44}$ g. of carbon

and $\dfrac{0·0127}{9}$ g. of hydrogen

$\therefore$ 100 g. of acetanilide contains $\dfrac{0·0565 \times 12 \times 100}{44 \times 0·0217}$ g. of carbon

and $\dfrac{0·0127 \times 100}{9 \times 0·0217}$ g. of hydrogen.

$= 71·0\%$ C and $6·51\%$ H.

Theoretical for C_8H_9NO; C $= 71·1\%$, H $= 6·67\%$.

Substances suitable for the estimation: acetanilide, sucrose, glucose, cinnamic acid, diphenylamine, salicylic acid, vanillin, *p*-bromoacetanilide, toluene *p*-sulphonamide.

Estimation of Nitrogen.

The two chief methods for estimating nitrogen in organic compounds are (i) the *Dumas* method, which can be applied to all organic compounds; (ii) the *Kjeldahl* method, which is of more restricted application, but which is frequently used in biochemical and physiological work. Its limitations are indicated in the description of the method (p. 492).

The Dumas Method.

Principle. A definite amount of the substance (*ca.* 25 mg.) is weighed out, transferred to a combustion tube and is burnt with a Bunsen flame in an atmosphere of air-free carbon dioxide, an oxidising filling (cupric oxide) of the tube being used as a source of oxygen. The carbon present is converted to carbon dioxide, the hydrogen to water, any sulphur to sulphur dioxide, and nitrogen and halogens are evolved in the free state. This resulting nitrogen is swept out of the heated tube by a stream of air-free carbon dioxide and collected in a graduated vessel (nitrometer) over 50% potassium hydroxide solution which absorbs the carrier gas. Any oxides of nitrogen that may have been produced during the combustion are reconverted to nitrogen by a heated copper spiral. From the measured volume of gas, reduced to normal temperature and pressure, the amount of nitrogen in the substance may be calculated.

The method depends for its success on the quantitative liberation of the nitrogen content of substances as molecular nitrogen; this can be rather difficult in certain cases (*e.g.*, polynitro compounds) but satisfactory determinations can be carried out by slight modification of the experimental conditions.

Apparatus.

The source of carbon dioxide. The main requirement of the carbon dioxide supply is that it shall be air-free. It is, however, almost impossible to generate carbon dioxide, by any fairly simple method, so that it is completely free from air. Nevertheless, it is possible to obtain the gas sufficiently pure so that no serious error is introduced into the determination.

The gas is usually generated by the action of hydrochloric acid on marble chips in a Kipp's apparatus **A** (Fig. 87). (It is advantageous to generate the carbon dioxide by using the Tucker all-glass apparatus, which, although more expensive, is extremely reliable. If this should prove too expensive, it is an advantage to use two "Kipp's" joined in series: the second supplies the CO_2 for the actual estimation, and the first ensures that the acid in the upper reservoir of the second is under an atmosphere of CO_2. The first must therefore be turned on before the second, and this order reversed on turning off.)

Before use, the marble chips are washed repeatedly with hot water, and then de-aerated by first etching them with concentrated hydrochloric acid and then boiling them with air-free water under reduced pressure. The chips are then rapidly transferred to the generator; small chips should be used and the bulb of the generator nearly filled so that there is as little air space left as possible. The acid to be used is made up from equal parts of concentrated hydrochloric acid (A.R. standard) and air-free water. Before the acid is transferred to the generator, a number of de-aerated marble chips are dissolved in it in order to expel any residual dissolved air and also to saturate it with carbon dioxide. The top portion of the generator **A** is then lifted several times in order to cause a rapid evolution of carbon dioxide so as to sweep out the air from the middle bulb. A number of pieces of marble, of such a size that they will not slip down the acid funnel, are then added to the acid in the upper bulb in order to sweep out any residual air in this part of the vessel. The stopper of this top bulb is provided with a non-return valve (a thin layer of mercury on a sintered

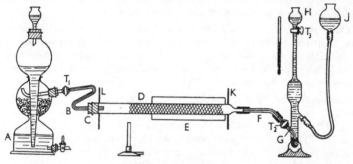

FIG. 87 (not to scale).

glass plate in a small funnel) to allow the escape of any excess of carbon dioxide and to prevent the leak of any air into the acid. Both these de-aeration processes are repeated a number of times over a period of hours. All bungs and stoppers should be tight-fitting and the bung carrying the gas delivery tap T_1 (Fig. 72) attached to the middle bulb should be wired in place; the gas take-off from this middle bulb should be by a glass tube bent round and reaching up to the top of the bulb to prevent, so far as possible, the carrying over of acid spray. Finally the generator should be allowed to deliver a slow stream of carbon dioxide until this is found to be sufficiently free of air (see below how to test the gas stream for this condition) for use in the estimation. If the generator, after standing, fails to supply sufficiently pure carbon dioxide, it should be allowed to flush several times, then run slowly until the pure gas is obtained.

The relatively concentrated hydrochloric acid is employed so that with ordinary use of the apparatus, spent liquor does not accumulate very rapidly; the concentrated acid also ensures a brisk and delicately controlled flow of gas. When the generator is replenished with acid, marble or both, the de-aeration procedure detailed above is repeated until a sufficiently air-free gas supply is obtained.

Z-tube. The tube **B** is made of capillary tubing (3 mm. internal bore) bent into the shape of a Z. It is attached by a length (5 cm.) of very tight-fitting rubber pressure tubing to the tap T_1, a glass-to-glass join being made inside the rubber tubing. The purpose of **B** is to act as a trap for any droplets of liquid that may be carried over in the gas stream from the generator **A**. The tube **B** is placed horizontally (*i.e.*, so that T_1 and the tube **D** are in the same horizontal plane—an arrangement which cannot be adequately indicated in Fig. 87): its further end is attached by a very tight-fitting rubber bung **C** to the end of the combustion tube **D**. This end of the capillary is drawn out into a beak 2·5 mm. long and 4 mm. in external diameter.

Combustion tube. This tube **D** is made of transparent silica or hard glass (50 cm. long and 1 cm. in diameter) and is provided at the right-hand end with a short, fine beak (3 cm. long, *ca.* 5 mm. in external diameter). The packing of the tube is considered in detail below. The tube carries at the left-hand end a small square of asbestos board **L** which prevents the heat of the Bunsen used during combustion from affecting the rubber bung **C**.

The furnace. For heating the tube packing, a small electric furnace **E** is used, similar to that described in the carbon and hydrogen determination. It is 22 cm. in length and 1·5 cm. in diameter. The furnace is maintained at 680°C., as before, by a calibrated Simmerstat and its temperature is checked from time to time with a bimetal pyrometer.

The angle tube. The beak of the combustion tube which protrudes from the furnace is attached to the side-arm of the nitrometer through an angle tube **F** made of thick-walled capillary glass tubing (30 cm. long by 2 mm. internal diameter). The tube forms a straight continuation of the combustion tube and is bent two-thirds of the way along at such an angle that it forms a straight join with the side-arm **G** of the nitrometer. The joints at both ends are made glass-to-glass with tight-fitting rubber pressure tubing (3 cm. lengths) to hold them in place. Both ends of the angle tube are drawn out into beaks 3 cm. long and 1 mm. internal diameter. A small square of asbestos board **K** is placed on the beak of the combustion tube in order to prevent the heat of the furnace reaching the rubber tubing joint and thus causing it to swell and perhaps to leak.

The Nitrometer. Before use, the glass nitrometer should be well washed with warm conc. nitric acid, followed by distilled water, alcohol, and ether, and allowed to dry. The taps T_2 and T_3 should then be lightly greased and turned until no striations are apparent. The bottom of the nitrometer fits into a metal or porcelain stand with a cork lining. This is carried by the baseplate of an ordinary metal clamp-stand and the nitrometer is held upright by a clamp gripping the upper part of its stem. A thermometer may be hung from this clamp with wire. The lower part of the nitrometer stem is supplied with two side-arms; one, which is attached by a length of pressure tubing to a glass reservoir **J**, is used for adjusting levels. As the pressure tubing will be in contact with very concentrated alkali for long periods, it is advisable to let it soak for some hours in a bath of aqueous potassium hydroxide before attaching to the apparatus. If this is omitted, sulphur is extracted from the rubber and then reacts with the mercury that is subsequently to be introduced into the apparatus, with formation of black particles of mercuric sulphide, which make reading of the gas volume difficult. The tubing should be wired on where it joins both the reservoir and the nitrometer side-arm. The other side-arm **G** is drawn out and carries a tap

T_2 for attachment to the angle tube **F**. The tap T_2 may have a length of glass rod fused to it so that it is capable of fine adjustment. The lower (internal) end of the capillary tube **G** is bent downwards and is also drawn out very slightly.

The main stem of the nitrometer widens into a bulb and then narrows to form a graduated tube. The usual graduation is of 8 ml. in 0·02 ml. divisions. The graduations continue to the tap T_3 at the top of the stem. Above T_3 there is a small reservoir **H** to prevent splashing of the concentrated alkali when gas is expelled from the nitrometer and also to ensure that a small excess of potash is left as a liquid seal above the tap T_3.

Clean dry mercury is first put into the nitrometer till it has just reached the bottom of the side-arm **G**. 50% Aqueous potassium hydroxide is then run into the reservoir **J** until the whole of the nitrometer is filled, and a little liquid has passed through the tap T_3 into the reservoir **H** above. The bulb **J** should be about one-third full of the potash when raised to the height of the liquid in the nitrometer. The stand to which the nitrometer is attached is provided with a ring that slides up and down for adjusting the level of **J**. The reservoirs **H** and **J** are provided with rubber bungs (not shown in Fig. 87), penetrated by short lengths of capillary tubing, so that even when the apparatus is in use, the concentrated potassium hydroxide solution may be kept almost out of contact with the atmosphere. If this is now done, the potassium hydroxide absorbs carbon dioxide from the air extremely rapidly and therefore soon requires replenishing. The concentrated potash gradually attacks the glass, ultimately causing the tap T_3 to leak, but effective greasing will in some part prevent this.

Packing of combustion tube. Before use, the silica tube **D** (Fig. 87) is washed in turn with warm concentrated nitric acid, distilled water, alcohol, ether and dried in an oven. Some ignited asbestos is first introduced and pushed along to the beak end of the combustion tube so that it forms a plug about 5 mm. in length. This is followed by a 100 mm.-long layer of M.A.R. "wire-form" copper oxide followed by a 3 mm. asbestos plug to hold it in place. Next a 50 mm. freshly reduced copper spiral is added. This is prepared by winding the correct width of copper gauze round a stout copper wire until the requisite thickness is attained: the wire is provided with small loops at both ends to prevent the gauze cylinder slipping off, and also to ensure easy removal of the spiral from the combustion tube. It is reduced by heating to a uniform red heat in a Bunsen flame and then dropping while still red hot into warm methyl alcohol in a boiling-tube. The alcohol vapour reduces the spiral to the characteristic rose colour and itself ignites at the top of the tube. The flame is blown out and an excess of methyl alcohol added to chill and immerse the spiral. The spiral is then withdrawn, washed well with dry ether and dried in an evacuated desiccator. This spiral is followed in the combustion tube by a further 3 mm. asbestos plug to hold it in place.

The above constitutes the permanent filling of the tube and need only be replaced at rare intervals. It is possible to perform up to 50 combustions before again reducing the copper spiral, but indication of the spiral being spent is afforded by the loss of its bright coppery appearance and, when more pronounced, by high values from the estimation. The purpose of this heated copper spiral is to reduce any oxides of nitrogen that may be formed in the course of the combustion. The main danger in this respect is the formation of nitric oxide. This, like nitrogen, is a neutral gas and is not absorbed by the potash in the nitrometer; every molecule of nitrogen derived from the original sample being estimated could form *two* molecules of nitric oxide, thus more than the theoretical volume of gas would be collected and high results would be obtained. This occurs to a marked extent with nitro-compounds and the reduced copper spiral may then be exhausted far more rapidly than usual.

The temporary filling of the combustion tube **D** is now inserted; this is in part replaced after every combustion. Sufficient "wire-form" copper oxide is added so that it just emerges to the left of the furnace **E** when the tube (not including the beak) is protruding 10–15 mm. at the beak end; this constitutes the main oxidative packing of the tube. This is followed by 25 mm. of M.A.R. "powder-form" copper oxide, followed by the sample suspended in more copper oxide, and backed by an oxidised copper spiral, 50 mm. in length.

Weighing of sample. Two separate tubes are used for weighing the sample and for mining it subsequently with copper oxide: they may conveniently be mounted in two holes cut in a large flat cork. The smaller tube, used for the actual weighing, is 7.5 c.m long and 9 mm. in diameter, and is fitted with a ground-glass stopper. It is supported on the balance pan by a small notched aluminium rider. This tube is roughly weighed and approximately 25 mg. of the material whose nitrogen content is to be estimated is transferred to the tube by means of a micro-spatula. The tube is then carefully weighed. It must be touched only with forceps and not with the fingers or its weight will be altered by the grease picked up from the hands. The contents are then transferred to the larger or mixing tube (7·5 cm. long and 1–2 cm. wide) which is also provided with a ground-glass stopper and which already contains a 15 mm. layer of "powder-form" copper oxide. The weighing tube is now carefully reweighed, again being handled only with forceps, and hence the weight of substance transferred to the mixing tube is known by difference. A further 10 mm. layer of "powder-form" copper oxide is now added to the mixing tube, the stopper carefully replaced and the mixture well shaken so that the sample is spread evenly throughout the whole of the mass of copper oxide. It is now ready to be transferred to the combustion tube.

Transferring the sample to the combustion tube. If we are dealing with the combustion tube **D** (Fig. 87) as it will have been left from a previous combustion, we have first to remove some proportion of the temporary element of the filling. The oxidised spiral is first removed, then all the "powder-form" copper oxide that had contained the original sample. This sometimes cakes and may be difficult to dislodge from the walls of the tube; a rigid copper or steel rod is useful for ensuring that all is removed. It will be found that a portion of the "wire-form" copper oxide that was situated just inside the furnace will have been converted to metallic copper; it is this portion of the packing that has provided the oxygen necessary for the combustion to take place. It is essential that this spent "wire-form" copper oxide is removed and a little more of the oxide beyond it, but it is not necessary to remove all the "wire-form" copper oxide on each occasion. The tube filling is replenished by adding fresh "wire-form" copper oxide until the packing would just protrude from the furnace if the tube (not including the beak) protruded about 10–15 mm. at the far end of the furnace.

When adding the fine "powder-form" copper oxide to the combustion tube it is an advantage to have the tube clamped loosely upright, the beak end resting on the bench. The powder is then added through a small glass funnel, part of whose stem has been cut off, the resulting butt end just fitting into the wide end of the combustion tube.

A layer of 25 mm. of "powder-form" copper oxide is now added.

Its purpose is twofold; first of all to prevent any particles of the analysis sample, which is to be added next, from percolating through the coarse porous "wire-form" copper oxide and so into that portion of the tube heated by the furnace; and secondly as a heat insulator, to prevent the sample being heated too rapidly by the nearby furnace. Both these safeguards are required, as otherwise some portion of the sample would be decomposed as soon as the furnace was switched on; the nitrogen so produced would be carried away during the initial sweeping of the air out of the tube with the carbon dioxide stream, and would not be collected. Low results would thus be obtained.

A chalk mark is now made on the tube to indicate the point reached by the filling. The copper oxide containing the dispersed sample in the mixing tube is now transferred to the combustion tube via the small funnel. The powder should be poured carefully down the hole at the bottom of the funnel so that as little as possible spreads on the sloping sides of the funnel or on the upper parts of the combustion tube. A further chalk mark is now made on the combustion tube to indicate the point reached by the filling. A 10 mm. layer of "powder-form" copper oxide is placed in the mixing tube, the stopper replaced, the whole well shaken, and this charge, in turn, transferred to the combustion tube. When removing the ground-glass stopper from the mixing tube at any time, care should be taken that powder caught at the bottom of the ground-glass seal is not removed with it; this is best prevented by carefully loosening the stopper, gently turning it round and then removing it. The copper oxide washings are repeated twice more, thus ensuring the removal of all the sample from the mixing tube and the effective washing of any particles adhering to the funnel into the combustion tube. After each washing, the funnel should be gently tapped in the top of the combustion tube, thus causing any particles that may be adhering to the funnel or the inside walls of the tube to settle down on to the rest of the filling. The copper oxide spiral is finally regenerated by heating it red-hot in a Bunsen flame and allowing it to cool in air; when cold it is added to the combustion tube which is then ready for use. The portion of the tube occupied by very nearly all the sample is clearly chalk-marked, which is a useful guide when carrying out the combustion with a burner.

As the tube ages it becomes opaque and it is not possible to see, at any stage, to what level the tube packing has reached. This may be overcome by using a steel rod as a "dip-stick" and making temporary chalk marks on the tube; these are removed as filling progresses and only the two indicating the position of the sample are left. Care should be taken that the metal rod is tapped well on the inside wall of the tube before withdrawal so that no portion of the copper oxide containing the sample is left adhering to it. The spent copper oxide of both varieties removed from the tube after each estimation may be regenerated by heating in a crucible or silica dish to 700–800° in air or in a muffle furnace for about half an hour. After cooling it is sieved and then used again as "wire or powder-form" copper oxide.

Assembling the apparatus. The combustion tube **D** (Fig. 87) is now placed in the cold furnace so that the first chalk mark is not less than 25 mm. from the furnace mouth. Connection is first made to the Z-tube **B** by pushing a tight-fitting, bored rubber bung as far as it will go into the wide end of the combustion tube and then inserting the drawn-out beak of **B** with a screwing motion until the glass tube has penetrated right through the bung and is clearly visible on the far side. This is the only means by which a satisfactory gas-tight joint may be obtained. The beak at the far end of the combustion tube is now attached to the drawn-out end of the tube **F**, which has previously been attached to the side-arm of the nitrometer. Both these joints are glass-to-glass and are made with impregnated pressure tubing. The small asbestos squares **K** and **L** are now placed on the combustion tube as shown (Fig. 72).

Testing the CO_2 supply As the combustion tube has been handled and packed in the air it will at this stage be full of air which requires sweeping out before the combustion takes place. The sweeping-out process usually takes longer with a freshly packed tube as the packing gives up its occluded air rather slowly. If a stream of carbon dioxide is passed into the nitrometer full of potash, the alkali will very rapidly be exhausted; so when sweeping out, it is usual to lower the reservoir **J**, open the tap **T₃** and allow the potash to sink so that the gas traverses a column of only 20–30 mm. of alkali before passing through the empty nitrometer and out at the tap **T₃**. After the level has been so lowered, the generator is turned on and the nitrometer tap **T₂** opened wide. After gas has passed for 5 minutes, most of the air will have been swept out of the combustion tube. This may be tested by closing tap **T₂**, raising the reservoir **J** till the alkali emerges into the bulb **H**, closing **T₃** and lowering the reservoir to its original position. Care should be taken to see that tap **T₂** is *always* closed before the reservoir **J** is raised or lowered (apart from the final adjusting of levels before reading the volume of nitrogen collected at the end of the experiment, it is easier to lift the reservoir **J** out of its rim for raising and lowering, rather than running the ring up and down the central stand on each ocasion). Tap **T₂** is now cautiously opened to such an extent that not more than one bubble of gas per second passes, and these bubbles are observed carefully as they rise in the nitrometer tube. Bubbles containing a large proportion of air are not absorbed, suffer little diminution in size and rise rapidly up the tube. Bubbles of carbon dioxide, however, are absorbed, diminish in size and rise more and more slowly as they ascend. When all the air has been swept **out** of the combustion tube, the so-called micro-bubbles are obtained; these should almost disappear and not be larger than a fine dust; they swirl in the wide part of the nitrometer as they rise, instead of travelling straight upwards, and they rise extremely slowly. These bubbles are so small that it should be possible to collect them for upwards of half an hour before any detectable volume is registered on the nitrometer graduations. If these micro-bubbles are not at first obtained, the sweeping out should be continued till a subsequent test shows all the air to have been swept out of the combustion tube.

The original adjustment of the generator for production of air-free carbon dioxide may be tested in a similar manner by attaching the generator **A** through the Z-tube **B** and angle-tube **F** to the nitrometer without the combustion tube being in place and allowing the gas to run until micro-bubbles are obtained, thus showing that air-free carbon dioxide is being produced. It sometimes proves unusually difficult to get to the stage of producing micro-bubbles; this is very often due to the potash in the nitrometer becoming exhausted. As a first step, this should be changed before further search is made for any leak or other source of the trouble.

The furnace **E** is now switched on, and takes about 20 minutes before the combustion tube packing has reached the required temperature. After 15 minutes, carbon dioxide is again passed for 5 minutes, and the apparatus tested as before for the appearance of micro-bubbles. If these are not at first obtained, the sweeping-out process must be continued until they do appear. Now that the combustion-tube packing is heated up to the required temperature and the apparatus filled with carbon dioxide, all air being swept out, the combustion may be started.

The combustion. The tap **T₂** is closed, **T₃** opened and the reservoir **J** raised (Fig. 87), to make sure that no air has been collected at the top of the nitrometer tube; a small quantity of potash is left in **H** when tap **T₃** is closed and the reservoir **J** then lowered again. The carbon dioxide generator is switched off and tap **T₂** slowly turned on until it is *fully* opened.

A lighted Bunsen burner, with the air-hole fully open and the barrel fitted with a metal cone, is now gently placed under the combustion tube just at the beginning of the oxidised copper spiral (Fig. 87). Care should be taken that the burner is applied gradually to the tube at the start to prevent a sudden rush of expanding gas through the potash in the nitrometer, for if carbon dioxide passes too rapidly through the alkali it may not be completely absorbed. The Bunsen is not placed so near the rubber bung **C** that charring takes place.

The rate at which bubbles of gas enter the nitrometer is now determined solely by the rate at which the heating is carried out; it should be controlled so as never to exceed one bubble of gas per second. The oxidised copper spiral is carefully heated to redness by very slowly moving the burner along it, and the heating of the powder copper oxide, containing the washings from the mixing tube, is then started. Up to this point, any gas that enters the nitrometer will be carbon dioxide, and even while heating the initial portion of copper oxide, the amount of nitrogeneous material contained in it is so small that very little nitrogen will be evolved. As the burner approaches the first chalk mark, however, extra care is required as very nearly all the sample is contained in this small section of tube filling, and overheating will cause rapid combustion with a consequent rapid stream of gas bubbles in the nitrometer. The great danger here is that these bubbles containing both nitrogen and carbon dioxide may rise rapidly through the potash and a considerable proportion of the constituent carbon dioxide will then never be absorbed by the alkali, thus leading to high results. Nearly all the errors made in nitrogen determinations arise from this source and the importance of a slow, regular evolution of gas controlled by careful combustion, cannot be overstressed. As soon as there is any sign of too rapid an evolution of gas the burner should immediately be moved 5 cm. back along the tube; rapidity of this movement is particularly important as there is usually a time lag between any overheating and the emergence of the offending bubbles in the nitrometer. Heating is continued until the burner arrives at the furnace mouth. The burner may then be extinguished.

Sweeping out. Although the combustion is now finished, a considerable proportion of the evolved nitrogen will still be left in the combustion tube and it is necessary to sweep this out into the nitrometer. The tap T_2 on the nitrometer is closed, the tap T_1 on the carbon dioxide generator opened and then tap T_2 reopened to such an extent that one bubble of gas per second is passing. The sweeping out is continued until micro-bubbles, similar to those obtained at the beginning of the experiment, are again obtained. This generally takes about ten minutes.

It sometimes happens that two or more bubbles coalesce to form one that hardly rises at all in the narrow part of the nitrometer tube; this may be driven up to the rest of the collected gas at the top of the tube by gently squeezing the rubber pressure tubing connecting the movable reservoir J with the nitrometer proper.

The tap T_2 is now closed. The furnace is switched off and the carbon dioxide generator left on until the combustion tube is cold; this ensures that the reduced copper spiral, by cooling in carbon dioxide, is maintained in the reduced state. (Despite this precaution it does become spent and should be replaced from time to time. A spent copper spiral leads to high results, but before this takes place there is usually sufficient indication by dulling and loss of colour of the spiral.) Finally the generator is switched off.

Reading the volume. The levelling bulb **J** is now raised on its carriage and clamped at the same level as the liquid in the graduated tube of the nitrometer. After standing for 10 minutes, the levels are finally adjusted and the volume of nitrogen read off with the aid of a lens. (If the meniscus is obscured by small bubbles which have collected at the gas-liquid interface, these may be dispersed as before by gently squeezing the rubber pressure tubing connecting the reservoir **J** with the nitrometer.) The temperature is read on the thermometer suspended from a clamp at the side of the graduated tube and the atmospheric pressure read off from an accurate barometer.

Blank on tube. It is advisable with a newly packed tube to carry out a determination on A.R. glucose (*ca.* 25 mg.); this serves to burn out the tube by removing occluded air from the permanent filling and also as an additional check on the quality of the carbon dioxide supply.

Example of Calculation.

Before using the observed gas volume to calculate the percentage of nitrogen in the sample being analysed, a correction has to be made for the vapour pressure of the potassium hydroxide solution and for the retention of some liquid near the top of the nitrometer due to the slow draining of the rather viscous potash solution down the walls of the narrow nitrometer tube. Both these factors will have the effect of making the observed value *larger* than the theoretical value; Pregl found that both could be adequately corrected for empirically by *subtracting* 2% from the measured volume before carrying out the calculation.

Estimation of N in acetanilide.

0·0237 g. of acetanilide gave 2·21 ml. of N_2 at 18°C. and 754 mm.

∴ 0·0237 g. of acetanilide gave

$$\frac{2·21 \times 0·98 \times 273 \times 754}{291 \times 760} \text{ ml. (corrected) at S.T.P.}$$

∴ 0·0237 g. of acetanilide contains

$$\frac{2·21 \times 0·98 \times 273 \times 754 \times 28}{291 \times 760 \times 22,400} \text{ g. of nitrogen}$$

∴ 100 g. of acetanilide contain

$$\frac{2·21 \times 0·98 \times 273 \times 754 \times 28 \times 100}{291 \times 760 \times 22,400 \times 0·0237} \text{ g. of nitrogen}$$

$$= 10·6\%.$$

Theoretical for C_8H_9NO; 10·4%.

Substances suitable for the estimation: acetanilide, diphenylamine, glycine, benzanilide.

The Kjeldhal Method.

Principle. A definite amount of the substance (*ca.* 25 mg.) is weighed out and transferred to a special Kjeldhal flask; it is decomposed by digesting with concentrated sulphuric acid and the nitrogen thereby converted quantitatively to ammonium sulphate. The acid solution is then transferred to a steam-distillation apparatus, made alkaline and the ammonia steam-distilled into saturated boric acid solution and finally titrated against standard acid.

The more easily the nitrogen is converted to ammonia, the more satisfactorily can the method be carried out. This method was originally utilised for the determination of nitrogen in amines, amino-acids, *etc.*, and was particularly useful for the nitrogen analysis of biological material. The sulphuric acid digestion may be expedited and improved by the use of catalysts such as selenium and mercuric sulphate. The direct method is unsuitable for a number of substances, especially azo compounds and substances where oxygen is attached to nitrogen as in nitro and nitroso compounds, as there is a tendency to lose some of the nitrogen as gaseous nitrogen or as an oxide. Such compounds may still be estimated by this method, however, if they are first reduced with hydrogen iodide and red phosphorus before undergoing the digestion process. It is indeed sometimes sufficient merely to add an excess of glucose to the digestion mixture thus avoiding the separate operation of reduction. Unless such substances can be reduced easily and without waste of time, it is probably desirable that more elementary students should use the Dumas method for the determination of nitrogen in these compounds.

Apparatus.

Steam-distillation unit. This consists of a steam generator **A** (Fig. 88) which is a 1-litre round-bottomed flask with a tight-fitting rubber bung wired in. The bung carries a tube **B** for delivering steam to the apparatus proper and a tap-funnel **C** for refilling the flask with water. Tube **B** is connected to a steam-trap **D** which is provided with a tap T_1 (or rubber tube and screw-clip) at the bottom for releasing any condensed water. The trap has a side-arm, also provided with a tap T_2, which is connected to the glass tube **E** (28 cm. × 3 mm.) reaching down to the bottom of the 150 ml. distillation bulb **F**. The end of this tube is bent down as shown to prevent the splashing over of liquid droplets. The tube **E** is provided with a small tap-funnel **G** which is closed either by the tap T_3 or by a rubber tube carrying a screw-clip. The solution to be steam-distilled is subsequently introduced through **G**.

The distillation bulb **F** is connected by a length of glass tubing (15 cm. × 2·5 cm.) to a double-bulb splash-head **H** which prevents any liquid droplets being carried right over during a distillation. The upper bulb carries an exit tube of transparent quartz **Q** (1 cm. in diameter) which is bent over twice at right angles. The short vertical limb is 10 cm. long and is bent as shown to form a further splash precaution. The horizontal limb is 20 cm. long and the vertical limb 40 cm. long; the latter is provided wth a 30 cm. water-jacket, converting it into a condenser, whose lower end **K** dips into a 100 ml. conical flask **J**, the level of which may be raised and lowered. It is necessary to make this part of the apparatus of quartz as the steam will dissolve traces of alkali from even hard glass. It is most convenient to have the apparatus arranged so that it may all be clamped around the same stand.

Before assembling, the constituent parts of the apparatus should be washed in turn with warm conc. nitric acid, distilled water, acetone, and dried in an oven.

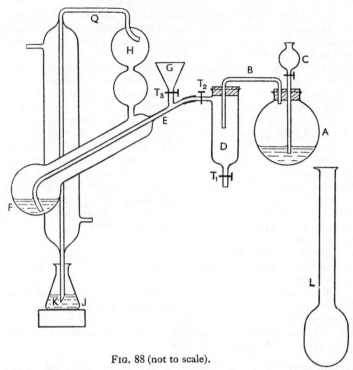

FIG. 88 (not to scale).

Digestion apparatus. The Kjeldhal flasks **L** of Pyrex glass are shaped as shown with a 50 ml. capacity bulb and a long neck (10 cm. × 1·5 cm.), provided with a small lip or spout. When digestion is proceeding they are supported over a micro-burner by an asbestos-centred gauze, and the top end is lightly clamped so that the flask is tilted slightly to the vertical. The flasks should be supplied with loosely fitting glass stoppers, made by drawing out and sealing off the bottom end of a hard glass boiling-tube. Digestions should *always* be carried out in a fume-cupboard as considerable quantities of sulphur di- and tri-oxides may be evolved.

Digestion. 20–25 mg. of the substance whose nitrogen content is to be estimated are weighed out in a stoppered weighing-tube and then transferred to the flask **L** that has been previously dried in an oven at 120°C. With care, the substance may be transferred directly into the bulb of the flask without any adhering to the sides. If any material sticks on the way down, the flask should be tapped gently to cause the substance to fall to the bottom. 2 G. of the catalyst mixture (32 g. of potassium sulphate, 5 g. of mercury sulphate and 1g. of selenium powder, well mixed) are added and 3 ml. of A.R. conc. sulphuric acid are measured out carefully and poured into the digestion flask. The acid should be poured straight into the bulb without touching the sides unless any of the nitrogenous sample has adhered to the walls of the flask, in which case the acid may be used to wash the particles down into the bulb of the digestion flask.

The loose stopper is now inserted into the flask with the drawn-off end downwards. The mixture is heated over the micro-burner so that the solution boils *gently* for 5 minutes, the heating is then increased so that the solution boils vigorously, and digestion continued for a further 45 minutes; the liquid should then be colourless. Many substances will have been decomposed quantitatively on shorter heating but the above period should suffice for all substances for which the method is suitable; the vigorous heating should in no circumstances be continued for longer than 45 minutes. As well as this Kjeldhal flask, another should be put on to digest at the same time, prepared in exactly the same way except that approximately 30 mg. of A.R. glucose (only roughly weighed out) are substituted for the nitrogenous material. This serves as a blank for the method and a test for the purity of the reagents.

As has been mentioned above, many substances which do not give satisfactory nitrogen analyses by this method can be made to do so if, before digestion, they are reduced with red phosphorus and hydrogen iodide. This procedure is rather tedious, however, and satisfactory results can often be obtained if 500 mg. of A.R. glucose are added to the digestion mixture—the digestion then being carried out in the usual way (Elek and Sobotka, *J. Amer. Chem. Soc.*, 1926, **48**, 501). Substances that do not yield to this modified procedure are best estimated by the Dumas method.

Steaming-out the steam-distillation apparatus. After the cleaned steam-distillation apparatus (Fig. 88) has been assembled, it is essential to pass steam through it for some time to remove readily soluble alkali. All the taps on the apparatus are opened and the water in the steam generator boiled vigorously. The steam will gradually pass into the apparatus. After a few minutes, the tap of the tap-funnel **C** may be closed and soon afterwards the tap T_1 of the steam-trap; finally the tap T_3 of the funnel **G** may be closed. Steaming-out should then be continued for not less than one hour, the receiver **J** not being in place.

During this process some water will have condensed in the steam-trap **D** and also in the distillation bulb **F**. If at the end of the steaming-out process, the Bunsen burner is removed from the generator **A**, the pressure in **A** will be reduced owing to steam condensation, and the liquid in **F** will be sucked back into **D**; provided that the bent-over tube is carefully adjusted, the bulb **F** may be almost completely emptied of liquid as desired. Finally the condensed water in the steam-trap **D** may be run out by opening the tap T_1.

Before each experiment the steam-distillation apparatus should be steamed-out for about half an hour; this may be carried out while the digestion is taking place.

Charging the steam-distillation apparatus. After steaming-out, and when the digestion in **L** is complete, the Bunsen burner is replaced under the steam-generator **A** and the tap on the tap-funnel **C**, and taps **T₂** and **T₃** closed; as steam is generated it is allowed to pass out of the steam-trap through **T₁**. A steady stream of water is now passed through the condenser. Exactly 20 ml. of a freshly mixed solution of 40% sodium hydroxide* and 40% sodium sulphide are run into the funnel **G**. (The 40% alkali and 40% sulphide solutions are made up in bulk and freshly mixed in the proportion of 9 vols. of alkali to 1 vol. of sulphide as required.) The tap **T₃** is opened and the alkali run into the bulb **F**. The tap is then closed and the funnel washed carefully round with a fine jet of distilled water; when washing is complete, **T₃** is opened and the wash-water allowed to run into **F**. The process is then repeated—the *total* washings being not more than 5–10 ml. Tap **T₃** is then left closed. 10 Ml. of saturated boric acid solution are poured into **J** which is then adjusted (seting at an angle if necessary) so that the end of the condenser is 2–3 mm. belowtth surface of the liquid but not touching the bottom of the flask.

The digestion mixture is allowed to cool in the Kjeldhal flask and then diluted with 10 ml. of distilled water. It is then carefully poured into the funnel **G** (Fig. 88), the last drop on the lip of the flask being washed off with a few drops of distilled water from a wash-bottle. The tap **T₃** is then carefully opened and the acid solution allowed to run down into the bulb **F**. A small quantity of the solution is prevented from flowing through **T₃** by closing the tap; this is to prevent the possibility of any of the ammonia, liberated when the acid ammonium sulphate solution is run into an excess of alkali, from escaping through **T₃** and thus introducing a large error into the determination. The flask **L** is now carefully washed out with 5 ml. of distilled water from a wash-bottle and the washings transferred to the funnel **G**. The washings are run into the bulb **F** by opening the tap **T₃**, but again a small liquid seal is left in **G** by closing **T₃** before all the liquid has passed through. This washing is repeated twice more; each time a small liquid seal being left in the funnel **G**. Finally, the walls of the funnel are washed with 5 ml. of distilled water and the wash allowed to flow through **T₃** into the bulb **F**; a small liquid seal is still left at **T₃** above the closed tap. The liquid in the bulb will now be black owing to the precipitation of mercury sulphide by the interaction of the sodium sulphide solution and the mercuric sulphate of the catalyst mixture— this prevents the possible formation of any mercury-ammonia complexes that might prevent the quantitative distillation of the latter.

Distillation of the ammonia. The ammonia which has been liberated quantitatively in the bulb **F** must now be distilled completely into the receiver **J**. The tap **T₁** on the steam-trap is therefore closed and tap **T₂** opened so that the steam is delivered into the bulb **F**, which at the same time is heated directly with the flame of a micro-Bunsen

---

* These solutions are obtained by dissolving 40 g. of the solid in water so that the final volume of the cold *solution* is 100 ml. With pure sodium hydroxide, the alkaline solution should be quite clear and free from insoluble material. The sodium sulphide used is the crystalline Na_2S, $9H_2O$.

burner. This prevents any considerable increase in the volume of liquid in the bulb **F** due to steam condensation. If too great a volume of liquid collects in **F**, the chance of minute droplets of concentrated sodium hydroxide splashing over into the receiver is much increased, and very small quantities of this alkaline liquid will introduce very large errors.

The steam-distillation is continued for 5 minutes after steam can first be seen entering the condenser; the ideal rate of distillation is about 4–5 ml. of distillate per minute, but this is not critical and may be varied within reasonable limits. The receiver **J** is then lowered from the lip **K** of the condenser and the steam-distillation continued for a further two minutes, thus ensuring that no traces of liquid containing ammonia are left on the inside of the condenser. At the end of this time any liquid on the lip **K** is rinsed with distilled water into **J**, which is then ready for titration. It is important that the receiver and its contents are kept cold during the distillation and it is advisable to interpose a piece of asbestos board or other screen so that it is not exposed to the heat from the burner under the steam generator.

Titration. The solution of ammonia absorbed in saturated boric acid may now be titrated as an alkali directly with 0·025 N.HCl (best obtained by dilution of commercially available standard N.HCl in a graduated flask). Three drops of indicator (mixed methyl-red/methylene-blue being most satisfactory) are added to the liquid in the receiver and the 0·025 N.HCl run in from an accurate burette.

Blank estimation. The distillation bulb is now emptied, as already described, by removing the burner from under the steam generator, only tap **T₂** being left open; the spent charge from **F** is thereby forced over into **D** and may be run out through **T₁**. The complete experiment, including titration, is then repeated with the digestion mixture from *ca.* 30 mg. of A.R. glucose in place of the nitrogenous material. The volume of acid used is *subtracted* from the titre obtained in the real experiment. The blank estimation serves as a check on (i) the purity of the reagents, (ii) any droplets of alkali that may have splashed over in the steam, and (iii) any other sources of error. (The blank estimation may advantageously be carried out before the actual estimation, to familiarise the student with the general manipulation.)

Example of Calculation.
Estimation of N in glycine.
0·02035 g. of glycine yielded an amount of NH_3 that required 10·96 ml. of 0·025 M.HCl. A blank estimation carried out on A.R. glucose (30 mg.) resulted in a titre of 0·20 ml. of 0·025 M.HCl.

10·76 ml. 0·025 M.HCl = 10·76 ml. 0·025 M.NH_3 solution

$$= \frac{10\cdot76 \times 14 \times 0\cdot025}{1000} \text{ g. nitrogen}$$

∴ 0·02035 g. glycine contains $\dfrac{10\cdot76 \times 14 \times 0\cdot025}{1000}$ g. nitrogen

$$\therefore \text{ 100 g. glycine contain } \frac{10 \cdot 76 \times 14 \times 0 \cdot 025 \times 100}{1000 \times 0 \cdot 02035} \text{ g. nitrogen}$$
$$= 18 \cdot 5\%.$$

Theoretical for $C_2H_5NO_2$; $18 \cdot 7\%$ N.

Substances suitable for the estimation: acetanilide, diphenylamine, glycine, benzanilide.

Estimation of Methoxyl (CH_3O-) Groups. (Zeisel's Method.)

Principle. A definite amount of the substance (*ca.* 25 mg.) is weighed out and transferred to the reaction bulb of the apparatus where it is decomposed by refluxing with constant-boiling hydriodic acid, the essential reaction being:

$$R \cdot OCH_3 + HI \longrightarrow R \cdot OH + CH_3I$$

The methyl iodide is transferred quantitatively (by means of a stream of a carrier gas such as carbon dioxide) to an absorption vessel where it either reacts with alcoholic silver nitrate solution and is finally estimated gravimetrically as AgI, or it is absorbed in an acetic acid solution containing bromine. In the latter case, iodine monobromide is first formed, further oxidation yielding iodic acid, which on subsequent treatment with acid KI solution liberates iodine which is finally estimated with thiosulphate (*cf.* p. 501). The advantage of this latter method is that six times the original quantity of iodine is finally liberated.

This method is not confined to methoxyl groups but can be used for ethoxyl as well, but higher alkyl groups do not yield iodides that are sufficiently volatile. The method may also be used for the estimation of methyl and ethyl groups attached to nitrogen, but the reaction with hydrogen iodide must now be carried out at a rather higher temperature. Sufficient control can readily be exercised so that the $-OCH_3$ and $-NCH_3$ groups in a compound containing both may be separately estimated; this is of particular value in the field of alkaloid chemistry where such compounds are often encountered.

The chief potential source of error to be avoided is the passing over of any of the concentrated hydrogen iodide with the methyl iodide, thus causing high results. This is prevented by a small water-condenser which does not keep back the methyl iodide, and also a gas-trap containing a suspension of red phosphorus in water. Another potential error is introduced by the low solubility of some methyl ethers in the aqueous hydrogen iodide, leading to incomplete decomposition and low results; this can be overcome, for instance, by the addition of a small quantity of phenol to the reaction mixture, thus increasing the solubility. A difficulty not so easy to surmount is the ease with which a number of ethers will sublime out of the hot hydrogen iodide before they have been decomposed (2-naphthyl methyl ether is a particularly marked example of this). It is also important that the flow of carrier gas should be slow to avoid any chance of some of the methyl iodide passing so rapidly through the absorbing liquid as to escape into the air. This is prevented by inserting a glass spiral into the receiver in order to increase the length of path the iodide must traverse.

Apparatus. The apparatus is made of Pyrex glass, in one piece. It consists of a shaped bulb **A** (Fig. 89) of about 30 ml. capacity in which the reaction takes place, provided with an inclined inlet **B** at the side and a vertical ascension tube **D**. **B** serves not only as an inlet for the admission of the carrier gas but also as the route by which the reagents and test sample are introduced into the apparatus. **B** ends in a small ground-glass joint into which fits a joint carrying a capillary-tube which projects well down into the bulb **A** (the end of the capillary should be just above the liquid level when the apparatus is charged for the determination). The upper extension of this capillary beyond the joint is provided with a tap **C** to control the rate of flow of the carrier gas.

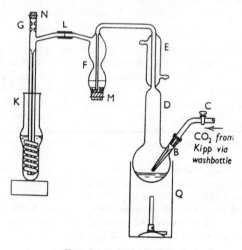

FIG. 89   (not to scale).

This tube is connected with rubber tubing of about 6 mm. bore to the carbon dioxide Kipp, via a wash-bottle containing sodium carbonate solution (to remove any dilute hydrochloric acid spray). It is very important, when the apparatus is in use, that there should be no constriction or bend in the rubber tube between the tap **C** and the wash-bottle. If these precautions are taken, a slow, even, and easily controlled flow of gas can be obtained.

The ascension tube **D** (*ca.* 1 cm. in diameter*) rises for about 8 cm. above **A**, then narrows (5 mm. in diameter) to form a small condenser **E** (8 cm. long). The ascension tube then bends over in a flattened U-shape and descends into the gas-washer **F** (*ca.* 8 cm. long). The tube continues to the bottom of the washer, leaving a gap of only 1–2 mm. when **F** is closed by the insertion of the rubber bung **M**. The tube in this section is 2–3 mm. in diameter. The outlet tube

---

* The dimensions given for the various tubes are those which have been found most suitable: they may however be varied within narrow limits.

opened bottle are not left standing about too long.) To prevent bromine vapour spreading in the laboratory, a lightly fitting plug of cotton-wool, moistened with 1–2 drops of formic acid, is inserted just into the wide part of the receiver **K**. The latter is then drawn up over the delivery-tube, so that there is a gap of only 1–2 mm. between the lower end of **H** and the bottom of **K**, and it is then held in place by a wooden block.

The test sample is now weighed out. This is best done by weighing 20–25 mg. into a small tinfoil cup: (the cup is best made by cutting the corners off a small square of tinfoil, and then pressing this circle into a cup by rubbing it into shape round the end of a glass rod). After the material has been introduced, the cup should be gently tapped on a metal block, while held with balance tweezers, to ensure that no particles of the sample are adhering to its outside edge; this also serves to settle the material down on to the floor of the cup. The cup, after weighing, is lightly closed by pinching the edges together and then slid carefully down the side-arm **B** into the reaction vessel **A**. For many substances it is quite satisfactory to weigh the material on a small square of cigarette paper (any gummed edge being cut off), which is finally folded over as before. If this is done, however, it is necessary to introduce a few minute pieces of unglazed porcelain into **A** in order to promote smooth boiling. With the tin cup this is unnecessary, as the stannic iodide produced by the dissolution of the cup promotes steady boiling and prevents bumping. About 20 mg. of pure phenol are then added. Finally 5 ml. of hydriodic acid* M.A.R. grade, d 1·7, are added from a pipette, the end of which should be inserted well into vessel **A**, and care taken in withdrawal so that no hydrogen iodide is left in the side-arm **B**. The ground-glass joint is now inserted into the side-arm and the rubber tube from the Kipp and wash-bottle attached. The tap **C** is now fully closed and the Kipp tap opened. Tap **C** is now very carefully opened until carbon dioxide begins to pass and adjusted so that not more than two bubbles are rising round the spiral in the receiver **K** at one time. It is very important to ensure at this stage that the rate is quite satisfactory, as too rapid a flow will almost certainly result in some methyl iodide escaping absorption. Finally a very slow stream of water is allowed to flow through the condenser **E**.

The Evolution of Methyl Iodide. The flask **A** (Fig. 89) is now heated with the non-luminous flame of the micro-burner. The immediate result of the heating will be an increase in the rate of bubbles passing up the absorption spiral; no endeavour should be made to decrease this flow, however, as it will return to the original rate as soon as the hydro-

---

* This should be free from sulphur, and obtained in small containers so that a specimen is rapidly used; it should be in dark bottles and stored in the dark. When withdrawing a specimen, the acid should be exposed to the air for as short a time as possible, as both air and light promote its decomposition to iodine.

opened bottle are not left standing about too long.) To prevent bromine vapour spreading in the laboratory, a lightly fitting plug of cotton-wool, moistened with 1–2 drops of formic acid, is inserted just into the wide part of the receiver **K**. The latter is then drawn up over the delivery-tube, so that there is a gap of only 1–2 mm. between the lower end of **H** and the bottom of **K**, and it is then held in place by a wooden block.

The test sample is now weighed out. This is best done by weighing 20–25 mg. into a small tinfoil cup: (the cup is best made by cutting the corners off a small square of tinfoil, and then pressing this circle into a cup by rubbing it into shape round the end of a glass rod). After the material has been introduced, the cup should be gently tapped on a metal block, while held with balance tweezers, to ensure that no particles of the sample are adhering to its outside edge; this also serves to settle the material down on to the floor of the cup. The cup, after weighing, is lightly closed by pinching the edges together and then slid carefully down the side-arm **B** into the reaction vessel **A**. For many substances it is quite satisfactory to weigh the material on a small square of cigarette paper (any gummed edge being cut off), which is finally folded over as before. If this is done, however, it is necessary to introduce a few minute pieces of unglazed porcelain into **A** in order to promote smooth boiling. With the tin cup this is unnecessary, as the stannic iodide produced by the dissolution of the cup promotes steady boiling and prevents bumping. About 20 mg. of pure phenol are then added. Finally 5 ml. of hydriodic acid* M.A.R. grade, d 1·7, are added from a pipette, the end of which should be inserted well into vessel **A**, and care taken in withdrawal so that no hydrogen iodide is left in the side-arm **B**. The ground-glass joint is now inserted into the side-arm and the rubber tube from the Kipp and wash-bottle attached. The tap **C** is now fully closed and the Kipp tap opened. Tap **C** is now very carefully opened until carbon dioxide begins to pass and adjusted so that not more than two bubbles are rising round the spiral in the receiver **K** at one time. It is very important to ensure at this stage that the rate is quite satisfactory, as too rapid a flow will almost certainly result in some methyl iodide escaping absorption. Finally a very slow stream of water is allowed to flow through the condenser **E**.

The Evolution of Methyl Iodide. The flask **A** (Fig. 89) is now heated with the non-luminous flame of the micro-burner. The immediate result of the heating will be an increase in the rate of bubbles passing up the absorption spiral; no endeavour should be made to decrease this flow, however, as it will return to the original rate as soon as the hydro-

* This should be free from sulphur, and obtained in small containers so that a specimen is rapidly used; it should be in dark bottles and stored in the dark. When withdrawing a specimen, the acid should be exposed to the air for as short a time as possible, as both air and light promote its decomposition to iodine.

gen iodide begins to boil. The mixture is kept boiling gently for 40 minutes. At the end of this period the vessel **K** containing the spiral **J** is lowered from the tube **H**, which is then rinsed inside and out with small quantities of distilled water from a wash-bottle provided with a fine nozzle; these washings are caught in **K**.

Titration. The contents of the receiver **K** (Fig. 89, p. 498) are then washed quantitatively into a 25 ml. conical flask containing 10 ml. of 20% sodium acetate solution; the sodium acetate/acetic acid is present in order to buffer the hydrobromic acid formed in Equation 2 (*b*) below. (It is an advantage to have these conical flasks provided with ground-in stoppers; alternatively, well-fitting dry rubber bungs can be used. In the latter case the flasks should be swirled well rather than shaken so that the liquid does not touch the rubber.) To destroy the excess of bromine, two drops of formic acid (not less than 80% concentration) are now added and the solution shaken; if necessary, more formic acid is added, one drop at a time, each addition being followed by shaking, until both the colour and smell of bromine have disappeared. 5 Ml. of 10% potassium iodide solution are added, the solution swirled, and then acidified with 10 ml. of $2N.H_2SO_4$. The solution is immediately stoppered, gently swirled, allowed to stand for 3 minutes and then titrated against $0.025 \ N.Na_2S_2O_3$ solution from an accurate burette. The thiosulphate is run in rapidly, the titration flask being swirled until a faint yellow colour is obtained; the burette reading is then noted and the solution carefully titrated till colourless, using a white glazed tile underneath the flask and another one behind it.

Blank estimation. A blank estimation in which A.R. glucose is used should be carried out exactly as above as a check on the method and on the purity of the reagents employed.

Reactions involved:

1. $R \cdot OCH_3 + HI \longrightarrow R \cdot OH + CH_3I$
2. (*a*) $CH_3I + Br_2 \longrightarrow CH_3Br + IBr$

   (*b*) $IBr + 3H_2O + 2Br_2 \longrightarrow HIO_3 + 5HBr$
3. $HIO_3 + 5KI + H_2SO_4 \longrightarrow 3I_2$
4. $3I_2 + 6Na_2S_2O_3 \longrightarrow 3Na_2S_4O_6 + 6NaI$

$\therefore$ **$-OCH_3 \equiv CH_3I \equiv HIO_3 \equiv 3I_2 \equiv 6Na_2S_2O_3$**

Example of Calculation.

Estimation of methoxyl group in vanillin.

0.02445 g. of vanillin yielded a solution that required 38.10 ml. $0.025 \ M.Na_2S_2O_3$ solution for decolorisation.

$6 \times 40,000$ ml. $0.025 \ M.Na_2S_2O_3$ solution $\equiv 31$ g. CH_3O group.

$\therefore 38.10$ ml. $0.025 \ M.Na_2S_2O_3$ solution $\equiv \dfrac{31 \times 38.10}{240,000}$ g. CH_3O group.

Hence 0.02445 g. of vanillin contains $\dfrac{31 \times 38.10}{240,000}$ g. CH_3O group

∴ 100 g. of vanillin contain $\dfrac{31 \times 38 \cdot 10 \times 100}{240,000 \times 0 \cdot 02445}$ g. CH$_3$O group

$= 20 \cdot 1\%$ Methoxyl Group.

Theoretical for C$_8$H$_8$O$_3$; $20 \cdot 4\%$ CH$_3$O.

Alternatively, since Molecular Weight of vanillin is $152 \cdot 1$,

$152 \cdot 1$ g. vanillin contain $\dfrac{31 \times 38 \cdot 10 \times 152 \cdot 1}{240,000 \times 0 \cdot 02445}$ g. CH$_3$O group.

(Weight CH$_3$O $= 31$)

$= \dfrac{38 \cdot 10 \times 152 \cdot 1}{240,000 \times 0 \cdot 02445}$ CH$_3$O group

$0 \cdot 99$ CH$_3$O group.

Substances suitable for the estimation: vanillin, veratrole.

Estimation of Halogens

Two simple methods for the semi-micro estimation of halogens are available, (*a*) the Carius method, and (*b*) the Parr "bomb" method. It should be emphasised that there are other methods available for these estimations on the true micro scale, but they do not lend themselves, by virtue of the balances, apparatus and manipulation required, to semi-micro work, or to the intermittent usage which class-work necessarily entails.

The Carius Method

Principle. This is essentially a small-scale modification of the macro method described on p. 416, the substance being completely oxidised in a sealed tube with fuming nitric acid in the presence of silver nitrate, the halogen being thus converted into silver halide. The collection and weighing of the silver halide require special techniques on the semi-micro scale.

Apparatus. Prepare an open strong-walled glass tube sealed at the lower end, precisely as in Fig. 72 (c) (p. 417), but about 35 cm. in length, and having internal and external diameters 9 and 13 mm. respectively (Fig. 90).

A weighing-cup **A** consists of a small glass cup about 2 cm. deep fused to a fine glass rod, the total length being about 8 cm. [For certain other purposes, *e.g.*, the semi-micro method for molecular weight determinations (pp. 436, 442), it is advantageous for this cup to have a small ground-glass stopper.] For general manipulation, the weighing cup **A** is held in a narrow glass "holding" tube **B**, and secured by a short collar of rubber tubing **C** (Fig. 90).

When weighing the cup **A**, it should be supported on the balance pan by a light aluminium carrier **D**, one upright end of which should preferably be *slightly* higher than the other, so that the cup is tilted slightly upwards during weighing.

A glass dropping-tube **E**, for the introduction of the nitric acid, is made with a small bulb just above the lower end, so that with care it can be withdrawn without the nitric acid coming in contact with the walls of the Carius tube.

The apparatus for collecting the silver halide is described later.

Method. Weighing the Sample. Remove the cup **A** from the holding-tube **B**, using a clean cloth and avoiding any contact of **A** with the hands, place it on the carrier **D** on the balance pan, and weigh it approximately (*i.e.*, to the nearest mg.). Then remove it from the pan, hold it upright in the cloth, and place *ca.* 25 mg. of the powdered compound under analysis in the cup: this transfer should be carried out with a micro-spatula in several separate operations, and the total amount must not exceed the limits of 20–30 mg. Then tap the cup gently with the spatula to settle the sample well down into the cup, and carefully remove with a clean cloth any solid still adhering to the outside or to the rim of the cup. Replace the cup on the carrier on the balance pan and weigh it carefully. If the weight proves to be outside the above limits, the compound must be added or removed before noting the weight.

Now refit the cup **A** carefully into the holding-tube **B**, and insert the whole to within 1 inch of the bottom of the Carius tube, which is meanwhile held horizontally. Then hold the Carius tube upright, and tap the cup *very gently* on the side of the tube to dislodge the sample; withdraw the holding-tube and cup carefully and slowly to avoid further contact with the sides of the tube. Remove the cup again from its holding-tube with a clean cloth and weigh it as before.

Filling and sealing the Carius tube. Introduce 100–150 mg. of powdered silver nitrate into the Carius tube, either through a spill of filter-paper rolled and inserted as described on p. 418, or through a small funnel, so that the powder falls freely to the bottom of the tube and does not touch or adhere to the walls.

Now pour *not more than* 0·5 ml. of fuming nitric acid (care in handling!) through a small funnel into the upper chamber of the dropping-tube **E** (Fig. 90). Insert the tube **E** to within 1 inch of the bottom of the Carius tube, open the tap slightly, and allow the acid (about 10 drops) to run in. Then withdraw the dropping-tube, taking great care that traces of nitric acid are not deposited on the upper sides of the tube.

Seal the tube precisely as described on p. 419. In view of the short length of the tube, a piece of stout glass rod can be temporarily fused to the open end to act as a handle whilst rotating the tube during the sealing (p. 419).

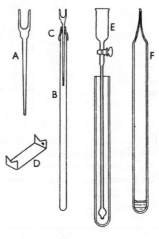

Fig. 90.

Place the sealed tube **F** (Fig. 90) in a strong iron tube, so that only the tip projects (*cf.* Fig. 74, p. 420), and heat it preferably in an electric furnace. The temperature should be increased to 280° over a period of *ca.* 45 minutes, and then maintained at this value for a further 4 hours. Then turn off the heating, and allow the tube to cool for several hours, and when possible overnight.

Opening the Carius tube. A considerable pressure will remain in the cold tube, and the precautions described in detail on p. 421 for opening the tube *must* be observed. (It is sufficient here to emphasise again that the tip of the Carius tube, whilst the latter is still in the iron tube, is cautiously heated with a small Bunsen flame until the glass softens and the gases blow out through a hole in the tip. The top of the tube is then cut off, taking precautions to ensure that no fragments of glass fall inside the tube.)

Collecting the silver halide. Meanwhile assemble the apparatus shown in Fig. 91. **G** is a filter-funnel having a sintered glass filter-plate

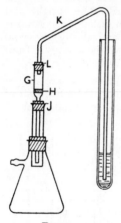

FIG. 91.

H. The stem of **G** fits through the bung **J** to the filter-flask as shown. A bent tube **K**, known as a Pregl filter-tube, is fitted through another bung **L** into the upper neck of the funnel **G**.

To prepare the funnel **G**, fit it to the filter-flask and wash it by passing distilled water, ethanol and acetone through the glass plate **H**. Remove **G** from the bung **J**, wipe it with a clean cloth, and dry it in an oven for 15 minutes at 140°. Then carefully wipe it again with the cloth, and place it in the balance case on the carrier **D** (Fig. 90) for 15 minutes to attain an equilibrium with the air. Then transfer it to the balance pan and weigh.

Add 3 ml. of distilled water slowly from a wash-bottle to the Carius tube, rotating the latter meanwhile so that any solid particles on the walls of the tube will be washed down. Now hold the tube in an oblique position, and *very gently* warm the extreme base of the tube in the flame of a small micro-Bunsen burner, until the liquid begins to boil, the tube being rotated and slightly shaken meanwhile to prevent "bumping." The object of this heating is to break up the cake of silver halide and to dissolve out the silver nitrate which it may contain. Unless very great care is taken, however, vigorous "bumping" may occur, and the silver halide may be flung out of the tube.

Now fit the weighed funnel **G** again to the filter-flask, and attach the Pregl filter-tube **K** as shown (Fig. 21). Apply a *gentle* suction from the water-pump, and dip the open limb of the tube **K** just below the surface of the liquid in the Carius tube. Draw off the supernatant liquid a little at a time until rather less than 1 ml. remains. Now gently shake the mixture in the Carius tube, and try to adjust the suction so

that almost all the suspended silver halide is drawn over in one operation. Then add 3 ml. of distilled water, shake the mixture, and draw
it over by suction a little at a time. Repeat this operation twice more,
first rubbing down gently with the end of the tube **K** any particles of
silver chloride adhering to the walls of the Carius tube. Finally add
two separate portions of ethanol, each of 5 ml., and draw them over.

Remove the tube **K** and the bung **L**. Examine the underside of the
bung for any particles of silver halide that might be adhering: wash
any such particles down into the funnel **G** with a small quantity of
ethanol. Then wash the inside walls of the funnel, under gentle
suction, with 5 ml. of ethanol from a wash-bottle, and finally the walls
and precipitate with two 5 ml. portions of acetone, and drain well.

Drying and weighing the silver halide. Remove the funnel **G**
from the bung **J**, wipe it with a clean cloth, and close the wide end by gently
inserting a small plug of cotton wool: the object of the plug is to prevent
any small granules of silver halide from falling out during handling, and it
must *not* be pressed down into the funnel. The funnel is then treated
precisely as before the first accurate weighing, namely, it is dried in an
oven at 140° for 15 minutes, then wiped all over with a clean cloth,
and transferred to the carrier in the balance case and allowed to mature
for 15 minutes. The cotton-wool plug is removed, and the funnel on
the carrier is weighed.

The calculation is identical in type with the example given on p. 423.

The Parr Bomb Method

Principle. An organic compound which contains chlorine is mixed with
sodium peroxide and ignited in a closed metal "bomb." The chlorine is thus
converted to sodium chloride, and after acidification the chloride is estimated
by the Volhard volumetric method. Bromine and iodine, when constituents of
organic compounds similarly treated, are converted largely into sodium bromate
and iodate respectively: these ions are therefore subsequently reduced by
hydrazine to bromide and iodide ions, and estimated as before.

Apparatus. The Parr Bomb is made of pure nickel, or of nickel-steel with
a very high nickel content: it remains clean and bright after many operations.
Stainless steel is not employed, as it is attacked under the conditions employed.

The bomb* consists of a strong thimble-shaped receptacle **A** (Fig. 92)
having a raised flange **B** as shown. The lid **C**, shown both vertically and horizontally in Fig. 92, has a circular groove **D**, which is filled with a lead washer.
When the lid **C** is fitted onto the bomb, this lead washer fits directly over the
top of the flange **B**, whereas the outside rim of the lid **C** almost reaches the
collar **E** of the bomb. Consequently if the lid **C** is pressed firmly down, the
lead washer gives a gas-tight seal on the flange **B**. The lid **C** has a short central
pillar **F** which is perforated, so that the bomb may be suspended by a wire or
metal rod if required.

* A convenient size of bomb for the quantities of material suggested is one
of 8 ml. volume. The apparatus is supplied by Messrs. Chas. W. Cook and
Sons, Ltd., University Works, 97 Walsall Road, Perry Barr, Birmingham 22B.

To obtain the necessary pressure on the lid, and for general protection when the bomb is being heated, the bomb is placed in a heavy metal case **G**, in which the collar **E** of the bomb rests in a circular recess at the top of **G**, and the base of **A** just appears through the bottom of **G**. The lid **H** of the case screws down over **G**, and has an orifice through which the pillar **F** of the bomb projects when **H** is screwed firmly down onto **G**. The bottom portion of **G** and the sides of **H** are made of hexagonal cross-section so that both can be firmly held with suitable tools whilst **H** is being screwed down and is thus thrusting the lid **C** of the bomb firmly down onto the base **A**.

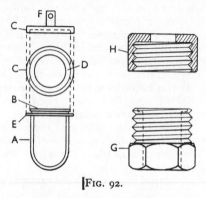

[FIG. 92.

Method. Clean and dry the bomb and its lid. The powdered compound to be analysed can now either be weighed directly into **A**, or weighed by difference using a weighing-cup of the type shown in Fig. 90. Weigh out thus 15–40 mg. of the material into **A**. Weigh out 0·4 g. of a finely powdered mixture* of equal parts of lactose and potassium nitrate, and pour about 0·3 g. of this carefully into **A**. Using a short length of 2 mm. glass rod, rounded at the end, mix the material thoroughly, with a grinding action, against the side of **A**, until an intimate mixture has been obtained. Add 4 g. of pure (A.R.) granular sodium peroxide and stir the mixture again. Finally clean off any traces of material on the rod by rubbing its end into the remaining lactose-nitrate mixture on a piece of glazed paper, and then adding this material to that in **A**. Then close the bomb tightly in the case **GH**, and tap sharply on a hard surface to consolidate the mixture.

Suspend the bomb by a wire or a metal rod through **F**. Fill with water the annular space between the pillar **F** and the hole in the top of **H**. Now heat the base of **A** with a pointed flame, *e.g.*, from a blowpipe pointing upwards. The time required for heating in this way is usually about 1 minute, but an ordinary Bunsen flame, used without concentration on the bottom of **A**, may require about 4 minutes. The

* In preparing this mixture, the lactose and the potassium nitrate should be powdered *separately* and then mixed solely by shaking. They should not be ground together in a mortar.

water in the top of **H** provides an indication of the time required: when the water begins to boil, the heating should be at once stopped. Then lower the bomb into cold water, and when it is thoroughly cold, unscrew and remove the outer case **GH**, rinse the outside of the bomb **A** with distilled water, dry it with a cloth. Prise off the lid **C**: if the ignition has occurred, fused lumps of peroxide will be seen, and the appearance of the mixture will have clearly changed. (If no ignition has occurred, replace the lid **C** and heat the encased bomb for a longer time: avoid overheating, which may melt the lead washer.)

Using distilled water from a wash-bottle, thoroughly rinse the inside of the lid **C** into a 150 ml. beaker. Carefully wash the *outside* of the bomb **A** similarly and discard the washings. Then place **A** on its side in the beaker, and add water until it is half-immersed. Cover the beaker with a watch-glass, and heat it gently until the peroxide has decomposed, and evolution of oxygen has ceased. Using stainless steel forceps or tongs, lift **A** above the solution, wash it thoroughly with a fine jet of distilled water, and remove it from the beaker.

Procedure for Chlorine Estimation. Again cover the beaker; using a teat-pipette inserted through the lip of the beaker, add concentrated nitric acid dropwise until the solution is acid, when carbon dioxide will be freely evolved.

Add a known volume of $0.02M.AgNO_3$ solution (in excess) and boil the solution until the silver chloride has coagulated. Filter through a conical 5 cm. funnel, ensuring that the filter-paper does not protrude above the rim of the funnel. Wash the silver chloride and the filter-paper several times with a fine jet of distilled water. To the united filtrate and washings add 1 ml. of saturated ferric alum solution. The solution should be almost colourless: if it is more than faintly coloured, add a few drops of concentrated nitric acid. Then titrate with $0.02M$-ammonium thiocyanate solution until the permanent colour of ferric thiocyanate is just perceptible. (Alternatively the chloride may be determined potentiometrically.)

Procedure for Bromine and Iodine Estimations. Again cover the beaker as before, but before adding the nitric acid add 1 g. of hydrazine sulphate and heat the solution on the water-bath until evolution of gas ceases. To ensure complete decomposition of an iodate, however, the heating should be continued for 1 hour.

Control experiment. This is not necessary if the sodium peroxide is known to be chlorine-free. If there is any doubt on this point, the whole operation should be repeated precisely as before, but omitting the organic halogen compound. A small thiocyanate titration value may be found, and this should be deducted from all determinations in which the above quantity of the particular batch of sodium peroxide is used.

NOTE. The massive construction of the bomb and its casing makes the risk of an explosion almost negligible. As an additional precaution however the bomb can be placed in a fume-cupboard, and a heavy iron plate or some loose bricks placed in front of the bomb, the gas supply being controlled from a protected position: safety goggles should also be worn. As a further precaution, the weight of material analysed may be reduced to *ca.* 10 mg., the lactose-nitrate mixture to 50 mg., and the sodium peroxide 1·0 g., the silver nitrate and the ammonium thio-cyanate solutions being 0·01M.concentration.

Example of Calculation

Estimation of Cl in *p*-dichlorobenzene.

Weight of sample taken . . . . . . 0·0210 g.
Volume of 0·02M.AgNO$_3$ solution added . . . . 25·00 ml.
,, ,, 0·02M.NH$_4$SCN ,, required . . . 10·70 ml.
,, ,, 0·02M.AgNO$_3$,, required to precipitate the
chlorine . . . 14·30 ml.

14·30 ml. 0·02M.AgNO$_3$ ≡ 35·46 × 0·02 × 14·30 g. chlorine.

∴0·021 g. of substance contains ,, ,, ,, ,,

∴100 g. of substance contain 35·46 × 0·02 × 14·30 × 100 g. chlorine.

$$\frac{35·46 \times 0·02 \times 14·30 \times 100}{0·0210}$$

$$= 48·28\%$$

Theoretical for C$_6$H$_4$Cl$_2$, 48·30%.

(Clearly it is not necessary to know the exact concentration of the ammonium thiocyanate solution, for it can be titrated against a known volume of the 0·02M.AgNO$_3$ solution, and this ratio used in the calculation.)

PART V

SIMPLE ENZYME REACTIONS

In the following pages an account is given of some of the more simple reactions which enzymes catalyse. The reactions have been selected partly because they are of particular interest to the organic chemist, and partly because they are capable of simple and ready demonstration in the laboratory.

The student who is unacquainted with the study of enzymes should first read the following brief theoretical introduction.

Enzymes may be described as organic catalysts of biological origin. The majority are obtained from the interior of cells, but some are obtained from natural secretions such as the digestive juices and milk. For a full discussion of the nature of enzymes and the mechanism of their reactions the student should consult a work such as *Chemistry and Methods of Enzymes*, by J. B. Sumner and G. F. Somers (Academic Press, New York), or *Enzymes*, by M. Dixon and E. C. Webb (Longman Group Ltd.). The following points should however be noted:

(1) Enzymes are proteins of high molecular weight, several of which have been isolated in a pure state; consequently their precise nature is in some instances still obscure. They form solutions in water and in dilute salt solutions, and are precipitated when such solutions are saturated with ammonium sulphate.

(2) They are highly specific in their reactions, *e.g.*, maltose attacks the α-glucosidic link (which occurs in maltose), but is without action on the β-glucosidic links.

(3) The effect of temperature is complex, but the majority of enzymes are most active about 45° and all are completely destroyed at 100°. At 0° the activity is reduced considerably but the enzyme is not destroyed.

(4) The activity of an enzyme varies considerably with acidity and there is generally a marked optimum pH* for each enzyme. Thus pepsin of the stomach has an optimum pH of 1·4, *i.e.*, it works best in a decidedly acid medium. It is inactive in neutral or alkaline solutions and the latter rapidly destroy it.

(5) Enzyme action is frequently accelerated or retarded by the presence of other substances both organic and inorganic. Such substances have been divided into three categories: (*a*) co-enzymes, without which certain enzymes are unable to function; (*b*) activators, and (*c*) inhibitors.

* The pH of a solution is defined as minus the logarithm of the hydrogen ion concentration: $pH = -\log [H]$. Thus if $[H] = 10^{-4}$, then $pH = 4$. Also if $[H] = 2 \times 10^{-4}$, then $[H] = 10^{0\cdot3010} \times 10^{-4} = 10^{-3\cdot699}$; ∴ $pH = 3\cdot699$. In any aqueous solution $[H] [OH] = 10^{-14}$ at ordinary temperatures. Therefore in a neutral solution $[H] = 10^{-7}$, or the pH of a neutral solution is 7. Hence the pH of an acid solution is <7, and the pH of an alkaline solution >7.

Nomenclature. The compound on which the enzyme acts is known as the *substrate*. The name of the enzyme is now usually obtained by adding the termination *-ase* to the name of the substrate. Thus an enzyme which hydrolyses an ester is known as an *esterase*. Nevertheless the older names of many enzymes still persist owing to their early discovery. In some cases the name of the enzyme indicates the reaction which it catalyses, *e.g.*, *oxidase*.

The isolation of enzymes in a pure state is frequently a matter of great difficulty owing to their instability, their low concentrations in plant and animal tissues, and also to their colloidal nature. The methods employed depend upon the physical and chemical nature of the enzyme in question. In the following experiments, no attempt has been made to isolate enzymes in a high state of purity.

The accompanying table gives details of a few of the simpler reactions which enzymes catalyse. Those for which practical directions are given in the following pages are marked with an asterisk.

It should be noted that a number of different enzyme preparations can now be purchased directly from manufacturing chemists. It must be emphasised that the activity of an enzyme, whether purchased or prepared in the laboratory, may vary between rather wide limits. The activity is dependent on the source of the enzyme, the presence of poisons and also on the temperature. It appears, for example, that the quality of horseradish peroxidase depends upon the season of the year at which the root is obtained from the ground. It cannot be expected therefore that all the experiments described below will work always with the precision characteristic of an organic reaction proceeding under accurately known conditions.

Lipase.

The action of esterases consists essentially in the hydrolysis (or synthesis) of carboxylic acid esters according to the equation:

$$RCOOR^1 + H_2O \rightleftharpoons RCOOH + R^1OH$$

If RCOOH is a comparatively simple organic acid and R^1OH a monohydric alcohol then the enzyme is called an esterase. Examples of such esters are ethyl butyrate, $C_3H_7COOC_2H_5$, and ethyl mandelate, $C_6H_5CH(OH)COOC_2H_5$.

If, on the other hand, RCOOH is a higher fatty acid and R^1OH a polyhydric alcohol, then the enzyme is called a lipase. Stearin or glyceryl tristearate (a fat) is

$$\begin{array}{l} CH_2 \cdot O \cdot CO \cdot C_{17}H_{35} \\ | \\ CH \cdot O \cdot CO \cdot C_{17}H_{35} \\ | \\ CH_2 \cdot O \cdot CO \cdot C_{17}H_{35} \end{array}$$

an example of this type of ester. The difference, however, is one of degree rather than kind. Thus the lipases which split natural fats are also capable of hydrolysing simple esters, although very much more slowly. Conversely esterases can hydrolyse fats, but only feebly.

A convenient source of the enzyme is castor oil seeds. The oil of the seeds is itself an ester, and therefore if the action of the enzyme is to be demonstrated on an extraneous ester, the castor oil must first be completely removed by extraction with ether. This, however, is a long process and may require several days for completion. The hydrolysing action of the enzyme on the oil in the seed can however be demonstrated as described on p. 512.

Enzyme	Origin	Substrate	Products	Optimum pH
Pancreatic lipase	pancreas	fats and other organic esters	organic acid and alcohol (often glycerol)	7·0
*Plant lipase	seeds rich in oil, e.g. castor oil seeds	,,	,,	5·0
*Diastase (or amylase)	liver, etc., malt	starch (amylum)	maltose and dextrin	6·0 (liver) 5·2 (malt)
*Ptyalin	saliva	,,	,,	6·7
Maltase	pancreas, small intestine, yeast	maitose	glucose	6·1 (gut) 6·6 (yeast)
*Invertase (sucrase)	small intestine, yeast	sucrose	glucose and fructose	6·2 (gut) 4·8 (yeast)
*Emulsin (β-glycosidase)	almond nuts	β-glucosides	glucose and a non-carbohydrate	4·1–4·5
Zymase (a mixture)	yeast	d-glucose, l-fructose	alcohol, CO_2 and small quantities of glycerol	4·5–6·5
Carboxylase	yeast	keto-acids	aldehydes and CO_2	4·8
Pepsin†	stomach	proteins	peptones	1·4
*Trypsin† (a mixture)	duodenum	proteins, peptones, polypeptides	amino-acids	8–11
*Urease	soya bean, jack bean	urea	ammonium carbonate	7·2–7·9
*Aldehyde oxidase	milk	aldehydes	fatty acid	approx. 7·0
*Peroxidase	horseradish, turnips, milk	activates H_2O_2 and a suitable substrate, e.g., aniline	quinone-imine dyes, induline, mauveine, aniline-black	4·5 varies with substrate
Catalase	living tissues of plants and animals	hydrogen peroxide	H_2O and inactive molecular O_2	7·0
Carbonic anhydrase	red blood corpuscles	carbonic acid	CO_2 and H_2O	6·8

* Practical directions provided.   † Secreted as inactive precursor.

ACTION OF LIPASE ON CASTOR OIL.

Remove the shells from 1 g. of the seeds* (about 5) and then grind up the latter thoroughly in a mortar. Add a few ml. of water and work into a paste. Proceed in this way adding a few ml. at a time until in all 25 ml. of water have been added. If this has been done thoroughly, a cream of uniform consistency will be obtained. Using a small measuring-cylinder, transfer 10 ml. of the lipase cream to each of two boiling-tubes **A** and **B**. Then using a 1 ml. pipette, add exactly 1 ml. of $M/10$ acetic acid to each and mix well: this activates the enzyme. Boil the contents of **B** for 2 minutes in order to destroy the enzyme, then place both tubes in a water-bath maintained at 40°, shaking well from time to time. After 45 minutes remove the tubes, cool, add 2 drops of phenolphthalein to each and titrate with $M/10$ sodium hydroxide solution. It will be found that more alkali is required to neutralise the acid in **A** than in **B**, showing that acid has been produced by enzymatic hydrolysis. An interesting feature, usually observable in the titration of **A**, is that when the end-point is approached the suspension becomes almost clear. This is due to the fact that the ester of the seeds has been hydrolysed to a fatty acid and an alcohol. The insoluble fatty acid is gradually replaced by its soluble sodium salt as the titration proceeds. The contents of **B** will of course remain cloudy.

The following are typical results using a lipase cream of average activity:

A required 6·9 ml. of $M/10$ NaOH solution.
B required 1·3 ml. of $M/10$ NaOH solution.

Diastase.

Diastase or amylase is formed when malt is produced by the germination of barley grains. Malt is therefore a good source of the enzyme. Diastase is also secreted by the salivary glands (when it is known as ptyalin), and also by the pancreas. Its function is to hydrolyse† starch to a mixture of maltose and dextrin:

$$(C_6H_{10}O_5)_n + H_2O = C_{12}H_{22}O_{11} + (C_6H_{10}O_5)_{n-2}$$

The optimum pH for ptyalin is 6·7 and that of malt diastase is 4·9. Hence it would seem that the enzyme differs in some way according to its origin.

Preparation of an extract containing malt diastase.

Grind 10 g. of malt‡ thoroughly in a mortar so that the grains are completely pulverised, add 50 ml. of water and macerate well. Allow to stand for about one hour, grinding up the mixture thoroughly from time to time, and then filter through a Buchner funnel.

---

* Care must be taken not to inhale dust from the seeds as they contain a poisonous protein: the grinding should therefore be carried out in a fume-cupboard.

† It has been shown that diastase consists of two distinct enzymes, α- and β-amylase, both of which are concerned with the hydrolysis of starch.

‡ Usually obtainable from a brewery.

(1) HYDROLYSIS OF STARCH BY DIASTASE.

Mix 3 g. of starch well with 10 ml. of water in a test-tube and pour the mixture into 90 ml. of boiling water contained in a 300 ml. conical flask, stirring at the same time. Cool to about 70° and then place in a water-bath maintained at 65–70°, but not higher. Now add 2–3 ml. of the malt extract prepared as above,* mix well and allow the hydrolysis to proceed. Take a series of test-tubes and in each put 10 ml. of water and 2 drops of a 1% iodine solution. At intervals of about 4 minutes (depending upon the activity of the enzyme solution), remove 1 ml. of the reaction mixture, cool and add it to one of the test-tubes and note the colour obtained. At the beginning of the experiment the colour will be blue due to the starch alone. As the reaction proceeds, the colour gradually becomes violet, reddish, yellowish and finally colourless.

The reason for this is that the starch is hydrolysed successively to dextrins of varying degrees of complexity and these give characteristic colours with iodine: for example, erythro-dextrin gives a reddish colour. The dextrin ultimately obtained, namely achroo-dextrin, gives no colour with iodine, as its name suggests. When this stage is reached, remove a few ml. of the reaction product and boil with Fehling's solution: a marked reduction takes place. This is due to maltose, the presence of which can be further demonstrated as follows.

To 50 ml. of the reaction product add 200 ml. of alcohol: a white precipitate of dextrin is produced. Stir well, allow to stand for about 15 minutes, and then filter through a Buchner funnel and transfer the filtrate to a 500 ml. distilling-flask. (The filtration is usually very slow and it may be found advantageous to use two Buchner funnels.) Add a few pieces of unglazed porcelain to the solution and distil off the alcohol (and some water) using a sand-bath. Transfer the residual liquid (about 40 ml.) to a 100 ml. conical flask, add a solution of 1 ml. of phenylhydrazine in 2 ml. of glacial acetic acid, and mix thoroughly. Heat in a boiling water-bath for 30 minutes. (If at the end of this period the solution is not absolutely clear, filter through a small fluted filter-paper into a previously warmed flask.) In either case allow to cool very slowly, preferably in a hot water-bath with the flame removed. Malto-sazone crystallises out when the solution is cold, and may be identified as described on p. 140.

(2) HYDROLYSIS OF STARCH BY PTYALIN.

When ptyalin acts on starch *in vitro*, the final product consists of about 80% of maltose and 20% of dextrin. The enzyme is destroyed in markedly acid solution, as it is also during full digestion in the stomach. But the presence of proteins, which act as buffers, prevents the hydrochloric acid secreted in the early stages of digestion from causing so high a concentration of hydrogen ions that the action of ptyalin is inhibited. This, together with the absence of active mechanical movement in the cardiac end of the stomach, permits the

* Or alternatively add 0·1–0·2 g. of the diastase obtainable from chemical dealers.

ptyalin to function in the stomach for about half an hour after the ingestion of food. Ptyalin works only in the presence of electrolytes, the chloride ion being the most effective.

Warm about 100 ml. of distilled water in a beaker to about 40° and with a portion of this thoroughly rinse out the mouth and reject the liquid. Again introduce about 20 ml. of the warm water into the mouth and mix with the saliva as completely as possible. Transfer the liquid so obtained into another beaker and then filter through a small fluted filter-paper into a small conical flask or boiling-tube.

Place 10 ml. of 1% starch solution (prepared as described above) in a boiling-tube, add 2 ml. of 1% sodium chloride solution and place the tube in a water-bath maintained at 38–40°. Place about 5 ml. of water in a series of test-tubes and to each add a few drops of 1% iodine solution. Now add 4 ml. of the diluted saliva solution to the starch solution, mix well and note the time. At intervals of about 30 seconds transfer 2 drops of the reacting mixture, by means of a dropping-tube, to one of the test-tubes, mix and note the colour. As in the previous experiment, the colour, which is blue at first, changes to blue-violet, red-violet, red-brown, pale brown, and finally disappears: at this stage the solution will reduce Fehling's solution. If the reaction proceeds too quickly for the colour changes to be observed, the saliva solution should be diluted.

Invertase (sucrase).

Yeast contains a number of enzymes, more particularly invertase and zymase. Invertase catalyses the hydrolysis of sucrose to glucose and fructose (*cf.* the catalysis of this reaction by acids, p. 369).

$$C_{12}H_{22}O_{11} + H_2O = C_6H_{12}O_6 + C_6H_{12}O_6$$
$$\text{sucrose} \qquad\qquad \text{glucose} \quad \text{fructose}$$

Sucrose is dextro-rotatory. Fructose shows a laevo-rotation greater in magnitude than the dextro-rotation shown by glucose. Hence as the hydrolysis of sucrose proceeds, the dextro-rotation gradually falls to zero and the solution finally shows a laevo-rotation. This hydrolysis is therefore sometimes called "inversion" and so the enzyme which catalyses the reaction is known as "invertase." Its more systematic name is, however, sucrase.

Preparation of an invertase solution.

Grind together in a mortar 25 g. of brewers' or of commercial pressed yeast and about an equal weight of silver sand, adding gradually 10 ml. of water. After the mixture has been well ground up and the yeast cells effectively ruptured, add about 50 ml. of water slowly with thorough mixing. Allow the mixture to stand for about 20 minutes, stirring from time to time. Filter through a Buchner funnel until a reasonably clear filtrate is obtained.

It is important to note that this solution does not contain any zymase.

In order to obtain an extract containing zymase, more complex methods of treatment must be employed.

HYDROLYSIS OF CANE SUGAR.

Dissolve 10 g. of cane sugar in water and make up to approximately 100 ml. Label three boiling-tubes **A**, **B** and **C**, and in them place the following:

(A) 20 ml. of sugar solution and 2 ml. of the invertase solution obtained above.

(B) 10 ml. of sugar solution and 1 ml. of the invertase solution which has previously been boiled thoroughly for 2–3 minutes.

(C) 10 ml. of sugar solution, 1 ml. of the invertase solution, and 1 ml. of 10% NaOH solution.

Mix each solution well and place the boiling-tubes in a water-bath maintained at 50°. After 10 minutes, transfer 1 ml. of each of the reaction mixtures to separate test-tubes, add 2 ml. of Fehling's solution to each and boil. A marked reduction is obtained in **A***, no reduction is obtained in **B**, and no reduction or only very slight reduction is obtained in **C**. This shows that the activity of the invertase is destroyed both by heat and alkali.

At the end of 30 minutes treat the mixture in **A** as follows: Dissolve 8 ml. of glacial acetic acid in 10 ml. of water, add 4 ml. of phenylhydrazine and mix well in order to obtain a clear solution. Add this to the solution in **A** and mix thoroughly: a slightly cloudy solution may be obtained, but this will clear on heating. Place the mixture in a boiling water-bath and note the formation of yellow crystals of glucosazone after about 15 minutes. At the end of about 1 hour, cool, filter off the precipitate and identify as directed on p. 139.

Emulsin.

Emulsin, an enzyme readily obtained from almonds, has the property of hydrolysing β-glycosides.

An account has been given on p. 144 of the α- and β-methylglucosides, formed by replacing the hydrogen atoms of the terminal OH groups of α- and β-glucose respectively by methyl groups. These hydrogen atoms can be replaced by various other radicals, and the compounds so formed belong to the general class of glycosides. A number of glycosides occur naturally and these are usually β-glycosides. For example, salicin (I) is a combination of salicyl alcohol (or saligenin) and glucose. Amygdalin (II) is a combination of two molecules of glucose, one molecule of hydrogen cyanide and one molecule

* Actually the optimum pH for the invertase reaction is about 4·8, and under these conditions the reaction proceeds even more rapidly. The solution can be adjusted approximately to this pH by adding 6 ml. of 1% acetic acid at the beginning of the experiment.

$HOCH_2C_6H_4O$ H

$$
\begin{array}{l}
\text{C} \\
\text{HCOH} \\
\text{HOCH} \qquad \text{O} \qquad C_6H_5CH(CN)-O \qquad H \qquad HOC_6H_4O \qquad H \\
\text{HCOH} \qquad\qquad\qquad\qquad\qquad C_{13}H_{20}O_{10} \qquad\qquad C_6H_{10}O_6 \\
\text{HC} \qquad\qquad\qquad\qquad\qquad\qquad (II) \qquad\qquad\qquad\qquad (III) \\
\text{CH}_2\text{OH} \\
\qquad (I)
\end{array}
$$

of benzaldehyde. Arbutin (III) is a combination of glucose with hydro-quinone (1,4-dihydroxy-benzene).

Emulsin does not hydrolyse α-methylglucoside, whereas it readily hydrolyses β-methylglucoside, salicin, amygdalin and arbutin. This is an excellent example of the specificity of enzymes:

$$C_6H_{11}O_5-OCH_3 + H_2O = C_6H_{12}O_6 + CH_3OH$$
$$\text{β-methyl-glucoside} \qquad\qquad \text{glucose}$$

$$C_6H_{11}O_5-OC_6H_4CH_2OH + H_2O = C_6H_{12}O_6 + HOC_6H_4CH_2OH$$
$$\text{salicin} \qquad\qquad\qquad\qquad \text{glucose} \qquad \text{salicyl alcohol}$$

Since an enzyme is a biological catalyst and therefore merely accelerates a reaction, it cannot alter the position of equilibrium in a reversible reaction. The hydrolysis of β-methylglucoside is reversible and emulsin should therefore be capable also of synthesising this compound from glucose and methanol. This synthesis can actually be carried out by the action of the enzyme on glucose dissolved in an excess of methanol, the excess of the alcohol throwing the equilibrium over to the left. Owing to experimental difficulties, this reaction is not here described.

In aqueous solution, the hydrolysis of a glucoside by emulsin goes to completion on account of the large proportion of water present.

Preparation of emulsin from almonds.

Place about 15 sweet almonds in boiling water for one minute. Pour off the water and remove the brown skins which have been loosened by the hot water. Grind up the "blanched" almonds in a mortar as thoroughly as possible. Add 40 ml. of water and grind into a paste, then add 10 ml. of 10% acetic acid and mix well: this causes the coagulation of the proteins present. Allow to stand for 10 minutes, stirring at intervals. Filter through a Buchner funnel: wash the residue in the funnel with a few ml. of water (allowing the washings to enter the filtrate) and drain well. Add 1 drop of 10% acetic acid to the filtrate; the solution should remain clear: if it does not, add the dilute acetic acid drop by drop until no more precipitate is formed, and then re-filter.

The clear filtrate is very active and may be used directly for the following experiments. Alternatively the solid enzyme may be isolated as follows. To the filtrate add an equal volume of alcohol to precipitate the enzyme: filter off the latter through a small Buchner funnel, wash with alcohol and then ether, and dry in a vacuum desiccator.

HYDROLYSIS OF SALICIN BY EMULSIN.

Salicin is a colourless crystalline substance, soluble in water. It does not reduce Fehling's solution nor does it give a coloration with ferric chloride. On hydrolysis with emulsin, glucose and salicyl alcohol are produced: the former reduces Fehling's solution and the latter gives a violet coloration with ferric chloride.

By gentle warming, dissolve 5 g. of salicin in 100 ml. of water contained in a 250 ml. conical flask. Add about 20 ml. of the emulsin solution as prepared above or 0·2–0·3 g. of the solid enzyme preparation,* mix well and place the flask in a water-bath maintained at 45°. Shake the mixture well from time to time and at the end of about 30 minutes transfer 1 ml. to a test-tube, cool and add ferric chloride solution: a violet coloration is produced. Also boil 1 ml. of the reaction mixture with Fehling's solution and note the reduction.

At the end of about an hour,† filter the solution and transfer 20 ml. of the clear filtrate to a boiling-tube. Dissolve 2·5 ml. of phenylhydrazine in 3 ml. of glacial acetic acid diluted with 3 ml. of water, and add this solution to that in the boiling-tube. Mix well and place the tube in a boiling water-bath. After about 15 minutes, crystals of glucosazone begin to separate. At the end of about 1 hour, filter off the precipitate and identify (p. 319).

Cool the remainder of the filtrate and extract three times with ether, using 20–30 ml. for each extraction. Dry the combined ethereal extracts over powdered anhydrous sodium sulphate. Filter into a small flask and distil off the ether on a water-bath. Pour the residual oil into a small dish or beaker: crystallisation takes place almost immediately. The salicyl alcohol so obtained is almost pure, but it may, if so desired, be recrystallised from a small quantity of benzene. It is a colourless crystalline solid, m.p. 86°, readily soluble in water; it gives a violet coloration with ferric chloride.

Trypsin.

The so-called "trypsin," obtainable from pancreatic juice and from fresh extracts of the pancreas, is not a simple enzyme but a mixture of trypsin proper (which hydrolyses proteins to proteoses and peptones) and a series of enzymes which hydrolyse these breakdown products to their constituent amino-acids. The term "trypsin," when used below, refers to this mixture.

Since trypsin is a mixture, it has no well-defined optimum pH. It should also be noted that trypsin is the only hydrolytic enzyme which is at all active in alkaline solution.

* 0·2–0·3 g. of the manufacturer's product also works satisfactorily.
† The time required for complete hydrolysis will naturally depend upon the activity of the emulsin, but preparations of average activity give a satisfactory yield of products after 1 hour.

The course of tryptic digestion of proteins.

On hydrolysing a protein, both NH_2 groups and COOH groups are set free in equal numbers by the splitting of – CONH – groups, and therefore the reaction cannot be followed by simple titration. One method of estimating the breakdown products (peptones, peptides, amino-acids, *etc.*) is Sørensen's formaldehyde titration method, the theory of which has been fully discussed under the Estimation of Glycine (p. 463). From the description given there it is obvious that the quantitative value of the formaldehyde titration will increase as the digestion proceeds, until finally a value is obtained which corresponds (theoretically at least) to the constituent amino-acids of the original protein.

Another important method of following protein hydrolysis is that due to Van Slyke, and consists in estimating the free amino groups liberated by treatment with nitrous acid, whereby gaseous nitrogen is evolved and measured in a special apparatus.

$$NH_2CH_2COOH + HNO_2 = HO \cdot CH_2COOH + N_2 + H_2O$$

Only Sørensen's method is employed in the following experiments. The student should therefore first acquaint himself with the theory of the estimation of glycine (p. 463).

It must be emphasised that these experiments are only roughly quantitative, for owing to the slight opalescence of the digesting mixture, accurate end-points using phenolphthalein can be obtained only by using an instrument known as a comparator.

HYDROLYSIS OF CASEIN.

Prepare a solution of casein as follows. Weigh out 15 g. of casein into a dry 500 ml. conical flask and add about 150 ml. of water. Dissolve 1·5 g. of anhydrous sodium carbonate and 1·5 g. of borax in about 20 ml. of hot water and add this solution to the casein. Warm until a solution is obtained, filter if necessary, and make up to a total volume of about 250 ml. with water. Add a few drops of toluene (to prevent putrefaction) and shake the solution.

Remove 25 ml. by means of a pipette, add a few drops of phenolphthalein: the colour is pink. Now add very cautiously, *drop by drop*, dilute acetic acid (say $M/100$) until the pink colour has *just* not disappeared. It is important not to add too much acid, otherwise the casein will be precipitated. Now add 5 ml. of neutralised formalin (see p. 464) and then titrate with $M/10$ NaOH solution. Note the amount required.

To the remainder of the casein solution add 0·5 to 0·8 g. of finely powdered commercial trypsin, shake to dissolve, and place in a thermostat (or in an incubator) at 40°. After 15 minutes, remove 25 ml. and add a few drops of phenolphthalein: it will now be found that the solution remains colourless. Run in carefully $M/10$ NaOH solution until the colour of the solution is just pink, add 5 ml. of neutralised formalin and then titrate against $M/10$ NaOH solution until the pink colour is just restored: note the amount required. Remove further quantities of 25 ml. at intervals which must be determined by the speed of the reaction. The following will probably make a suitable series: $\frac{1}{2}$, $\frac{3}{4}$, 1, 2, 3, 6 and 24 hours. It will be found that, as the reaction proceeds, the titration value increases fairly rapidly at first and then more slowly.

HYDROLYSIS OF GELATIN.

Dissolve 6 g. of gelatin in about 250 ml. of warm water. Carry out the formaldehyde titration on 25 ml. of the solution: note in this case that the solution is acid to phenolphthalein.

To the remainder of the gelatin solution, add 0·5 to 0·8 g. of finely powdered commercial trypsin and incubate at 40°. Carry out the formaldehyde titration on 25 ml. samples at intervals as above.

Note that the original solution sets to a gel on standing, but is fluid at 40°, and when removed from the bath usually remains so sufficiently long for a titration to be carried out. It is interesting to observe that, after several hours' digestion, the mixture no longer sets to a gel on standing at room temperature, showing that the gelatin is now replaced by completely water-soluble amino-acids.

Urease.

The chief sources of this important enzyme are (a) the jack bean (*Canavalia ensiformis*), (b) the soy (or soja) bean (*Glycine hispida*). The enzyme is of great value in identifying and estimating urea. The action of urease on urea is specific, the reaction catalysed being:

$$(NH_2)_2CO + 2H_2O = (NH_4)_2CO_3$$

Urease is one of the enzymes which have been obtained in the crystalline state. This has been done by stirring jack bean meal with 30% aqueous acetone, filtering and allowing the filtrate to remain at 0° for several hours. The urease which crystallises out is separated by centrifuging and is then recrystallised. Like crystalline pepsin and trypsin, it is a protein.

SPECIFIC UREASE TEST FOR UREA.

The principle of this test is as follows: The liquid suspected of containing urea is treated with dilute acid or alkali until its pH is about 7. A solution of the enzyme is also made and its pH adjusted to 7. The two solutions are mixed and the resulting conversion of urea to ammonium carbonate causes the pH of the solution to rise to over 8; this change is noted by the use of a suitable indicator, phenol-red being the one usually employed. Proteins do not interfere with the test, but the reaction is inhibited by traces of heavy metals.

Place about 0·2 g. of jack-bean meal in a test-tube, add 2 ml. of water and about 5 drops of phenol-red. Mix thoroughly and allow the faintly yellow solution to stand while the urea solution is being made up.

Dissolve about 0·2 g. of urea in 5 ml. of water, add about 5 drops of phenol-red and 1 drop of dil. HCl: the colour is now yellow. Divide the solution into two portions. To one portion, add very dilute (about 1%) NaOH solution until the colour is red: now add the second portion, *drop by drop*, until the red colour is *just* discharged. The solution is now at about pH 7.

To this yellow solution add the enzyme solution, mix well and allow to stand at room temperature. The mixture becomes red as the pH rises to 8.

ESTIMATION OF UREA BY UREASE.

This method of estimating urea is more accurate than the hypobromite method (p. 458) and is used extensively for accurate metabolic work.

The method is based on the conversion of urea to ammonium carbonate and the estimation of the latter by titration with standard acid. For this purpose, two equal quantities of urea (or urine) are measured out into two flasks **A** and **B**. **A** is treated with 10 ml. of a strong urease preparation and some phenolphthalein, warm water is added and the mixture is adjusted by the addition of $M/10$ HCl from a burette **A**[1] until the red colour is just discharged. This brings the mixture to about pH 8 (the optimum for urease) and also prevents loss of ammonia.

The contents of **B**, which act as a control, are treated with mercuric chloride in order to inhibit the action of the enzyme, and then 10 ml. of urease solution are added. The solution is diluted with water and ammonium chloride added (in order to balance the ammonium chloride subsequently formed in **A**). Methyl-red is then added and the solution is titrated with $M/10$ HCl from a second burette **B**[1] until a bright red colour is obtained.

The solution in **A** is now treated with mercuric chloride and methyl-red, and then titrated with $M/10$ HCl until its colour matches that of the solution in **B**. The difference in the volume of HCl run in from the burettes **A**[1] and **B**[1] is a measure of the amount of urea present.

Urease solution. Place about 5 g. of jack-bean meal in a mortar and grind up with about 10 ml. of water. Then add about 90 ml. of water, mix *thoroughly* and allow to stand for some time in order to deposit starch and other insoluble substances. Decant off the supernatant liquid into a conical flask and cork the latter.

The estimation. Label two 250 ml. conical flasks **A** and **B**, and into each measure 5 ml. of urine solution (or about 0·1 g. of solid urea, accurately weighed). Add to each about 20 ml. of water and bring the temperature to about 60°. To **A** add 3 drops of phenolphthalein solution and to **B** add 1 ml. of 0·5% mercuric chloride solution. Now to each solution, add 10 ml. of the urease solution and mix well. The mixture **A** soon turns red.

Fill two burettes **A**[1] and **B**[1] with $M/10$ HCl. Run in from **A**[1], drop by drop, sufficient $M/10$ hydrochloric acid *just* to discharge the red colour in **A**. Maintain the temperature at about 60° and keep the colour just discharged by cautiously adding the HCl from time to time. Care must be taken not to add an excess of acid, otherwise the proteins will be precipitated and the enzyme rendered inactive. The reaction is complete in about 5 minutes, but allow the mixture to stand for a further 5 minutes after the final discharge of the colour.

Meanwhile add 4 drops of methyl-red and 1 ml. of 10% ammonium chloride solution to **B**. The colour will normally be yellow; if so, add $M/10$ HCl from **B**[1], drop by drop, until a red colour is just obtained.

Now add 1 ml. of the mercuric chloride solution to **A** and 4 drops of methyl-red. Run in $M/10$ HCl from the first burette A^1 until a red colour is obtained identical with that in **B**. Note the difference in the volume of acid run in from A^1 and B^1.

Calculation.
    The equations for the above reactions are:

$$CO(NH_2)_2 + 2H_2O = (NH_4)_2CO_3$$
$$(NH_4)_2CO_3 + 2HCl = 2NH_4Cl + CO_2 + H_2O$$

1 gram-molecule of urea $\equiv$ 2000 ml. of M.HCl solution

i.e., 60 g. of urea $\equiv$ 2000 ml. of M.HCl solution

$\therefore$ 0·003 g. of urea $\equiv$ 1 ml. of $M/10$ HCl solution

Aldehyde oxidase (or dehydrogenase).

This enzyme, sometimes also called the Schardinger enzyme, occurs in milk. It is capable of "oxidising" acetaldehyde to acetic acid, and also the purine bases xanthine and hypoxanthine to uric acid. The former reaction is not a simple direct oxidation and is assumed to take place as follows. The enzyme "activates" the hydrated form of the aldehyde so that it readily parts with two hydrogen atoms in the presence of a suitable hydrogen acceptor such as methylene-blue the latter being reduced to the colourless leuco-compound. The oxidation of certain substrates will not take place in the absence of such a hydrogen acceptor.

$$CH_3CH\begin{smallmatrix}OH\\\\OH\end{smallmatrix} + \underset{\text{methylene-blue}}{M} \longrightarrow CH_3COOH + \underset{\substack{\text{leuco-methylene-}\\\text{blue}}}{MH_2}$$

Make up an approximately 5% solution of acetaldehyde in water, add a few drops of phenolphthalein and then add dilute Na_2CO_3 until the solution just turns pink, thus removing any free acid.

Make up a methylene-blue solution by grinding 0·1 g. with water and making up to 1 litre with water.

Place 5 ml. of milk in each of two test-tubes **A** and **B**. Boil the milk in **B** thoroughly for 2 minutes to destroy the enzyme, and cool. Then in each test-tube place 1 ml. of the acetaldehyde solution and 1 ml. of the methylene-blue solution. Mix gently by inverting the tubes: avoid shaking with air. Now place **A** and **B** in a water-bath maintained at 40–50°. After a time (usually about 20 minutes) the dye in **A** is completely decolorised except at the surface, while **B** is unaffected.

This reaction can also be carried out in the absence of air or oxygen, *i.e.*, anaerobically.

Peroxidase.*

This enzyme is widely distributed, more particularly in plants. Three important sources of the enzyme are horse-radish, turnips and milk. Peroxidase is capable of activating both hydrogen peroxide and a suitable substrate so that the latter is oxidised, although hydrogen peroxide alone may be incapable of affecting this change. It sometimes happens that hydrogen per-

* See *Peroxidase*, by B. C. Saunders, A. G. Holmes-Siedle and B. P. Stark, Butterworths, London, 1964.

oxide alone does, in fact, oxidise a given substrate slowly and feebly, but on adding the enzyme the reaction is not only accelerated, but appears to have its course altered and thus gives rise to entirely different end-products. An interesting example of this is shown by aniline, which under certain conditions is oxidised by hydrogen peroxide alone to azobenzene, azoxybenzene and nitrobenzene: in the presence of peroxidase, however, entirely different substances are produced, *viz.*, a quinone-imine dye, an induline, a mauveine and aniline-black.

Other substances can activate hydrogen peroxide, for example, ferrous iron (p. 352). The products however are usually less well defined and different from those obtained when using peroxidase.

Isolation of Peroxidase.

The activity of the specimen isolated will depend largely upon the extent and thoroughness of the extraction. By following the details outlined below, a specimen of peroxidase sufficiently active for all ordinary purposes is obtained.

Cut the tops off some turnips, wash the latter if necessary and then weigh out 300 g. Cut up into small pieces and mince in a small mincing-machine. Place the macerated product in a 1-litre beaker or jar, add 300 ml. of water and stir thoroughly with a strong glass rod at intervals during 20 minutes. Decant off as much as possible of the supernatant liquid on to a Buchner funnel, transferring as little of the pulp as possible to the filter-paper. Now place the pulp in a strong cotton cloth and extract as much liquid as possible by squeezing. Combine this liquid with the filtrate in the Buchner funnel, measure the total volume and transfer to a beaker. Saturate with ammonium sulphate by adding about 70 g. of powdered ammonium sulphate for each 100 ml. of filtrate. Stir well and then allow to stand. After a few minutes the crude peroxidase is precipitated, and may rise to the surface or sink to the bottom of the liquid. If the latter happens, decant off as much of the supernatant liquid as possible and filter off the remainder through a small Buchner funnel. If the precipitate rises to the top of the liquid, it is usually advisable to transfer to a separating-funnel, allow to settle, run off as much of the lower liquid as possible, and then filter the remainder through a Buchner funnel. Place the funnel in a vacuum desiccator and allow to dry overnight. Detach as much of the dried precipitate as possible from the filter-paper, grind up in a mortar and preserve in a small stoppered tube. This preparation will retain its activity for several months, particularly if kept in a refrigerator.

It should be noted that the aqueous extract of the turnips shows weak peroxidase activity before precipitation with ammonium sulphate.

QUALITATIVE TESTS FOR AROMATIC AMINES.

Place about 0·1 g. (or 0·1 ml.) of the amine in a test-tube, add 0·1 ml. of glacial acetic acid to dissolve the amine and then add water until the test-tube is half-full Next place about 0·3 g. of the peroxidase preparation in a very small mortar and grind up with about 15 ml. of water. Filter through a small fluted filter-paper into a test-tube.

With the aid of a small pipette or a fine-bore dropping-tube (Fig. 30, p. 60), add about 4 drops of the filtered enzyme solution to the amine acetate solution. Using another dropping-tube add 1 drop of "20 volume" hydrogen peroxide solution and shake well. Note the colour change which takes place.

The rate of colour change will depend upon the activity of the enzyme preparation. The changes enumerated below are usually, however, easily observable.

Aniline. Purple, gradually turning brown. A brown precipitate on standing.

o-*Toluidine.* Transient green, deep blue and then a deep blue precipitate. Usually a very fast reaction.

m-*Toluidine.* Reddish-purple, gradually darkening.

p-*Toluidine.* Orange-red, then a deep blood red: finally a red precipitate is formed.

1-*Naphthylamine.* Opalescent indigo blue.

2-*Naphthylamine.* Brown solution with a very slight pale blue fluorescence.

Monomethylaniline. Deep blue, changing to a slate blue.

Dimethylaniline. Yellow, changing through olive green to a deep green. On long standing becomes bluish green.

Diphenylamine (suspension). Bluish-purple changing to a deep permanganate colour.

Triphenylamine (suspension). Almost negative. A very pale rose-pink coloration may slowly form.

o-*Phenylene diamine.* Yellow, darkening to the colour of dichromate.

m-*Phenylene diamine.* Dark brown. The colour change is sometimes difficult to observe, as the original solution is often brown.

p-*Phenylene diamine.* A transient yellow which almost immediately changes to a deep green. On standing the solution turns brown. A very sensitive test for peroxidase. In fact, a slice of turnip or horse-radish will develop a green colour when treated with hydrogen peroxide and a solution of *p*-phenylene diamine in dilute acetic acid.

Repeat one or two of the above experiments using however, in place of the active enzyme, a sample of the enzyme solution which has been thoroughly boiled for 2 minutes. Note that the above colour changes do not now occur.

Peroxidase in milk.

Dissolve about 0·1 g. of *p*-phenylene diamine in about 10 ml. of water. Place 5 ml. of milk in each of two test-tubes **A** and **B**. Boil the milk in **B** thoroughly for 2 minutes and then cool. In each test-tube place 5 drops of the phenylene diamine solution and then add 1 drop of "20 vol." hydrogen peroxide solution, and mix. A green coloration is produced in **A**, and then very rapidly changes to a slate-blue. No coloration is produced in **B**. This test therefore readily differentiates fresh from boiled milk.

APPENDIX

PREPARATION OF REAGENTS

Throughout this book, the reagents referred to, unless otherwise stated, have been prepared as described below.

ACIDS.

ACETIC ACID, DILUTE. Approx. $4M$. Dilute 230 ml. of glacial acetic acid with water until total volume is 1 litre.

HYDROCHLORIC ACID, DILUTE. 1 vol. of conc. HCl to 3 vols. of water.

NITRIC ACID, DILUTE. 1 vol. of conc. HNO_3 to 10 vols. of water.

SULPHURIC ACID, DILUTE. 1 vol. of conc. H_2SO_4 to 8 vols. of water.

SULPHUROUS ACID. Water saturated with SO_2.

BASES.

AMMONIUM HYDROXIDE SOLUTION, DILUTE. 1 vol. of conc. ammonia (d, 0·880) to 3 vols. of water.

POTASSIUM HYDROXIDE, ALCOHOLIC. Boil under reflux a mixture of 10 g. of powdered KOH and 100 ml. of rectified spirit for 30 minutes. Cool and if solid material remains, decant through a filter of glass-wool.

SODIUM HYDROXIDE, 10% AQUEOUS. 100 g. NaOH dissolved in water, and the cold solution diluted to 1 litre.

SODIUM HYDROXIDE, 30% AQUEOUS. As above, using 300 g. NaOH.

SALTS.

BARIUM CHLORIDE. 10% solution, i.e., 100 g. of $BaCl_2,2H_2O$ dissolved in water and the solution made up to 1 litre.

BLEACHING POWDER. Shake a mixture of 125 g. of bleaching powder and 1 litre of water at intervals for 2 hours, then filter.

CALCIUM CHLORIDE. Dissolve 100 g. of $CaCl_2,6H_2O$ (or 50 g. of anhydrous $CaCl_2$) in water and make up to 1 litre.

COPPER SULPHATE. 10% solution of $CuSO_4,5H_2O$.

FERRIC CHLORIDE. Approx. 4·5%. Dissolve 75 ml. of "liquid $FeCl_3$"* in water and make up to 1 litre. Alternatively, dissolve 75 g. of $FeCl_3,6H_2O$ in water, add 10 ml. of conc. HCl, and make up to 1 litre.

FERROUS SULPHATE. Dissolve 10 g. of $FeSO_4,7H_2O$ in water, add 10 ml. of dil. H_2SO_4 and make up to 100 ml. with water. It should, whenever possible, be prepared immediately before use.

MERCURIC CHLORIDE. Saturated aqueous solution (approx. 6%).

MERCURIC NITRATE. 5% solution of $Hg(NO_3)_2$.

* As supplied by chemical dealers; a concentrated solution of $FeCl_3$ acidified with HCl.

MERCUROUS NITRATE. 5% solution of $HgNO_3,H_2O$.

POTASSIUM IODIDE. 10% solution.

POTASSIUM PERMANGANATE. 1% solution.

SILVER NITRATE. 2% solution.

SODIUM BISULPHITE.* Dissolve 600 g. of $NaHSO_3$ in water, make up to 1 litre and pass in SO_2 for a few minutes to ensure absence of Na_2SO_3.

SODIUM CARBONATE. 20% solution of $Na_2CO_3,10H_2O$.

SODIUM HYPOBROMITE. Dissolve 200 g. of NaOH in water, make up to 1 litre, chill in ice-water, and slowly add 50 ml. of bromine with stirring.

SODIUM HYPOCHLORITE. $2M$. This may be prepared with sufficient accuracy by dissolving 100 g. of NaOH in 200 ml. of water in a large beaker, cooling the solution, and then adding about 500 g. of crushed ice. Now counterpoise the beaker on a rough set of scales, and pass in chlorine from a cylinder until an increase in weight of 72 g. is obtained. Make up the solution to 1 litre and stir well. The solution must be kept in a cool dark place, but even then slowly decomposes.

SODIUM NITROPRUSSIDE. Dissolve a few crystals in water as required.

SPECIAL REAGENTS.

ACETYLATING MIXTURE. Equal vols. of acetic anhydride and glacial acetic acid (p. 107). (A special mixture is used for quantitative acetylation; see p. 451.)

AMMONIACAL SILVER NITRATE. Add 1 drop of 10% aqueous NaOH solution to about 5 ml. of silver nitrate solution in a test-tube: then add *dilute* NH_3 drop by drop with shaking until only a trace of undissolved Ag_2O remains. A number of reductions require the presence of Ag^+ ions. It is often advisable, therefore, after adding the ammonia to add silver nitrate solution until a faint but permanent precipitate is obtained. The solution should always be prepared in small quantities immediately before use, and any unexpended solution thrown away afterwards. If the solution is kept for some time, it may form explosive by-products.

BROMINE-WATER. Shake about 5 ml. of bromine with 100 ml. of water, and decant off the clear aqueous solution as required (concentration about 3%).

CHLORINE-WATER. Water saturated in the cold with chlorine gas (about 0·7%).

FEHLING'S SOLUTION. *Solution* **A**. Dissolve 69·28 g. of $CuSO_4,5H_2O$ in water and make up to 1 litre.

Solution **B**. Dissolve 346 g. of sodium potassium tartrate ($C_4H_4O_6NaK,4H_2O$, "Rochelle salt") and 120 g. of NaOH in water and make the mixed tartrate and hydroxide solution up to 1 litre.

To prepare Fehling's solution, mix equal volumes of Solutions

* Alternatively named sodium hydrogen sulphite.

A and **B**. Fehling's solution should be prepared only in sufficient quantity for immediate needs, as it slowly deteriorates on standing, while Solutions **A** and **B** keep almost indefinitely.

HYDROGEN PEROXIDE. "10 volumes" solution (as purchased).

IODINE SOLUTION. Cold saturated aqueous solution. (If a more concentrated solution is required, add 1 g. of powdered iodine to a solution of 2 g. of potassium iodide in a minimum of water, and dilute the solution to 100 ml.)

1-NAPHTHOL, ETHANOLIC, 1%. Dissolve 1 g. of 1-naphthol in methylated spirit and make up to 100 ml. with spirit.

1-NAPHTHOL, ETHANOLIC, 20%. As above, using 20 g. of 1-naphthol.

SCHIFF'S REAGENT. Dissolve 1 g. of rosaniline in 50 ml. of water with gentle warming. Cool, saturate with SO_2, add about 1 g. of animal charcoal, shake and filter: make up to 1 litre with water. If the pink colour reappears on standing, add a few drops of SO_2-water carefully with stirring until the colour *just* disappears.

2,4-DINITROPHENYLHYDRAZINE. Reagent A, in hydrochloric acid: Reagent B, in methanol-sulphuric acid. For preparation, see p. 261.

INDICATORS.

METHYLENE-BLUE. Dissolve 1 g. of powdered methylene-blue in water and make up to 500 ml.

METHYL-ORANGE. Dissolve 1 g. of methyl-orange in 1·5 litres of boiling water.

METHYL-RED. Dissolve 1 g. in 1 litre of ethanol.

THYMOL-BLUE. Dissolve 0·266 g. in 50 ml. of ethanol, and add 100 ml. of water.

PHENOLPHTHALEIN. Dissolve 1 g. of phenolphthalein in 100 ml. of methylated spirit.

PHENOL-RED. Grind up 0·1 g. of phenol-red with 29 ml. of $N/100$ NaOH and make up to 250 ml. with water.

Johnson Universal Test Papers, $_pH1$ to $_pH11$.

LABORATORY FIRST-AID, TREATMENT OF FIRES, Etc.

A First-Aid Box, clearly labelled, should be kept in a readily accessible place in the laboratory, and should contain the following articles. *All bottles and packages should be clearly labelled.*

Bandages, lint, gauze, cotton-wool, adhesive plaster, and a sling.

Delicate forceps, needles, thread, safety-pins, and scissors.

Fine glass dropping-tube. Glass eye-bath.

Vaseline, Castor oil, Olive oil, Sal volatile. Zinc oxide ointment. Boric acid (powder). Chloramine-T (fine hydrated crystals, obtainable from B. D. H. Ltd., Poole, Dorset, BHI2 4NN). Savlon Antiseptic cream and emulsion (I.C.I. Ltd.) Savlon cream is a very effective and harmless antiseptic; it is unnaffected by long storage.

Bottles of the following:

Acriflavine Emulsion (in quantity).

Savlon Antiseptic (aqueous solution).

Lime-water (in quantity).

2% Iodine solution. 1% Boric acid. 1% Acetic acid.

8% Sodium bicarbonate solution (*i.e.*, saturated in the cold).

1% Sodium bicarbonate solution.

Amyl nitrite capsules.

Burns.

Whatever the cause of the burn or scald, *e.g.*, flames, hot metal, hot liquid, acids, caustic alkalis, *etc.*:

(1) Remove any smouldering or acid/alkali-soaked clothing.

(2) Thoroughly and profusely wash the burnt area with cold tap water.

(3) *Gently* dry with a clean (or preferably sterile) towel or cotton wool.

(4) Cover burnt or scalded area with sterile dressing.

(5) Transfer patient to hospital or doctor for consideration of further treatment (a course of anti-tetanus toxoid is frequently indicated if the patient is not already immunised, *i.e.*, has had a full course of booster doses of ATT within the last five years).

Minor scalds may be treated as above (1 to 3) and then savlon or acriflavine emulsion applied before application of a sterile dressing.

Special cases

Bromine Burns. When experiments involving the use of liquid bromine are being performed, small bottles of petroleum (b.p. 80–100°) should be immediately available. If bromine is spilt on the hands, immediately wash it off with an ample supply of petroleum, when the bromine will be completely removed from the skin. (If subsequently the skin which has been in contact with the petrol feels tender and "smarts" owing to removal of the normal film of grease, cover gently with savlon emulsion or with olive oil.)

Sodium Burns. Most frequently caused by small molten pellets ejected from heated tubes. If a small pellet of sodium can still be seen, remove carefully with forceps. Then wash the burn thoroughly in cold water, then in 1% aqueous acetic acid and then cover with gauze soaked in savlon emulsion or olive oil.

Phosphorus Burns. Wash well in cold water, and then immerse in *ca.* 1% aqueous silver nitrate solution. If serious, wash again with water, and apply the savlon or acriflavine treatment.

Methyl sulphate. If spilt on hands: wash *immediately* with an ample supply of concentrated ammonia solution. Then dab *gently* with a wad of cotton wool soaked in the ammonia solution. (See also p. 220.)

EYE ACCIDENTS See use of eye goggles, p. 531.

Whatever liquid (*e.g.*, acid or caustic alkali) or solid (*e.g.*, glass) has entered the eye, the eye should be thoroughly and profusely washed with tap water (*e.g.*, put head under tap) and the eye-lids should be held widely open, especially where caustic alkalis have entered the eye.

No attempt should be made to remove imbedded glass. This is a *hazardous* procedure and should be left to a doctor—more damage can result if attempted by someone not skilled in this technique.

Soreness which may follow very minor accidents to the eye may be relieved by placing 1 drop of castor oil in the corner of the eye.

Cuts

Minor—wash thoroughly with soap or disinfectant and water until absolutely clean. Apply sterile dressing.

For more serious cuts, where bleeding is profuse, apply pressure with a thick sterile (or at least clean) pad, dressing, or towel over the area. If an artery is spurting, try to minimise bleeding by applying pressure immediately above and below the cut.

If glass is still thought to be present in the cut, wash thoroughly before applying pressure. If bleeding is profuse, the application of pressure to prevent bleeding is more important than the removal of the glass.

In all cases the patient should be transferred to hospital or to a doctor, for further treatment of the wound, and also for a course of anti-tetanus toxoid, which is indicated if the patient is not already fully immunised.

Poisons

Solid and Liquid Poisons

(*a*) In the mouth but not swallowed. Spit out at once, and wash the mouth out repeatedly with water.

(*b*) If swallowed. Whatever the substance swallowed (*e.g.*, acids, alkalis, arsenic or mercury compounds, *etc.*), dilute by drinking approximately one pint of milk, preferably, or water.

No attempt to make the patient vomit should be carried out, especially in the cases of swallowed acids or alkalis.

Hydrogen cyanide (inhaled) or alkali cyanides (taken by mouth, *cf*. p. 192); inhale amyl nitrite from freshly opened capsules. Obtain medical attention urgently.

Gas Poisoning

Remove the patient to the fresh air, and loosen clothing at the neck. If breathing has stopped or is extremely weak, give artificial respiration and continue until the patient is transferred to hospital or until a doctor arrives.

To counteract chlorine or bromine fumes if inhaled in only small amounts, inhale ammonia vapour. Afterwards suck eucalyptus pastilles, or drink warm dilute peppermint or cinnamon essence, to soothe the throat and lungs.

ELECTRIC SHOCK

Switch off. Treat for burns as necessary.

If the patient is in a state of "shock" (*i.e.*, pale, faint or collapsed, sweating, cold) treat by lying flat, or preferably with the legs raised approximately one foot, loosen clothing around the neck, keep warm but not hot (one to two blankets) and transfer to hospital or obtain medical attention urgently.

TREATMENT OF FIRES.

Clothes. Laboratories should be equipped with a sufficient number of fireproof blankets, so that a blanket is available at any point of the laboratory at a few seconds' notice. Each blanket should be kept in a clearly labelled box, the lid of which is closed *by its own weight* and not by any mechanical fastening, which might delay removal of the blanket. The box itself should be kept in some open and unencumbered position in the laboratory.

The blanket when required should be at once wrapped firmly around the person whose clothes are on fire, the person then placed in a prone position on the floor with the ignited portion upwards, and water poured freely both over the blanket and in between the blanket and the person's clothes until the fire is extinguished.

BENCH FIRES.

Most of the available fire-extinguishers are unsuitable for chemical laboratory use. Those which give a stream of water are useless for extinguishing burning ether, benzene, petrol, *etc.*, and exceedingly dangerous if metallic sodium or potassium are present. Those which give a vigorous and fine stream of carbon tetrachloride, frequently serve merely to fling the burning material (and particularly burning solvents) along the surface of the bench without extinguishing the fire, the area of which is thus actually increased. Contact of the tetrachloride with metallic sodium or potassium may cause violent explosions.

The following methods should therefore generally be used:

(1) *Sand.* Buckets of dry sand for fire-extinguishing should be available in the laboratory and should be *strictly reserved* for this purpose, and not encumbered with sand-baths, waste-paper, *etc.* Most fires on the bench may be quickly smothered by the ample use of sand. Sand once used for this purpose should always be thrown away afterwards, and *not* returned to the buckets, as it may contain appreciable quantities of inflammable, non-volatile materials (*e.g.*, nitrobenzene), and be dangerous if used a second time.

(2) *Carbon tetrachloride.* Although sand is of great value for extinguishing fires, it has the disadvantage that any glass apparatus around which the fire centres is usually smashed under the weight of the sand. Alternatively, therefore, for *small* fires carbon tetrachloride may be poured in a copious stream from a Winchester Bottle on to the

fire, when the "blanketing" effect of the heavy carbon tetrachloride vapour will quickly extinguish the fire. In such cases it should be remembered, however, (a) not to use carbon tetrachloride if metallic sodium or potassium is present, as violent explosions may result, (b) to ventilate the laboratory immediately after extinguishing the fire, in order to disperse the phosgene vapour which is always formed when carbon tetrachloride is used in this way.

(3) *Carbon dioxide.* The above disadvantages of carbon tetra-chloride have caused it to be now superseded by carbon dioxide, which is available in $2\frac{1}{2}$ lb. ($1 \cdot 13$ Kgm.) and 5 lb. ($2 \cdot 26$ Kgm.) extinguishers; these are the most effective extinguishers for use in the laboratory.

Carbon dioxide has the advantages that in use (a) adverse chemical reactions are extremely unlikely, (b) there is no electrical hazard, and (c) damage to apparatus is minimal.

(4) If a liquid which is being heated in a beaker or a conical flask catches fire, it is frequently sufficient to turn off the gas (or other source of heating) below and then at once to stretch a clean duster tightly over the mouth of the vessel. The fire quickly dies out from lack of air, and the (probably valuable) solution is recovered unharmed.

Students should bear in mind that the majority of bench fires arise from one of three causes, all of which result from careless manipulation by the student himself. These causes are: (1) the cracking of glass vessels which are being heated (usually for distillation purposes) whilst containing inflammable liquids. This cracking may occasionally be due to faulty apparatus, but is almost invariably caused by an unsuitable method of heating, the latter furthermore being often hastily applied. (2) The addition of unglazed porcelain to a heated liquid which is "bumping" badly—with the result that the previously superheated liquid suddenly froths over and catches fire. Porcelain should never be added to a "bumping" liquid until the latter has been allowed to cool for a few minutes and therefore has fallen in temperature below its boiling-point. (3) The heating of volatile, inflammable liquids in flasks *not* fitted with reflux condensers.

The most dangerous solvent in the laboratory is carbon disulphide, the flash-point of which is so low that its vapour is ignited, *e.g.*, by a gas-ring 3–4 minutes after the gas has been turned out. Carbon disulphide should therefore never be used in the laboratory unless an adequate substitute as a solvent cannot be found. Probably the next most dangerous liquid for general manipulation is ether, which, however, has frequently to be employed. If the precautions described on pp. 79, 163, are *always* followed, the manipulation of ether should however be quite safe.

EXPLOSIONS.

Gaseous explosions also rank among those accidents which are almost invariably due to careless work. They are usually caused by:

(i) Faulty condensation of a heavy inflammable vapour, such as ether.

The precautions mentioned in the previous paragraph if observed will prevent this occurrence.

(ii) Igniting an inflammable gas before all air has been removed from the containing vessel. Whenever an inflammable gas is collected, a sample in a small test-tube should first be ignited at a safe distance from the main experiment. If it burns quietly, without any sign of even a gentle explosion, the main body of the gas can be safely ignited —although even then, this should be done with the smallest volume of gas suitable for the purpose concerned.

(iii) Experiments in which metallic sodium has been used (*e.g.*, the preparation of ethyl acetoacetate), and in which the product has subsequently to be treated with water. Great care should be taken to ensure that no unchanged sodium remains when the water is added.

SPECIAL CAUTION.

Safety goggles should always be worn over the eyes when carrying out potentially dangerous operations, *e.g.* vacuum distillations, distillation of large volumes of inflammable liquids and experiments employing large quantities of metallic sodium.

Table		Page
I.	Atomic Weights	534
II.	Vapour Pressure of Water at Various Temperatures	534
III.	Conversion Factors for Gravimetric Analysis	534
IV.	Alcohols and Derivatives	536
V.	Aryl-substituted Alcohols and Derivatives	537
VI.	Phenols and Derivatives	538
VII.	Aliphatic Aldehydes and Derivatives. Acetals	539
VIII.	Aromatic Aldehydes and Derivatives	540
IX.	Aliphatic Ketones and Derivatives	541
X.	Aromatic Ketones and Derivatives	542
XI.	Aliphatic Carboxylic Acids and Derivatives	543
XII.	Aromatic Carboxylic Acids and Derivatives	544
XIII.	Esters	546
XIV.	Sulphonic Acids and Derivatives	548
XV.	Quinones	549
XVI.	Primary Amines and Derivatives	550
XVII.	Secondary Amines	552
XVIII.	Tertiary Amines and Derivatives	553
XIX.	Amino-acids and Derivatives	555
XX.	Nitroso-compounds	556
XXI.	Nitro-compounds	557
XXII.	Azo-compounds	557
XXIII.	Azoxy-compounds	558
XXIV.	Ureas and Thioureas	558
XXV.	Substituted Hydrazines	558
XXVI.	Halogeno-hydrocarbons	559
XXVII.	Aromatic Hydrocarbons and Derivatives	560
XXVIII.	Ethers	560
	Logarithms	562
	Anti-logarithms	564

TABLE I. ATOMIC WEIGHTS.

	Symbol	At. Wt.		Symbol	At. Wt.
Antimony	Sb	121·76	Manganese	Mn	54·93
Arsenic	As	74·91	Mercury	Hg	200·61
Barium	Ba	137·36	Nitrogen	N	14·01
Bromine	Br	79·92	Oxygen	O	16·00
Calcium	Ca	40·08	Phosphorus	P	31·02
Carbon	C	12·00	Platinum	Pt	195·23
Chlorine	Cl	35·46	Potassium	K	39·10
Chromium	Cr	52·01	Silver	Ag	107·88
Copper	Cu	63·57	Sodium	Na	23·00
Hydrogen	H	1·008	Strontium	Sr	87·63
Iodine	I	126·92	Sulphur	S	32·06
Iron	Fe	55·84	Tin	Sn	118·70
Lead	Pb	207·22	Zinc	Zn	65·38
Magnesium	Mg	24·32			

TABLE II. VAPOUR PRESSURE (p) OF WATER AT VARIOUS TEMPERATURES (t).

t (°C)	8	9	10	11	12	13	14	15	16
p (mm.)	8·0	8·6	9·2	9·8	10·5	11·2	11·9	12·7	13·5
t (°C)	17	18	19	20	21	22	23	24	25
p (mm.)	14·4	15·4	16·3	17·4	18·5	19·7	20·9	22·2	23·6

TABLE III. CONVERSION FACTORS FOR GRAVIMETRIC ANALYSIS.

Sought.	Weighed as	Factor.	Log. of Factor
C	CO_2	0·2727	1·4357
H	H_2O	0·1119	1·0488
Cl	AgCl	0·2474	1·3934
Br	AgBr	0·4256	1·6290
I	AgI	0·5406	1·7329
S	$BaSO_4$	0·1374	1·1379
CH_3O	AgI	0·1321	1·1209

The factor represents the fraction by weight of the element sought (Column 1) in the final compound weighed (Column 2), e.g., the weight of carbon in x g. of carbon dioxide is therefore 0·2727x g.

Physical Constants of Organic Compounds.

The following classes of organic compounds are arranged approximately in the order of the Sections 9–25 given on pp. 316–318. In the case of compounds having more than one reactive group, the derivatives noted are the fully substituted derivatives that would normally be obtained if an excess of reagent were used: *e.g.*, the methyl ether of a dihydric phenol is the di-methyl ether, the benzoyl derivative of a diamine is the dibenzoyl derivative, *etc.* The following abbreviations are used: *anhyd.*, anhydrous; *d.*, with decomposition; *subl.*, sublimes.

When, in a column headed "M.p.," a value is given in parenthesis, it indicates that the compound is liquid at room temperature and that the value given is consequently the boiling-point. Conversely in a column headed "B.p.," values given in parenthesis are those of the melting-point. A blank space indicates that the compound has not apparently been recorded.

536 TABLE IV. ALCOHOLS AND DERIVATIVES.

	M.p.	B.p.	3,5-Dinitro-benzoates M.p.	Phenyl-urethanes M.p.	1-Naphthyl-urethanes M.p.	p-Nitro-benzoates M.p.
Methyl . . .		64·5°	109°	47°	124°	96°
Ethyl . . .		78	94	52	79	57
n-Propyl . . .		97	75	51	80	35
iso- ,, . . .		82	122	90	106	110
Allyl . . .		97	50	70	109	30
n-Butyl . . .		118	64	61	72	35
iso- ,, . . .		108	88	86	104	69
sec- ,, . . .		100	76	64	98	26
tert- ,, . . .	25	82	142	136	101	116
n-Amyl . . .		138	46	46	68	11
2-Pentanol . .		119	62		76	17
3-Pentanol . .		116	100	49	95	17
n-Hexyl . . .		156	61	42	59	5
n-Hexan-2-ol . .		140	39		60	40
n-Heptyl . . .		176	48	65	62	10
n-Heptan-2-ol .		159	49	60	54	
n-Octyl . . .		194	62	74	66	12
n-Octan-2-ol .		179	32	(oil)	64	28
n-Nonyl . . .		214	52	62	65	66
n-Decyl . . .	6	231	57	60	71	30
2-Methoxy-ethanol .		125			113	51
2-Ethoxy- ,,		135	75		67	
2-n-Propoxy ,,		153				
2-n-Butoxy- ,,		172		62		120
Furfuryl . . .		170	81	45	129	76
Tetrahydro-furfuryl .		177	84	61	90	47
Cyclo-pentanol . .		141	115	132	118	62
Cyclo-hexanol . .	25	161	113	82	129	50
Mono-ethanolamine[1] .		171				
Di- ,, [2] .	28	270				
Tri- ,, [3] .		360				
Ethylene-glycol . .		197	169*	157*	176*	140*
Propylene-glycol (1,2) .		187	147*	153*		127*
Tri-methylene-glycol .		216	178*	137*	164*	119*
Tetra- ,, ,, .	19	230		183*	198*	175*
Penta- ,, ,, .		239		176*	147*	105*
Hexa- ,, ,, .	42	250		171*		
Glycerol . . .		290d.		180†	192†	188†
Pentaerythritol . .	253					
d-Mannitol . .	166			303d.[5]		
d-Sorbitol . .	55[4]					

[1] 2-Amino-ethanol. [2] Di(2-hydroxyethyl)amine. [3] Tri(2-hydroxyethyl)amine.
[4] Monohydrate. [5] Hexa-deriv.
* Di-substituted derivs. † Tri-substituted derivs.

(continued on p. 537)

TABLE IV. ALCOHOLS AND DERIVATIVES (*continued*).   537

	M.p.	B.p.	3,5-Dinitro-benzoates M.p.	Phenyl-urethanes M.p.	1-Naphthyl-urethanes M.p.	p-Nitro-benzoates M.p.
Ethylene-chlorohydrin .		128·5	92	51	101	56
,, -bromohydrin .		149	86	86	86	52
Trimethylene-chlorohydrin		161d.	77	36	76	
,, -bromohydrin		176d.			73	42
Glycerol-1-chloro-hydrin		213d.				108*
,, -1,2-dichloro- ,,		183		73	93	37
,, -1,3- ,, ,,		176	129	73	115	62

TABLE V. ARYL-SUBSTITUTED ALCOHOLS AND DERIVATIVES.

	M.p.	B.p.	3,5-Dinitro-benzoates M.p.	Phenyl-urethanes M.p.	1-Naphthyl-urethanes M.p.	p-Nitro-benzoates M.p.
Benzyl . .		205°	113°	76°	134°	85°
o-Methylbenzyl[1] .	36	219		79		101
m- ,, [2] .		217	111		116	89
p- ,, [3] .	60	217	118	79		
o-Chlorobenzyl .	74	230				94
m- ,, .		234				
p- ,, .	73	235		94		
o-Bromobenzyl .	80					
m- ,, .		254				
p- ,, .	77					121
o-Iodobenzyl .	90					
m- ,, .		165/16				
p- ,, .	72					
o-Nitrobenzyl .	74	270				
m- ,, .	27					
p- ,, .	93	185/12				171
o-Hydroxybenzyl[4] .	87					
m- ,, .	73					
p- ,, .	125					
o-Methoxybenzyl .		249			136	82
m- ,, .		252	121	105		
p- ,, .	25	259		93		94
1-Phenylethyl[5] .	20	203	95	94	106	48
2- ,, .		220	108	80	119	62
Diphenylcarbinol[6] .	69	299	141	140	136	131
Triphenyl ,, .	165	380				
Cinnamyl . .	33	257	121	91	114	78
Benzoin . .	137	344		165	140	123
Furoin[7] . .	135					

[1], [2], [3] o-, m-, p-Tolylcarbinols.   [4] Saligenin.   [5] Methyl-phenylcarbinol.
[6] Benzhydrol.   [7] See Table IX.

	M.p.	B.p.	Toluene-p-sulphonate M.p.	p-Nitro-benzoate M.p.	3,5-Dinitro-benzoate M.p.	Phenyl urethane M.p.	1-Naphthyl urethane M.p.
Phenol	43°	182°	96°	126°	146°	126°	133°
o-Cresol	30	191	55	94	138	145	142
m- ,,	12	202	51	90	165	125	128
p- ,,	36	202	70	98	189	115	146
o-Chlorophenol		176	74	115	143	120	120
m- ,,	31	214		99	156		158
p- ,,	43	220	71	168	186	138	166
o-Bromophenol	5	195	78				129
m- ,,	33	236	53				108
p- ,,	64	238	94	180	191	144	168
o-Iodophenol	43		80			122	
m- ,,	40		61	133	183	138	
p- ,,	94		99			148	
Catechol	105	245		169*	152*	169*	175*
Resorcinol	110	280	81*	182*	201*	164*	206*
Hydroquinone	170	286	159*	263*	317*	224*	247*
o-Methoxyphenol[1]	32	205	85	93	142	136	118
m- ,, ,,		244					129
p- ,, ,,	56	243		116	166		
o-Nitrophenol	45	216	83	141	155	107	113
m- ,,	97	194/70	113	174	159	129	167
p- ,,	114		97	159	188	148	151
o-, m-, p-Amino-phenol[2]							
Salicylic acid[3]	159		155	205			
Saligenin[4]	87						283
2,4-Dichlorophenol	45	210	125				
2,4-Dibromophenol	40	239	120	184			
2,4,6-Trichloro-phenol	69	246		106	136		188
2,4,6-Tribromo-phenol	94		113	153	174	168	153
Picric Acid	122			143			
Pyrogallol (1,2,3)	133	309		230†	205†	173†	
Phloroglucinol (1,3,5)	218			283†	162†	191†	
Carvacrol[5]		238	44	51	77	135	116
Thymol[6]	51	233	71	70	103	107	160
Eugenol[7]		254	85	81	131	96	122

[1]Guaiacol.   [2]See Table XVI.   [3]See Table XII.   [4]See Table V.
[5]Pr,Me,OH = 1,4,3.   [6]Pr,Me,OH = 1,4,2.   [7]Allyl, OMe,OH = 1,3,4.
* Di-substituted deriv.   † Tri-substituted deriv.

(continued on page 539)

TABLE VI. PHENOLS AND DERIVATIVES (*continued*) 539

	M.p.	B.p.	Toluene-*p*-sulphonate M.p.	*p*-Nitrobenzoate M.p.	3,5-Dinitrobenzoate M.p.	Phenyl urethane M.p.	1-Naphthyl urethane M.p.
1-Naphthol .	94	279	88	143	217	178	155
2- ,, . .	123	285	125	169	210	155	157
1,3-Dihydroxy-naphthalene[8]	124						
1,5- ,, ,, .[9]	265						
1,8- ,, ,, [10]	142						220

Diacetyl derivs., [8]56°, [9]159°, [10]55°.

TABLE VII. ALIPHATIC ALDEHYDES AND DERIVATIVES. ACETALS.

	B.p.	Phenylhydrazone M.p.	2,4-Dinitrophenylhydrazone M.p.	Semicarbazone M.p.
Formaldehyde . .	−21°	145°	166°	169*d*.°
Acetaldehyde . .	21	57, 99[1]	147, 168[1]*	162
Paraldehyde . .	(13) 124			
Propionaldehyde .	49	(oil)	155	89, 154[1]
n-Butyraldehyde .	74	94	126	95, 106[1]
iso- ,, . .	64	(oil)	187	125
Aldol . .	77/16			194
Crotonaldehyde .	104	56	190	201
n-Valeraldehyde .	103		108	
n-Hexaldehyde .	131		107	109
n-Heptaldehyde .	156	(203)	108	109
n-Octaldehyde .	170		106	101
Chloral . . .	98[3]		131	90*d*.
Bromal . . .	174			87*d*.
Phenylacetaldehyde .	(34) 194	58	121	156
Cinnamaldehyde .	250*d*.	168	255*d*.	215
Dihydro ,, [2]. .	224		149	127
Furfural . .	161	97	229	202
Tetrahydro-furfural .	145/740		204	166
Hexahydro-benzaldehyde	162		172	173
Methylal $CH_2(OCH_3)_2$.	42			
Ethylal $CH_2(OC_2H_5)_2$.	89			
"Dimethyl-acetal" $CH_3CH(OCH_3)_2$.	64			
Acetal $CH_3CH(OC_2H_5)_2$	102			
"Di-*n*-propyl-acetal" $CH_3CH(OCH_2CH_2CH_3)_2$	147			

Values given in parentheses before B.p. are M.ps.
Values given in parentheses in Phenylhydrazone column are B.ps.
[1] Two forms. [2] β-Phenylpropionaldehyde. [3] "Monohydrate."
* The form, m.p. 147°, is usually obtained.

TABLE VIII. AROMATIC ALDEHYDES AND DERIVATIVES.

	M.p.	B.p.	Phenyl-hydrazone M.p.	2,4-Dinitro-phenyl-hydrazone M.p.	Semi-carbazone M.p.
Benzaldehyde . . .	Liq.	179	158	237	222
o-Chloro-benzaldehyde .	11	213	86	207	225
m- ,, ,, . .	17	213	134	248	228
p- ,, ,, .	47	214	127	218, 265[5]	230
o-Bromo- ,, .	22	230			214
m- ,, ,, .	Liq.	234	141	25	205
p- ,, ,, .	57		113	260	228
o-Nitro- ,, .	44	252	156	250d.	256
m- ,, ,, .	58		120	293d.	246
p- ,, ,, .	106		159	320	221
o-Amino ,, .	40		227	250	247
m- ,, ,, .			162	270d.	280d.
p- ,, ,, .	72		156	194	173d.
Salicylaldehyde . .		196	142	252d.	231
m-Hydroxy-benzaldehyde .	104	240	130, 147[5]	260d.	198
p- ,, ,, .	115		177	280d.	224, 280[5]
o-Methoxy- ,, .		243	120	253	215
m- ,, ,, .	4	230	76	219	233d.
p- ,, ,, [1] .	2·5	248	120	254d.	210
o-Tolualdehyde . . .		200	106	193	212
m- ,, . . .		199	91	212	216
p- ,, . . .		204	121	234	234
Vanillin[2] . . .	80	285d.	105	271	229d.
Veratraldehyde[3] . .	44	285	121	265	177
p-Dimethylamino-benzaldehyde . .	74	176/17	148	237	222
Phenylacetaldehyde . .	34	194	58	121	156
Cinnamaldehyde . .		252d.	168	255d.	215
Dihydro- ,, [4] . .		224		149	127
1-Naphthaldehyde . .	34	292	80	270	221
2- ,, . .	60		206d.		245
o-Phthalaldehyde . .	56		196d.*		
m- ,, . . .	90		248*		
(p)-Tere ,, . . .	116	245	154† 278d.*		

[1] Anisaldehyde. [2] 4-Hydroxy-3-methoxy-benzaldehyde. [3] 3,4-Dimethoxy-benzaldehyde. [4] β-Phenylpropionaldehyde. [5] Two forms.
* Di-substituted derivative. † Monosubstituted derivative.

TABLE IX. ALIPHATIC AND ALICYCLIC KETONES AND DERIVATIVES.

	B.p.	Phenyl-hydrazone M.p.	2,4-Dinitro-phenyl-hydrazone M.p.	Semi-carbazone M.p.
Acetone	56°	42°	126°	190°
Ethyl methyl ketone . .	80	Liq.	115	146
Diethyl ketone . . .	102	,,	156	139
Methyl n-propyl ketone .	102	,,	144	112
,, iso- ,, ,, . .	94	,,	120	113
Di-n-propyl ketone . .	144	,,	75	133
Di-iso- ,, ,, .	124	,,	98	160
n-Butyl methyl ,, . .	128	,,	106	122
Isobutyl methyl,, . .	117		95	132
Di-n-butyl ,, .	188			90
Di-iso- ,, ,, .	168		66	122
Chloroacetone . . .	119		125	164d.
Bromoacetone . . .	137/725			
Diacetyl	88	243	315	279
Acetylacetone . . .	139	(273)	209	185d.†
				107*
Acetonylacetone . .	194	120	257	224
Mesityl oxide . . .	130	142	203	133, 164[1]
Diacetone alcohol . .	166		203	
Pinacolone . . .	106	Liq.	125	157
Phorone	(28) 199		118	221
Ethyl acetoacetate . .	181	50	96	133
Cyclopentanone . .	131	55	147	209
Cyclohexanone . . .	156	81	162	166
2-Methyl-cyclohexanone .	165	46	137	197
3- ,, ,, .	170	94	155	190
4- ,, ,, .	171	110	134	198
Cycloheptanone . .	180	72	148	163
Furoin	(135)	81	217	
Furil	(165)	187	215	
(d-)Camphor . . .	(179) 209	233	177	237

Values given in parentheses before B.p. are M.ps.
Values given in parentheses in Phenylhydrazone column are B.ps.
* Di-deriv.   † Mono-deriv.   [1] Two forms.

TABLE X. AROMATIC KETONES AND DERIVATIVES.

	M.p.	B.p.	Phenyl-hydrazone M.p.	2,4-Dinitro-phenyl-hydrazone M.p.	Semi-carbazone M.p.
Acetophenone . . .	20°	202°	105°	250°	198°
o-Chloro-acetophenone .		229		206	160
m- ,, ,, .		228			232
p- ,, ,, .	20	232	114	231	200
o-Bromo- ,, . .		112/10		189	177
m- ,, ,, .		131/16			238
p- ,, ,, .	51	256	126	230	208
ω- ,, ,, [1]					
o-Hydroxy- ,, . .	28	215	110		210
m- ,, ,, .	96	296			195
p- ,, ,, .	109	240	151	261	199
o-Methoxy- ,, .		245	114	159	183
m- ,, ,, .		240		207	196
p- ,, ,, .	38	258	142	220	198
o-Nitro- ,, .	28	218			
m- ,, ,, .	81	202	128	228	257
p- ,, ,, .	81		132		
Propiophenone . . .	19	218	147	191	181
Benzyl methyl ketone . .	27	216	87	156	198
Benzyl ethyl ,, . .		226			135
Benzophenone . . .	49	306	137	239	164
p-Chloro- ,, . . .	78	323	106	185	
p-Bromo- ,, . . .	82	350	126	230	
Phenyl p-tolyl ketone . .	60	326	109	199	121
Benzyl phenyl ,, . .	60	320	116	204	148
Di-p-tolyl ,, . .	95	335	100	229	140
Dibenzyl ketone . . .	35	331	128	100	146
Methyl-1-naphthyl ketone .	34	302	146		229
Methyl-2- ,, ,, .	54	301	177	262	236
Benzoin	137	344	106[2]	245	206d.
Benzil	95	347d.	{ 134† / 235*	– / 189*	182† / 244d.*
Phenacyl chloride . .	59	244		212	156
Phenacyl bromide . .	50	135/18		230	146
p-Bromophenacyl bromide .	109				
Benzalacetone . . .	42	262	157	227	187
Dibenzalacetone . .	112		153	180	190
1-Tetralone . . .		129/12	84	257	217
Fluorenone . . .	83	341	151	283	

[1] See Phenacyl bromide (below). [2] Second form, m.p. 159°.

* Di-deriv. † Mono-deriv.

TABLE XI. ALIPHATIC CARBOXYLIC ACIDS AND DERIVATIVES.

Acid	M.p.	B.p.	Esters — Methyl B.p.	Esters — Ethyl B.p.	Esters — Phenyl B.p.	Esters — p-Nitro-benzyl M.p.	Esters — Phen-acyl M.p.	Esters — p-Bromo-phenacyl M.p.	Benzyl-thiouronium salt M.p.	Amide M.p.	Anilide M.p.	Benzyl-amide M.p.	Chloride B.p.	Anhydride B.p.	Nitrile B.p.
Formic	8°	100°	32°	54°	173°	31°	Liq.	135°	152°	3°	50°	60°			25°
Acetic	17	118	57	77	196	78	50	85	134	82	113	60	52°	138°	82
Glycollic	79		151	160	(100)	107		138	146	120	97	103		130	183d.
Propionic		140	79	98	(20)211	31	Liq.	59	153	79	105	43	80	168	97
n-Butyric		163	102	120	227	35		63	146	115	96	38	100	198	117
iso- ,,		155	92	110					143	129	105	87	92	182	108
Pyruvic	13	165	136	155				77	158	124	104				93
Monochloro-acetic	63	189	130	145	(45)235			105	160	119	137	94	105	(46)	127
Dichloro-acetic		194	143	158	(33)247			99	178	97	119	96	107	215	112
Trichloro-acetic	58	197	152	167	255d.	80			149	141	94	94	118	223	83
Bromo-acetic	50	208	144d.	169	(32)	89			145	91	130	107	134	(42)245	149
Cyan-acetic	66		201	207						123	198	124			(30)220
Carbonic			90	126	(78)306					132	238	169	8		
Oxalic	101[1]		(54)163	186	(130)	204	Liq.	244d.	196	418d.	245	223	64		
Malonic	133d.		181	198	(50)	85	Liq.	Liq.	146d.	170	225	142		(120)250	(30)222
Succinic	185	235d.	(19)195	218	(121)	88	148	211	154	242[3]	226	206	190	(120)250	(56)268
Glutaric	98	303	214	237	(54)	69	105	137	153	174	224	170	217	(56)288	286
Adipic	153		115/3	245	(106)	106	88	155	163	220	238	189		(22)	295
dl-Lactic	18	119/12	144	155	Liq.	Liq.	96	112	153	74	59	59			182
l-Malic	100		242	253		124	106	179	158	157	197	156			
d-Tartaric	169		(48)280	(17)280	102	163	130	216d.		196d.	264d.	199			
Citric	75–80[2]		(79)	294	(124)	102	104	148		210d.	199	169			
Fumaric	286		(102)192	218	(162)	150	197	257d.	183	266d.	314	204	162	202	(96)186
Maleic	132		205	225	(73)	89	129	169d.	173	181d.[4]	187	148		(56)202	

Values in parentheses in the columns for Methyl, Ethyl, and Phenyl Esters and for Anhydrides and Nitriles are M.ps.

[1] Dihydrate; anhydrous, m.p. 190 d.   [2] Monohydrate; anhydrous, m.p. 153.   [3] Imide, m.p. 125.   [4] Imide, m.p. 93.

TABLE XII. AROMATIC CARBOXYLIC

Acid	M.p.	Esters				
		Methyl B.p.	Ethyl B.p.	Phenyl M.p.	p-Nitro-benzyl M.p.	Phenacyl M.p.
(1) Benzoic	121	198°	213°	69°	89°	119°
(2) Salicylic	158	223	234	42	98	110
(3) Acetylsalicylic	135	(49)	272	97	90	105
(4) m-Hydroxybenzoic	201	(70)	(72) 295		108	147
(5) p- ,,	213	(131)	(116) 297	176	181	178
(6) o-Chlorobenzoic	141	234	243	37	106	83
(7) m- ,,	158	234	245		107	116
(8) p- ,,	243	(44)	238		130	90
(9) o-Bromobenzoic	150	244	254		110	83
(10) m- ,,	155	(32)	261	65	105	113
(11) p- ,,	252	(81)	262	117	141	90
(12) o-Methoxybenzoic	101	245	261	59	113	
(13) m- ,,	110	(32) 250	250			
(14) p- ,, [1]	184	(48) 256	263	76	132	134
(15) o-Nitrobenzoic	147	275	(30) 275		112	125
(16) m- ,,	141	(78) 279	(47) 298	99	142	106
(17) p- ,,	239	(96)	(56)	129	169	128
(18) 2,4-Dinitrobenzoic	183	(70)	(41)		142	
(19) 3,5- ,,	207	(108)	(95)	146	157	
(20) Anthranilic	146	(24) 300	(13) 226	70	205	181[4]
(21) m-Aminobenzoic	174	(38)	294		201	
(22) p- ,,	188	(112)	(92)	173	>248	186[4]
(23) o-Toluic	105	215	227	(306)	91	75
(24) m- ,,	111	215	(47) 230		87	
(25) p- ,,	178	(33) 217	228	83	104	103
(26) Phthalic	196–9d.	283	298	70	155	154
(27) Isophthalic	347	(68)	(11) 285	120	203	191
(28) Terephthalic	300 subl.	(141)	(42) 302	191	264	192
(29) Phenylacetic	76	215	227	42	65	50
(30) α-Phenylpropionic	(265)	221	230			
(31) β- ,,	48	238	247		36	42
(32) Cinnamic	133	(36) 261	271	72	117	140
(33) o-Nitrocinnamic	240	(72)	(44)		132	126
(34) p- ,,	287	(161)	(142)	152	186	146
(35) dl-Mandelic	118	(58) 250	(37) 255		124	84
(36) 1-Naphthoic	162		309	99	132	135
(37) 2-Naphthoic	185	(77) 290	(32) 308			
(38) Hexahydrobenzoic	30	183	196			
(39) Phenoxyacetic	100	245	251	60		148

Values in parentheses in the columns for Methyl, Ethyl and Phenyl Esters and for Anhydrides and Nitriles are M.ps.   [1] Anisic acid.

ACIDS AND DERIVATIVES.

p-Bromophenacyl M.p.	Benzyl thiouronium salt M.p.	Amide M.p.	Anilide M.p.	Benzylamide M.p.	Chloride M.p.	Chloride B.p.	Anhydride M.p.	Nitrile M.p.	Nitrile B.p.	
119°	167°	129°	162°	105°		197°	42°		190	(1)
140	148	139	135	137	20	92/15		98		(2)
	144	138	136	102	49	135/12	85		254	(3)
176	162	167	157	142				82		(4)
191	145	162	197					113		(5)
107	169	141	118	101		238	79	43	232	(6)
117	164	134	124			225	95	41		(7)
128	194	179	194	173	16	222	194	96	224	(8)
102	171	155	141		11	245		53	253	(9)
126	168	155	146			243		38	225	(10)
134	196	189	197		42	247	218	112	237	(11)
113	164	129	131			254	72	25	256	(12)
	176	134				244	67			(13)
152	185	163	171	131	22	145/15	99	61	240	(14)
101	159	175	161	141	20	148/9	135	110		(15)
132	163	142	154	101	35	278d.	160	118		(16)
136	182	200	211	142	75	150/15	189	147		(17)
158	181	204	193		46		160	104		(18)
159	179	183	234		69	196/11	219			(19)
172[5]	144	109	131	125				50	266	(20)
190[5]	160	111[2]	140		42			53	290	(21)
200[5]	166	179[3]	162	89	31			86		(22)
57	145	143	125	110		208	39		205	(23)
108	164	95	126	99		219	71		212	(24)
153	190	159	148	133		214	95	27	217	(25)
153	158	220	251	178		281	132	141		(26)
119	216	280			44	276		162		(27)
225	206	>250	337	266	84	261		222		(28)
89	165	157	118	122		210	72		234	(29)
	146	91	133			97/12			230	(30)
104	152	105	98	85		225			261	(31)
146	183	147	153	226	36	257	136	20	256	(32)
142		185			65		65	92		(33)
191	209	217								(34)
113	166	134	152					22	170d.	(35)
134	149	202	163	180	20	297	145	37	299	(36)
144	184	192	170	143	43	304	133	66	305	(37)
91	166	185	146			180	25		185	(38)
148	181	101	99	90		226	68		240	(39)

[2] Hydrate, m.p. 79°. [3] Hydrate, m.p. 114°. [4] Di-deriv., (N-phenacyl)-phenacyl ester. [5] Di-deriv., as [4].

TABLE XIII. ESTERS.

In view of the difficulty of arranging esters in a chemically logical sequence they have in the following table been arranged in order of increasing b.ps (liquid) and m.ps (solid). Other esters are given in Tables XI and XII (pp. 543–545). The values for esters of polybasic acids refer to the fully esterified product.

LIQUID

	B.P.			B.P.
Methyl formate	31·5°	Dimethyl succinate	(18)	196°
Ethyl formate	54·2	Phenyl acetate		196
Methyl acetate	57·1	Ethyl acetoacetate		198
Iso-propyl formate	71	Diethyl malonate		199
Ethyl acetate	77	Methyl benzoate		199
Methyl propionate	80	Benzyl formate		203
n-Propyl formate	81	Phenyl propionate	(20)	211
Iso-propyl acetate	91	n-Propyl oxalate		213
Methyl iso-butyrate	93	Ethyl benzoate		213
Iso-butyl formate	98	Benzyl acetate		217
Ethyl propionate	99	Diethyl succinate		218
n-Propyl acetate	101	Iso-propyl benzoate		218
Methyl butyrate	102	Methyl salicylate		223
n-Butyl formate	107	Phenyl n-butyrate		227
Ethyl iso-butyrate	110	Iso-butyl oxalate		229
Iso-butyl acetate	117	n-Propyl benzoate		230
Ethyl butyrate	122	Ethyl salicylate		234
n-Propyl propionate	122	Iso-propyl salicylate		237
Iso-amyl formate	123	Benzyl n-butyrate		238
n-Butyl acetate	126	n-Propyl salicylate		239
Iso-propyl n-butyrate	128	Isobutyl benzoate		241
Iso-butyl propionate	137	n-Butyl oxalate		243
n-Propyl n-butyrate	143	n-Propyl succinate		246
n-Butyl propionate	147	n-Butyl benzoate		249
Iso-butyl isobutyrate	149	Glyceryl triacetate		258
Ethyl lactate	154·5	Ethyl cinnamate	(6·5)	271
Iso-butyl butyrate	157	Diethyl d-tartrate	(19)	280
Cyclohexyl formate	162	Dimethyl phthalate		284
n-Butyl n-butyrate	165	Triethyl citrate		294
Iso-propyl lactate	168	Diethyl phthalate		298
Cyclohexyl acetate	175	Glyceryl tributyrate		309
Diethyl oxalate	185	Benzyl salicylate		320
Di-iso-propyl oxalate	189			

Values in parentheses are M.ps.

(continued on p. 547)

SOLID

	M.P.			M.P.
Phenyl propionate	(211°) 20°	Phenyl phthalate . . .		70°
Methyl anthranilate	(300) 24·4	2-Naphthyl acetate .	.	71
Methyl cinnamate. . (261)	36	Glyceryl tristearate .	.	71
Benzyl cinnamate . . .	39	Glyceryl tribenzoate .	.	72
Phenyl salicylate . . .	42	Phenyl cinnamate .	.	72
Cyclo-hexyl oxalate . .	42	Glycol dibenzoate . (360)		73
Benzyl succinate . . .	48	Trimethyl citrate .	.	79
Dimethyl d-tartrate . . (280)	48	Benzyl oxalate . .	.	80
1-Naphthyl acetate . .	49	Dimethyl dl-tartrate . (282)		90
Dimethyl oxalate . (163)	54	Diphenyl succinate . (330)		121
Phenyl benzoate . . (314)	69			

Values in parentheses are B.ps.

TABLE XIV. SULPHONIC ACIDS AND DERIVATIVES.

	Benzyl-thiouronium salt M.p.	Sulphonyl chloride M.p.	Sulphon-amide M.p.	Sulphon-anilide M.p.
Benzene sulphonic . .	150°	15	153°	110°
Toluene-o-sulphonic . .	170	10°	156	136
Toluene-m- ,, . .		12	108	96
Toluene-p- ,, . .	182	71	137	103
o-Chlorobenzene sulphonic .		28	188	
m- ,, ,, .		Liq.	148	
p- ,, ,, .	175	53	144	104
o-Bromobenzene ,, .		51	186	
m- ,, ,, .		Liq.	154	
p- ,, ,, .	170	75	166	119
o-Nitrobenzene ,, .		69	193	115
m- ,, ,, .	146	64	168	126
p- ,, ,, .		80	179	136
Orthanilic[1] . .	132		153	
Metanilic[2] . .	148		142	
Sulphanilic . .	187		164	200
p-Acetamido-benzene sulphonic . .	248	150	219	
Phenol-p-sulphonic . .	169		177	141
o-Carboxy-benzene sulphonic[3]	206*	40, 79[4]*	†	195*
m- ,, ,, [3]	133*	20*	170*	
p- ,, ,, [3]	213*	57*	236*	252*
Naphthalene-1-sulphonic .	137	68	150	112, 157
Naphthalene-2- ,, .	191	79	217	132
1-Naphthylamine-4-,, .	195		206	190
2-Naphthylamine-1-sulphonic	139			
2- ,, -6- ,,	184			
1-Naphthol-2-sulphonic .	170			
1- ,, -4- ,, .	104			200
2-Naphthol-1-sulphonic .	136	124		161[5]
2- ,, -6- ,, .	217		238	161
Anthraquionne-1-sulphonic	191	217		216
Anthraquinone-2- ,, .	211	197	261	193
Benzene-o-disulphonic .	206	143	254	241
Benzene-m- ,, . .	214	63	229	144
Benzene-p- ,, . .		141	288	249

[1] o-Aminobenzene sulphonic acid.   [2] m-Aminobenzene sulphonic acid.
[3] o-, m-, p-Sulphobenzoic acids.   [4] Two forms.   [5] Dihydrate, m.p. 105°.
* Di-substituted deriv.   † Imide (saccharin) has m.p 224°.

(continued on p. 549)

TABLE XIV. SULPHONIC ACIDS AND DERIVATIVES (*continued*).

	Benzyl-thiouronium salt M.p.	Sulphonyl chloride M.p.	Sulphon-amide M.p.	Sulphon-anilide M.p.
Naphthalene-1,4-disulphonic		160	273	179
Naphthalene-1,6- ,, .	235	129	297	
Naphthalene-2,6-disulphonic	256	225	305	
Naphthalene-2,7- ,,	211	159	243	
(+)-Camphor-10-sulphonic	210	68	132	120
(+)-3-Bromocamphor-8-sulphonic . . .	10	137	145	

Carbohydrates

In view of the indefinite melting-points of many sugars and of their readily obtainable derivatives (*e.g.*, osazones, *cf.* p. 139), their identification should be based primarily on their chemical properties. Their rotatory power can often be used for identification purposes, but is not considered in this book.

TABLE XV. QUINONES.

	Colour	M.p.	Oxime M.p.	Semi-carbazone M.p.
Benzoquinone . .	Yellow	115°	240°d.	243°
Toluquinone . .	,,	69	234d.	240d.
1,4-Naphthoquinone .	,,	125	207d.	247*
1,2-Naphthoquinone .	Red	115–120 d.	169	184*
Anthraquinone . .	Pale yellow	277	224d.*	
Alizarin[1] . . .	,,	290		
Phenanthraquinone .	Orange	206	202	220d.*
d-Camphorquinone .	Pale yellow	198	140	147

M.ps. of oximes and semicarbazones are those of the di-derivatives, except those marked * which are mono-derivatives.

[1] 1,2-Dihydroxyanthraquinone; diacetyl deriv., m.p. 184°.

TABLE XVI. PRIMARY AMINES AND DERIVATIVES.

	M.p.	B.p.	Picrate M.p.	Acetyl deriv. M.p.	Benzoyl deriv. M.p.	Benzene sulphonyl deriv. M.p.	Toluene p-sulphonyl deriv. M.p.	Phenyl-urea deriv. M.p.
Methylamine		−7°	215°	28°	80°	30°	75°	151°
Ethylamine		19	170	(205)	71	58	63	99
n-Propylamine		49	135	47	84	36	52	116
iso-Propylamine		34	156		100	26	51	156
Allylamine		56	140	(215)	17	39	64	115
n-Butylamine		77	151	(229)	70			130
iso- ,,		69	156	(227)	57	53	78	147
sec.- ,,		63	140		76	70	55	156
n-Amylamine		105	143		31			238
n-Hexylamine		129	127		40	96		
n-Heptylamine		155	121					63
Benzylamine		185	199	60	105	88	116	168
1-Phenylethylamine		187	189	57	120			
2-Phenylethylamine		198	172	52	116	69	64	
Cyclohexylamine		134		104	149	89	88	
Ethylenediamine	8	117	234*	172*	249*	168*	160*	263*
Aniline		184	189	114	163	112	103	239
o-Toluidine		200	214	112	143	124	110	196
m- ,,		203	195	66	125	95	114	174
p- ,,	45	200	181	152	158	120	118	212
o-Chloroaniline		209	134	88	99	129	105	181
m- ,,		230	177	79	122	121	138	184
p- ,,	71	232	178	179	192	121	95	238
o-Bromo-aniline	32	229	129	99	116		90	
m- ,,	18	251	180	87	120	100		189
p- ,,	66	245	180	167	204	134	101	246d.
o-Iodo-aniline	60		112	110	139			
m- ,,	30			119	157		128	
p- ,,	64			184	222	162		
o-Nitro-aniline	72		73	94	98	104	114	223
m- ,,	114	225	143	155	157	136	139	198
p- ,,	148		100	216	199	137	191	212
o-Anisidine	5	225	200	88	60	89	127	144
m- ,,		251	169d.	81	112	82	68	
p- ,,	57	246	165d.	130	153	95	114	
o-Phenetidine		229	158	79	104	102	164	169
m- ,,		248	69	96	103	143	157	
p- ,,		254		138	173	143	107	178

(continued on p. 551)

TABLE XVI. PRIMARY AMINES AND DERIVATIVES—*continued*.

	M.p.	B.p.	Picrate M.p.	Acetyl deriv. M.p.	Benzoyl deriv. M.p.	Benzene sulphonyl deriv. M.p.	Toluene p-sulphonyl deriv. M.p.	Phenyl-urea deriv. M.p.
o-Aminophenol . .	174			124*	184*	134*	139[1]	166
m- ,, . .	123			101*	153*	153*	157[2]	232
p- ,, . .	186			151*	234*	125*	143[3]	221
2,4-Dichloro-aniline .	63	245	106	146	117	128	126	
2,4-Dibromo- ,, .	79		124	146	134		134	
2,4,6-Trichloro- ,,	78	262	83	206	174			
2,4,6-Tribomo- ,,	120	300		238	198	232		
1-Naphthylamine .	50	300	163	160	161	167	157	222d.
2- ,, .	113	294	195	134	162	102	133	220
o-Phenylene-diamine .	102	257	208	186	303*	185	202	
m- ,, ,,	64	283	184	191	240*	194	172	
p- ,, ,,	141	267		304	300*	247	266	
p-Amino-dimethylaniline	41	262	188	132	228			
p-Amino-diethyl ,, .		261		104	172			
2-Amino-biphenyl .	50	299		121	102		99	
4- ,, ,, .	53	302		171	230		160	
4,4'-Diamino- ,, . (benzidine)	127	400		317*	352*	232*	243*	

[1] N-deriv.; O-deriv. has m.p. 101°.
[2] N-deriv.; O-deriv. has m.p. 96°; di-deriv. m.p. 110°.
[3] N-deriv.; O-deriv. has m.p. 143°; di-deriv., m.p. 169°.
* Indicates di-substituted derivative.

TABLE XVII. SECONDARY AMINES.

	M.p.	B.p.	Picrate M.p.	Acetyl deriv. M.p.	Benzoyl deriv. M.p.	Benzene sulphonyl deriv. M.p.	Toluene p-sulphonyl deriv. M.p.	Phenyl-urea deriv. M.p.	Nitrosamine M.p.	Nitrosamine B.p.
Dimethylamine		7·5°	158°	(166)	41°	47‾	79°			
Diethylamine		56	155	(186)	42	42	60	85	Liq.	177
Di-n-propylamine		111	75	(210)		51			Liq.	205
Di-iso-propylamine		84	140						46	195
Diallylamine		111								
Di-n-butylamine		159	59					85		237
Di-iso-butylamine		139	119	86		55		105	Liq.	214
Di-sec.-butylamine		135								
Di-n-amylamine		205								
Dibenzylamine		300d.		93	112	68	81	127	61	
Dicyclohexylamine		256	173	102	77		119	169	105	
N-Methyl-aniline		194	145	103	63	79	94	104	Liq.	121†
N-Ethyl-aniline		206	138	54	60		88	91		134†
N-n-propyl-aniline		222		47		54	56			
N-n-butyl- ,,		240		Liq.	56		56			
N-Benzyl- ,,	38	306	48	58	107	119	140		58	
N-Methyl-o-toluidine		208	90	56	66		120			
N-Methyl-m- ,,		206		66						
N-Methyl-p- ,,		210	131	83	53	64	60		54	
N-Ethyl-o- ,,		218		(255)	72	62	75			
N-Ethyl-m- ,,		221		(254)	72					
N-Ethyl-p- ,,		217		(258)	40	66	71			
Diphenylamine ,,	54	302	182	103	180	124	142	136	67	
Di-o-tolylamine		312²								
Di-m- ,,		322		43						
Di-p- ,,	79	330		85	125				101	
Pyrrolidine		89	112				123			
Piperidine		105	152	Liq.	48	94	103	171	Liq.	218
Tetrahydro-quinoline	20	250	142	(295)	76	67				214d
Tetrahydro-iso- ,,		232	195	46	129	154		144	53	
Piperazine[1]	104	145	280*	144*	196*	282*	298*		158*	
Morpholine		130	148		75	118	147		29	245
Carbazole	238	354	185	69	98				84	

[1] Hexahydrate, m.p. 44°.   ² At 730 mm.
* Di-substituted derivs.   † At 14–15 mm.   Values in parentheses are B.ps.

TABLE XVIII. TERTIARY AMINES AND DERIVATIVES.

	M.p.	B.p.	Picrate M.p.	Meth-iodide M.p.	Metho-picrate M.p.	Metho-toluene-p-sul-phonate M.p.	Nitroso deriv. M.p.
Trimethylamine . . .		3·5°	216°	230°			
Triethylamine . . .		90	173				
Tri-n-propylamine . . .		156	117	208			
Tri-iso-propylamine . . .							
Tri-n-butylamine . . .		216	106	180			
Triallylamine		155					
Tribenzylamine . . .	92	380	190	184			
Tricyclohexylamine . . .			179				
Dimethylaniline . . .		193	163	228d.	122	161	87
Ethylmethylaniline . . .		201	134	125		49	66
Diethylaniline		216	142	102			84
Di-n-propylaniline . . .		245	261	156			
Di-iso-propylaniline . . .		221					
Di-n-butylaniline . . .		271	125			180	
Dibenzylaniline . . .	70	300	132	135			91
Benzylmethylaniline . . .		306	127	164			44
Benzylethylaniline . . .		312	121	141			62
p-Chloro-dimethylaniline . .	35	230					
p-Bromo- ,, . .	55	264		185d.			
p-Iodo- ,, . . .				212			
Dimethyl-o-toluidine . .		185	122	210	114		
Dimethyl-m- ,, . .		212	131	177	108		
Dimethyl-p- ,, . .		211	130	220	197	85	
Dimethyl-1-naphthylamine .		273	145	164		83	
Dimethyl-2- ,, . .	47	305	206	193d.	195d.		
Methyldiphenylamine . .		295		163	168		
Triphenylamine . . .	127	365					
Tri-o-tolylamine . . .							
Tri-m- ,, . . .							
Tri-p ,, . . .	117						
Pyridine		115	167	118	115	139	
2-Methylpyridine (2-picoline) .		129	170	229	113	150	
3- ,, (3- ,,) .		144	150	99	120		
4- ,, (4- ,,) .		143	167	152	150		
2,4-Dimethylpyridine (lutidine) .		157	183	113			
2,6- ,, (,,) .		142	163	238			
2,4,6-Trimethylpyridine (collidine)		172	156				
2-Chloropyridine . . .		170				120	
3- ,, . . .		149	135				
2-Bromopyridine . . .		194				127	
3- ,, . . .		170		146		156	

(continued on p. 554)

TABLE XVIII. TERTIARY AMINES AND DERIVATIVES—*continued*.

	M.p.	B.p.	Picrate M.p.	Meth-iodide M.p.	Metho-picrate M.p.	Metho-toluene-p-sulphonate M.p.	Nitroso deriv M.p.
Quinoline		238°	203°	134°[1]	169°d.	126°	
2-Methylquinoline (quinaldine) .		247	194	195	141	161	
4- ,, (lepidine) .	10°	262	211	174	161		
5- ,, ...	49	263	218	105			
6- ,, ...		258	229	219		154	
7- ,, ...	39	252	237	193			
8- ,, ...		248	200				
6-Hydroxyquinoline . . .			236				
8- ,, ...	76	267	204	143d.			
2-Chloroquinoline . . .	38	267	122				
6- ,, . . .	41	262			248d.	143	
2-Bromoquinoline . . .	49				210d.		
6- ,, . . .	19	278	217		278	152	
6-Nitroquinoline . . .	154				245d.		
8- ,, . . .	92				176		
Isoquinoline	24	242	223	159	169	163	
Acridine	111s.	345	258	223			
Hexamethylene tetramine . .	280			179	190	215	105

[1] Anhydrous; monohydrate, 68–70°.
s. sublimes.

TABLE XIX. AMINO-ACIDS AND DERIVATIVES.

	Formula	M.p.	Methyl ester M.p.	Ethyl ester M.p.	Acetyl deriv M.p.	Benzoyl deriv M.p.	3,5-Dinitro-benzoyl deriv. M.p.	z-Naphthal-ene sulphonyl deriv. M.p.
Glycine .	$NH_2 \cdot CH_2COOH$	232° d.	Liq.	Liq.	206°	187°	179°	159°
Alanine (dl) .	$CH_3 \cdot CH(NH_2)COOH$	295 „	„	„	138	165	177	152
Sarcosine .	$CH_3NH \cdot CH_2COOH$	212 „	„	„	135	104	154	
Phenylglycine	$C_6H_5NH \cdot CH_2COOH$	127	48	58	194	63	—	
Aspartic (l) .	$HOOC \cdot CH_2 \cdot CH(NH_2)COOH$	*271 d.	Liq.	Liq.		185	—	153
Cystine (l) .	$[-S \cdot CH_2 \cdot CH(NH_2)COOH]_2$	*260 „	„			180	180	230
Valine (dl) .	$(CH_3)_2CH \cdot CH(NH_2)COOH$	*298 „				132	158	
„ (l) .	„	*315 „				127	158	
Leucine (l) .	$(CH_3)_2CH \cdot CH_2 \cdot CH(NH_2)COOH$	*294 „	„	„	181	106†	187	
Phenylalanine (dl) .	$C_6H_5CH_2 \cdot CH(NH_2)COOH$	256		„		187		
„ „ (l)	„	*283 d.		„		145	93	
Hippuric .	$C_6H_5CO \cdot NH \cdot CH_2COOH$	187	85	67			—	
Tyrosine (l) .	$p\text{-}HOC_6H_4 \cdot CH_2 \cdot CH(NH_2)COOH$	344	135	108	172	166	—	
Anthranilic .	$NH_2 \cdot C_6H_4COOH$	144	25	Liq.	185	181	278	
m-Amino-benzoic	„	174	37	„	250	248	270	
p- „ „	„	186		89	252	278	>290	

* The m.ps. of these acids vary with the rate of heating, and the values given are those obtained on rapid heating in sealed tubes.
† Anhydrous.

TABLE XX. NITROSO-COMPOUNDS.

	Formula	M.p.
Methyl-phenyl-nitrosamine . .	$C_6H_5(CH_3)N \cdot NO$	Liq.
Ethyl- ,, ,, .	$C_6H_5(C_2H_5)N \cdot NO$	,,
Nitroso-benzene . . .	$C_6H_5 \cdot NO$	$67°$
p-Nitroso-phenol . . .	$HO \cdot C_6H_4 \cdot NO$	$125d.$
p-Nitroso-monomethyl-aniline .	$NO \cdot C_6H_4 \cdot NH \cdot CH_3$	118
p- ,, -dimethyl- ,, .	$NO \cdot C_6H_4 \cdot N(CH_3)_2$	$85d.$
p- ,, -monoethyl- ,, .	$NO \cdot C_6H_4 \cdot NH \cdot C_2H_5$	78
p- ,, -diethyl- ,, .	$NO \cdot C_6H_4 \cdot N(C_2H_5)_2$	87
Diphenyl-nitrosamine . .	$(C_6H_5)_2N \cdot NO$	67
p-Nitroso-diphenylamine . .	$NO \cdot C_6H_4NH \cdot C_6H_5$	144
1-Nitroso-2-naphthol . .	$NO \cdot C_{10}H_6 \cdot OH$	109
2- ,, -1- ,, . . .	,,	$163d.$
4- ,, -1- ,, . . .	,,	198

TABLE XXI. NITRO-COMPOUNDS.

	M.p.	B.p.		M.p.	B.p.
Nitro-methane . .	Liq.	101°	o-Nitro-benzyl chloride .	48°	
Nitro-ethane . .	,,	114	m- ,, ,, .	45	
Nitrobenzene . .	,,	210	p- ,, ,, .	71	
m-Dinitrobenzene .	90	302	p-Nitro-benzyl bromide .	99	
o-Nitro-toluene .	Liq.	220	p-Nitro ,, iodide .	127	
p- ,, ,, .	52	238	o-Nitro-benzaldehyde .	44	
2,4-Dinitro- ,, .	70		m- ,, ,,	58	
sym-Trinitro- ,, .	82		p- ,, ,, .	106	
o-Nitro-phenol .	46	216	o-Nitro-benzoic acid .	148	
m- ,, ,, .	97		m- ,, ,, ,, .	141	
p- ,, ,, .	114		p- ,, ,, ,, .	241	
2,4-Dinitro- ,, .	114		o-Nitro-benzoyl chloride .	25	
Picric acid . .	122		m- ,, ,, ,, .	35	277
o-Nitro-aniline .	71		p- ,, ,, ,, .	75	
m- ,, ,, .	114	285	3,5-Dinitro-benzoyl		
p- ,, ,, .	148		chloride . . .	70	
o-Nitro-acetanilide .	92		o-Chloro-nitrobenzene .	33	244
m- ,, ,,	155		p- ,, - ,, .	83	242
p- ,, ,,	212		o-Bromo- ,, .	43	261
o-Nitro-anisole .	10	265	p- ,, - ,, .	126	259
p- ,, - ,, .	54	259	o-Iodo- ,, .	54	
o- ,, -phenetole .	Liq.	268	p- ,, - ,, .	172	
p- ,, - ,, .	60	283	Chloro- 2,4-dinitro-		
2,4-Dinitro-anisole .	94		benzene.	51	315
2,4- ,, -phenetole .	86		Bromo- 2,4-dinitro-		
o-Nitro-benzyl alcohol .	74	270d.	benzene .	75	
m- ,, ,, ,, .	27		1-Nitro-naphthalene .	61	304
p- ,, ,, ,, .	93		2- ,, ,, .	79	

TABLE XXII. AZO-COMPOUNDS.

	Formula	M.p.
Azo-benzene	$C_6H_5 \cdot N{:}N \cdot C_6H_5$	68°
p-Amino-azo-benzene . .	$NH_2 \cdot C_6H_4 \cdot N{:}N \cdot C_6H_5$	126
p-Dimethylamino-azo-benzene .	$(CH_3)_2N \cdot C_6H_4 \cdot N{:}N \cdot C_6H_5$	115
Benzene-azo-(p)-phenol . .	$C_6H_5 \cdot N{:}N \cdot C_6H_4OH$	152
Benzene-azo-2-naphthol . .	$C_6H_5 \cdot N{:}N \cdot C_{10}H_6OH$	134
Azo-o-toluene	$CH_3C_6H_4 \cdot N{:}N \cdot C_6H_4CH_3$	55
Azo-p-toluene	,,	144

TABLE XXIII. AZOXY-COMPOUNDS.

	Formula	M.p.
Azoxybenzene	$C_6H_5N{:}NO{\cdot}C_6H_5$	36°
o-Azoxytoluene . . .	$CH_3C_6H_5N{\cdot}NO{\cdot}C_6H_4CH_3$	59, 82[1]
p- ,, . . .	,,	75

[1] Two forms.

TABLE XXIV. UREAS AND THIOUREAS.

(for Amides, see under Carboxylic acids)

	Formula	M.p.
Urea	NH_2CONH_2	132°
Guanidine	$NH_2C({:}NH)NH_2$	50d.
Semicarbazide . . .	$NH_2CONH{\cdot}NH_2$	96
Biuret	$NH_2CONH{\cdot}CONH_2$	192d.
Phenyl-urea . . .	$C_6H_5{\cdot}NHCONH_2$	147d.
sym-Diphenyl-urea .	$C_6H_5{\cdot}NHCONH{\cdot}C_6H_5$	237
Tetraphenyl-urea . .	$(C_6H_5)_2NCON(C_6H_5)_2$	183
Benzyl-urea . . .	$C_6H_5CH_2{\cdot}NHCONH_2$	149
o-Tolyl-urea . . .	$CH_3C_6H_4{\cdot}NHCONH_2$	191
p- ,, - ,, . . .	,,	181
Thiourea	NH_2CSNH_2	180
Thio-semicarbazide . .	$NH_2CSNH{\cdot}NH_2$	182
Phenyl-thiourea . .	$C_6H_5{\cdot}NHCSNH_2$	154
Thio-carbanilide . .	$C_6H_5{\cdot}NHCSNH{\cdot}C_2H_5$	153
Tetraphenyl-thiourea . .	$(C_6H_5)_2NCSN(C_6H_5)_2$	195

TABLE XXV. SUBSTITUTED HYDRAZINES.

	Formula	M.p.	B.p.	Acetyl deriv. M.p.	Benzoyl deriv. M.p.
Phenyl-hydrazine . .	$C_6H_5NH{\cdot}NH_2$	23°	243°*	128°	168°
Methyl-phenyl-hydrazine	$C_6H_5(CH_3)N{\cdot}NH_2$	Liq.	227 *	92	153
p-Tolyl-hydrazine .	$CH_3C_6H_4NH{\cdot}NH_2$	65	242 *	121	146
Diphenyl-hydrazine .	$(C_6H_5)_2N{\cdot}NH_2$	34		184	192
Hydrazobenzene .	$C_6H_5NH{\cdot}NHC_6H_5$	131		105	138
2,4–Dinitrophenylhydraz-ine	$(NO_2)_2C_6H_3NH{\cdot}NH_2$	200		197	206

*With partial decomp.

TABLE XXVI. HALOGENO-HYDROCARBONS.

	d.	B.p.		d.	B.p.
Methyl chloride .	Gas	−24°	Benzyl chloride .	1·105	179°
,, bromide .	,,	4·5	,, bromide .	1·440	198
,, iodide .	2·285	43	,, iodide .	(m.p.	d.
Ethyl chloride . .	Gas	12·5		24)	
,, bromide .	1·450	38	Benzal chloride .	1·296	207
,, iodide .	1·943	72	Benzo-trichloride .	1·380	220
n-Propyl chloride .	0·805	46	Chloro-benzene .	1·110	132
,, bromide .	1·354	71	Bromo- ,, .	1·495	156
,, iodide .	1·746	102	Iodo- ,, .	1·835	188
iso-Propyl chloride .	0·860	37	o-Dichloro-benzene .	1·315	179
,, bromide .	1·312	60	m- ,, ,, .	1·290	172
,, iodide .	1·706	89	p- ,, ,, .	(m.p.	172
n-Butyl chloride .	0·890	77		53)	
,, bromide .	1·280	100	o-Dibromo-benzene .	1·978	224
,, iodide .	1·615	130	m- ,, ,, .	1·955	219
iso-Butyl chloride .	0·880	68	p- ,, ,, .	(m.p.	219
,, ,, bromide .	1·273	91		89)	
,, ,, iodide .	1·611	120	o-Chloro-toluene .	1·085	159
Allyl chloride .	0·940	46	m- ,, ,, .	1·075	162
,, bromide .	1·436	70	p- ,, ,, .	1·075	162
,, iodide .	1·845	104	o-Bromo-toluene .	1·425	181
Methylene dichloride .	1·364	42	m- ,, ,, .	1·415	183
,, dibromide	2·498	97	p- ,, ,, .	(m.p.	185
,, di-iodide .	3·285	170d.		28)	
			o-Iodo-toluene .	1·700	207
Chloroform . .	1·504	61	m- ,, ,, .	1·702	204
Bromoform . .	2·904	151	p- ,, ,, .	(m.p.	211
Iodoform . . .	(m.p.	d.		35)	
	120)		1-Chloro-naphthalene	1·196	262
Carbon tetrachloride .	1·606	77	2 ,, ,, .	(m.p.	265
,, tetrabromide .	(m.p.	189d.		61)	
	92)		1-Bromo-naphthalene	1·490	281
,, tetra-iodide .	(subl.)	d.	2- ,, ,, .	(m.p.	281
Ethylene dichloride .	1·254	83		59)	
,, dibromide .	2·180	130	1-Iodo-naphthalene	1·734	303
,, di-iodide .	(m.p.		2- ,, ,, .	(m.p.	309
	81)			54)	
Ethylidene dichloride .	1·186	60			

For Nitro-halogeno-compounds, see Table XXI.

TABLE XXVII. AROMATIC HYDROCARBONS AND DERIVATIVES.

	M.p.	B.p.		Nitro Compounds Derivs. M.p.	Picrate M.p.
Benzene . .	5°	81°	1,3	89°	84°*
Toluene . .	−95	111	2,4	70	88*
o-Xylene . .	−25	144	4,5	118	81*
m-Xylene . .	−47	139	2,4,6	183	91*
p-Xylene . .	15	138	2,3,5	139	90*
Mesitylene .	−57	165	2,4,6	235	97*
Ethylbenzene .	−94	136	2,4,6	37	96*
Styrene . .	−31	145			
Stilbene . .	125	306			95
Naphthalene .	80	218	1	61	152
Anthracene .	216	351			135*
Phenanthrene .	98	340			144
Biphenyl . .	69	254	4,4'	237	
Dibenzyl . .	53	284	4,4'	180	100
Diphenylmethane	25	261	2,4,2',4'	172	
Triphenylmethane	92	358	4,4'4''	206	
Fluorene	114	294			228

* Unstable.
Figures given before the M.ps. of Nitro-derivatives indicate position of nitro groups.

TABLE XXVIII. ETHERS.

	M.p.	B.p.	Picrate M.p.
Ethyl methyl		10°	
Diethyl		35	
Di-n-propyl . . .		91	
Di-isopropyl . . .		68	
Di-n-butyl . . .		140	
Di-isobutyl . . .		123	
Di-sec-butyl . . .		121	
Di-isoamyl . . .		170	
Glycol mono-methyl . .		125	
,, ,, -ethyl . .		135	
,, ,, -n-propyl .		153	
,, ,, -n-butyl .		172	92
Glycol dimethyl . .		83	
,, diethyl . . .		124	
Glycerol trimethyl . .		148	
,, triethyl . . .		185	

(continued on p. 561)

TABLE XXVIII. ETHERS *(continued)*.

	M.p.	B.p.	Picrate M.p.
Benzyl methyl		169	116
Benzyl ethyl		189	
Dibenzyl	4	295	78
Diphenyl.	28	259	110
Monochlorodimethyl. . .		59	
1,1'-Dichlorodiethyl . . .		117	
2-Monochlorodiethyl . .		107	
2,2'-Dichlorodiethyl . . .		177	
Anisole		154	80
Phenetole		172	92
o-Chloroanisole . . .		195	
m- ,, ...		193	
p- ,, ...		198	
o-Bromoanisole . . .		220	
m- ,, ...	21	236	
p- ,, ...	11	216	
Catechyl monomethyl[1] . .	32	205	89[3]
,, dimethyl[2] . .	22	207	57
Resorcinyl monomethyl . .		243	
,, dimethyl . . .		216	57
Hydroquinone monomethyl .	52	243	
,, dimethyl . .	56	212	
o-Cresyl methyl . . .		171	119
m- ,, ,, . . .		177	114
p- ,, ,, . . .		176	89
Methyl-1-naphthyl . . .		263	130
,, -2- ,, . . .	73	273	117
Ethyl-2-naphthyl . . .	36	282	101
2-Naphthyl n-propyl . .	40	297	81
,, isopropyl . .	40	285	95
n-Butyl-2-naphthyl . . .	36	309	67
sec-Butyl-2- ,, . . .	34	298	86
tert-Butyl-2- ,, . . .			
Benzyl-1-naphthyl . . .	77		
Benzyl-2-naphthyl . . .	102		123

[1] Guaiacol. [2] Veratrol. [3] Unstable.

LOGARITHMS

	0	1	2	3	4	5	6	7	8	9	Differences								
											1	2	3	4	5	6	7	8	9
10	0000	0043	0086	0128	0170	0212	0253	0294	0334	0374	4	8	12	17	21	25	29	33	37
11	0414	0453	0492	0531	0569	0607	0645	0682	0719	0755	4	8	11	15	19	23	26	30	34
12	0792	0828	0864	0899	0934	0969	1004	1038	1072	1106	3	7	10	14	17	21	24	28	31
13	1139	1173	1206	1239	1271	1303	1335	1367	1399	1430	3	6	10	13	16	19	23	26	29
14	1461	1492	1523	1553	1584	1614	1644	1673	1703	1732	3	6	9	12	15	18	21	24	27
15	1761	1790	1818	1847	1875	1903	1931	1959	1987	2014	3	6	8	11	14	17	20	22	25
16	2041	2068	2095	2122	2148	2175	2201	2227	2253	2279	3	5	8	11	13	16	18	21	24
17	2304	2330	2355	2380	2405	2430	2455	2480	2504	2529	2	5	7	10	12	15	17	20	22
18	2553	2577	2601	2625	2648	2672	2695	2718	2742	2765	2	5	7	9	12	14	16	19	21
19	2788	2810	2833	2856	2878	2900	2923	2945	2967	2989	2	4	7	9	11	13	16	18	20
20	3010	3032	3054	3075	3096	3118	3139	3160	3181	3201	2	4	6	8	11	13	15	17	19
21	3222	3243	3263	3284	3304	3324	3345	3365	3385	3404	2	4	6	8	10	12	14	16	18
22	3424	3444	3464	3483	3502	3522	3541	3560	3579	3598	2	4	6	8	10	12	14	15	17
23	3617	3636	3655	3674	3692	3711	3729	3747	3766	3784	2	4	6	7	9	11	13	15	17
24	3802	3820	3838	3856	3874	3892	3909	3927	3945	3962	2	4	5	7	9	11	12	14	16
25	3979	3997	4014	4031	4048	4065	4082	4099	4116	4133	2	3	5	7	9	10	12	14	15
26	4150	4166	4183	4200	4216	4232	4249	4265	4281	4298	2	3	5	7	8	10	11	13	15
27	4314	4330	4346	4362	4378	4393	4409	4425	4440	4456	2	3	5	6	8	9	11	13	14
28	4472	4487	4502	4518	4533	4548	4564	4579	4594	4609	2	3	5	6	8	9	11	12	14
29	4624	4639	4654	4669	4683	4698	4713	4728	4742	4757	1	3	4	6	7	9	10	12	13
30	4771	4786	4800	4814	4829	4843	4857	4871	4886	4900	1	3	4	6	7	9	10	11	13
31	4914	4928	4942	4955	4969	4983	4997	5011	5024	5038	1	3	4	6	7	8	10	11	12
32	5051	5065	5079	5092	5105	5119	5132	5145	5159	5172	1	3	4	5	7	8	9	11	12
33	5185	5198	5211	5224	5237	5250	5263	5276	5289	5302	1	3	4	5	6	8	9	10	12
34	5315	5328	5340	5353	5366	5378	5391	5403	5416	5428	1	3	4	5	6	8	9	10	11
35	5441	5453	5465	5478	5490	5502	5514	5527	5539	5551	1	2	4	5	6	7	9	10	11
36	5563	5575	5587	5599	5611	5623	5635	5647	5658	5670	1	2	4	5	6	7	8	10	11
37	5682	5694	5705	5717	5729	5740	5752	5763	5775	5786	1	2	3	5	6	7	8	9	10
38	5798	5809	5821	5832	5843	5855	5866	5877	5888	5899	1	2	3	5	6	7	8	9	10
39	5911	5922	5933	5944	5955	5966	5977	5988	5999	6010	1	2	3	4	5	7	8	9	10
40	6021	6031	6042	6053	6064	6075	6085	6096	6107	6117	1	2	3	4	5	6	8	9	10
41	6128	6138	6149	6160	6170	6180	6191	6201	6212	6222	1	2	3	4	5	6	7	8	9
42	6232	6243	6253	6263	6274	6284	6294	6304	6314	6325	1	2	3	4	5	6	7	8	9
43	6335	6345	6355	6365	6375	6385	6395	6405	6415	6425	1	2	3	4	5	6	7	8	9
44	6435	6444	6454	6464	6474	6484	6493	6503	6513	6522	1	2	3	4	5	6	7	8	9
45	6532	6542	6551	6561	6571	6580	6590	6599	6609	6618	1	2	3	4	5	6	7	8	9
46	6628	6637	6646	6656	6665	6675	6684	6693	6702	6712	1	2	3	4	5	6	7	7	8
47	6721	6730	6739	6749	6758	6767	6776	6785	6794	6803	1	2	3	4	5	5	6	7	8
48	6812	6821	6830	6839	6848	6857	6866	6875	6884	6893	1	2	3	4	4	5	6	7	8
49	6902	6911	6920	6928	6937	6946	6955	6964	6972	6981	1	2	3	4	4	5	6	7	8
50	6990	6998	7007	7016	7024	7033	7042	7050	7059	7067	1	2	3	3	4	5	6	7	8
51	7076	7084	7093	7101	7110	7118	7126	7135	7143	7152	1	2	3	3	4	5	6	7	8
52	7160	7168	7177	7185	7193	7202	7210	7218	7226	7235	1	2	3	3	4	5	6	7	7
53	7243	7251	7259	7267	7275	7284	7292	7300	7308	7316	1	2	2	3	4	5	6	6	7
54	7324	7332	7340	7348	7356	7364	7372	7380	7388	7396	1	2	2	3	4	5	6	6	7

LOGARITHMS

	0	1	2	3	4	5	6	7	8	9	1	2	3	4	5	6	7	8	9
														Differences					
55	7404	7412	7419	7427	7435	7443	7451	7459	7466	7474	1	2	2	3	4	5	5	6	7
56	7482	7490	7497	7505	7513	7520	7528	7536	7543	7551	1	2	2	3	4	5	5	6	7
57	7559	7566	7574	7582	7589	7597	7604	7612	7619	7627	1	2	2	3	4	5	5	6	7
58	7634	7642	7649	7657	7664	7672	7679	7686	7694	7701	1	1	2	3	4	4	5	6	7
59	7709	7716	7723	7731	7738	7745	7752	7760	7767	7774	1	1	2	3	4	4	5	6	7
60	7782	7789	7796	7803	7810	7818	7825	7832	7839	7846	1	1	2	3	4	4	5	6	6
61	7853	7860	7868	7875	7882	7889	7896	7903	7910	7917	1	1	2	3	4	4	5	6	6
62	7924	7931	7938	7945	7952	7959	7966	7973	7980	7987	1	1	2	3	3	4	5	6	6
63	7993	8000	8007	8014	8021	8028	8035	8041	8048	8055	1	1	2	3	3	4	5	5	6
64	8062	8069	8075	8082	8089	8096	8102	8109	8116	8122	1	1	2	3	3	4	5	5	6
65	8129	8136	8142	8149	8156	8162	8169	8176	8182	8189	1	1	2	3	3	4	5	5	6
66	8195	8202	8209	8215	8222	8228	8235	8241	8248	8254	1	1	2	3	3	4	5	5	6
67	8261	8267	8274	8280	8287	8293	8299	8306	8312	8319	1	1	2	3	3	4	5	5	6
68	8325	8331	8338	8344	8351	8357	8363	8370	8376	8382	1	1	2	3	3	4	4	5	6
69	8388	8395	8401	8407	8414	8420	8426	8432	8439	8445	1	1	2	2	3	4	4	5	6
70	8451	8457	8463	8470	8476	8482	8488	8494	8500	8506	1	1	2	2	3	4	4	5	6
71	8513	8519	8525	8531	8537	8543	8549	8555	8561	8567	1	1	2	2	3	4	4	5	5
72	8573	8579	8585	8591	8597	8603	8609	8615	8621	8627	1	1	2	2	3	4	4	5	5
73	8633	8639	8645	8651	8657	8663	8669	8675	8681	8686	1	1	2	2	3	4	4	5	5
74	8692	8698	8704	8710	8716	8722	8727	8733	8739	8745	1	1	2	2	3	4	4	5	5
75	8751	8756	8762	8768	8774	8779	8785	8791	8797	8802	1	1	2	2	3	3	4	5	5
76	8808	8814	8820	8825	8831	8837	8842	8848	8854	8859	1	1	2	2	3	3	4	5	5
77	8865	8871	8876	8882	8887	8893	8899	8904	8910	8915	1	1	2	2	3	3	4	4	5
78	8921	8927	8932	8938	8943	8949	8954	8960	8965	8971	1	1	2	2	3	3	4	4	5
79	8976	8982	8987	8993	8998	9004	9009	9015	9020	9025	1	1	2	2	3	3	4	4	5
80	9031	9036	9042	9047	9053	9058	9063	9069	9074	9079	1	1	2	2	3	3	4	4	5
81	9085	9090	9096	9101	9106	9112	9117	9122	9128	9133	1	1	2	2	3	3	4	4	5
82	9138	9143	9149	9154	9159	9165	9170	9175	9180	9186	1	1	2	2	3	3	4	4	5
83	9191	9196	9201	9206	9212	9217	9222	9227	9232	9238	1	1	2	2	3	3	4	4	5
84	9243	9248	9253	9258	9263	9269	9274	9279	9284	9289	1	1	2	2	3	3	4	4	5
85	9294	9299	9304	9309	9315	9320	9325	9330	9335	9340	1	1	2	2	3	3	4	4	5
86	9345	9350	9355	9360	9365	9370	9375	9380	9385	9390	1	1	2	2	3	3	4	4	5
87	9395	9400	9405	9410	9415	9420	9425	9430	9435	9440	0	1	1	2	2	3	3	4	4
88	9445	9450	9455	9460	9465	9469	9474	9479	9484	9489	0	1	1	2	2	3	3	4	4
89	9494	9499	9504	9509	9513	9518	9523	9528	9533	9538	0	1	1	2	2	3	3	4	4
90	9542	9547	9552	9557	9562	9566	9571	9576	9581	9586	0	1	1	2	2	3	3	4	4
91	9590	9595	9600	9605	9609	9614	9619	9624	9628	9633	0	1	1	2	2	3	3	4	4
92	9638	9643	9647	9652	9657	9661	9666	9671	9675	9680	0	1	1	2	2	3	3	4	4
93	9685	9689	9694	9699	9703	9708	9713	9717	9722	9727	0	1	1	2	2	3	3	4	4
94	9731	9736	9741	9745	9750	9754	9759	9763	9768	9773	0	1	1	2	2	3	3	4	4
95	9777	9782	9786	9791	9795	9800	9805	9809	9814	9818	0	1	1	2	2	3	3	4	4
96	9823	9827	9832	9836	9841	9845	9850	9854	9859	9863	0	1	1	2	2	3	3	4	4
97	9868	9872	9877	9881	9886	9890	9894	9899	9903	9908	0	1	1	2	2	3	3	4	4
98	9912	9917	9921	9926	9930	9934	9939	9943	9948	9952	0	1	1	2	2	3	3	3	4
99	9956	9961	9965	9969	9974	9978	9983	9987	9991	9996	0	1	1	2	2	3	3	3	4

	0	1	2	3	4	5	6	7	8	9	Differences								
											1	2	3	4	5	6	7	8	9
·00	1000	1002	1005	1007	1009	1012	1014	1016	1019	1021	0	0	1	1	1	1	2	2	2
·01	1023	1026	1028	1030	1033	1035	1038	1040	1042	1045	0	0	1	1	1	1	2	2	2
·02	1047	1050	1052	1054	1057	1059	1062	1064	1067	1069	0	0	1	1	1	1	2	2	2
·03	1072	1074	1076	1079	1081	1084	1086	1089	1091	1094	0	0	1	1	1	1	2	2	2
·04	1096	1099	1102	1104	1107	1109	1112	1114	1117	1119	0	1	1	1	1	2	2	2	2
·05	1122	1125	1127	1130	1132	1135	1138	1140	1143	1146	0	1	1	1	1	2	2	2	2
·06	1148	1151	1153	1156	1159	1161	1164	1167	1169	1172	0	1	1	1	1	2	2	2	2
·07	1175	1178	1180	1183	1186	1189	1191	1194	1197	1199	0	1	1	1	1	2	2	2	2
·08	1202	1205	1208	1211	1213	1216	1219	1222	1225	1227	0	1	1	1	1	2	2	2	3
·09	1230	1233	1236	1239	1242	1245	1247	1250	1253	1256	0	1	1	1	1	2	2	2	3
·10	1259	1262	1265	1268	1271	1274	1276	1279	1282	1285	0	1	1	1	1	2	2	2	3
·11	1288	1291	1294	1297	1300	1303	1306	1309	1312	1315	0	1	1	1	2	2	2	2	3
·12	1318	1321	1324	1327	1330	1334	1337	1340	1343	1346	0	1	1	1	2	2	2	3	3
·13	1349	1352	1355	1358	1361	1365	1368	1371	1374	1377	0	1	1	1	2	2	2	3	3
·14	1380	1384	1387	1390	1393	1396	1400	1403	1406	1409	0	1	1	1	2	2	2	3	3
·15	1413	1416	1419	1422	1426	1429	1432	1435	1439	1442	0	1	1	1	2	2	2	3	3
·16	1445	1449	1452	1455	1459	1462	1466	1469	1472	1476	0	1	1	1	2	2	2	3	3
·17	1479	1483	1486	1489	1493	1496	1500	1503	1507	1510	0	1	1	1	2	2	2	3	3
·18	1514	1517	1521	1524	1528	1531	1535	1538	1542	1545	0	1	1	1	2	2	2	3	3
·19	1549	1552	1556	1560	1563	1567	1570	1574	1578	1581	0	1	1	1	2	2	2	3	3
·20	1585	1589	1592	1596	1600	1603	1607	1611	1614	1618	0	1	1	1	2	2	3	3	3
·21	1622	1626	1629	1633	1637	1641	1644	1648	1652	1656	0	1	1	2	2	2	3	3	3
·22	1660	1663	1667	1671	1675	1679	1683	1687	1690	1694	0	1	1	2	2	2	3	3	3
·23	1698	1702	1706	1710	1714	1718	1722	1726	1730	1734	0	1	1	2	2	2	3	3	4
·24	1738	1742	1746	1750	1754	1758	1762	1766	1770	1774	0	1	1	2	2	2	3	3	4
·25	1778	1782	1786	1791	1795	1799	1803	1807	1811	1816	0	1	1	2	2	2	3	3	4
·26	1820	1824	1828	1832	1837	1841	1845	1849	1854	1858	0	1	1	2	2	3	3	3	4
·27	1862	1866	1871	1875	1879	1884	1888	1892	1897	1901	0	1	1	2	2	3	3	3	4
·28	1905	1910	1914	1919	1923	1928	1932	1936	1941	1945	0	1	1	2	2	3	3	4	4
·29	1950	1954	1959	1963	1968	1972	1977	1982	1986	1991	0	1	1	2	2	3	3	4	4
·30	1995	2000	2004	2009	2014	2018	2023	2028	2032	2037	0	1	1	2	2	3	3	4	4
·31	2042	2046	2051	2056	2061	2065	2070	2075	2080	2084	0	1	1	2	2	3	3	4	4
·32	2089	2094	2099	2104	2109	2113	2118	2123	2128	2133	0	1	1	2	2	3	3	4	4
·33	2138	2143	2148	2153	2158	2163	2168	2173	2178	2183	0	1	1	2	2	3	3	4	4
·34	2188	2193	2198	2203	2208	2213	2218	2223	2228	2234	1	1	2	2	3	3	4	4	5
·35	2239	2244	2249	2254	2259	2265	2270	2275	2280	2286	1	1	2	2	3	3	4	4	5
·36	2291	2296	2301	2307	2312	2317	2323	2328	2333	2339	1	1	2	2	3	3	4	4	5
·37	2344	2350	2355	2360	2366	2371	2377	2382	2388	2393	1	1	2	2	3	3	4	4	5
·38	2399	2404	2410	2415	2421	2427	2432	2438	2443	2449	1	1	2	2	3	3	4	4	5
·39	2455	2460	2466	2472	2477	2483	2489	2495	2500	2506	1	1	2	2	3	3	4	5	5
·40	2512	2518	2523	2529	2535	2541	2547	2553	2559	2564	1	1	2	2	3	4	4	5	5
·41	2570	2576	2582	2588	2594	2600	2606	2612	2618	2624	1	1	2	2	3	4	4	5	5
·42	2630	2636	2642	2649	2655	2661	2667	2673	2679	2685	1	1	2	2	3	4	4	5	6
·43	2692	2698	2704	2710	2716	2723	2729	2735	2742	2748	1	1	2	3	3	4	4	5	6
·44	2754	2761	2767	2773	2780	2786	2793	2799	2805	2812	1	1	2	3	3	4	4	5	6
·45	2818	2825	2831	2838	2844	2851	2858	2864	2871	2877	1	1	2	3	3	4	5	5	6
·46	2884	2891	2897	2904	2911	2917	2924	2931	2938	2944	1	1	2	3	3	4	5	5	6
·47	2951	2958	2965	2972	2979	2985	2992	2999	3006	3013	1	1	2	3	3	4	5	5	6
·48	3020	3027	3034	3041	3048	3055	3062	3069	3076	3083	1	1	2	3	4	4	5	6	6
·49	3090	3097	3105	3112	3119	3126	3133	3141	3148	3155	1	1	2	3	4	4	5	6	6

ANTI-LOGARITHMS

	0	1	2	3	4	5	6	7	8	9	1	2	3	4	5	6	7	8	9
·50	3162	3170	3177	3184	3192	3199	3206	3214	3221	3228	1	1	2	3	4	4	5	6	7
·51	3236	3243	3251	3258	3266	3273	3281	3289	3296	3304	1	2	2	3	4	5	5	6	7
·52	3311	3319	3327	3334	3342	3350	3357	3365	3373	3381	1	2	2	3	4	5	5	6	7
·53	3388	3396	3404	3412	3420	3428	3436	3443	3451	3459	1	2	2	3	4	5	6	6	7
·54	3467	3475	3483	3491	3499	3508	3516	3524	3532	3540	1	2	2	3	4	5	6	6	7
·55	3548	3556	3565	3573	3581	3589	3597	3606	3614	3622	1	2	2	3	4	5	6	7	7
·56	3631	3639	3648	3656	3664	3673	3681	3690	3698	3707	1	2	3	3	4	5	6	7	8
·57	3715	3724	3733	3741	3750	3758	3767	3776	3784	3793	1	2	3	3	4	5	6	7	8
·58	3802	3811	3819	3828	3837	3846	3855	3864	3873	3882	1	2	3	4	4	5	6	7	8
·59	3890	3899	3908	3917	3926	3936	3945	3954	3963	3972	1	2	3	4	5	5	6	7	8
·60	3981	3990	3999	4009	4018	4027	4036	4046	4055	4064	1	2	3	4	5	6	6	7	8
·61	4074	4083	4093	4102	4111	4121	4130	4140	4150	4159	1	2	3	4	5	6	7	8	9
·62	4169	4178	4188	4198	4207	4217	4227	4236	4246	4256	1	2	3	4	5	6	7	8	9
·63	4266	4276	4285	4295	4305	4315	4325	4335	4345	4355	1	2	3	4	5	6	7	8	9
·64	4365	4375	4385	4395	4406	4416	4426	4436	4446	4457	1	2	3	4	5	6	7	8	9
·65	4467	4477	4487	4498	4508	4519	4529	4539	4550	4560	1	2	3	4	5	6	7	8	9
·66	4571	4581	4592	4603	4613	4624	4634	4645	4656	4667	1	2	3	4	5	6	7	9	10
·67	4677	4688	4699	4710	4721	4732	4742	4753	4764	4775	1	2	3	4	5	7	8	9	10
·68	4786	4797	4808	4819	4831	4842	4853	4864	4875	4887	1	2	3	4	6	7	8	9	10
·69	4898	4909	4920	4932	4943	4955	4966	4977	4989	5000	1	2	3	5	6	7	8	9	10
·70	5012	5023	5035	5047	5058	5070	5082	5093	5105	5117	1	2	4	5	6	7	8	9	11
·71	5129	5140	5152	5164	5176	5188	5200	5212	5224	5236	1	2	4	5	6	7	8	10	11
·72	5248	5260	5272	5284	5297	5309	5321	5333	5346	5358	1	2	4	5	6	7	9	10	11
·73	5370	5383	5395	5408	5420	5433	5445	5458	5470	5483	1	3	4	5	6	8	9	10	11
·74	5495	5508	5521	5534	5546	5559	5572	5585	5598	5610	1	3	4	5	6	8	9	10	12
·75	5623	5636	5649	5662	5675	5689	5702	5715	5728	5741	1	3	4	5	7	8	9	10	12
·76	5754	5768	5781	5794	5808	5821	5834	5848	5861	5875	1	3	4	5	7	8	9	11	12
·77	5888	5902	5916	5929	5943	5957	5970	5984	5998	6012	1	3	4	5	7	8	10	11	12
·78	6026	6039	6053	6067	6081	6095	6109	6124	6138	6152	1	3	4	6	7	8	10	11	13
·79	6166	6180	6194	6209	6223	6237	6252	6266	6281	6295	1	3	4	6	7	9	10	11	13
·80	6310	6324	6339	6353	6368	6383	6397	6412	6427	6442	1	3	4	6	7	9	10	12	13
·81	6457	6471	6486	6501	6516	6531	6546	6561	6577	6592	2	3	5	6	8	9	11	12	14
·82	6607	6622	6637	6653	6668	6683	6699	6714	6730	6745	2	3	5	6	8	9	11	12	14
·83	6761	6776	6792	6808	6823	6839	6855	6871	6887	6902	2	3	5	6	8	9	11	13	14
·84	6918	6934	6950	6966	6982	6998	7015	7031	7047	7063	2	3	5	6	8	10	11	13	15
·85	7079	7096	7112	7129	7145	7161	7178	7194	7211	7228	2	3	5	7	8	10	12	13	15
·86	7244	7261	7278	7295	7311	7328	7345	7362	7379	7396	2	3	5	7	8	10	12	13	15
·87	7413	7430	7447	7464	7482	7499	7516	7534	7551	7568	2	3	5	7	9	10	12	14	16
·88	7586	7603	7621	7638	7656	7674	7691	7709	7727	7745	2	4	5	7	9	11	12	14	16
·89	7762	7780	7798	7816	7834	7852	7870	7889	7907	7925	2	4	5	7	9	11	13	14	16
·90	7943	7962	7980	7998	8017	8035	8054	8072	8091	8110	2	4	6	7	9	11	13	15	17
·91	8128	8147	8166	8185	8204	8222	8241	8260	8279	8299	2	4	6	8	9	11	13	15	17
·92	8318	8337	8356	8375	8395	8414	8433	8453	8472	8492	2	4	6	8	10	12	14	15	17
·93	8511	8531	8551	8570	8590	8610	8630	8650	8670	8690	2	4	6	8	10	12	14	16	18
·94	8710	8730	8750	8770	8790	8810	8831	8851	8872	8892	2	4	6	8	10	12	14	16	18
·95	8913	8933	8954	8974	8995	9016	9036	9057	9078	9099	2	4	6	8	10	12	15	17	19
·96	9120	9141	9162	9183	9204	9226	9247	9268	9290	9311	2	4	6	8	11	13	15	17	19
·97	9333	9354	9376	9397	9419	9441	9462	9484	9506	9528	2	4	7	9	11	13	15	17	20
·98	9550	9572	9594	9616	9638	9661	9683	9705	9727	9750	2	4	7	9	11	13	16	18	20
·99	9772	9795	9817	9840	9863	9886	9908	9931	9954	9977	2	5	7	9	11	14	16	18	20

Differences columns correspond to 1 2 3 4 5 6 7 8 9.

INDEX

Accidents, laboratory, 526
Acetal, 73
Acetals, table of, 539
Acetaldehyde, oxidation by oxidase, 521
  preparation, 74
  reactions of, 341, 344
Acetaldehyde-ammonia, use in *Hantzsch* reaction, 295
Acetaldehyde cyanhydrin, 121
Acetaldoxime, 93
Acetamide, bromination, 127
  preparation, 117
  hydroxylamine test for, 334
  reactions of, 360
  reaction with benzylamine, 362
p-Acetamidobenzenesulphonyl chloride, preparation, 181
p-Acetamidobenzenesulphonamide, preparation, 181
  hydrolysis, 181
Acetanilide, hydrolysis, 108
  nitration, 167
  preparation, 108
    semi-micro, 108
  reactions of, 379
  sulphonation, 181
Acet-bromoamide, 127
Acetic acid, as solvent, 15, 436
  molecular weight of, 446
  preparation (glacial), 74
    (in aqueous solution), 75
  reactions of, 347, 351
  use in acetylation, 107
Acetic anhydride, preparation, 115
  reactions of, 364
  use in acetylation, 107-109, 450, 452, 453
Acetoacetic ester—*see* Ethyl acetoacetate
Acetone, as solvent, 15, 440
  reactions of, 345
  reduction to pinacol, 148
  use in iodoform preparation, 92
Acetone cyanhydrin, 121
Acetone sodium bisulphite, 345, 346
  effect of heat on, 320
Acetonitrile, hydrolysis, 122
  preparation, 121
  reactions of, 359, 360
  use in *Hoesch* reaction, 258
Acetonylacetone, dehydrogenation, 147
  derivatives of, 541
Acetophenone, preparation, 255
  semi-micro, 256

conversion to 1-phenylethylamine 223
  reactions of, 345
  semi-micro preparation, 256
  use in *Mannich* reaction, 261
Acetophenone oxime, 258
Acetophenone phenylhydrazone, preparation, semi-micro, 257
  use in *Fischer* indolisation, 294
Acetophenone semicarbazone, preparation, semi-micro, 258
Acetoxime, hydrolysis, 94
  preparation, 93
Acetylacetone, derivatives of, 541
Acetyl chloride, reactions of, 364
  use in acetylation, 107, 110
Acetyl groups, estimation of, 455
Acetylation, methods and uses, 107
  of amines and phenols, 107 *et seq.*
  glucose and mannitol, 141 *et seq.*, 452
  nitro-anilines, 387
  nitro-phenols, 386
  primary amines, 373
  secondary amines, 376
Acetylene, preparation from calcium carbine, 86
  from ethylene dibromide, 87
  tests for, 87
  storage in cylinders. 86
Acetylene dicarboxylic esters, use in *Diels-Alder* reaction, 292
Acetylsalicylic acid, preparation, 110, 352
  reactions and uses, 111
Achroo-dextrin, 513
Acid amides, preparation, 117
  reactions of, 359
  tables of, 543-5
Acid anhydrides, reactions of, 364
  tables of, 543-5
Acid chlorides, reactions of, 364
  tables of, 543-5
Acids, amino—*see* Amino-acids
  carboxylic, reactions of, 348
    tables of derivs, 543, 544, 555
    table of reactions of, 412
  equivalent weight of, 447, 448
  isolation from its salt, 56, 349
  molecular weight of, by alkali titration, 447
    by silver salts, 445
  removal by ion exchange, 57

Acids, amino—*contd.*
 sulphonic, preparation, 178
 properties, 353
 reactions, 353
 table of derivatives, 548
Acraldehyde, use in *Diels-Alder* reaction, 292—*see also* Acrolein
Acridone, preparation, 303
 structure, 303
Acriflavine emulsion, 527
Acrolein, test for glycerol, 337
Adams, R., preparation of pinacol, 149
Adaptors, for condensers, 44
 flasks, 44
 steam-distillation, 44
Adipic acid, formation, 347
Adsorption chromatography, 48
Advanced techniques, 48
Air-condensers, 8
Alcohol, use in reduction of diazo-compounds, 202
 ethyl—*see* Ethanol
Alcohols, esterification of, 95
 estimation of hydroxyl groups in, 450
 reactions of, 333
 reaction with phosphorus trichloride, 96, 308
 tables of derivatives, 536-7
Aldehyde oxidase, 511, 521
Aldehydes, reactions of, 341
 tables of derivatives, 539, 540
 table of reactions of, 411
Alizarin, formation from catechol, 339
 reactions of, 390
Alkyl phosphites, preparation, 308
Allocinnamic acid, 236
Allyl alcohol, 114
Almonds, preparation of emulsin from, 516
Alumina, use in chromatographic absorption, 48
Aluminium chloride, storage, 255
 use in *Friedel-Crafts'* reaction, 254
Aluminium isopropoxide,
 mechanism in carbonyl reductions, 153
 use of, 153
Amberlite, resin for ion-exchange, 57
Amides, preparation, 117
 reactions of, 359, 360
 tables of, 543-5
Amines,
 action of nitrous acid on,
  primary, 182, 372
  secondary, 204, 376
  tertiary, 204, 377
 identification of, as crystalline derivatives, 374, 376, 378

reactions of, 372-379
 table of reactions of, 415
 tables of derivatives, 550-1
Amino-acetic acid—*see* Glycine
Amino-acids, estimation of, 463
 from proteins by tryptic digestion, 517-18
 reactions of, 380
Amino-aliphatic carboxylic acids, reactions of, 380
 benzoylation of, 381, 382
 crystalline derivatives, 382
 estimation, 463
 separation by chromatography, 51, *et seq.*
 sulphonylation of, 382
 tables of, with derivatives, 555
Amino-aromatic carboxylic acids, reactions of, 383
Amino-aromatic sulphonic acids, reactions of, 384
Aminoazobenzene, preparation, 208
p-Aminobenzenesulphonamide—*see* Sulphanilamide
p-Aminobenzenesulphonic acid—*see* Sulphanilic acid
ε-Amino-caproic acid, lactam of, 227
Amino-groups, estimation of, 452
1-Amino-2-hydroxy-naphthalene—*see* 1-Amino-2-naphthol
α-Amino-ketones, 293
2-Amino-4-methylthiazole, 305
 preparation, 305
 nitrate, 305
1-Amino-2-naphthol, preparation, 211
2-Amino-n-octane, 224
 methylation, 226
 preparation, 225
 hydrochloride, 225
Amino-phenols, 386
 benzoylation, 387
Amino-urea—*see* Semicarbazide
Ammoniacal cuprous chloride,
 preparation, 87
 test for acetylene, 87
Ammoniacal silver nitrate, preparation, 525
 treatment of compounds with, 408
Ammonium cyanate, conversion to urea, 123
Ammonium formate,
 use in *Leuckert* reaction, 223
Ammonium molybate, test for sugars, 368
Ammonium salts, reactions of, 359
Amygdalin, hydrolysis by emulsin, 515
Amylase—*see* Diastase
Analysis, qualitative analysis of a compound, 401 *et seq.*

Analysis—*contd.*
  qualitative analysis of a mixture, 397 *et seq.*
  quantitative analysis,
    macro, 416 *et seq.*
    semi-micro, 465 *et seq.*
Anhydrides, tables of, 543
Anhydrone—*see* Magnesium perchlorate
Anilides, reactions of, 379
  hydrolysis, 108, 168, 379
Aniline, estimation of amino groups in, 452
  isolation by ion-exchange, 57
  molecular weight of, 447, 452, 454
  preparation, 162
    semi-micro, 164
  reactions of, 373
    with sulphuric acid, 179
    sulphonylation, 250
Aniline chlorostannate, 161
Aniline hydrochloride, estimation of, 454
Animal charcoal, 22-23
Anion exchange resin, 55, 57
Anisole, preparation, 219
  reactions of, 396
Anthracene, oxidation, 259
  picrate, 174, 394
  reactions of, 393
  use in *Diels-Alder* reaction, 292
Anthrahydroquinone diacetate, preparation, 371
Anthranilic acid,
  conversion to diphenic acid, 200
  diazotisation, 200
  methylation, 222
  reactions of, 383
  use in paper chromatography, 53
Anthraquinone, preparation, 259
  semi-micro, 261
  reactions of, 370, 371
Antipyrine, 272
Apparatus, assembling, 40
  drying, 40
  ground-glass, 42-47
  small scale, 59, 71
Arbusov reaction, 311
Arbutin, hydrolysis by emulsin, 516
Aromatic hydrocarbons, reactions of, 393
  with unsaturated side-chains, 295
Aromatic monoamines, table of reactions of, 320
Aromatic substitution, 159
Arsenic acid, use in preparation of quinoline, 298
Arsinic acids, 314
  preparation, 314

Arsonic acids, 312
  crystalline salts, 314
  preparation, 312
  reduction to dichloro-arsines, 314
Aryl-substituted alcohols, table of, 537
Aspirin—*see* Acetylsalicylic acid
Assemblies of ground-glass apparatus, 44
Atomic weights, 435
Avertin, 91, 153
Azobenzene, 212
  preparation, 213
Azo-compounds, preparation, 209
  reduction, 210
  table of, 557
Azo-dye formation, 209, 339, 373, 383, 387
Azoxybenzene, preparation, 212
  constitution, 212
Azoxy-compounds, table of, 558

Balance, sensitivity of, 465
Barbituric acid, 306
Bart reaction, 312
Bases, equivalent weight of, 450
  molecular weight of, as chloroplatinates, 448
Beckmann, rearrangement, of oximes, 93, 227
  thermometer, 429
Beilstein test for halogens, 323
Benzaldehyde, reactions of, 341
Benzaldehyde phenylhydrazone, preparation, semi-micro, 229
Benzamide, hydrolysis, 120
  preparation, from benzoyl chloride, 119
  from benzonitrile, 193
  reactions of, 360
Benzanilide, 245
  hydrolysis, 246
  preparation,
    semi-micro, 245
  reactions of, 379
Benzene, bromination, 175
  as solvent for molecular weight determinations, 433, 435, 440
  from diazo-compounds, 189
  mechanism, 175
  reactions of, 393
Benzene and toluene, separation, 28
Benzeneazo-*p*-dimethylaniline, 186
Benzeneazo-2-naphthol, 188, 210
  preparation, 210
  reduction to 1-amino-2-naphthol, 211
Benzeneazophenol, 188

Benzenediazonium hydrogen sulphate, preparation (in solution), 187
reactions of, 188
Benzenesulphonamide, 247
Benzenesulphon-diethylamide, 248
Benzenesulphon-ethylamide, 248
Benzenesulphonyl-aniline, 247
Benzenesulphonyl chloride, use in sulphonylation, 247, 248
Benzenesulphonyl-methylaniline, 247
Benzhydrol, preparation, 153
Benzidine, preparation, 215
transformation, 215
Benzil, preparation, 234
Benzil osazone, preparation, semi-micro, 234
Benzilic acid, preparation, 235
rearrangement, 235
Benzoic acid molecular weight of, 447
preparation from benzaldehyde, 232
from benzyl chloride, 239
by hydrolysis of benzanilide, 246
of benzamide, 120
of benzonitrile, 193
of phenyl benzoate, 244
reactions of, 347, 352
Benzoic anhydride, 241
Benzoin, preparation, 233
conversion to benzil osazone, 234
Benzonitrile, hydrolysis benzamide, 192-193
benzoic acid, 193
preparation, 191
reactions of, 359, 360
Benzophenone, reactions of, 345, 347
reduction to diphenylcarbinol, 152
to tetraphenyl-ethylene glycol, 151
Benzoquinone, reactions of, 370
use in Diels-Alder reaction, 292
Benzoylaniline—see Benzanilide
Benzoylation, 243-244
of amino-carboxylic acids, 383
of amino-phenols, 386
of nitro-anilines, 387
of phenols, 244, 338
of primary amines, 245, 374
of secondary amines, 376
Benzoyl chloride, preparation, 240
reactions of, 364
use in benzoylation, 243
Benzoyl peroxide, in radical production, 177
Benzyl acetate, reactions of, 354
Benzyl alcohol, preparation, 231
oxidation to benzoic acid, 301, 336
reactions of, 335, 337
Benzylamides, preparation, 350, 357, 360, 362

reactions, 360
Benzylamine, reactions, 373
isolation by ion-exchange, 57
use in identify acids, 350
amides, 362
ammonium salts, 360
esters, 357
Benzyl chloride, oxidation of, 239, 393
reactions of, 390, 393
Benzyl p-nitrobenzoate, preparation, semi-micro, 246
Benzylidene-acetone, 231
Benzylidene-aniline, preparation, semi-micro, 230
Benzylphenylarsinic acid, 314
preparation, 314
Benzylthiouronium chloride, 126
preparation, 127
use in identifying arsonic acids, 314
carboxylic acids, 349
sulphonic acids, 353
Biphenyl, formation in Grignard reaction, 284
nitration, 393
reactions of, 393
Biuret reaction, 362
Bismarck brown, 388
Bleaching powder, colorations with, 374
Boiling-points, 8
determination of, 7, 8, 9
semi-micro, 61
elevation of, 440
tables of, 536 et seq.
Bolt-head flasks, 17
Bromal, conversion to tribromoethanol, 153
derivations, 539
Bromination of acetamide, 128
acetanilide, 167
aniline, 165
benzene, 175
mechanism, 175
ethyl acetoacetate, 268
ethyl crotonate, 177
phenols, 188, 339
using N-bromo-succinimide, 177
Bromine, detection, 323, 327
estimation (Carius), 416
semi-micro, 502
bomb method, 505
reagent for unsaturation, 85
precautions in using, 527
Bromine burns, treatment of, 527
p-Bromoacetanilide, preparation, semi-micro, 166
Bromo-anilines, m.ps. 160

p-Bromoaniline, conversion to 4-bromodiphenyl, 201
Bromobenzene, preparation, 175
  mechanism, 177
  reactions of, 390
4-Bromobiphenyl,
  preparation, 201
  mechanism, 201
Bromoform, as solvent for molecular weight determinations, 433, 435
Bromo-phenols, m.ps., 160
p-Bromophenylhydrazine, 179
N-Bromosuccinimide, 177
  use in bromination, 177
  mechanism, 177
Bromostyrene, 353
Bromo-toluenes, m.ps., 160
p-Bromophenacyl bromide, 349
  for identification of acids, 349
  of ammonium salts, 360
p-Bromophenacyl esters, 543-545
  identification of acids, 349
Buchner flasks, 10
  funnels, 10
Burette, semi-micro, 59, 60
Burns, treatment of, 527
Butadiene, use in *Diels-Alder* reaction, 292
n-Butanol, conversion to butyl bromide, 102
  reactions of, 390
Butyl alcohol—*see n*-Butanol
n-Butyl bromide, preparation, 102

Calcium carbide, 86
Calcium chloride (drying agent), 24
Calcium chloride tubes, 104
Calcium ethyl sulphate, 78
Calcium oxide (drying agent), 24
  for ethanol, 87
Calcium sulphate (drying agent), 24
Camphor, depression of freezing-point, 437
  derivatives of, 541
  oxidation to camphorquinone, 148
Camphorquinone, preparation, 148
Cane sugar—*see* Sucrose
Cannizzaro's Reaction, 231, 342
Capillary tubes,
  for low-pressure distillation, 28
  for m.p. determinations, 2
  for *Rast* determinations, 437
Caprolactam, 227
  preparation, 227
Carbamide—*see* Urea
Carbanilide—*see* Diphenyl-urea
Carbasorb, 468, 470
Carbohydrates, estimation of, 460

general, 134
  reactions of, 366
  table of reactions of, 414
Carbon, detection of, 320
Carbon and hydrogen estimation, semi-micro, 467
Carbon dioxide, air-free, 482
Carbon disulphide, danger of use as solvent, 15
Carbon tetrachloride, as solvent, 15
  explosions with, in sodium test, 321
  reactions of, 390, 392
Carbonic anhydrase, 511
Carbonium ion formation, 254
Carbonyl chloride, 91
Carborundum, 8, 455
o-Carboxydiphenylamine, preparation, 217
Carboxylase, 511
Carboxylic Acids, isolation from salts, 56, 349
  reactions of, 347
  table of reactions of, 412
  tables of derivatives, 543-545
Carbylamine—*see* Isocyanide
Carius's halogen estimation,
  macro, 416
  semi-micro, 502, 505
  sulphur estimation, 423
Carvacrol, derivatives, 538
Casein, hydrolysis of, by trypsin, 518
Castor oil seeds, 510, 512
Catalase, 511
Catechol, reactions, 337
  derivatives, 538
Cation exchange resin, 55, 57
Caustic potash (drying agent), 24—*see also* Potassium hydroxide
Cellosolve, as solvent, 15
Charcoal, animal, 21, 22
  purification, 21
  wood, 21
Chattaway's method, for acetylation 109
Chloral (hydrate), 91
  reactions of, 341, 344
Chloramine-T, estimation, 253
  preparation, 252, 253
Chloretone, 91
Chloroacetic acid,
  conversion to ethyl malonate, 282
  to nitromethane, 132
Chloroacetone, 305
  synthetic use, 305
Chlorine, detection, 323, 327
  estimation (*Carius*), 416
  semi-micro, 502
  bomb method, 505
Chloro-anilines, m.ps., 160

Chlorobenzene, preparation, 189
    reactions of, 290
o-Chlorobenzoic acid, use in *Ullmann*
    condensation, 217
    bromophenacyl ester of, 350
    phenacyl ester of, 350
Chloro-bromo-benzenes, m.ps., 160
α-Chlorocarboxylic acids, conversion
    to nitro-hydrocarbons, 131
Chloro-2,4-dinitrobenzene,
    reactivity, 185, 262
Chloroform, as solvent, 15, 440
    explosions with, in sodium test, 321
    extraction, continuous, 35
    preparation, 90
    reactions of, 390, 392
    uses, 91
Chloroplatinates, 448
Chlorosulphonic acid, use in sulphon-
    ation, 181
Chromatography, 48
    adsorption, 48
    ion-exchange, 55
    paper, 50
Chromium trioxide, use as oxidising
    agent, 259
Cinnamaldehyde, conversion to di-
    phenyl-octatetrene, 238
    derivatives of, 540
    formation of, 231
Cinnamic acid, preparation, 236
    reactions of, 347, 353
Allo-Cinnamic acid, 236
Cinnamic aldehyde—*see* Cinna-
    maldehyde
Cis-trans isomerism, 236, 238
Citric acid, from sodium salt by ion-
    exchange, 55
    reactions of, 347, 352
Claisen, ester, condensation, 264
    flask, 28, 32, 44
    reaction, 231
CO₂-free water, preparation, 448
Cleaning mixtures, 27
Clemmensen Reduction, 290
Co-enzyme, 509
"Cold-finger," 62
Collidine, derivatives of, 553
Collidine-3,5-dicarboxylic acid,
    preparation, 297
Colour, of compounds, 403
Columns, fractionating, 25, 26, 64
Compounds, catalogue of, for identifi-
    cation, 316, *et seq.*
Condensers, air, 8, 43
    semi-micro, 63
    water, 8, 9, 43
Constant b.p. mixtures, 8
Continuous extraction, 35

of liquids by solvents, 35, 36
of solids, by solvents, 37, 47
Copper acetate—*see* Cupric acetate
Copper derivative of ethyl acetoace-
    tate, 268
    derivative of glycine, 129, 382
Corks, 40
Control experiments, 445
Conversion Factors, 534
Coumarin, preparation, 307
o-Cresol, reactions of, 410
m-Cresol, reactions of, 410
p-Cresol, reactions of, 410
Criteria of Purity, liquid compounds, 6
    solid compounds, 1
Crotonaldehyde, reaction with malonic
    acid, 280
Cryoscopic method of molecular weight
    determination, 432
    semi-micro, 436
Crystalline derivatives preparation of,
    acid anhydrides 366
    acid chlorides, 366
    acids, carboxylic, 349
        sulphonic, 353
    alcohols, 336
    aldehydes, 343
    amides, 361
    amines, primary, 374
        secondary, 376
        tertiary, 377
    amino-carboxylic acids, 383
    amino-aromatic sulphonic acids, 384
    anilides, 380
    esters, 358
    ethers, 397
    hydrocarbons (aromatic), 394
    imides, 361
    ketones, 345
    nitriles, 367
    nitro-anilines, 388
    nitro-hydrocarbons, 385
    nitro-phenols, 388
    phenols, 340
    quinones, 370
Crystallisation—*see* Recrystallisation
Cupric acetate, preparation, 75
Cupric salt of glycine, 129, 382
Cuprous acetylide, 77
Cuprous chloride, preparation, 189
Cuts, treatment of, 528
Cyanides (organic)—*see* Nitriles
Cyanine dyes, 303
Cyclohexane, as solvent for mol. wt.
    determinations, 433, 435, 440
Cyclohexan-1,2-dione,
    benzilic acid rearrangement, 235
Cyclohexanol, oxidation, 335
    reactions of, 335

Cyclohexanone, oxidation, 347
use in *Fischer* Indolisation reaction, 294
Cyclohexanone oxime, 227
preparation, 228
use in *Beckmann* rearrangement, 227
Cysteine, from cystine, 383
Cystine, reactions of, 380, 383

Decolorisation by animal charcoal, 22
Dehydrogenation,
of dihydro-pyridine derivative, 296
of dihydro-quinoline derivative, 297 300
by selenium dioxide, 146
Dehydrogenase—*see* Aldehyde oxidase
Depression of freezing-point, 432-439
Derivatives, crystalline for identification purposes—*see* Crystalline derivatives
Desiccators, calcium chloride, 20
vacuum, 20
Detection—*see* Identification
Determination of number of acetyl groups, 455
number of hydroxyl groups, 450
m.p. of camphor, 438
Molecular Depression Constant of camphor, 438
molecular weights, 424 *et seq.—see also* Estimation of
Dextrin, 511, 512, 513
Dextrose—*see* Glucose
Diacetyl-ethylene, 147
Dialkylarylamines, 373
reactions, 377
Dialkyl hydrogen phosphites, 308
preparation, 309
4,4'-Diaminobiphenyl, preparation, 215
Diastase, 511, 512, 513
Diazoaminobenzene, 183, 188
preparation, 207
Diazo-benzene hydrogen sulphate, preparation (in solution), 187
Diazo-compounds—*see also* Diazonium compounds
Diazonium-compounds, general preparation, 183
reactions, 188
Iso-Diazo-compounds—*see* Isodiazotates
Diazomethane, use in methylation, 218
Diazotates, formation, 182
free radical formation from, 201
Diazotisation, 182
of primary amines, 182, 374

of anthranilic acid, 200
of sulphanilic acid, 214, 384
of nitro-anilines, 387
Dibenzal-acetone, preparation, semi-micro, 231
1,2-Dibromoethane—*see* ethylene dibromide
Dichloramine-T, estimation, 252
preparation, 251
Dichloro-benzene, m.p., 160
Dichlorophenylarsine, 314
preparation, 314
p-Dibromobenzene, as by-product, 176
Dibromobenzene, m.p., 160
Diels-Alder reaction, 292
application to anthracene, 292
1,8-diphenyloctatetrene, 238
Diethyl collidine-3,5-dicarboxylate, hydrolysis, 297
preparation, 295
Diethyl ether—*see* Ether
Diethyl ethylphosphonate, preparation, 311
Diethyl hydrogen phosphite, preparation, 310
Diethylamine, reactions, 375
Diethylaniline, reactions, 377
Diethylene dioxide, 15
Diethyl ketone, reactions, 345
Diethyl malonate—*see* Ethyl malonate
Diethyl succinate, dehydrogenation to diethyl fumarate, 147
9,10-Dihydroanthracene-9,10-*endo*-αβ-succinic anhydride, preparation, 292
2,4-Dihydroxyacetophenone, preparation, 258
Di-isopropyl hydrogen phosphite, preparation, 309
Di-isopropylamine, reactions, 375
1,2-Diketones, Benzilic acid rearrangement, 225
conversion to quinoxalines, 304, 372
1,3-Diketones, condensation with α-amino-ketones, 293
Dimedone—*see* 5,5-Dimethyl-cyclohexan-1,3-dione
Dimethylamine, from *p*-nitroso-dimethylaniline, 206
from toluene-*p*-sulphon-dimethylamide, 221
use in *Mannich* reaction, 261
2-Dimethylamino-*n*-octane, 224
preparation, 226
hydrochloride, 227
Dimethylaminoazobenzene, 207, 208
ω-Dimethylaminopropiophenone hydrochloride, preparation, 261

p-Dimethylaminostyryl-quinoline, preparation, 302
    reaction with acids, 302
Dimethylaniline, conversion to *p*-nitroso-dimethylaniline, 204
    to benzene-azo-*p*-dimethylaniline, 188
    reactions of, 373, 377
5,5-Dimethylcyclohexan-1,3-dione, condensation with aldehydes, 146, 279
Dimethylformamide, as solvent, 15
2,4-Dimethylpyrrole-3,5-dicarboxylic acid, diethyl ester, 293
    preparation, 293
Dimethyl succinate, conversion to succinamide, 119
    reactions of, 354
Dimethyl sulphate, treatment if spilt on hands, 220, 527
    precautions in use, 220
    use for methylation, 218, 220, 221
Di-1-naphthylurea, 375
m-Dinitrobenzene, preparation, 161
    reactions of, 385, 386
    reduction 168, 385
    test for –CH₂CO– group, 274, 346
3,5-Dinitrobenzoic acid, preparation, 242
    test for –CH₂CO– group, 274, 346
3,5-Dinitrobenzoyl chloride, 242
    preparation, 242
3,5-Dinitrobenzoyl derivatives, of alcohols, 247, 335, 336
    amino-acids, 381
    esters, 358
    ethers, 396
    phenols, 338, 340
3,5-Dinitrobenzoylation, 335· 337, 381
2,4-Dinitrophenylhydrazine, 279
    preparation, 262
    preparation, as reagent, 263
    reaction with aldehydes and ketones, 334, 341
2,4-Dinitrophenylhydrazones, preparation, 263, 264
1,2-Diols, periodate oxidation, 145
Dioxan, 15, 263
Diphenyl—*see* Biphenyl
Diphenic acid, preparation, 200
Diphenylamine, conversion to diphenylnitrosamine, 204, 376
    reactions of, 204, 376
Diphenylamines, preparation by *Ullmann* condensation, 217
Diphenylcarbinol, preparation, 152
Diphenylnitrosamine, preparation, semi-micro, 204

1,8-Diphenyloctatetrene, 238
    preparation, 238
2,3-Diphenylquinoxaline, 304
    preparation, semi-micro, 305
Diphenylurea, preparation, 125
Di-*n*-propylamine, reactions, 375
Disaccharides, 134 *et seq.*
Distillation, 25
    fractional, 25-26, 28
        of mixture of benzene and toluene, 28
    fractional, under reduced pressure, 30-31
        semi-micro, 64
    steam-, 32-33, 44
        semi-micro, 66
    under reduced pressure, 28-29
        semi-micro, 66
Distillation head, 33, 43, 44
Disubstituted benzenes, m.ps. of, 160
"Drierite," 24
Doebner-Miller synthesis, of quinaldine, 300
Drying of liquid compounds, 24
    of apparatus, 40
    of recrystallised material, 19, 68
    of solids in vacuo, 19, 68
    pistol, 68-69
Dumas' nitrogen estimation, 482

Ebullioscopic method of molecular weight determinations, 440-445
Electric shock, treatment for, 529
Elements, identification by *Lassaigne's* method, 321 *et seq.*
    by *Middleton's* method, 326 *et seq.*
Eelevation of Boiling-point, 440-445
Emulsin, 511, 515-516
    preparation from almonds, 516
Enzymes, simple, nomenclature, 510
    reactions of, 509 *et seq.*
    table of reactions of, 511—*see also* under appropriate enzyme
Equipment, standard semi-micro, 71
Equivalent weight of acids, 447
                  bases, 450
Erythro-dextrin, 513
Esterase, 510
Esterification, mechanism of, 96
    methods of, 96, 97
Esters, action of enzymes on, 510
    benzylamides from, 357
    boiling-points and melting-points table of, 546
    3,5-dinitrobenzoates from, 358
    hydroxamic acid test for, 334, 355
    hydrolysis, 355, 356, 413

Esters—*contd.*
    preparation, 96-98
    reaction with hydroxylamine, 334,
      355
    reactions of, 354
    tables of, 543-547
    table of reactions, 413
Estimation of acetyl groups, 455
    amino-acids, 463
    amino groups, 452
    aniline, 452
    aniline hydrochloride, 454
    bromine (*Carius*), 416
      semi-micro, 502
      bomb method, 505
    carbon and hydrogen,
      semi-micro, 467
    chlorine (*Carius*), 416
      semi-micro, 502
      bomb method, 505
    formaldehyde, 457
    glucose, 462
    glycine, 463
    halogens (*Carius*), 416, 422
      semi-micro, 502
    hydrogen, 467
    hydroxyl groups, 450
    iodine (*Carius*), 416
      bomb method, 505
      semi-micro, 502
    methoxyl groups,
      semi-micro, 497
    nitrogen (*Dumas*),
      semi-micro, 482
    nitrogen (*Kjeldahl*), 416
      semi-micro, 491
    sucrose, 462
    sugars, 460
    sulphur (*Carius*), 423
    urea (hypobromite), 458
    urea (urease), 520
    see also Determination of
Ethane tetracarboxylic acid ester,
    preparation and hydrolysis, 276
Ethanol, absolute, preparation, 89
    oxidation of, 73
    reaction with sulphuric acid, 78
      mechanism, 78
    reactions of, 335, 337
Ether, as solvent, 15, 440
    extraction, 34
      continuous, 36
    preparation, 79
    purification, 82
    distillation, precautions, 35, 80, 81
    peroxide, 83
Ethers, reactions of, 395
    table of, 560-561

2-Ethoxyethanol,
    as solvent, 15
Ethyl acetate, as solvent for molecu-
    lar weight determinations, 440
    hydrolysis, 99
      semi-micro, 100
    preparation,
      semi-micro, 98
    reactions of, 354
Ethyl acetoacetate, bromo-derivative,
      268
    conversion to methyl-phenyl-pyra-
      zolone, 271
    copper derivative, 268
    hydrolysis, 270
    interconversion of *keto* and *enol*
      forms, 268
    preparation, 264
    properties, 268
    sodium bisulphite derivative, 269
    substitution derivatives, 269
    synthetic use of, 269
    use in coumarin synthesis, 307
      in *Hantzsch* collidine reaction, 295
      in *Knorr's* pyrrole synthesis, 293
      in *Michael* reaction, 277
Ethyl alcohol—*see* Ethanol
Ethylbenzene, preparation, 288
Ethyl benzoate, preparation, 104
    reactions of, 354
Ethyl bromide, hydrolysis, 102
    preparation, 100
    reactions of, 103, 390
Ethyl chloride, 97
Ethyl *v*-bromocrotonate, preparation,
      177
Ethyl cinnamate, preparation, 237
    reactions of, 354
Ethyl crotonate, bromination, 177
Ethyl cyanacetate
    in *Michael* reaction, 277
Ethyl formate, reactions of, 177
Ethyl hydrogen sulphate, 77, 95
Ethyl iodide, preparation, 106
    reactions of, 103, 390, 392
Ethyl malonate, conversion to ethane
      tetracarboxylic acid ester, 276
    hydrolysis, 275
    preparation, 272
    reactions of *enol* form, 274
    substitution derivatives, 275
    use in *Michael* reaction, 277
      in thiobarbituric acid synthesis,
      306
Ethyl methyl ketone, reactions, 345
Ethyl nitrite, 103
Ethyl oxalate, reactions, 354
Ethyl phenyl ether—*see* Phenetole

Ethyl β-phenyl-β-hydroxy-propionate, preparation, 286
Ethyl phthalate, reactions of, 354
Ethyl salicylate, reactions of, 354
Ethyl succinate, reactions of, 354
Ethyl tartrate, reactions of, 354
p-Ethyltoluene, preparation, 290
Ethylation, of phenol, 220
Ethylene, preparation, 83
 tests, 84
Ethylene dibromide, 84, 87
 as solvent for molecular weight
  determinations, 433, 436, 440
 conversion to acetylene, 87
 effect of heat on, 319
Ethylene glycol—see also Glycol
 ethers of, 15
 formation, 85
 oxidation by periodate, 145
 reactions of, 335
Ethylene oxide, reaction with Grignard
 reagents, 283
Ethylene tetracarboxylic acid, ethyl
 ester, 276
Evaporation, semi-micro, 69
Eugenol, derivatives, 538
Explosions, prevention of, 530
Extraction, Soxhlet, 37, 47
 continuous with chloroform, 36
  with ether, 35
Eye accidents, treatment of, 527

Fats, action of lipase on, 510
Fehling's solution, preparation, 461,
 525
 reaction with phenylhydrazine, 199
 standardisation, 460
 treatment of compounds with, 408
Fenton's reagent, 352
Ferric chloride, reactions with, 332,
 348, 408
 neutral solution of, 332
Filter cylinder, Irvine, 11
Filter-paper, fluted, 12
Filtration, 9
 of hot solutions, 11
 semi-micro, 66
Fires, prevention and treatment, 529
Fischer Indolisation reaction, 294
Fischer-Speier method of esterifica-
 tion, 96, 104, 237
First-aid, 526
First-aid Box, equipment, 526
Fittig's Reaction, 288
Flame coloration, by metals, 404
Flasks, Buchner, 10
 bolt-head, 17
 ground-glass, 42

Fluorescein test, 351, 353, 363
Fluted filter-paper, 12
Formaldehyde detection of
 with dimedone, 146, 279
 estimation of, 457
 reactions of, 341
  with Grignard reagents, 282
Formaldehyde-formic acid,
 methylations with, 218, 226
Formalin solution, 241
 estimation, 457
Formamide, reactions of, 359, 362
Formic acid, anhydrous, 114
 preparation (in solution), 113
 reactions of, 347, 350
Fractional crystallisation, 13 et seq.
 distillation, 25
 under reduced pressure, 28
Fractionating columns, 25, 26
 semi-micro, 64
Free Radicals,
 from N-bromosuccinimide, 177
 diazotates, 201
 Gomberg's reaction, 201
 sodio-benzophenone, 347
Freezing-point, depression of, 432
 tables of, 536 et seq.
Friedel-Crafts' Reaction, 254, 288, 290
Fructose, α- and β-, 134, 461
 action of zymase on, 511
 reactions of, 366, 368
Fruit sugar—see Fructose
Funnels, Buchner, 10
 hot-water, 12
 separating, 34
 semi-micro, 68
  Hirsch, 10, 68
Furfural, derivatives of, 539
Furfuryl alcohol, derivatives of, 536
Furil, derivatives of, 541
Furoin, derivatives of, 541

Galactose 136, 461
Gas poisoning, treatment for, 528
Gases, semi-micro identification, 69
Gatterman's method, for preparation
 of chlorobenzene, 189
Gelatin, hydrolysis of, by trypsin, 519
Glucosazone, 137
 preparation, 138, 368
  from fructose, 137, 368
   salicin, 517
   sucrose, 515
Glucose, α- and β-, 135
 action of zymase on, 514
 estimation of hydroxyl groups in,
  452
 estimation with Fehling's solution,
  462

Glucose—*contd.*
  isolation by ion-exchange, 58
  reactions of, 366, 367
β-Glucosidase—*see* Emulsin
β-Glucosides, action of emulsin on, 515, 516
Glycerol, conversion to formic acid, 113
  dehydration, 114
  estimation of hydroxyl groups in, 452
  periodate oxidation, 146
  reactions of, 335, 337
  use as heating-bath, 60
Glyceryl monoformate, 113, 114
  monoxalate, 113
  oxalate, 114
  triacetate—*see* Triacetin
  tristearate, action of lipase on, 510
Glycine, copper derivative, 129 382
  estimation of, 463
  preparation, 130
  reactions of, 130, 381
  separation by paper chromatography, 51
Glycol, estimation of hydroxyl groups in, 452
  periodate oxidation of, 145
  reactions of, 335
Glycosides, oxidation by periodate, 145
Gomberg reaction, 201
Grape sugar—*see* Glucose
Grignard reagent, preparation, 280
  synthetic use of, 282-284
Ground-glass apparatus, 42
Guaiacol, derivatives, 538

Halogen, detection of, 323, 327
  estimation (*Carius*), 416
  semi-micro, 502, 504
Halogeno-hydrocarbons, reactions of, 390
  table of, 559
Hammick and Illingworth's Rules of aromatic substitution, 159
Hantzsch synthesis,
  of collidine-3,5-dicarboxylic acid diethyl ester, 295
  2-amino-4-methylthiazole, 305
Heating, under reflux, 17
  semi-micro, 62
Heating substances on a crucible lid, 319, 404
Heterocyclic amines, reactions of, 373, 377
Hempel gas-burette, 427, 460
Hexacetylmannitol, estimation of acetyl groups in, 456

preparation, 143
Hexamethylenetetramine, reactions of, 373, 379
n-Hexyl methyl ketone, 224
  preparation, 225
n-Hexyl methyl ketoxime, 224
  preparation, 225
  reduction, 225
Hinsberg's method for separating amines, 248, 249
Hirsch funnel, 10, 68
Hoesch reaction, 258
Hofmann's primary amine synthesis, 127
Hot-water funnels, 12
Hydrazine, as reducing agent,
  use in analysis, 507
Hydrazines, table of, 558
Hydrazobenzene, purification, 216
Hydriodic acid, for *Zeisel* estimation, 500
Hydrobenzamide, preparation, 229
Hydrocarbons, reactions of, 393
  identification, 394
  table of derivatives, 560
Hydrochloric acid, treatments of compounds with, 408
Hydrogen, detection of, in an organic compound, 320
  estimation,
  semi-micro, 467,
Hydrogen chloride, anhydrous, 104, 237
Hydrogen peroxide, for hydrolysis of nitrites, 194
Hydrolysis, by enzymes, 510 *et seq.*
  of *p*-acetamidobenzene sulphonamide, 181
  acetanilide, 108
  acetonitrile, 122
  acetoxime, 94
  acid annydrides, 364
  acid chlorides, 364
  alkyl halides, 390
  anilides, 108, 168, 379
  amides, 361
  aspirin, 111
  benzamide, 120
  benzanilide, 246
  benzonitrile, 193
  collidine-3,5-dicarboxylic acid, diethyl ester, 297
  diazonium compounds, 183, 187
  discaccharides, 136
  esters, 99, 355, 357
  esters, table of, 413
  ethyl acetate, 100
  ethyl acetoacetate, 270
  ethyl bromide, 102

Hydrolysis—*contd.*
 ethyl malonate, 275
 ethyl nitrite, 131
 Grignard reagent, 282-283
 imides, 361
 methyl isocyanate, 127
 methyl oxalate, 357
 nitriles, 122
 p-nitroacetanilide, 167
 p-nitrosodimethylaniline, 206
 phenyl benzoate, 244
 starch, 370, 512, 513
 sucrose, 136, 369, 462, 515
 p-tolunitrile, 195
 quantitative—of acetyl groups, 455 *et seq.*
Hydroquinone, oxidation, 255
Hydroxamic acids,
 from acid anhydrides, 364
 from acid chlorides, 364
 from esters, 334
o-Hydroxybenzyl alcohol (Saligenin), preparation, 155
 using emulsin, 517
1-Hydroxycyclopentane-carboxylic acid, 235
Hydroxyl groups, estimation of, 450
Hydroxylamine, 93
 as reducing agent, 99, 200
 for oxime formation, 334
 test for, 94
 use in testing for esters, 334
  for acid anhydrides, 364
  for acid chlorides, 364
7-Hydroxy-4-methyl-coumarin, 307
 preparation, 307
Hypnone—*see* Acetophenone

Identification, by mixed melting-points, 5, 6
 by preparation of crystalline derivatives—*see* Crystalline derivatives
 scheme for the—of an organic compound, 401
Identification of (in a compound),
 carbon, 320
 halogen, 323, 327
 hydrogen, 320
 nitrogen, 321, 327
 sulphur, 325, 327
Imides, reactions of, 359, 360
Indicators, preparation, 526
Indoles, preparation by *Fischer* reaction, 294
Indolisation, by *Fischer* reaction, 294
"Industrial" spirit, as solvent, 15
Ingold, mechanism of nitration, 157
Inversion, of cane sugar, 514

Invertase, 511, 514
Iodine, colours in ethers and aromatic hydrocarbons, 396
 detection, 323, 327
 estimation (*Carius*), 416
  semi-micro, 502
  bomb method, 505
Iodobenzene, preparation, 184, 188
 reactions, 390
Iodobenzene, diacetate, preparation, 187
Iodobenzene dichloride, preparation, 185
Iodoform, preparation, 92
 semi-micro, 93
 reactions of, 390-392
Iodoform Reaction, 91, 336, 346, 352
Iodosobenzene, preparation, 186
Iodoxybenzene, preparation, 187
Ion-exchange,
 chromatography, 55
 resins, 55
Iron filings, use in reduction, 213
Irvine filter-cylinder, 11
Isopropanol,
 oxidation to acetone, 153
 reactions, 335
Isopropyl alcohol—*see* Isopropanol
Isocyanide, 121
 Reaction, 373, 379, 392
Isodiazotates, formation, 183
Isoquinoline, derivatives of, 554

Jack bean, 363, 519, 520

Ketene, 116
Keto-acids, action of carboxylase on, 511
Keto-imines, hydrolysis, 259
Ketones, aliphatic, 91, 93, 224
 aromatic, 254
 reactions of, 345
 table of reactions, 411
 tables of derivatives, 541, 542
Kipp's apparatus, for semi-micro analysis, 482
Kjeldahl's nitrogen estimation 416, semi-micro, 492
Knoevenagel condensation, 279
 mechanism, 279
Knorr's synthesis of pyrroles, 293
Kon's modification of vacuum triangle, 31
Kuhn R. synthesis of polyenes, 238

Lactic acid, reactions of, 347, 351

Lactonitrile, 121
Lactosazone, preparation, 140, 369
Lactose, general, 134, 461
  reactions of, 367, 369
Laevulose—*see* Fructose
Lassaigne, sodium test, 321, 324, 325
Lead acetate, distinction from lead formate, 114
Lead formate, preparation, 113
  properties and uses, 114
Lead peroxide, use in analysis, 472, 473
Lepidine, reactions, 302
  derivatives of, 554
Leuckert reaction, 223
Liebermann's reaction, 204, 340, 376
Lipase, 510, 511
Lithium aluminium hydride,
  reduction with, 155
  manipulation, 155
  uses, 155
Logarithm tables, 562

Macroanalysis, 416
Magnesium, for *Grignard* reactions, 281
Magnesium amalgam, 149
  reduction with, 150
Magnesium perchlorate, as drying agent, 467 *et seq.*
Magnesium sulphate (drying agent), 24
Magnetic stirrer, 62
Maleic anhydride use in *Diels-Alder* reaction, 292
Malonic acid, reaction with crotonaldehyde, 280
Malonic ester—*see* Ethyl malonate
Malt, 512
Maltase, 511
Maltosazone, preparation, 139, 369
  from starch, 513
Maltose, general, 134, 461
  reactions of, 367, 369
  from starch, 512
Malt sugar—*see* Maltose
Mandelic acid,
  derivatives of, 544
Manipulation, 1
  semi-micro, 59 *et seq.*
Mannich reaction, 261
Mannitol, acetylation, 143
  derivatives, 536
  estimation of hydroxyl groups, 452
Mannose, 461
Manometer, 30
Mariotte bottle, 472
Mechanism of,
  Arbusov reaction, 311

bromation, aromatic, 175
  by N-bromosuccinimide, 177
Claisen ester condensation, 265
  ester formation, 95
  ethanol-sulphuric acid interaction, 95
Friedel-Crafts' reaction, 254
Gomberg reaction, 201
Hofmann's amine synthesis, 128
Knoevenagel condensation, 279
Liebermann's Nitroso-reaction, 340
Meerwein-Ponndorf-Verley reduction, 153
Michael addition reaction, 277
  nitration, aromatic, 156
  pinacol-pinacolone rearrangement, 152
  sulphonation, aromatic, 178
Meerwein-Ponndorf-Verley, reduction, 152
Melting-points, 1
  apparatus, 3
    electrical, 61
    hot-stage, 61
  determination of, 2, 5, 61
    in preheated bath, 131, 140
  identification by mixed m.ps., 5
  tables of, 536 *et seq.*
Mercurous nitrate, test for cyanide and halide, 324
Mercury benzamide, preparation semi-micro, 120
Mercury derivatives, of amides, 120
Mesityl oxide, 278
  in *Michael* reaction, 278
  derivatives of, 541
Metaformaldehyde, reactions of, 341, 344
Metallic salts, reactions of, 349
Metals, flame colorations of, 404
Metanilic acid,
  derivatives of, 548
Methanol, absolute, 89
  derivatives of, 536
  reactions of, 335, 337
  use as solvent, 14
Methiodides, 378, 392
Methods and manipulation, 1
  semi-micro, 59
2-Methoxyethanol, as solvent, 15
Methoxyl groups, estimation, semi-micro, 497
Methyl acetate, reactions of, 269
Methyl alcohol—*see* Methanol
N-Methylanthranilic acid,
  preparation, 222
  separation by, paper chromatography, 53

Methyl benzoate, reactions of, 354
Methyl cellosolve, as solvent, 15
Methyl cinnamate, reactions of, 354
Methyl cyanide—see Acetonitrile
Methyl 3,5-dinitrobenzoate, preparation, semi-micro, 247
Methyl ethylketone—see Ethyl methyl ketone
Methyl formate, reactions of, 354
Methyl iodide, reactions of, 390, 392
Methyl isocyanate, 127
Methyl 1-naphthyl ether, 221
Methyl 2-naphthyl ether, preparation, 220
  difficulty in Zeisel estimation, 497
Methyl-orange, constitution, 215
  preparation, 214, 384
  as indicator, 526
  test for sulphanilic acid, 384
Methyl oxalate, reactions of, 354, 357
  hydrolysis, 357
Methyl phenyl ether—see Anisole
Methyl-phenyl-pyrazolone, preparation, 271
Methyl phthalate, reactions of, 354
Methyl-red, as indicator, 526
Methyl salicylate, reactions of, 354
Methyl succinate, reactions of, 354
Methyl sulphate—see Dimethyl sulphate
Methyl tartrate, reactions of, 354
Methyl toluene-p-sulphonate, as quarternising agent, 378
Methyl p-tolyl ketone, preparation, 290
p-Methylacetophenone, preparation, 290
  reduction, 291
Methylamine, from nitromethane, 133
  hydrochloride, preparation, 128
Methylated spirit, as solvent, 14
Methylation, general methods of, 217
  of 2-amino-n-octane, 226
  anthranilic acid, 222
  2-naphthol, 220
  phenol, 219
  toluene-p-sylphonamide, 221
Methylene-blue, reduction of, 521
  use in sugar analysis, 463
  as indicator, 463, 526
Methylglucoside, α and β, 143
  α, preparation, 144
    reactions of, 145
  β, hydrolysis by emulsin, 516
Meyer reaction, 314
Michael reaction, 277
Michaelis-Arbusov reaction, 311
Middleton, identification of elements, 326

Milk sugar—see Lactose
Millon's reaction, 382
Milk, aldehyde oxidase in, 521
  peroxidase in, 523
  test for boiled —, 523
Mixtures, separation of, 397
Molecular, Depression Constant, 432
  Elevation Constant, 440
Molecular rearrangement, of cyanates to ureas, 123-125
  of diazoaminobenzene to aminoazobenzene, 208
  See also Rearrangements
Moleculat weights, determination by analysis of chloroplatinates, 448
  analysis of silver salts, 445
  boiling-point method, 440
    semi-micro, 442
  freezing-point method, 432
    semi-micro, 436
  Rast's method, 437
  Sucharda-Bobranski method, 442
  titration with alkali, 447
  Victor Meyer's method, 425
Molisch's test, 367
Monobromo-acetamide, 127
Monomethylaniline, reactions of, 375
  sulphonylation, 250
Monophenyl-urea, preparation, 125
Monosaccharides, reactions of, 134, 366
Morpholine, derivatives of, 552
Mortar, thermostatic, 470
Murexide test, 389

Naphthalene, reactions of, 393
Naphthalene picrate, 174
Naphthalene-2-sulphonyl chloride, 382, 554
1-Naphthol, reactions of, 337
2-Naphthol, reactions of, 337
1,2-Naphthoquinone, reactions, 370
1,4-Naphthoquinone, reactions, 370
2-Naphthyl acetate, preparation, 110
2-Naphthyl esters, tests for halides, 391
1-Naphthylisocyanate, 336, 375
1-Naphthyl methyl ether, 221
2-Naphthyl methyl ether, preparation, 220
  difficulty, in Zeisel estimation, 497
1-Naphthylamine, reactions of, 373
2-Naphthylamine, reactions, 373
1-Naphthylurea, 375
1-Naphthyl-urethanes, 337, 536-9
Nerolin—see Methyl 2-naphthyl ether
Ninhydrin, colour with amino-acids, 51

Nitration of benzene, 157
  mechanism, 157
  of halogeno-hydrocarbons, 391
    hydrocarbons, 157, 393
    nitrobenzene, 157, 395
    phenol to o- and p-nitrophenol, 170
    phenol to picric acid, 173
Nitriles preparation, 120
  reaction with Grignard reagents, 283
  reactions of, 359, 360
  tables of, 543-545
p-Nitroacetanilide, preparation, 167
  hydrolysis, 168
o-Nitroaniline, reactions of, 387
m-Nitroaniline, preparation, 168
  reactions of, 387
p-Nitroaniline, preparation, 167, 168
  reactions, 387
Nitroanilines, m.ps., 160, 557
  crystalline derivatives, 388
  chromatographic separation, 49
  reactions of, 287
  reduction, 387
Nitrobenzene, as solvent for molecular
    weight determinations, 433, 435
  preparation, 157
    semi-micro, 158
  reactions of, 384
  reduction to aniline, 162
p-Nitrobenzoyl chloride, 244
  for identifying alcohols, 244, 336
    phenols, 244, 246, 339, 340
p-Nitrobenzyl bromide, 348
p-Nitrobenzyl esters, use in, identi-
    fication of acids, 350
Nitro-compounds, aliphatic, 131
  reactions of, 133
Nitro-compounds, aromatic, re-
    actions, 384
  table of, 557
Nitroethane, 131
Nitrogen, detection of, 321
  detection of, in carbon-free com-
    pounds, 323
Nitrogen, estimation (Dumas),
    semi-micro, 482
  (Kjeldahl), 482, 491
Nitro-hydrocarbons
  aliphatic, preparation, 131
    properties, 132, 133
  aromatic, preparation, 157
    properties, 384
  reactions, 385
  reduction, 162, 385
  table of, 557
Nitrolic acids, 134
Nitrometer, semi-micro, 482
Nitromethane, preparation, 132
  reactions of, 133

o-Nitrophenol, preparation, 170
  reactions of, 386
p-Nitrophenol, preparation, 170
  reactions of, 386
Nitrophenols, m.ps., 161, 538-9
  crystalline derivatives, 387
  reactions of, 386
  reduction, 386
p-Nitrophetylhydrazine, 229
Nitroprusside reaction—see Sodium
    nitroprusside
Nitrosamines, 376
Nitrosobenzene, conversion to azo-
    benzene, 210
p-Nitrosodimethylaniline, prepara-
    tion, 204, 378
  reactions, 206
Nitro-toluenes, m.ps., 160
p-Nitrotoluene, reactions, 385
Nitrous acid, reaction with amides, 360
  amino-acids, 381, 518
  aromatic amines, 182, 374
  nitro-paraffins, 134
  phenols, 340
  m-phenylene diamine, 385
  primary amines, 181
  secondary amines, 203
  tertiary amines, 204
Nomenclature of enzymes, 510

n-Octan-2-ol, oxidation, 224
sec-Octyl alcohol, see n-Octan-2-ol
Odour of compounds, 403
Optimum pH, for enzyme reactions,
    509, 511
Organo-arsenic compounds, 312, 314
    lithium compounds, 155
    phosphorus compounds, 308-
    311
Orientation of aromatic compounds,
    159
Orthanilic acid, derivatives of, 548-9
Osazone of benzil, 234
    fructose, 137, 368
    glucose, 137, 368, 515, 517
    lactose, 140, 369
    maltose, 139, 369
Osazones, 134 et seq.
Oxalic acid, preparation, 112
  reactions of, 347, 351
Oxamide, preparation, 118
  reactions of, 359, 363
Oxanthranol, 371
Oxidase, aldehyde —, 511, 521
Oxidation, by Fenton's reagent, 352
  of acetaldehyde by oxidase, 521
    alcohols, 335
    amines, 372 et seq.

Oxidation—*contd.*
amines, by peroxidase, 522
anthracene, 259
aromatic aldehydes, 343
benzoin, 234
benzoquinone, 372
benzyl alcohol, 336
benzyl chloride, 239, 393
n-butanol, 335
camphor, 147
cane sugar, 112
cinnamic acid, 353
cylcohexanol, 335
ethanol to acetaldehyde, 74, 335
ethanol to acetic acid, 75, 335
ethylene, 83
formaldehyde, quantitative, 457
glycerol, 146
glycol, 335
Grignard reagent, 282
isopropanol, 335
n-octan-2-ol, 224
methanol, 335
1,2-naphthoquinone, 372
phenanthraquinone, 372
phenylhydrazine, 199
side-chain, 239, 395
toluene, 395
Oximes, *Beckmann* rearrangement, 93, 227
preparation and uses, 93
reduction, with sodium and ethanol, 235
with zinc and acetic acid, 293

Paper chromatography, 50
Paraffin wax, as drying agent, 19
Paraformaldehyde, use in *Mannich* reaction, 262
Paraldehyde, reactions of, 341, 344
Parr bomb, for halogen determination, 505
Pellet press, 431
Pepsin, 511
Pentacetylglucose, 141
estimation of, acetyl groups in, 456
α. preparation, 141
β, preparation, 142
conversion β to α, 142
Periodate oxidation, 145
of pinacol, 146
glycerol, 146
Perkin reaction, for cinnamic acid, 236
for coumarin, 307
triangle, 31, 45
Peroxidase, 521
isolation of, 522
qualitative test for amines, 522

Petroleum, as solvent, 14
reactions of, 393
pH, definition of, 509
optimum, of enzymes, 509
Phenacyl bromide, for identification of acids, 349
Phenacyl esters, for identicfication of acids, 349
preparation, 349
Phenanthraquinone, 370
reactions and properties, 370
reaction with *o*-phenylenediamine, 305, 372
Phenanthrene,
oxidation, 254
reactions, 393
Phenetole, 188
preparation, 220
Phenol, methylation, 219
nitration, 170
preparation, 195
properties, 197
reactions of, 337
Phenols, estimation of hydroxyl groups in, 450
reactions of, 337
table of derivatives, 538-9
table of reactions of, 410
Phenolphthalein, as indicator, 526
Phenoxyacetic acid,
derivatives of, 544-5
Phenyl acetate, preparation, 109
reactions of, 355
Phenylalanine,
separation by paper chromatography, 51
N-Phenylanthranilic acid, preparation, 217
conversion to acridone, 303
Phenylarsonic acid, 312
preparation, 312
benzylthiuronium, salt, 314
reduction, 314
Phenyl benzoate, 244
hydrolysis, 244
preparation,
semi-micro, 244
reactions of, 355
Phenyl bromide—*see* Bromobenzene
Phenyl chloride—*see* Chlorobenzene
Phenyl cyanide—*see* Benzonitrile
1-Phenyl-ethylamine,
preparation, 223, 258
use in optical resolutions, 258
Phenyl ethyl ether—*see* Phenetole
Phenyl-glucosazone—*see* Glucosazone
Phenylhydrazine, preparation, 197
oxidation, 199
propérties, 199

Phenylhydrazine—*contd.*
reduction, 199
use in preparation of phenylhydrazones and ozasones, 137-41, 229,
234, 257, 341, 368, 369
Phenylhydrazone of acetophenone,
257, 345
of benzaldehyde, 229
of cyclohexanone, 295
of salicylaldehyde, 341
Phenyl iodide—*see* Iodobenzene
Phenyl-lactosazone—*see* Lactosazone
Phenyl-maltosazone—*see* Maltosazone
Phenyl magnesium bromide,
preparation in solution, 284
Phenyl methyl ether—*see* Anisole
Phenyl-osazones—*see* Osazones
Phenyl salicylate, reactions of, 355
N-Phenylsulphonamides, 247
preparation. 247, 249
Phenyl toluene-*p*-sulphonate, preparation, semi-micro, 249
Phenylurethanes,
preparation, 336, 340
o-Phenylenediamine, condensation
with benzil, 304
phenanthraquinone, 304, 372
quinoxaline formation, 304, 372
reactions of, 388
m-Phenylenediamine, reactions of, 388
p-Phenylenediamine, reactions of, 388
test for peroxidase, 523
Phloroglucinol, derivatives, 538
Phosgene, 91
Phosphites, alkyl, 308
preparation, 308
Phosphorus burns, treatment of, 527
Phosphorus pentachloride, for con-
version of acids to acyl chlorides,
240, 242
Phosphorus pentoxide, for dehydration of amides, 121
Phosphorus trichloride,
reaction with alcohols, 96, 308
Photographic sensitisers, 203
Phthalein reaction, 339, 353, 363
Phthalic acid, reactions of, 347, 353
Phthalic anhydride, reactions of, 364,
366
Phthalimide, reactions of, 361, 363
Physical constants, 535 *et seq.*
Physical properties, 403—*see also*
under appropriate compound
Picolines, derivatives of, 553
Picrates, of amines, 174, 374, 376, 378
anthracene, 174, 394
aryl ethers, 397
naphthalene, 174, 394
pyridine, 174, 392

quinaldine, 377
quinoline, 174, 377
Picric acid, preparation, 173
reactions and uses, 174
"Pig," for fractional distillation, 31,
45, 65
Pinacol, preparation, 149
conversion to pinacolone, 152
oxidation to acetone, 146
Pinacol-pinacolone rearrangement,
152
Pinacolone, preparation, 152
Piperazine, derivatives of, 552
reactions, 375
Piperidine, derivatives of, 552
reactions, 375
Pipettes, semi-micro, 59-60
Platinum, recovery, 449
Poisons, treatment for, 528
Potassium, detection in presence of
sodium, 174
Potassium antimonyl tartrate, preparation, 115
Potassium carbonate (drying agent),
24, 197
dehydration, 197
use in *Ullmann* condensation, 217
Potassium cupro-cyanide, preparation,
191
Potassium cyanide, precautions in use,
191
Potassium ethyl sulphate, hydrolysis,
79
preparation, 78
Potassium hydroxide (drying agent),
24, 163
Potassium permanganate, reagent for,
unsaturation, 85, 87, 353
Preparations, 73
semi-micro, 70
Primary amines, 373-5
table of derivatives, 550
Primary aromatic amines, reactions of,
373
table of, 550
Proline, separation by paper chroma-
tography, 50
Propyl alcohol(*iso*)—*see* Isopropanol
n-Propanol, reactions, 335
Proteins, hydrolysis by trypsin, 518
Pseudo-acids, 131
Pseudo-nitrol, 134
Ptyalin, 511, 513
Purdie's method of methylation, 218
Purification, of liquid substances, 23
et seq.
of solid substances, 13 *et seq.*
Purines, reactions of, 389
Pyknometer, 434

Pyramidon, 272
Pyridine, reactions of, 377
    use in acetylation, 110, 270, 450, 452
    use in benzoylation, 339
    use in bromination, 175
Pyridine ethiodide, 392
    methiodide, 392
    picrate, 174, 392
Pyrogallol, derivatives, 538
Pyrroles, synthesis, 293
Pyrrolidine, derivatives of, 552

Qualitative analysis of a compound, 401 et seq.
    of a mixture, 397 et seq.
Quantitative analysis, 416 et seq.
Quaternary salts of tertiary amines, preparation, 377-8
    table of, 553-4
Quicklime—see Calcium oxide
Quinaldine, preparation, 300
    methiodide, 302
    methopicrate, 302
    reactions of, 302, 303
Quinoline, preparation, 297
    derivatives of, 554
    reactions of, 373, 379
Quinoline chlorozincate, 298
Quinoline picrate, 174, 378
Quinones, preparation, 254
    reactions of, 370
    table of derivatives, 549
Quinoxalines, 304
    preparation, semi-micro, 305

Radicals, Free—see Free Radicals
Rapid furfural test, 368 et seq.
Rast's camphor method, 437
Reactions and identification of organic compounds, 316 et seq.
Reagents, preparation, 524
Rearrangements,
    amine cyanates to ureas (Wohler), 123-6
    Beckmann, 93, 227
    benzidine, 215
    benzilic acid, 235
    diazo-aminobenzene to amino-azo-benzene, 208
    pinacol to pinacolone, 152
Recrystallisation, 13
    experimental directions, 15
    semi-micro, 66
Rectified spirit, as solvent, 14, 440
Reducing agent, test for, by ammonia-cal silver nitrate, 408
    by Fehling's solution, 408

Reduction, of acetone, 149
    of anthraquinone, 371
    azo-compounds, 210
    azoxybenzene, 212
    benzeneazo-2-naphthol, 210
    benzophenone, 152, 154
    benzoquinone, 371
    diazonium compounds, 189, 197
    m-Dinitrobenzene to m-nitroaniline 169
    to m-phenylenediamine, 385
    n-hexyl methyl ketoxime, 224
    1,2-naphthoquinone, 371
    nitroanilines, 387
    nitrobenzene to aniline, 162, 385
    nitrobenzene to azoxybenzene, 212
    nitro-ethane, 131
    nitrophenols, 386
    oximes, 93
    phenanthraquinone, 371
    phenylhydrazine, 137, 199
    reductive acetylation, 371
    salicylic acid, 155
Reflux condenser, 17, 43
    semi-micro, 63, 64
Reformatsky reaction, 286
Resacetophenone,
    preparation, 258
Resorcinol, reactions of, 338
    use in coumarin synthesis, 307
    Hoesch reaction, 258
Rochelle salt, 115, 461, 525
Ring enlargement, by Beckmann re-arrangement, 227

Salicin, hydrolysis of, by emulsin, 515, 517
Salicyl alcohol, preparation, 155
    by enzymes, 515
    derivatives of, 537
Salicylaldehyde, reactions of, 341, 344
Salicylamide, reactions of, 359, 368
Salicylic acid, acetylation, 111, 268
    reactions of, 347, 352
    reduction to saligenin, 156
Saligenin—see Salicyl alcohol
Salts, ammonium, reactions of, 359
    metallic, effect of heat on, 319-20, 404-5
    reactions of, 348
    of amines, reactions of, 373
Sand, use for extinguishing fires, 529
Sandmeyer's method for preparation of benzonitrile, 190
    chlorobenzene, 189
    p-tolunitrile, 194
Saponification, 99

Saunders, action of phosphorus trichloride on alcohols, 97
identification of amino-
acids, 381
iodoform reaction, 91
S-benzylthiouronium chloride—*see*
benzylthiouronium chloride
Scalds, treatment of, 527
Schardinger enzyme—*see* Aldehyde
oxidase
Scheme, for the identification of an
organic compound, 401 *et seq.*
for the separation of a binary mixture, 397 *et seq.*
Schiff's bases, 230
nitrometer, 484
reagent, use of, 341, 345
preparation, 525
test for uric acid, 389
Schotten-Baumann reaction, benzoylation, 243
sulphonylation, 247
Secondary amines, reactions of, 375
table of, 552
"Seeding" of solutions, for crystallisa-
tion, 17
Selenium dioxide,
dehydrogenation with, 146
oxidation with, 147
Semicarbazide, use in preparation of
semicarbazones, 258
Semicarbazone formation, 258, 341,
342, 346
Semi-microanalysis, 465
Semi-micro equipment, 59
standard for students, 70
Sensitisers, photographic, 303
Separation of simple binary mixtures,
397 *et seq.*
Separating-funnels, 34, 59
Side-chain, oxidation of, 239, 395
Silica gel, as drying agent, 19
Silicone for baths, 4
Silicone grease, as lubricant, 42, 62
Silver acetylide, 87
Silver nitrate
ammoniacal, preparation, 525
ammoniacal, treatment of com-
pounds with, 408
Silver oxalate, thermal decomposition,
447
Silver oxide, use in methylation, 218
Silver salts, analysis of, 445
preparation, 445
Skraup's synthesis of quinoline, 297
Small scale apparatus, 59
advantages of, 59
Soda-lime, heating substances with,
327, 406

Sodium, burns, treatment of, 527
as condensing agent, 103, 264, 288
as drying agent, 24
for drying ether, 82
conversion to wire, 82
use in *Lassaigne's* test, 321
Sodium acetate, dehydration of, 117
Sodium ammonium tartrate, 115
Sodium benzoate, effect of heat on, 319
Sodium bisulphite, addition product
with acetone, 346
ethyl acetoacetate, 269
benzaldehyde, 344
addition products with aldehydes
and ketones, 257
preparation, 525
Sodium, citrate, conversion to citric
acid, 56
Sodium dichromate, 74
Sodium hydroxide, "flake," 19
treatment with, 327, 405
Sodium hypobromite, preparation,
525
Sodium hypochlorite, 2*M*-solution,
preparation, 525
Sodium *meta*periodate, for glycol
oxidation, 145
Sodium nitroprusside, test for sulphide, 325
test for –CH$_2$CO– group, 274, 344,
346
test for cysteine, 383
Sodium periodate, for glycol oxida-
tion, 145
Sodium potassium tartrate, 115
Sodium press, 82
Sodium sulphanilate, effect of heat on,
320
Sodium sulphate (drying agent), 24
Solubility of compounds, 15, 403
Solvent, choice of, 14, 21
Sorbic acid, 279
preparation, 280
Sorensen's estimation of glycine, 463
test for amino-acids, 381
method of observing protein hydro-
lysis, 518
Soxhlet extraction, 37, 46
Soy bean—*see* Jack bean
Specimens, storage of, 40
Spray apparatus, 52
Stannous chloride, use in reduction,
162, 197, 211
Starch, reactions of, 366, 369
action of diastase on, 511, 512
action of ptyalin on, 513
Starch iodide coloration, 369
Steam-distillation, 32
semi-micro, 66, 494

Steam-generator, 33
  semi-micro, 66
Steam splash-heads, 33
Stearin, action of lipase on, 510
Stilbene, tests for, 395
Still-head, for distillation, 33, 44, 89
Stirrer, magnetic, 62
Stirrers, with mercury seal, 38
  with rubber sleeve, 38, 44
Stirring, 38
  semi-micro, 62
Styrene, tests for, 395
Sublimation, 23
  of anthraquinone, 260
  semi-micro, 69
Substrate, definition of, 510
Substrates, table of, 511
Succinamide, preparation, 119
Succinic acid,
  dehydration, 115
  molecular weight of, 448
  reactions of, 347, 351
Succinic anhydride, 115
  reactions of, 364
Succinimide, 119
  reactions of, 359, 363
Sucharda-Bobranski method,
  for molecular weights, 442
Sucrase—*see* Invertase
Sucrose, estimation, 462
  general, 134
  hydrolysis (inversion), 135, 514
  hydrolysis by invertase, 135, 514,
    515
  oxidation to oxalic acid, 112
  reactions of, 367
"Sugar of lead"—*see* Lead acetate
Sugars estimation of, 460
  general properties, 134
  reactions of, 367
  See also Carbohyrates
Sulphanilamide, action of soda-lime
    on, 329
  preparation, 181
Sulphanilate, sodium, action of heat
    on, 320
Sulphanilic acid, conversion to
    methyl orange, 214, 384
  decolorisation, 22
  preparation, 179
  reactions of, 384
Sulphapyridine, 181
Sulphathiazole, 181
Sulphonamides, preparation, 354
Sulphonanilides, preparation, 354
Sulphonation, 178
  of aniline, 179
  of hydrocarbons, 178, 394
Sulphonic acids, reactions, 353

aliphatic, preparation, 179
aromatic, derivatives, 353
  identification, 353
  preparation, 178
  table of derivatives, 548-9
Sulphonylation, 247-9
Sulpho-urea—*see* Thio-urea
Sulphur, detection of, 325, 327
  estimation (*Carius*), 423
Sulphuric acid, action of, 331, 407
  70%, preparation, 109
  70%, use as hydrolysing agent,
    109, 168, 222, 246, 251, 379
  90%, as hydrolysing agent, 193
Sym-Tribromoaniline, preparation,
  166
Sym-Tribromobenzene, preparation,
  202

Table of atomic weights, 534
  of conversion factors for gravi-
    metric analysis, 534
    acetals, 539
    acid anhydrides, 543-5
      amides, 543-5
      N-benzylamides, 543-5
      chlorides, 543-5
    acids,
      aliphatic, 543
      amino, 555
      aromatic, 544-5
      sulphonic, 548
    alcohols, 536-7
      aryl substituted, 537
    aldehydes, aliphatic, 539
      aromatic, 540
    alkyl halides, 559
    amides, 543, 545
    amines, primary, 550-1
      secondary, 552
      tertiary, 553-4
    amino-acids, 555
    amino-phenols, 551
    anilides, 543, 545
    axo-compounds, 557
    azoxy-compounds, 558
    esters, 543, 544, 546
    ethers, 560-1
    halogeno-hydrocarbons 559
    hydrazines, 558
    hydrocarbons, aromatic, 560
    ketones, aliphatic, 541
      aromatic, 542
    nitro-hydrocarbons, 557
    nitro-phenols, 538
    nitrosamines, 552
    nitroso-compounds, 556
    phenols, 538-9

Table of Atomic Weights—*contd.*
quinones, 549
sulphonamides, 548-9
sulphonic acids, 548-9
thioureas, 558
ureas, 558
logarithms, 562-5
reactions of aldehydes, 411
reactions of aromatic amines, 415
reactions of carbohydrates, 414
reactions of carboxylic acids, 412
reactions of esters, 413
reactions of ketones, 411
reactions of phenols, 410
vapour pressure of water, 534
Tabloid press, 431
Tartar emetic—*see* Potassium antimonyl tartrate
Tartaric acid, reactions of, 347, 352
Tautomerism, of aliphatic nitro-compounds, 131
of camphor, 437
ethyl acetoacetate, 268
ethyl malonate, 274
methyl-phenyl-pyrazolone, 272
nitromethane, 132
uric acid, 389
Tertiary amines, reactions of, 377
table of, 553-4
use in preparing phosphorus esters, 308
1,2,3,4-Tetrahydrocarbazole, preparation, 294
picrate 295
Tetraphenylethylene glycol 151
preparation 152
Thermometer *Beckmann* 429
"pocket," 43
Thiazoles preparation, 305
Thiobarbituric acid, 306
preparation 307
Thiols, oxidation, 178
Thionyl chloride, for preparation of acid chlorides, 240
Thiourea, properties, and reactions, 359, 361
use in preparing,
benzyl thiuronium chloride, 126
thiols, 127
Thioureas, table of, 558
Thymol, derivatives, 538
Thymol-blue, as indicator, 526
Tin, use in reduction, 161, 385 *et seq.*
Toluene reactions of, 393
Toluene-*p*-sulphonamide, conversion to chloramine-T, 253
to the dimethylamide, 221
to sodium derivative, 252

preparation, 251
Toluene-*p*-sulphon-dichloro-amide—*see* Dichloramine-T
Toluene-*p*-sulphon-dimethylamide, preparation, 221
Toluene-*p*-sulphonic acid, preparation, 178
Toluene-*p*-sulphonchlorosodio-amide—*see* Chloramine-T
Toluene-*p*-sulphonyl-aniline, preparation, 250
Toluene-*p*-sulphonyl chloride, conversion to amide, 250
properties and uses, 249
use for identifying,
amines, 374, 375, 376
amino-acids, 382
phenols, 340
Toluene-sulphonyl chlorides, m.ps., 160
Toluene-*p*-sulphonyl-methylaniline, preparation, 250
p-Toluic acid, from *p*-tolunitrile, 195
o-Toluidine, reactions of, 373
m-Toluidine, reactions of, 373
p-Toluidine, conversion to *p*-tolunitrile, 194
reactions of, 373
p-Tolunitrile, hydrolysis, 195
preparation, 194
Toluqinone,
reactions, 370
p-Tolyl cyanide—*see* *p*-Tolunitrile
p-Tolyl methyl ketone—*see* *p*-Methylacetophenone
Transformations,
amine cyanates to ureas (*Wohler*), 123-6
Beckmann, 93, 227
benzidine, 215
benzilic acid, 235
diazo-aminobenzene to amino-azobenzene, 208
Fischer indole synthesis, 294
pinacol to pinacolone, 152
Triacetin, estimation of acetyl groups in, 455
Triacetyl-glycerol—*see* Triacetin
Trialkyl phosphites
preparation, 308
Triarylamines, 377
reactions, 377
2,4,6-Tribromoaniline, 165
preparation, 165
1,3,5-Tribromobenzene, preparation, 202
Tribromophenol, 188
Tri-*n*-butylamine, 377
Triethylamine, reactions, 377

Triethyl phosphite, preparation, 308
2,6,8-Trihydroxypurine, 389
2,4,6-Trimethylpyridine-3,5-dicarbo-
  xylic acid, diethyl ester, preparation,
  295
2,4,6-Trinitrophenol—see Picric acid
Trioxymethylene, reactions of, 341
1,2,3-Triols, periodate oxidation, 146
Triphenylamine, reactions of, 377
Triphenyl-carbinol, preparation, 284
  semi-micro, 285
Tri-n-propylamine, reactions, 377
Trypsin, 511, 517
Turnips, peroxidase from, 522
Tyrosine, reactions of, 380, 382

Ullmann condensation, 217
Ultraviolet light,
  in chromatography, 51, 53
Unglazed porcelain, for m.ps., 2
  for use in distillation, 8
Units of ground-glass apparatus, 42
Unsaturation, tests for, 85, 353
Urea, estimation (hypobromite
    method), 458
  estimation (urease method), 520
  in Beilstein's test, 323
  preparation, 123
  reactions of, 362
  specific (urease) test, 519
Urea nitrate, 123, 362
  oxalate, 124, 362
Ureas, table of, 558
Urease, 519
  estimation of urea by, 520
  qualitative test for urea, 519
Urethanes, for identification of,
    alcohols, 335, 336
    phenols, 340
Uric acid, reactions of, 389
Urine, estimation of urea in, 458,
  520

Urotropine—see Hexamethylene-tet
  ramine

Vacuum distillation, 28-32
Van Slyke, method of following pro-
    tein hydrolysis, 518
Vanillin, use in Zeisel estimation, 501
Vapour pressure, of water, 435
Vapour Density, determination by
    Victor Meyer's method, 425
Victor Meyer, vapour. density deter-
    mination, 425
Vorlander's Rules of Aromatic Sub-
    stitution, 159

Water, as solvent for molecular weight
    determinations, 433, 436, 440, 442
  free from carbon dioxide, 448
  vapour pressure of, 533
Water-condensers, 8
  reflux, 17, 43
  semi-micro, 64
Weighing, for semi-micro estimations,
    465-7
  of absorption tubes, 475
  of semi-micro samples, 476, 486
Williamson's ether preparations, 103,
    217
Wohler's urea synthesis, 123
Wood charcoal, 21
Wurtz Reaction, 103, 288

Yeast, invertase from, 514
Yield, calculation of, 98

Zeisel's method, semi-micro, 497
Zinc, amalgamated, 291
  for reduction, 291, 293
Zwitterion, 130
Zymase, 511